PROPAGATION OF PLANTS

PROPAGATION
OF PLANTS

*A Complete Guide for Professional and Amateur Growers of
Plants by Seeds, Layers, Grafting and Budding, with Chapters
on Nursery and Greenhouse Management*

by

M. G. KAINS

*Formerly Professor of Horticulture, Pennsylvania State College
and Lecturer on Horticulture, Columbia
University, New York*

and

L. M. McQUESTEN

*Formerly Associate in Pomology, College of Agriculture,
University of California*

REVISED AND ENLARGED
EDITION

NEW YORK
ORANGE JUDD PUBLISHING COMPANY, INC.
1952

PREFACE

For the past twenty-two years the original edition of this book has been the standard American text on plant propagation. It has been, and still is, relied upon alike by commercial and amateur plant propagators and by teachers in farm schools, agricultural and forestry colleges for its succinctly stated principles and methods. Now, however, it is out of date and out of print; for during these years, especially during the past five, so many important discoveries and improvements in methods have been made that nurserymen and greenhousemen as well as teachers, students and experimenters have demanded a new, adequately illustrated volume to replace it and thus bring the scattered information between the covers of one book.

For the better part of two years, therefore, the authors have been reviewing the plant propagation literature of the world, collecting material, collating processes, culling out the effete, conserving the important and cooperatively condensing the vital into the present all-embracing volume.

In order to elucidate the text to the fullest possible extent they have scrutinized more than 2,000 photographs and line drawings from which they have chosen nearly 600 pictures that have been made into 350 plates to illustrate the text. Used singly or in combinations of two to six or more they constitute a pictorial exegesis which, step by step, makes the subject clear, even to the novice.

The text has been so arranged that the propagator, whether professional or amateur, can get a clear exposition of whatever subject interests him, without being annoyed by pedagogical material. On the other hand, the teacher, the experimenter, and the student will find abundant reference to text and illustrations in the 50 practicums placed toward the close of the book.

Professional propagators, teachers and amateurs will also find the plant lists and condensed rules for propagation of special value when they have unfamiliar plant material with which to deal; for thus they can gain information with which to start and proceed in the development of new plants.

Finally, the index not only covers the entire text but lists the tables, section subjects, illustrations, important variety names, institutions and the authors whose work has been cited. Thus it will be easy to trace the location of any desired item by looking for any of these various keys.

Among the many persons to whom the authors are indebted for help are Doctor W. W. Robbins, Head of the Division of Botany, College of Agriculture, University of California, at Davis, for suggestions, and to Doctor William Crocker, Director of The Boyce Thompson Institute of Plant Research at Yonkers, N. Y., for scanning and editing the text on seedage, spores and germination; to Doctor W. P. Tufts, Head, and Professor Leonard Day, both of the Pomological Division of the College of Agriculture, University of California, and to Doctor H. B. Tukey, Chief in Research at the New York Agricultural Experiment Station in Geneva, for reviewing the manuscript on rootstocks; to Professor W. L. Howard, Director of the College of Agriculture, University of California, for information and the illustrations on layerage-propagation of fruit tree stocks; to Doctors P. W. Zimmerman and A. E. Hitchcock, of The Boyce Thompson Institute of Plant Research for scansion of the text on methods of cuttage propagation, especially the chapter on "growth substances"; to Professor A. F. Camp, Horticulturist in Charge of the University of Florida Citrus Experiment Station at Lake Alfred, Fla., for reviewing and extending the section on citrus stocks; and to the late Doctor F. V. Coville, Botanist of the United States Department of Agriculture, at Washington, D. C., for bringing the information on blueberry, rhododendron and other acid tolerant plant propagation up to the date of his passing.

In addition to these the authors express their thanks to the nurseries, greenhouse construction companies, experiment stations colleges and other institutions credited throughout the text for photographs and drawings from which many of the illustrations have been made.

M. G. Kains,
L. M. McQuesten.

CONTENTS

vii

CONTENTS

ILLUSTRATIONS AND TABLES

To facilitate the location of each of the 350 figures throughout the book, the authors have departed from the usual space- and time-wasting "List of Illustrations" and have indexed both halftones and line drawings by means of key words (several in most cases) that will readily come to mind. The searcher will thus save time and annoyance when he desires to find any specific illustration. In the index the numbers that follow the contraction "Fig." refer to *pages*, not figure numbers.

The tables have been similarly indexed, but the first number that follows the word "Table" is the number of the table itself.

I

INTRODUCTION

1. Plant propagation is the multiplication or increase in number of plants in the perpetuation of the species. As applied by man, it includes knowledge of the proper time, place and manner in which best results may be secured. Fundamentally it is based upon (a) certain natural laws or principles which constitute the *science*, and (b) certain methods of manipulation which constitute the *art* of the processes as a whole.

2. Art and science contrasted.—*Art* is merely the knowledge of methods without reference to reasons whereby results may be secured. It is the actual doing of the operation, the "HOW." It therefore implies skill gained through practice. *Science* deals with the underlying reasons for certain forms of procedure, or answers the question "WHY?" and the conditions which affect the process without considering the skill involved in manipulation.

To illustrate: A workman in a nursery may easily transplant 4,000 potted dahlia plants in a day of 10 hours without knowing anything specific of the underlying principles; whereas, the proprietor may know the principles and give proper orders for their application without being able to transplant half as many plants in the same time, yet he may be a master workman because of his knowledge of both the art and the science. The art is best acquired by following the example of a skilled workman; the science best from books and instructors.

3. Methods of propagating plants naturally divide themselves into two general classes—*sexual* and *asexual* propagation or reproduction. Below are given the methods or divisions of plant propagation.

SUMMARY OF THE METHODS OR DIVISIONS OF PLANT PROPAGATION [1]

I. Seeds (Seedage—Sexual Propagation).

    A. *Requiring Preparatory Treatment before Planting:*

        1. Chemical—Honey locust, asparagus, alfalfa, hard seed.

        2. Mechanical—Canna, sour or bitter clover.

        3. Scalding—Honey locust, Kentucky coffee tree.

        4. Soaking—Black locust.

        5. Stratification—Black walnut, peach, cherry.

    B. *Requiring no Preparatory Treatment:*

    Many annuals and perennials.

II. Spores (Asexual Propagation).

III. Buds (Asexual Propagation).

    A. *On their Own Roots:*

        1. Parts not Detached Before Rooting.

          a. Suckers—Red raspberry, blackberry.

          b. Runners—Strawberry.

          c. Layers (Layerage).

             (1) Tip Layerage—Loganberry, black raspberry, dewberry.

             (2) Simple layerage—Spirea, pyracantha.

             (3) Continuous layerage—Filbert, snowball.

             (4) Mound layerage—Quince, apple (Paradise or Doucin).

             (5) Pot or Chinese layerage—Rubber plant, oleander.

             (6) Compound layerage—Grape.

             (7) Laying down—Apple, plum, cherry.

        2. Parts Generally Detached Before Rooting.

          a. Separation.

             (1) Bulbs—Hyacinth, Easter lily.

             (2) Corms—Crocus, gladiolus.

          b. Division.

             (1) Rhizomes or rootstocks—Canna, iris.

             (2) Crowns—Lily-of-the-valley, asparagus.

             (3) Offsets—Houseleek, artichoke, pineapple.

             (4) Tubers.

                (a) Fleshy underground stems—Irish potato.

                (b) Enlarged roots—Sweet potato, dahlia.

---

[1] Taken from University of Missouri publication *Principles and Practice of Plant Propagation*, by W. L. Howard, now director of the Branch of the College of Agriculture, University of California, Davis, California.

3. Parts Always Detached Before Rooting (Cuttage).
   a. Root cuttings.
      (1) Common—Blackberry, horseradish.
      (2) Tuber—Sweet potato.
   b. Stem cuttings.
      (1) Hardwood—Pyracantha, privet.
      (2) Semi-hardwood—Privet, oleander, veronica.
      (3) Softwood—Privet, geranium, coleus, begonia.
      (4) Tuber—Irish potato.
   c. Leaf cuttings—Begonia rex, bryophyllum.

B. *On the Roots of Other Plants (Graftage):*
   1. Scion grafting.
      a. Root grafting.
         (1) Piece root graft ⎫ Apple, pear.
         (2) Whole root graft ⎭
      b. Top Grafting.
         (1) Cleft graft—Apple, pear.
         (2) Saw-kerf or notch graft—Apple, pear, walnut.
         (3) Bark graft—Apple, pear, walnut.
         (4) Side graft—Apple, pear.
         (5) Whip graft—Apple, pear.
      c. Bridge grafting—Apple, pear.
      d. Inarching or Grafting by Approach.
         (1) Inarching proper—Pear, orange, mango.
         (2) Cordons—Apple, pear.
         (3) Living braces—Apple, pear.
         (4) Living arches—Ornamental trees, etc.

   2. Bud Grafting (Budding).
      a. Shield bud or "T" bud—Peach, plum.
      b. Flute bud—Nut trees.
      c. Ring bud—Nut trees.
      d. Patch bud and its modifications—Nut trees.
      e. And others.

1. SEXUAL REPRODUCTION

4. **Seedage** is Nature's most common method of disseminating and propagating higher plants. Most farm and garden crops are thus propagated because they produce viable seed freely and give rise to plants true to type or whose exact parental form is not essential (cereals, most vegetables, forest trees and seedlings for graftage).

Seeds often offer the readiest and least expensive means for the reproduction of *species*. Seedlings usually vary somewhat in their characteristics; hence dependence cannot always be placed on them to furnish exact reproductions of their parents.

5. Sexual reproduction is carried on by the use of seed bodies (seeds) which result from the fusion *(fertilization)* of two or three masses of protoplasm, male and female, hence the term *sexual reproduction*. Seeds are fertilized ovules; structures which when matured include rudimentary plants *(embryos)* protected, while dormant, by seed coats and containing nutrients either in or around the cotyledons to supply the needs of growth.

Seeds include the following parts: 1, Embryo, 2, seed coats, 3, and often endosperm. This last, when present, results from the fusion of three protoplasmic masses, one from the pollen tube and two from the ovule (Fig. 1). A seed is essentially a young plant in the resting stage or in a state of arrested development.

6. Mechanism for seed production.—Seeds are produced by flowers (Fig. 2). The ultimate purpose of flowering is seed production to perpetuate the species. Examination shows the flower (apple, tomato, violet) to consist of four sets of organs arranged in whorls (or often spirals) about a central axis. The lowest whorl, called the *calyx*, consists of usually green, leaf-like structures (sepals). The next, composed of generally delicate, colored *petals,* is the *corolla*. Above the petals (when present) are *stamens,* usually

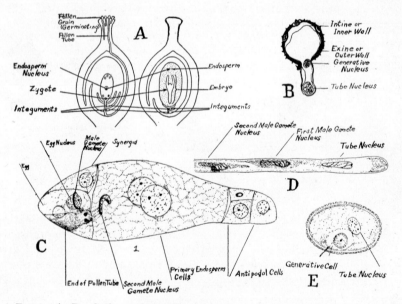

Fig. 1.—A, Developing embryo, B, germinating pollen grain; C, embryo sac, showing fertilization process, fertilized ovule; D, end section of germinating pollen tube; E, pollen grain.

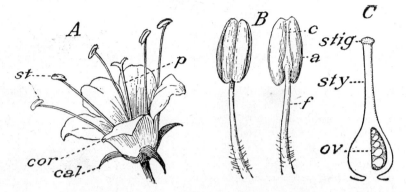

FIG. 2.—Complete flower. A. *cal*, calyx; *cor*, corolla; *st*, stamen; *p*, pistil. B. Front and back of stamen. *a*, anther; *c*, connective; *f*, filament. C. Pistil. *ov*, ovule; *sty*, style; *stig*, stigma.

thread-like and each almost always bearing a yellow or brown body (anther) at its apex. The center whorl is a group of *pistils* (often reduced to only one).

Flowers that contain all four whorls are called *complete* (pear). The two outer sets are *non-essential organs* since they do not play a direct part in reproduction and in some plants, one or both are partly or wholly lacking—Euphorbia without calyx; Croton without corolla, pepper family lacking both. The two inner whorls (stamens and pistils) are the *essential organs*. A flower which contains both sets of *essential* organs is *perfect*, though it may lack one or the other or both the outer whorls. If one of the sets of essential organs is missing (some varieties of strawberry, lack stamens, Fig. 3) the flowers are *imperfect*. An imperfect flower may be

A   B

FIG. 3.—Strawberry flowers. A, Perfect; B, Imperfect or pistillate —lacking stamens.

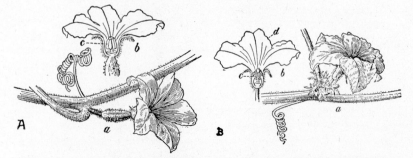

Fig. 4.—Monœcious flowers (cucumber). A. Pistillate; *a*, ovary; *b*, longitudinal section showing *c*, stigmas. B. *a*, Staminate; *b*, longitudinal section; *c*, stamens; *d*, corolla.

either *pistillate* or *staminate*, depending upon the presence of pistils in the one and stamens in the other.

When a plant bears both kinds of imperfect flowers separately it is *monœcious* (cucumber, Fig. 4). In Indian corn the tassel consists of staminate flowers and the young ear of pistillate flowers (Fig. 5). When individual plants bear flowers of only one sex they are *diœcious*, or of two households (holly, date palm, hop). In plant propagation and culture whenever fruits or seeds are desired

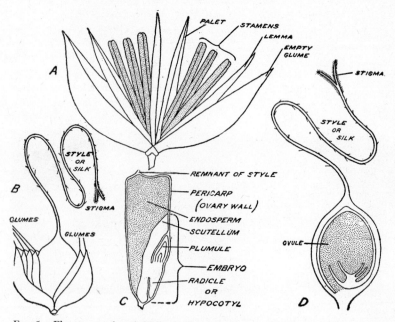

Fig. 5.—Flowers, seed and fruit of corn. A. Flower; B, pistil; C, Kernel; D, pistil enlarged showing developing embryo.

of sexually differentiated species, plantings must include both sexes to insure pollination. For example, pistachio and holly trees will produce no fruit or seed (exceptions rare) unless at least two individuals, a staminate and a pistillate tree, grow near enough together for the pollen of the former to be transferred to the pistils of the latter.

The typical stamen consists of two parts: a slender stalk-like *filament* which at its free end bears one or more *pollen sacs* or *anthers* (Fig. 6). Filament and anther both present many differences in shape, size, color and manner of attachment each to the other and to the rest of the flower. These are of considerable importance to the plant classifier in establishing natural relationships. The anther is the essential part of the stamen. It produces pollen grains, the male reproductive bodies. The filament is of use only as it holds the anther in the most favorable position for the disposal of pollen. In many flowers it is wanting.

A nearly mature typical anther examination will show a wall of sterile tissue enclosing several locules or sacs, more or less completely filled with minute pollen grains (Fig. 7). In most plants

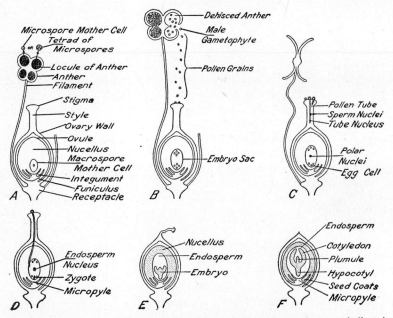

Fig. 6.—Stages of seed development. A, essential organs of flower—pistil and stamen; B, pollination—anther splitting and releasing pollen, seen falling on stigma of pistil; C, germination of pollen grains on stigmatic surface and beginning growth down style; D, fertilization; E, embryo in early stage of development; F, mature fruit containing developed embryo.

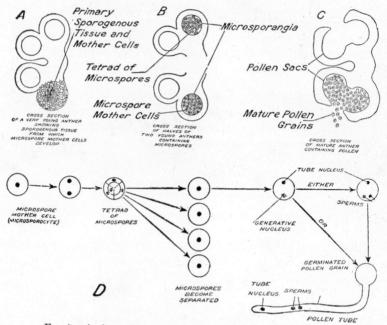

FIG. 7.—Anther. Development and growth of pollen grains.

there are four locules in each anther. As the anther approaches maturity, however, two of the walls separating the locules usually break down so that at the time of pollen dispersal each anther has but two large locules. In the early stages of anther growth each locule is filled with delicate tissue, the cells of which are known as *"mother cells."* Each one of these eventually divides to form (usually) four *"daughter cells,"* which each later develop into a pollen grain. Upon reaching maturity the anther opens *(dehisces)* and liberates its pollen.

Microscopic examination shows a pollen grain to consist of a mass of protoplasm surrounded by two walls. [1] The inner wall is a thin elastic membrane *(intine)*. The outer wall *(extine)* is thick, more or less rigid and acts as a protection for the contents. It is sometimes absent. In some species this outer is characteristically marked. Careful examination at the time pollen grains are liberated from the anther shows that the protoplasm usually contains several more or less distinct structures, two or three *nuclei,* whose substance

---

[1] Note: To observe germinating pollen place anthers from flowers in a petri dish under a glass cover in a warm place to dry for 24 hours. Then place a drop of 12% sugar solution on a slide. Sprinkle pollen on this drop and invert slide over a Van Tieghen cell partly filled with water (Fig. 8). The cell is made by imbedding a ring of glass in paraffin on a slide. In two to twelve hours the pollen will germinate.

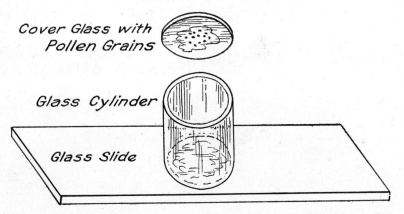

Cover Glass with Pollen Grains

Glass Cylinder

Glass Slide

FIG. 8.—Van Tieghen cell, glass ring fastened to microscope slide with paraffin or balsam.

is relatively dense. These are the *generative nucleus* and the *tube nucleus.* Usually these *nuclei* may be distinguished from each other, either in form or size.

A typical pistil consists of three parts, *ovary* or enlarged base, *style* or stalk, and *stigma,* its *tip* which is receptive to pollen. In many flowers the style is lacking, the stigma resting directly upon the ovary. Within the ovary one or more ovules may be developed from the tissues of the interior surface. Their number and attachment vary greatly, from two (peach) to thousands (poppy). They

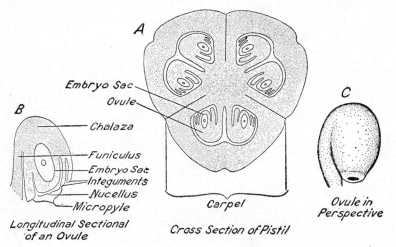

A

B

C

Embryo Sac

Ovule

Chalaza

Funiculus

Embryo Sac

Integuments

Nucellus

Micropyle

Carpel

Ovule in Perspective

Longitudinal Sectional of an Ovule

Cross Section of Pistil

FIG. 9.—Cross section of pistil showing: A, position of ovules in ovary and B, C, *ovules.*

may stand erect on the bottom, be suspended from the central axis, or attached along the sides.

Ovules vary widely in size, structure, and shape (globular, elongated, flattened, oval). Many are so small they cannot be seen by the naked eye; some are more than an eighth of an inch in diameter. Each is attached to the *placenta* of the ovary by a short stalk (chalaza) through which food is carried from the placenta to the nucellus (Fig. 9).

A high power microscope shows a typical, fully formed ovule to consist of delicate tissue, differentiated into a central portion (nucellus) and an enveloping layer *(integument)* grown together at one point originating in a single narrow area not completely in-

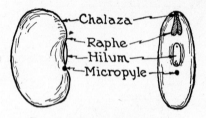

FIG. 10.—Sketch of bean seed showing parts.

closing the nucellus but leaving a small opening *(micropyle)*. One of the cells in the center of the nucellus develops into the *embryo sac*. When the seeds separate from the placenta they show a small scar *(hilum)* at the point of rupture (Fig. 10). The slight ridge made by the chalaza is the *raphe*.

7. Pollination and fertilization.—After studying pollen and ovule separately as they exist in the flower the next step is to bring them together. This step involves pollination and fertilization.

Pollination is the transfer of pollen from the anther to the stigma of the same or another flower. *Fertilization* is the actual union of male and female elements in the ovule. Every species of plant has some distinctive method to effect this transfer. Where the pollen from one flower fertilizes the ovules of the same flower (garden pea) the process is known as "selfing." Anthers need merely to close in and deposit their pollen upon the stigma. Many plants, however, have cross fertilization—by wind (Indian corn, Fig. 5), insects (clover), water (eel grass) or other means.

In some cases they have developed peculiar devices and habits to secure it. Some flowers (bean, orchid) are so shaped that self pollination is prevented; others (dandelion, tomato) mature their stamens and pistils at different times. Some are self sterile, that is, fertilization does not usually follow pollination with their own pollen, such as almond, cherry and certain varieties of grapes, plums, pears and apples.

These facts explain many phenomena observed in crop production. For instance, rainy weather during corn blossoming is likely to cause a poor set of kernels because corn is wind pollinated. Dry

weather is necessary that
the pollen may fly. Clover
is pollinated largely by
bumble bees; hence when
these insects are scarce a
poor seed crop is almost
certain, and when there are
no bumble bees red clover
seed production fails en-
tirely.

8. **Artificial pollina-
tion** (Fig. 11) is merely
transferring pollen from
stamen to stigma by human
means. It is practiced
where cucumbers, tomatoes
and other fruits are raised
in greenhouses, except
where bees are kept for this
special function. It is also
practiced in all crossing and
hybridization to produce

Fig. 11.—Artificial fertilization of lily. Note
that anthers have been removed previous to
their maturity.

new varieties of plants. The flowers are not allowed to self-polli-
nate; but pollen is used from flowers of plants with the desired
characteristics.

Artificial pollination has been practiced also in determining the
proper pollinators for various varieties of fruit trees. When determining pollinators and when creating new varieties it is necessary
to remove the stamens of the flowers to be used as the female parents. This *emasculation* is done with tweezers or the nails of thumb

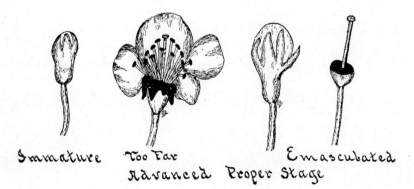

Immature   Too Far   Emasculated
          Advanced Proper Stage

Fig. 12.—Correct and incorrect stages for emasculating flowers for
artificial pollenation.

and middle finger.   The corolla and sometimes the calyx tube are pinched off along with the stamens (Fig. 12).

Pollen is collected and cared for as follows: Stamens with ripe pollen are removed from the desired flowers and placed in petri dishes in a warm place for 24 to 48 hours to dry.   It is separated from the anthers by using a fine screen, placed in a glass vial and

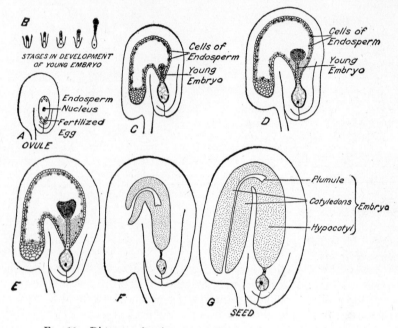

FIG. 13.—Diagrams showing growth of embryo and endosperm in shepherd's purse.

corked.   When to be applied the vial is opened against the thumb and inverted.   Some adheres to the thumb and may be brushed on the stigma of the emasculated flower, or applied with a fine camel's hair brush (Fig. 11).

Pollination is ordinarily followed by germination of the pollen grain.   The grain absorbs moisture and food from the stigmatic surface and swells.   The outer coat *(extine)* of the grain bursts and the inner one *(intine)* begins to protrude as a tube which enters the stigma.   An excretion of enzyme into the tissues of the style takes place and the reserve materials stored there are gradually digested as the tube grows and advances.   The pollen tube usually enters the ovule through the micropyle.

The time required for the pollen tube to make its way from the stigma to the ovule is influenced by length and structure of style, temperature, species of plant and many other factors. In some cases it takes only a day or two, in others it may require several months. In some fall flowering woody plants (witch-hazel) pollination takes place in the autumn but the growth of the pollen tube, checked by cold weather, does not resume until warm spring weather.

9. **Fertilization.**—Once through the micropyle, the pollen tube penetrates the nucellus and enters the embryo sac where it disintegrates and discharges its protoplasmic contents into the embryo sac. The tube disappears. If not already divided (in the pollen tube) the generative nucleus divides into two sperm nuclei. One of these unites with the egg cell of the embryo sac thus causing fertilization. The cell resulting from this fusion develops into the young plant or embryo.

The egg nucleus of the embryo sac fuses with one of the sperm nuclei from the pollen tube resulting in the body *(zygote)* which will develop into a new plant. The other sperm nucleus fuses with a protoplasmic body in the embryo sac formed by the union of two nuclei. The result of this triple fusion is the nuclear mass which will develop into endosperm (Fig. 13).

10. **Seed development.**—The plant starts its life as a result of fertilization when the male (or sperm) nucleus of the pollen tube from the pollen grain fuses with the egg (or female) nucleus in the embryo sac of the ovule (Fig. 13). The cell which results from this fusion is the beginning of the new individual.

As the ovule develops, its parts become differentiated and its coats (one or two *integuments*) become more or less hardened into the *testa* or impervious covering of the fully ripened seed (Fig. 14).

Internally a typical seed consists essentially of an embryo and one or more cotyledons. These last characters have suggested two of the chief groups of plants: *monocotyledons* (plants with only one cotyledon) and *dicotyledons* (those with two—conifers normally have more than two).

In the corn seed (a monocotyledon) the embryo is embedded in the *endosperm* or albumen of the seed. In dicotyledonous plants, (bean) it is differentiated into three main

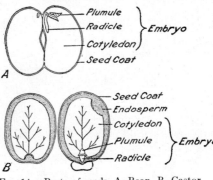
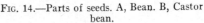

FIG. 14.—Parts of seeds. A, Bean. B, Castor bean.

parts; 1, *Hypocotyl,* terminating in the radicle or primary root with its tip directed to the *micropyle,* or "little gate," (the opening for the entrance of water); 2, the two *cotyledons* or seed leaves attached above the hypocotyl; and 3, the *epicotyl (plumule)* or bud between the cotyledons (Fig. 14).

The cotyledons may be thick and serve only for food storage (pea); they may be thin, leaf-like and serve as foliage leaves from the beginning (castor-bean) or they may combine both functions (squash).

In monocotyledonous plants the endosperm is always well developed and the embryo comparatively small. In corn, for example, the embryo consists of a shield-shaped structure; the *cotyledon* (and *scutellum*), an upward pointing, sheathed *plumule* or bud and a downward-pointing miniature *root.* In similar seeds the cotyledon absorbs food from the endosperm and transmits it to the growing point of the embryo. Normally a period of rest follows the maturity of the seed. During this time growth and development of the embryo are at a standstill although internal chemical changes may occur. (Fig. 15).

Certain seeds (wheat, corn) consist largely of endosperm. In cocoanut the endosperm reaches enormous development, the hollow center containing milk being the central cavity of the embryo sac surrounded by the closely-packed endosperm cells which form the edible portion. Endosperm is rich in food materials (starch, sugar, protein and fat) to supply the young embryo.

Immediately after fertilization the new embryo cell divides and produces more or less extensive tissue through subsequent and continued growth and re-division of the daughter cells. Gradually the various parts of the embryo found in the mature seed become discernible. In the developing seeds of many plants the embryo makes such rapid, vigorous growth that the endosperm has little or no chance to develop. What does form is broken down and the food material it contains is used by the embryo. The result is an *exalbuminous* seed in which the cotyledons are usually gorged with the food (bean—Figs. 14 and 15).

11. Secondary Effects of Fertilization.—The stimulus which fertilization imparts to the ovule and which results in the development of the seed is also transmitted to associated tissues. A few days after blossoming, apple and tomato flowers that have been fertilized have stalks more turgid than those not fertilized, and those of Japanese honeysuckle turn from white to yellow. Rapid changes also occur in the ovary wall which develops into the fleshy part of the fruit. In the strawberry the stimulus is carried to the receptacle of the flower which becomes fleshy and later edible. In the pineapple the entire inflorescence becomes fleshy to form the fruit.

In various fruits (banana, pineapple, and seedless apples, pears, plums and grapes) which never or rarely contain seeds the ovules never develop but the stimulus given by the proper pollination of the flower is usually required to develop the fleshy parts of these fruits.

12. Limits of Cross Fertilization.—Though most species of plants prefer cross to self fertilization there is a limit beyond which they will not cross. There must be a definite affinity between the two parents. Except self-sterile varieties (Brighton grape) and inter-sterile fruits (certain sweet cherries), seed plants in the same species nearly always cross. Those in different penera but in

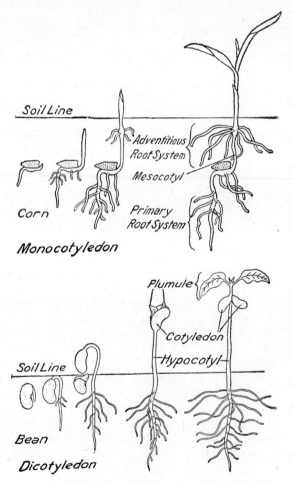

Fig. 15.—Germination of seeds and growth of seedlings.

the same family sometimes do. Those which belong to different families rarely if ever do so. If the plants concerned in the process are closely related the act is termed *crossing;* if more distantly related, that is, belonging to different species, it is hybridization.

13. Seed Dissemination.—The three important agencies in seed dissemination are wind, water, and animals. *Wind* plays an important part in transporting light seeds—often long distances—especially those with appendages which buoy them up (willow, poplar, thistle, dandelion, milkweed, sycamore). It also helps carry heavier winged seeds that whirl or flutter in the air and thus check descent more or less (maple, elm, tulip tree, boxelder, basswood, ash) carrying them several hundred or thousand feet, depending upon its velocity.

Water transports seeds that float readily (apples, walnuts, acorns) much greater distances than those that sink (chestnuts, hickory nuts). It also transports seeds carried by wind and by animals, therefore is the most general distributing agent of the three.

Animals carry seeds in one or the other of three ways: either attached to their bodies (burs and various species of *Bidens* or beggar-lice); second, in their intestines, where the juices of digestion fail to break down the protective seed coverings (blackberry, cherry, pokeberry, plum); or, third, by burying them for later use as food and then failing to dig them up. Squirrels are perhaps most active in this third way.

Man is the greatest of all seed distributors. Purposely he collects seed in all parts of the world and transports it to places where he wants to plant it; unknowingly, he carries weed seeds in bedding and packing, on ships, trains, autos and airplanes. He may accidentally or purposely mix such seeds with valuable ones and thus introduce them where the shipments are distributed. The progress of the race westward from India, Assyria, Palestine, Egypt, Mediterranean countries and Northern Europe to America and Australasia may thus be traced by weeds as well as by cultivated plants carried by man.

Seed transportation is conducted upon an extensive scale by hundreds of wholesale and retail seed merchants in all parts of the world. Seeds such as acorns are difficult to transport long distances. Usually thick-coated and bony seeds require moist, confined air; thin-shelled ones, dry conditions. For shipping to or through the tropics seed is usually sealed in tin cases or oiled packages. Most seeds, however, sent through ordinary cool climates, after being thoroughly air dried, need be placed only in cotton sacks, large paper packages or manila envelopes. Apple, pear and other small seeds are often mixed with powdered charcoal which absorbs excess moisture.

Species difficult to ship in seed form may often be more satisfactorily transported as seedlings either actively growing in Wardian cases or dormant as nursery stock. The former method is not much practiced; the latter is the favorite method of nurserymen.

14. Handling seeds of Fleshy Fruits.—Seeds of many fruits must be freed from their fleshy or pulpy coverings before they can be stored or planted. When there is no danger of injury to the seeds, the fruits may be crushed or ground; for instance, apples, the pomace is mixed with water, stirred vigorously and often for one to three weeks until the pulp has partially fermented. After the seeds

FIG. 16.—Screen to separate seeds from decayed pulpy fruits. Frame 16" x 5'. Wire mesh ⅛". Fruit crushed by hand is worked through with water into tub. After good seeds sink, pulp is poured off, seeds re-washed and spread out to dry.

sink to the bottom the pulp may be poured off, the seeds collected, rewashed and dried.

Soft fruits (blueberry, raspberry, strawberry, cranberry) are often so treated (Fig. 16) though they are perhaps as often handled like soft fruits (tomato, cucumber, melon)—merely crushed under water, the pulp poured off, the seeds washed and dried. Practicum II.

Chemical treatment of the coverings is sometimes needed to separate membranes and seeds (persimmon). Seeds are sometimes soaked in weak caustic potash solution (a stick to a pailful of water). Fresh wood ashes, lime and lye also help to free many seeds of their resinous coverings.

II. PROPAGATION BY SPORES

15. Spores.—Propagation by spores is so nearly akin to that by seeds that the two are usually classed under the one head *seedage*.

Spores are asexual, usually one-celled, reproductive bodies of flowerless plants. A striking difference between them and seeds is that they contain no embryo. While reproduction of plants from spores is not dependent on sex, as in flowering plants, the process is akin to it.

The black or brown spots *(sori)* of many ferns, (Fig. 17) produce hundreds or thousands of spores. These germinate on moist surfaces and produce small plant bodies *(prothallia)* which develop the sex organs *(archegonia* and *antheridia)* and these in turn develop the sex elements *(gametes)* which fuse, the fusion body developing into the fern plant.

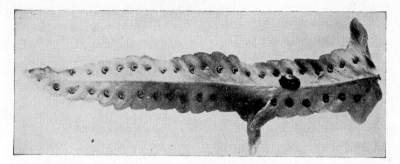

FIG. 17.—Part of fern frond showing sori which produce spores.

Spores are of interest to the horticulturist because they are employed in the propagation of ferns, mosses, and mushrooms. Many plant diseases are spread by their means (apple scab, wheat rust, black knot of cherry, downy mildew of grape).

III. ASEXUAL REPRODUCTION

16. Asexual Reproduction is the development of new individual plants or animals without the function of sex. Among seed plants it is performed by means of buds either still attached to or separated from the so-called "parent" plants. Each new individual plant possesses the characteristics of its parent except in cases of bud variations or "sports," in which there are more or less distinct differences. The various asexual methods, natural and artificial, adopted and adapted by man are of special value in propagating named varieties of many fruits and ornamentals. Some plants (Jerusalem artichoke, sweet potato, tarragon and horseradish) no longer produce seed under ordinary conditions so must be propagated by asexual methods.

17. Natural and artificial methods.—All methods employed by man are adaptations or improvements upon natural methods, instances of which may be found in nature. For this reason they should hardly be called artificial, though often so termed.

18. Natural methods of propagation differ in the three general classes of plants. Annuals and biennials all propagate themselves by seeds, of which they usually produce abundance. Except in special cases (as in increasing stock usually by cuttings of some specially individual plant) they are not propagated artificially by any asexual method; first, because the abundance of seed obviates

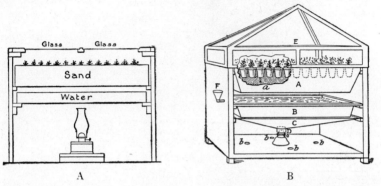

Fig. 17x.—Propagating ovens. A, Home made. B, Elaborate style. A, Galvanized iron earth tray, *a*, plants in pots; B, water tank filled by funnel, F; C, chamber heated by lamp, D, *b*, air intakes; *e*, removable top.

the need of doing so, and, second, because few of them can be so propagated.

Many warm climate plants used for ornamental bedding in gardens (coleus, geranium), though perennials in their native countries, are made to live as "stock plants" (148) from year to year in greenhouses, though outdoors they are treated as annuals. They are, therefore, so propagated.

Perennials (including trees and shrubs) may or may not propagate by seeds. Hence, they may or may not be propagated by one or both these methods according to convenience, economy or some other consideration. When they do not propagate by seeds, they do so by buds, of which they generally produce abundantly, either upon the branches and sometimes the leaves, or on roots or other underground parts. Thus, though the parent plant may die, man (and sometimes the plant itself) may take advantage of either its seeds or its buds in perpetuation.

For instance, the underground stems of quack grass are capable of producing a new plant from every joint. Again, should it be deemed necessary, the California big tree which, at the estimated age of 5,000 years, is on the road to extinction, mainly due to human activity, might be given another 5,000-year start by propagating it from buds or cuttings (Fig. 106). The process might again be repeated 50 centuries later, and so on without limit.

19. Life cycles of plants.—Every plant normally passes through a life cycle of history. The seed germinates, the plant vegetates, blooms, bears seeds and sooner or later dies. Life cycles vary in duration from a few days or weeks (peppergrass and portulaca) to many centuries (redwood, various oaks and pines). Under normal (or natural) conditions, the duration of the life cycle of any species may vary considerably because perhaps of inherited vigor or environment or both.

For instance, in a sowing of garden carrots a few plants may "run to seed" the first season, though the general life cycle of this vegetable is two years; conversely, some annuals, as radish, may fail to seed the first year, but send up flower stalks the following season. Such cases, however, are exceptional.

So far as known, no plant lives indefinitely, though by the application of certain methods of propagation existence may be continued beyond the duration of the normal life cycle of the plant so treated.

For instance, the geranium, which is normally a warm climate plant, easily killed in cold climates by frost, may be propagated by cuttings, and thus not only its numbers increased indefinitely, but its life extended by asexual generation. In one sense this is not strictly extending the life cycle of the individual plant, for the original stem and roots are generally thrown away as having served their purpose.

Because all plants normally reach the limits of their life cycles, some method of propagation is necessary if they are to be perpetuated; otherwise they will be lost. To prevent this contingency flowering plants, usually provide ample seed, though in some cases they have developed asexual methods. Strawberries propagate by means of runners (106); certain dogwoods by stolons (109); black raspberries by tip layers (100); houseleeks by rosettes (111, 114); cannas by rhizomes (108); banyan trees by aërial roots from limbs; mangroves by "knees" or prop roots; Irish potatoes by tubers (116); and so on.

20. The term environment is used to include all the external influences that, as a whole, affect a living organism in any way. Among the principal factors that make up environment are heat, light, moisture and food supply.

21. Duration of life cycle determines the three general groups of plants; annuals, biennials and perennials.

a. *Annuals* complete their life cycle in one season or less—oat, radish, cosmos, purslane.

b. *Biennials* require two growing seasons or parts of two—hollyhock, turnip, mullein. The root lives through the winter in a cold climate or has a dormant period in a warm or an arid one, and resumes activity when conditions again become favorable to growth.

Before the second season of growth closes they mature their seeds and die.

Apparent exceptions to these two groups are "winter annuals," plants which start to grow late in one season, live over winter and reach maturity early the following season (crimson clover, shepherd's purse).

c. *Perennials* live from year to year and produce seed or fail to do so. They are divided into three classes—herbaceous, woody and shrubs and trees. a. Herbaceous perennials (or perennial herbs) have perennial roots but annual tops (asparagus, peony, bindweed). b. Woody perennials have perennial roots but biennial stems (raspberry). c. Shrubs and trees are woody in both root and stem and persist from year to year without definite loss.

II

GERMINATION

22. **Germination** or sprouting is the resumption of growth by the dormant embryo or young plant in the seed. It is complete when growth has ruptured the seed coats and the embryo has emerged.

Seedlings push through the soil by the extension of their radicles, aided in some cases by their cotyledons. Though in some instances (corn) the cotyledon or cotyledons (pea) remain beneath the surface of the ground, they usually "come up" above the surface (bean, castor-bean) often turn green and perform for a time the functions of true leaves (maple, tomato, nasturtium) but cease this role when true leaves are developed.

23. **Factors that control germination:** *viability, water, free oxygen, heat* and *age* and *stage of maturity of the seed.* The seed of each species and even some varieties of a single species, seem to demand different degrees or quantities of one or more of these factors to produce best results. The most favorable combination of these factors for each kind of seed is, therefore, called the *optimum* for that species. Presupposing viability, or ability to live, the stages of germination are: 1, Absorption of moisture by the seed. 2, Conversion of stored food under favorable temperature into sugars by enzymes or natural ferments. 3, Stimulation of the embryo cells into growth. 4, Bursting the seed coat by the swelled embryo, etc.

24. **Water is necessary** because plant food must be in solution to be of service to the embryo. In practice it is, perhaps, more important than oxygen and heat because too much or too little may prevent germination. Therefore, in practice, it requires careful regulation. Generally it reaches the seed through the soil, though many seeds and spores sprout on any surface moist enough, or any material which will supply their needs.

In nature there are many variations. Cocoanuts will sprout among rocks where thrown up by the sea, their roots sustained by the "milk" while "searching" perhaps several yards for crevices in which to secure a hold and food. Countless kinds of seeds, blown by wind or carried by water, sprout among mountain rocks where both soil and water are in small supply. Long moss (Spanish moss *Tillandsia*) seeds germinate on the limbs of trees. Mistletoe does this also, but the sprouts become parasitic in the tissues of the trees to which they attach themselves.

Still water retards germination of dry land species; but little, if at all, of water plants. In the case of buckwheat grown experimentally, most seeds sprouted in 24 hours in running water, but those in still water took two days or more. Doubtless this is because of the differences in content of oxygen, the former containing the larger percent. Morinagu and others showed that many seeds germinate in water and that O_2 is the controlling factor. (Note experiments by Zimmerman with cuttings.)

25. Temperature variations influence seeds in germination less than do those of moisture (Fig. 18). Both, however, should be

Fig. 18.—Effect of temperature on germination. A. Flat in warm room germinated seed readily. B. Flat placed in ice box failed to germinate bean seed.

avoided. Seeds will stand much heat and cold if dry, but if wet, frost may injure them and heat may "cook" them. In seed storage, every precaution against decay must be observed. Especially must the seed be kept as dry as possible. The room may be even hot, provided it is not damp. This rule applies to small as well as large quantities of seeds. Often corn, wheat and other cereals imperfectly dried before shipment heat in transit and are ruined both for seed-age and food. Sometimes the heat is high enough to cause great losses in warehouses and ships.

26. Time of sowing outdoors, as well as depth, influences temperature. Seeds planted deeply in spring may rot because they are too cold; and those planted shallow in summer may continue dry and thus fail to sprout. Hence early spring sowing of any kind of seed should be shallower than that of the same kind in late spring or summer. No general rule can be given, because each species has its own preferences; but large seeds may be sown two to four times their diameters and small ones only slightly covered—just enough to hide them from light. Fresh and strong seeds may be sown

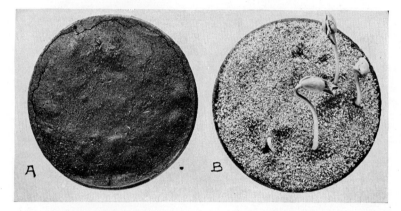

FIG. 19.—Oxygen effect on germination. A. Bean seed failed in puddled clay, it is believed, because oxygen supply was reduced. B, Beans grew when puddled clay was covered with sand which permitted free entrance of oxygen.

deeper than old or weak ones, because the seedlings should reach the surface with comparative ease.

Oxygen is usually in ample supply for germination. It is always present in soils neither tightly packed nor water-soaked (Fig. 19). Water plant seeds (lotus, waterlily) will germinate under water.

Deep planting is unfavorable to germination, first, because the supply of oxygen may be restricted (Fig. 20), second, because the seedlings may be unable to reach the surface, especially if the soil is hard. Under glass and in sand the same species of seeds may be planted at twice the depth employed in the open. After planting,

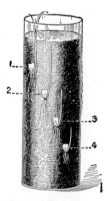

FIG. 20.—Deep planting effects. Corn seeds planted all at one time.

the soil should be firmed lightly to avoid washing the seeds out when watering. If the soil is hard and likely to bake, a light mulch of old compost should be applied in the rows.

27. Light affects germination in various ways, depending on the species of plant. Seeds of many species are indifferent; those of others slightly inhibited (*Amaranthus retroflexus*—pigweed—and larkspur); others completely or partially inhibited (*Phacelia tanacetifolia* and *Nigella arvensis*); still others require it and germinate best without cover, provided moisture is present (mistletoe, *Gesneriaceæ*). Many that are favored by it need only low intensity.

Though the value of shading is probably a question of moisture in many cases, it is considered advisable to shade fine seeds and spores

while germinating. Nothing is to be gained by the reverse
process. When covered with soil they are usually shaded enough,
but when sown upon or near the surface they sprout better when
shaded at least partially. Parsley, thyme, marjoram and other slow
sprouting and small seeds sown outdoors do best under shade (Fig.
21). However, this is more because of controlled moisture than

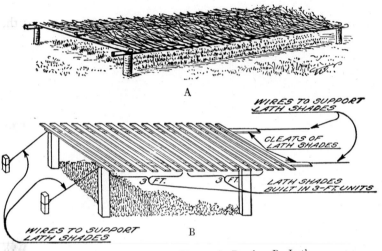

Fig. 21.—Shade for seedlings. A. Brush. B. Lath.

because of light. Paper and muslin are often used for shading.
When the seedlings have two or more true leaves shade may be
removed. In most cases, it may be said, light is not essential for
germination; on the other hand it may retard germination of many
seeds (Fig. 22).

28. Size of seed generally influences the proportionate size of
seedlings, not only as to species but as to specimen. A mere glance
at a lima bean would suggest that the seedling would be many times
larger than a begonia seedling! The same generally holds true of
the larger, heavier specimens as compared with the smaller, lighter
ones of the same species.

Influence of Seed Size. Superiority in germination of large *vs* small seeds
has been shown by M. B. Cummings in Vermont with sweet peas, sweet pump-
kins, Hubbard squash, lettuce, beans, parsley, radishes and garden peas. In
this experiment large bean seeds gave an earlier product even though it took
longer for them to germinate than smaller seeds. Experiments as a whole show
distinct advantage in using large and heavy seed.

29. Very small seeds (begonia, thyme) are merely dusted on
the soil in a seed "pan" sunk in moist sand or moss, water never

being applied directly. Sometimes another method is practiced—the water being contained in an exterior section of a flower pot. In each case the water seeps through the porous pot and keeps the soil moist. Seeds the size of celery are often watered after sowing by standing the pans in shallow water until the surface soil becomes moist. By these methods the watering is quickly done without danger of washing the seeds out of the soil.

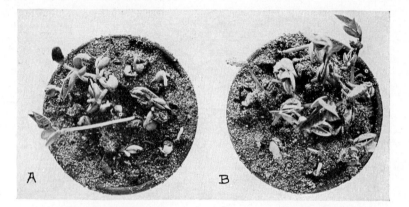

Fig. 22.—Bean seeds germinate as well in darkness (A) as in light (B). Neither light nor darkness is essential with most plants, but there are exceptions.

Too much water is as bad as too little, because the soil becomes water-logged and the seeds decay. Dampness throughout the whole soil is all that is needed in a seed bed, except for aquatic plants (water lily, rice). A wet surface over a dry soil is bad because the roots cannot grow properly. Hence seeds and seedlings should be watered from below whenever possible.

For large numbers of seeds and for large seed beds, watering with hose (or sprinkler) is necessary. Never should a strong stream or an open hose be used for such work, because these may either wash out or bury the seeds, pack the soil or do all three. Florists and gardeners who grow many plants under glass use great care in watering seeds. They aim to keep the soil moist, not wet, and never water-logged, because excess moisture weakens the seedlings and favors damping-off (73).

30. Delayed germination.—When conditions are normal, many seeds will sprout in less than three days (mustard family); others seem to require three or more weeks (parsley family); still others do not germinate under ordinary conditions for a year or more (holly, thorn, mountain ash). These differences may be due to the form of stored food, the character of seed coats, the nature of the

plant, the necessity for the rest period to be broken, the dryness of the seeds or the soil, etc. For instance, ginseng seeds if sown as soon as ripe, should sprout the following spring; if dried they may take 18 months or more. Clover and alfalfa "hard seeds" are slow to germinate unless treated with sulphuric acid. Kentucky coffee tree seeds are also slow but when treated thus are quick (Fig. 23).

FIG. 23.—Kentucky coffee tree seedling 40 days old from seed treated with sulphuric acid.

Slow, irregular germination is understandable for usually the sooner a seed germinates after it is planted, the better, because the risk of being destroyed by animals or fungi is reduced and the seedling given a better chance to develop. Weeds may gain a start if germination is delayed. Therefore, the seeds and the soil should always be treated in ways that favor prompt germination.

30A. Freezing.—Corn often suffers from freezing of water in its tissues before the grain is thoroughly dry. When it contains 13% or less moisture it will withstand considerable frost.

31. The germination test. In testing germination it is advisable to take duplicate samples each containing 200 seeds of small seeded crops and 100 of large seeded ones. The germinator may be a piece of flannel, white blotting paper or other material placed in a shallow dish (Fig. 24). The seed should be spread uniformly, covered with another blotter, cloth, etc., and another plate or glass placed over the whole and examined daily. For small seeds Petri dishes used by bacteriologists are more convenient than soup plates because they occupy less space. Seed pans and flower pots are useful in a larger way. For work in colleges, germinating ovens are more convenient and useful. Other methods are shown in Figure 17x. Water enough to keep the seeds moist during the test should be supplied but the seeds should not stand in water. A place should be selected where day and night temperature are fairly uniform. The length of time the test should continue varies with species of seed (Table 2 and Practicum X).

Selecting seeds for germination test must be done indiscriminately without regard to the appearance of the seed. Beginners are likely to choose the more promising looking seeds. When such are used the results will be deceiving in favor of the dealer.

32. Value of laboratory tests as related to field conditions. Experiments carried on at the Montana Experiment Station show that laboratory tests indicate rather closely the percentage of seeds which, in a given lot, will produce healthy plants under normal conditions. Results show that the number of plants produced from 100 seeds in the field may be 75% to 85% of what is called "actual planting value of seeds," a value obtained by multiplying the purity percentage by the germination percentage of any given lot of seeds. This relation between laboratory tests and field germination holds true more generally among cereals and other large seeded plants than with small-seeded plants (flax, alfalfa).

33. Value of "trial grounds" to seedsmen and to the public cannot be over-estimated (Fig. 25). The firm's stocks and those of competitors are grown side by side, and as the season advances, critical observations are made, with the result that inferior stock is discovered and disposed of in ways that will do no harm.

34. Importance of seed analysis is threefold: a, seeds are the most variable materials farmers have to buy; b, weight for weight they are most costly; c, the success or failure of the immediate crops and often of several generations of crops depends largely or perhaps even wholly upon the character of the seed. Hence seed

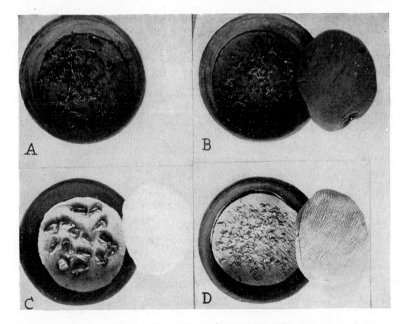

Fig. 24.—Seeds germinating: A, alfalfa on blotter only; B, white clover between two blotters; C, corn between folds of canton flannel; D, lettuce between paper toweling. Seedlings to be counted daily and recorded with dates.

FIG. 25.—Seedsmen grow samples of their own and other stocks side by side to test the character of each.

testing is almost essential to the modern farmer who must leave no point to chance.

Borlase furnished an example in the following table and comment:

TABLE 1.—VALUE OF SEED ANALYSIS ILLUSTRATED

Sample	Pound Price, Cents	% Good Seeds	% Inferior Seeds	% Weed Seeds	Number Seeds in Pound	Number Good Seed for a Cent
1	*25	97.1	1.7	1.2	213,620	8,906
2	*20	78.6	13.4	8.0	172,920	8,640
3	*18	60.3	28.1	11.6	132,660	7,370

*Price approximate, hence "number good seed for a cent" also approximate.

35. Stratification[1] is a modification of nature's method of handling seeds. In cold climates the seeds are broken open through the action of water and by frost; in warm ones by the help of moisture alone, usually abundant during the rainy season. Stratification may consist in fully exposing the seeds to the action of the weather;

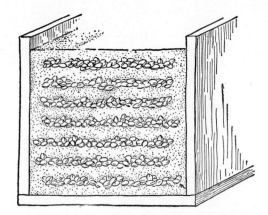

FIG. 26.—Box of stratified seed in cross section.

usually this consists of alternate layers of seeds and moist sand or sifted soil (Fig. 26) either in shallow boxes, flats, pits, or trenches. The flats are placed on the ground outdoors to be moistened by rain and snow and to freeze and thaw. The north side of a building is an excellent place to store them. Nearly all hard and bony seeds fail to germinate evenly if allowed to become thoroughly dry. In many

---

[1] Compare and contrast these methods with that developed by the Boyce Thompson Institute (36, 37).

TABLE 2.—SUGGESTED PROCEDURE FOR GERMINATION TESTS

Kind of seed	Substra-tum [1]	Tempera-ture (° C.)[2]	Usual duration of test	
			Prelimi-nary count (days)	Final count (days)
Field crops:				
Barley [3]	B	20	3	5
Beans	T, S	20–30	3	6
Beet [4], [5]	B	20–30	4	10
Buckwheat	B	20–30	3	5
Corn	T, S	20–30	3	5
Cotton [6]	T, S	20–30	4	7
Flax	TB	20–30	2	5
Hemp	B	20–30	3	5
Oats [3]	B	20	3	5
Peas	T, S	20	4	8
Rice	B	20–30	3	6
Rye [3]	B	20	3	5
Tobacco	TB	20–30	7	14
Wheat [3]	B	20	3	5
Wheat, durum [3]	B	20	4	6
Forage plants:				
Alfalfa	B	20	3	5
Bermuda grass [7]	BJ	20–35	10	21
Bluegrass, Canada [7]	BJ	20–30	14	28
Bluegrass, Kentucky	BJ, TB	20–30	14	28
Brome grass	B	20–30	5	10
Carpet grass	BJ	20–35	10	21
Clover, alsike	B	20	3	5
Clover, crimson	B	20	3	6
Clover, Japan	B	20–35	6	14
Clover, red	B	20	3	5
Clover, sweet	B	20	3	5
Clover, white	B	20	3	5
Cowpeas	T, S	20–30	4	10
Crested dog's-tail	B	20–30	10	18
Bent grass	BJ	20–30	10	21
Dallis grass	BJ	20–35	10	21
Fescues (except meadow)	B	20–30	10	21
Fescue, meadow	B	20–30	5	10
Meadow foxtail	B	20–30	6	10
Millet	B	20–30	3	5
Johnson grass	B	20–35	6	10
Orchard grass	B	20–30	6	14
Paspalum	B	20–35	6	14
Rape	B	20	3	5
Redtop	TB	20–30	5	10

[1] B = between blotters; TB = on top of blotters; T = between folds of absorbent paper towels or of Canton flannel; S = sand or soil boxes; BJ = bell jar or other modification of Jacobsen apparatus such as Copenhagen apparatus or Petri dishes.

[2] Where two temperatures are given (as 20–30° C.) the test should be alternated between the given temperatures. It does *not* mean that temperature may fluctuate within these limits.

[3] Freshly harvested cereals that do not germinate readily by usual method should be germinated at 15° C. or by the prechilling method; i.e., test should be kept in ice box for three to five days, and then test should be completed at room temperature.

[4] Soak in water at 20° C. for two hours before testing for germination.

[5] It is recommended that beet germination be confined to determination of percentage of balls which sprout.

[6] Samples of cotton seed from Southwest, when tested by this method, often decay badly, although seed can be shown to have a high viability. When this condition is suspected supplementary germination tests should be made by thoroughly wetting fuzz of seed before putting it to germinate. If supplementary test is higher than standard test, report both standard germination and live seed (as indicated by result of supplementary test).

[7] Test should be exposed to light for portion of day (3 to 8 hours). Also complete germination is hastened markedly by moistening substratum with 0.2 per cent solution of potassium nitrate.

U. S. Dept. of Agr. Circular 406.

TABLE 2.— *Continued*

Kind of seed	Substra-tum [1]	Tempera-ture (° C.)[2]	Usual duration of test	
			Prelimi-nary count (days)	Final count (days)
Forage plants—Continued.				
Rescue grass	BJ	20–35	10	21
Rhodes grass	B	20–30	6	10
Ryegrass	B	20–30	6	10
Sorghum	B	20–30	3	5
Sudan grass	B	20–30	3	5
Soy beans	T, S	20–30	4	8
Sweet vernal grass	B	20–30	6	14
Tall oat grass	B	20–30	6	10
Timothy	TB	20–30	5	8
Turnip	B	20	3	5
Velvet grass	B	20–30	6	10
Vetch	T, S	20	4	14
Vegetables:				
Asparagus	T	20–30	6	14
Beans	T, S	20–20	3	6
Beet [4], [5]	B	20–30	4	10
Cabbage	B	20	3	5
Carrot	B	20–30	6	14
Cauliflower	B	20	3	5
Celery	B	20–30	10	21
Cucumber	B	20–30	3	5
Eggplant	TB	20–30	8	14
Kale	B	20	3	5
Lettuce [8]	B	20	2	4
Muskmelon	B	20–30	3	5
Okra	T	20–30	4	14
Onion	B	20	5	10
Parsley	B	20–30	14	28
Parsnip	B	20–30	6	21
Peas	T, S	20	3	6
Pepper	TB	20–30	4	10
Pumpkin	T	20–20	3	6
Radish	B	20	3	5
Salsify	T	20–30	5	10
Spinach	TB	20	5	10
Squash	T	20–30	3	6
Sweet corn	T, S	20–30	3	5
Tomato	B	20–30	4	10
Turnip	B	20	3	5
Watermelon	B	20–30	4	6
Flowers: [9]				
Ageratum	TB	20–30	6	10
Aster	B	20	5	12
Alyssum	TB	20	5	10
Balsam (Impatiens)	B	20	3	5
California poppy	B	20	4	12
Calendula	B	20	3	10
Candytuft	TB	20	3	8
Coreopsis	B	20	5	10
Cosmos	B	20	3	10
Hollyhock	B	20	5	16
Larkspur [10]	B	15	8	21
Morning-glory	B	20–30	5	14
Mignonette	B	20	4	10
Nasturtium	T	15	7	10
Pansy	TB	20	6	12

[8] Soak for two hours in water not above 20° C. Samples which remain dormant may be germinated by prechilling method, or may be placed on moist absorbent cotton in Petri dishes.
[9] A longer list of flowers is available through the Department.
[10] May also be germinated by prechilling method, as noted in footnote 3.

TABLE 2.— *Continued*

Kind of seed	Substratum [1]	Temperature (° C.)[2]	Usual duration of test	
			Preliminary count (days)	Final count (days)
Petunia	TB	20–30	5	10
Poppy	TB	15	5	10
Portulaca	TB	20	3	8
Snapdragon	TB	20	6	10
Summer cypress (Kochia)................	TB	20–30	3	6
Sunflower	B	20–30	6	14
Sweet pea................................	T	20	5	10
Zinnia	B	20–30	4	8

cases, the shells must also be broken before the embryo can grow. Therefore, stratification is practiced as a rule with most nuts and the seeds of forest trees, shrubs, roses and of many common fruits. (See Table 3.)

When large quantities of seeds are to be stratified, or when stratification is done on a commercial scale, the best plan is to dig a pit 8″ or 10″ deep in a well drained place and dump the seeds into this in bulk and mix them with sifted soil or preferably sand. The

TABLE 3.—SEED WHICH MAY BE STRATIFIED AS SOON AS PROCURED

Apple (*Malus*).
Apricot [1] (*Prunus armeniaca*).
Ash (*Fraxinus*).
Barberry (*Berberis*).
Beech (*Fagus*).
Bittersweet (*Celastrus*).
Boxwood (*Buxus*).
Chestnut (*Castanea*).
Cherry (*Prunus*).
Cork tree (*Phellodendron*).
Cotoneaster (*Cotoneaster*).
Cranberry bush (*Viburnum*).
Dogwood (*Cornus*).
False indigo (*Amorpha*).
Firethorn (*Pyracantha*).
Flowering Quince (*Cydonia*).
Peach (*Amygdalus*).
Pear, French (*Pyrus communis*).
Pearlbush (*Exochorda*).
Persimmon (*Diospyros*).
Plum (*Prunus*).
Privet (*Ligustrum*).
Russian olive (*Elæagnus*).
Shadblow (*Amelanchier*).

Fringe tree (*Chionanthus*).
Hackberry (*Celtis*).
Hawthorn (*Cratægus*).
Holly (*Ilex*).
Honeysuckle (*Lonicera*).
Hornbeam (*Carpinus*).
Horsechestnut (*Æsculus*).
Juniper, redcedar (*Juniperus*).
Linden (*Tilia*).
Locust (*Robinia* and *Gleditsia*).
Magnolia (*Magnolia*).
Maidenhair tree (*Ginkgo*).
Maple (*Acer*), species that ripen in fall.
Nandina (*Nandina*).
Oak (*Quercus*).
Papaw (*Asimina*).
Siberian pea-tree (*Caragana*).
Silver-bell (*Halesia*).
Snowbell (*Styrax*).
Sweet gum (*Liquidambar*).
Tulip tree (*Liridodendron*).
Yellowwood (*Cladrastis*).
Yew (*Taxus*).

[1] Apricot seed should not be stratified until three weeks before planting It germinates too quickly.

mass may even extend above ground level. Finally, the top layer of seeds is mounded with sand 3″ or 4″ above the ground surface. If water stands at the bottom of the pit the seeds will be drowned.

Some seeds should be stratified as soon as procured. Some planted immediately (oak, chestnut) when ripened. Others should be kept dry over winter and planted in spring (Tables 4 and 5).

TABLE 4.—SEEDS WHICH MAY BE KEPT DRY AND PLANTED IN SPRING

Althæa (*Hibiscus syriacus*).
American arbor vitæ (*Thuja occident-alis*).
Bald cypress (*Taxodium*).
Bluebeard (*Caryopteris*).
Catalpa (*Catalpa*).
Cedar (*Cedrus*).
Chaste-tree (*Vitex*).
Crape myrtle (*Lagerstrœmia*).
Cryptomeria (*Cryptomeria*).
Cypress (*Cupressus* and *Chamœcyparis*).
Hemlock (*Tsuga*).
Larch (*Larix*).

Mock orange (*Philadelphus*).
Mulberry (*Morus*).
Oriental arborvitæ (*Thuja orientalis*).
Pear, oriental species (*Pyrus calleryana* and *P. ussuriensis*).
Plane tree (*Platanus*).
Redbud (*Cercis*).
Sophora (*Sophora*).
Spruce (*Picea*).
Sweetshrub (*Calycanthus*).
Umbrella pine (*Sciadopitys*).
Wisteria (*Wisteria*).

TABLE 5.—THESE SEEDS SHOULD BE PLANTED AS SOON AS RIPE

Birch (*Betula*).
Elm (*Ulmus*).

Maple(*Acer*), species that ripen in spring.
Oak (*Quercus*).

The California method of stratifying almond and apricot seeds is to stratify in spring. Three or four weeks before planting time boards laid on the ground are covered with an inch of sand on which almonds are spread. Alternate layers are made until the pile is complete. If kept wet during warm weather the seeds will swell or burst open and be ready to plant in drills one or two inches deep. The sprouts should not be more than one half inch long when planted. If stratified earlier they germinate and are ready to plant before the ground has warmed up enough for favorable growth. During unusually dry springs it may be necessary to sprinkle the stratified seeds as they must always be kept moist. They may also be stratified in flats or boxes.

Stratifying peach, plum and cherry seeds in California, for best results should be done in early November or at about the time the fall rains begin. On a small scale they may be stratified in flats well drained by holes in the bottoms, placed flat on the ground outdoors on the north side of a building and left uncovered to receive all rain. The seeds must not lie long in standing water or water-logged soil or sand. If rain does not fall the sand must be kept moist by sprinkling.

Peach pits usually germinate well if stored in moist sand and subjected to freezing which helps to loosen the sutures. However, freezing is not essential; in the Southern States good results are obtained by keeping the pits moist from the time they are collected or, if the ground is moist, by planting them soon after collection.

Poor peach pits with aborted kernels may be separated from the viable seed by dumping the suspected lot into water. The defective ones will float.

Stratification of nuts should be done in the fall in well drained boxes, flats, pits or trenches. The shells of butternuts and black walnuts are so impervious, that moisture is greatly delayed in reaching the germs. Hence stratification is necessary. The nuts are stratified in moist sand and exposed to frost which splits the two united parts of the shell thus permitting moisture to reach the embryo. In February and later, the seeds should be examined. When they begin to show signs of sprouting they should be planted in nursery rows. In the Western and Eastern states this means that the soil must be prepared in late Autumn. By plowing deeply then it can be put in condition for the seeds in February, March or April shortly after a heavy rain, as only the surface need then be made fine.

Chestnuts and acorns should be stratified during November or December in fine, barely moist sawdust and placed in cold storage at 32° to 40° F. They will start to germinate during February or later in storage and should then be planted. If it is not possible to plant in February, they should be kept in storage below 32°.

Myrobalan plum seeds may be treated with various solutions to hasten germination. Home grown myrobalan seeds, however, may be stratified like those of other stone fruits.

Stratification of pine seeds in moist acid peat at 5° C. (41° F.) for two months at the Boyce Thompson Institute hastened germination and in most cases resulted in a larger number of seedlings. The above storage conditions are recommended for all species tested except *Pinus palustris*, for which one month at 5° C. or one to two months at zero are recommended (Fig. 28). The species tested were Pinus excelsa, cembra, palustris, tæda, echinata, carabæa, and Sequoia sempervirens, *Amer. Jour. Bot.*, 17.

36. Seed storage.[1]—Though some seeds germinate quickly if slightly immature, in general it is best to harvest all when fully ripe, for such seeds keep better than unripe ones. Proper stratification or other treatments will overcome any tardiness due to thorough ripening.

As seeds vary greatly in the amount of drying they can stand and perhaps in their behavior to other storage factors, best storage

---

[1] Harvesting, Storing and Stratification of Seeds in Relation to Nursery Practise. William Crocker, *Florists Review*, 65, No. 1684, March 6, 1930.

conditions for any sort of seed can be learned only by experiment.

Some seeds will withstand little drying so must be sown immediately after harvest or stratified in a moist medium at a low temperature. For example, red and silver maple seed which when newly ripe contain 50 to 65% of moisture are killed if the moisture falls much below 35%; yet when stored moist just above freezing they have been kept fully viable for more than a year. It is practical, however, to sow them immediately after gathering and before they become dry. Poplar and willow seeds also.

In the New York climate the critical moisture content is approximately that of thoroughly air-dried seeds. Fluctuation in moisture content also seems to shorten the life of seeds. This is one of the factors that make for the success of seed storage in hermetically sealed vessels (various conifers and delphinium). Possibly the accumulation of carbon dioxide or the depletion of oxygen in such containers may also have an influence. When seeds are to be stored thus their moisture content must be low—certainly well air-dried, probably even drier, especially if to be stored at relatively high temperatures.

Though the moisture remains the same, seed vitality is prolonged directly as the temperature drops. For instance, parsnip seed keeps much better at 40° than at 70°, even though the former contains 50% more water. Lowering the temperatures will partly offset the ill effects of high temperatures. According to *The Forest Worker*, "noble pine" seeds kept in sealed storage at 7° to 14° F. germinated as well after three or four years as they did after only one year of ordinary storage.

37. Oxygen influences vitality of stored seeds.—There is great need of thorough study of the combined effects of moisture, low temperature and absence of oxygen as affecting vitality in stored seeds. Possibly the vitality of any seeds that withstand moderate artificial drying may be lengthened many years by proper combination of these three factors.

Guillaumin kept soy beans in perfect condition for six years in a vacuum and in an atmosphere of nitrogen, whereas in ordinary air they failed to germinate. Fatty seeds, especially, seem sensitive to oxygen in storage.

Studies along these lines at the Boyce Thompson Institute show that delphinium seeds in ordinary storage lose their vitality almost completely after two or three years but that air-dried seeds in sealed jars retain their vitality well at all temperatures, that lowering improves their keeping quality and that seeds under the better storage conditions show little fall of vitality after being stored three years. These experiments may have to run several years longer to decide whether 7° F. or 40° F. is the better temperature and whether extra artificial drying is ultimately beneficial or injurious.

Rosaceous seeds, when handled and shipped in the fruits, are often injured by heating. They give best results when freed from the ripe, fleshy parts, washed clean, dried and so stored until time for stratification. American plum, *(Prunus americana)* so handled and stored in a dry seed locker at the Institute for 31 months gave 94% germination. Because of this high rate other seeds of this same lot stored at lower temperatures and with special drying have not been tested yet for germination. Japanese rose *(Rosa multiflora)* similarly handled but stratified for 60 to 70 days gave good germination and fine seedlings the second spring after being harvested. Apple seeds which are sometimes said not to stand dry storage for even a short time, treated in this manner and stored 30 months showed little degeneration. Hence the conclusion that it is safe to clean, dry and store rosaceous seeds in the dry state from harvest time until winter stratification.

38. Modern stratification.—The term "stratification" formerly applied to storing seeds in alternate layers with moist sand and subjecting them to cold or, more generally, freezing temperatures. The Boyce Thompson Institute has proved mixing to be far better than stratification, though this term is still used for the new method. It has also proved granulated peat moss to be a better medium than sand, muck or soil.

Peat is superior because it can be pressed free enough from moisture to give good air supply and yet be moist enough to prevent excessive drying. It holds more than ten times as much water as sand when each contain the most favorable amounts of water for stratification. As it is normally acid it might be thought injurious to seeds, yet in all tests except one (bearberry—*Arctostaphylos uva-ursi*) natural peat gave as good results as washed or neutralized samples. So it is recommended. Washing was done by leaching which left the material only slightly acid; neutralizing by thoroughly mixing about one half pound of 200-mesh limestone powder with about half a bushel of packed peat to insure neutralization of all parts.

Stratification (in the mixing way) gives best results when moisture and air are properly regulated—no part of the medium being water-logged or too dry. This condition may be best maintained by shifting the material from one box to another at intervals of three or four weeks, loosening any parts that become compact and adding water when needed.

Alternate freezing and thawing has long been considered essential to most successful stratification, but exhaustive studies at the Institute have proved this practice a mistake. Best results have invariably occurred in a range from just above freezing to 50° F. No benefit was observed from either permanent or temporary freezing. Even the splitting of stony seeds is not hastened by freezing. Damson plum seeds crack first at 59° and still later at 41°, which is the best after-ripening temperature for these seeds. Freezing has not proved either beneficial or necessary. On the contrary, considerable freezing after the seeds are ready to germinate is likely to be injurious. Certainly it stops those chemical changes which generally occur in seeds stratified at temperatures above freezing.

Practical stratification in the production of seedlings depends upon maintaining the best temperature for the most favorable length of time for each species of seed. When the producer knows these he may start stratifying at the beginning of the required time to have the seed ready for sowing when spring opens. For instance, apple seeds require 60 to 70 days at 40° for complete after-ripening. As they then begin to germinate in the stratification material they must be sown immediately. Hence they should be stored dry until two months before needed for sowing, then stratified until sowing time. When to be sown on April first they must by stored dry until February first, then stratified. Another instance: Flowering dogwood (*Cornus florida*) seed to be sown May first must be stored dry until January first, then stratified at 40° F. Seeds that germinate at stratification temperatures cannot be stratified much earlier than their after-ripening period. But those that do not germinate at a temperature as low as that of stratification can be carried in stratification for some time after they are ready to germinate (Table 6).

Nurserymen often complain of little or no germination of birch seeds. Experiments at the Institute show that when first harvested they germinate poorly at any temperature. When thoroughly air dried for a month or more they will germinate only at relatively high temperatures. If stratified at a low temperature they gradually fall at the temperature at which they will germinate until after five or six months of stratification they will germinate at the freezing point.

From these statements it is evident that dry, stored birch seeds will not germinate in the cold seed beds of early spring. With proper stratification, however, there should be no difficulty in spring seedling production. Birch seeds are the only ones the Institute has found where the germination falls greatly with stratification.

Though in most cases studied temperatures above 50° F. are not effective for stratification, but are likely to make the seeds more dormant rather than to prepare them for germination, in the cases of three southern pines (*Pinus echinata, P. caribæa* and *P. tæda*) temperatures up to 59° are effective. In these, however, 32° to 40° are far more practical, for they largely prevent germination while the seeds are in stratification. It is possible that with more southerly forms generally higher stratification temperatures than 50° will be effective, but probably not practical on account of excessive germination during stratification.

In certain species of cotoneaster low temperature stratification previous to spring sowing is not the most effective way of producing seedlings. This is also true of American holly (*Ilex opaca*) and English holly (*I. aquifolium*). Good seedling production is obtained by cleaning the seeds in the fall and storing dry until spring, then sowing them in coldframes, mulching lightly during the following winter. The next spring gives much higher seedling production, often running the total to over 40%. Many thousand seedlings have been produced by this method. In one case English holly seeds were kept in laboratory germinators for 18 months, then sowed outside in spring. The following spring they produced 66% of seedlings, the highest seedling yield. This, of course, is not a practical method. When common winterberry (*I. verticillata*) seeds are sown in spring in open coldframes they give good seedling production the following spring. They do not do well if mulched during winter. It is possible that many germinate and die before the removal of the mulch in spring. Yaupon (*I. vomitoria*) seeds will germinate even in a greenhouse in about nine months.

The only method of hastening the germination of holly seeds that has been tried at the Institute is breaking the hard coats, but it is not practical.

Every kind of seed stratified at the Institute is also planted in the fall in three sorts of coldframes—uncovered, covered, with board cover and those mulched and board covered. With few exceptions this method of growing seedlings has certain innate disadvantages. First, the seeds must be protected with wire netting to keep out rodents. Second, most seeds do not get the proper temperature in the open and the board covered frames. Third, though proper mulching will give the desired temperature (a little above freezing point) it also leads to germination and death of many seedlings during winter, especially in cases of one, two or three months of stratification.

With seeds that respond to low-temperature stratification, fall planting in coldframes, mulched or otherwise, is a poor substitute for proper stratification in a cold cellar or a refrigerator room.

Now that we know the proper temperature and time for stratification of many nursery seeds, seedling production can be put on an efficient and exact basis. The fact that a rather large range of temperature is effective (about 40° F. and a range from 32° to 50°) makes control of temperature simple. Artificial refrigeration will give best results. If not available a good stratification cellar can be kept at temperatures that will give good results.

39. When to plant stratified seeds.—Stratified seeds should always be planted early in spring before germination starts, because many species sprout while the ground is still cold (pear, beech, oak, apple). If sprouting starts before sowing, the percentage of loss will be high. Hence the seed bed should be prepared the previous fall so as to lose no time in spring. Peach and plum seeds do not suffer as much as do apple and pear seeds. Should it ever be necessary to sow the seeds, especially of small kinds, such as apple, strawberry, raspberry, while the soil is wet and cold, it is a good plan to open furrows and cover the seeds with well-decayed, fibrous compost, sawdust or similar material, so as to prevent baking. A good mixture for this purpose is rotted sod, sharp sand and cow manure which has been rotted a year or more and turned over twice or oftener to secure uniformity.

40. Vitality of seeds.—Most lots contain some seeds that will not germinate at all. They are dead even though freshly gathered and properly handled. Among viable seeds vitality varies greatly (Table 7) but unless the embryos be vigorous they will not sprout well nor produce strong plants. Hence the importance of using only the best. Since the price paid for good seed is little compared with the value of the crop the best farmers never haggle over the "high prices" of seeds sold by reputable seedsmen (34). For instance, The Long Island Cauliflower Growers Association members never pay less than 75 cents an ounce for seed, all of which is purchased in large lots on contract. The lowest retail price quoted at this writing by a well-known seed house is 75 cents an ounce for an old standard variety; the highest $8, but this last is for a new variety.

TABLE 6—TIME AND TEMPERATURE EFFECTIVE FOR STRATIFICATION

Name of seeds	Temperature Best	Effective range	Best time (Days)	Name of seeds	Temperature Best	Effective range	Best time (Days)
Pinus austriaca	41	32–50	30–60	French crab apple	41	41–46	84
P. banksiana	32	32–41	60	French pear (stored dry 6 months)	41	41–50	90
P. contorta	41	32–50	60	Japan pear (stored dry 6 months)	41	41–50	100
P. coulteri	41	32–41	30	Sorbus aucuparia	32	32–41	90
P. densiflora	50	32–50	30	Photinia glabra	50	41–50	38
P. flexilis	41	32–50	30–60	Aronia arbutifolia	32	32–41	90
P. insignis	41	32–50	60	A. arb. var. atropurpurea	50	32–41	60
P. lambertiana	50	32–50	90	Amelanchier canadensis	46	32–50	120
P. monticola	32	32–50	90	Rubus chamaemorus	32	32–41	180
P. ponderosa	32–41	32–50	30–60	Rosa multiflora	41	41–46	50
P. resinosa	32–50	32–50	30	R. rugosa	41	32–50	84
P. rigida	41	32–50	30	R. canina	41	32–50	270
P. strobus	50	32–50	60	R. fendleri	41	32–50	300
P. thunbergii	41	32–50	30	R. helene	41	32–50	210
Picea excelsa	32	32–41	60	R. carolina	41	32–50	90
P. canadensis	32	32–41	60	R. setigera	41	32–50	100
P. omorika	41	32–50	30	R. rubrifolia	41	32–50	360
P. pungens	41	32–50	30	Prunus americana	41	32–50	150
P. sitchensis	32	32–50	30–60	P.simonii (apricot-plum) carpel intact	50	32–50	45
Abies arizonica	32	32–41	30	P.simonii (apricot-plum) out of carpel	41	32–50	25
Taxodium distichum	41	32–50	30	Peach (carpel intact)	41–50	32–50	60–100
Libocedrus decurrens	32–41	32–50	30–60	Peach (out of carpel)	41	32–50	35–60
Thuja gigantea	41	32–50	30–60	Prunus tomentosa (carpel intact)	41	32–50	75
Thuja occidentalis	32	32–50	60	P. tomentosa (out of carpel)	41	41–50	42
Cupressus macrocarpa	32	32–50	60	Damson plum (carpel intact)	41	41–50	110
Juniperus virginiana	50	32–50	65	Damson plum (out of carpel)	41	32–50	84

Smilacina racemosa	41	32–50	90–120
Maianthemum canadense	41–50	32–50	140
Convallaria (Lily-of-the-valley)	41	32–50	150
Iris pseudacorus	41	32–50	75
I. versicolor	41	32–50	75
Belamcanda	41	41–50	120
Betula lenta	41	32–50	60–75
B. papyrifera	41	32–50	60–75
B. lutea	41	32–50	60–75
Liriodendron tulipifera (daily or weekly alternation)	32–50	32–60	70
Exochorda	41	32–50	50
Cotoneaster horizontalis*	50	50	70
C. dielsiana	50	50	70
C. zabelii	50	50	70
Pyrus ussuriensis (fresh seeds)	45	41–50	50
Domestic apple	41	41–46	60–70

P. avium (Mazzard)	41	32–50	90
P. cerasus (Montmorency)	41	32–50	120
P. cerasus (Early Richmond) (carpel intact)	32	32–41	90
P. cerasus (Early Richmond) (out of carpel)	32	32–50	60
Acer palmatum (Red Jap. maple)	41	32–50	100–120
Carica papaya (Pawpaw)	50	32–50	100
Cornus florida	41	32–50	120
C. kousa	41	32–50	120
C. nuttallii	32	32–50	140
C. canadensis	41	32–43	120–150
C. mas	50	50	120
C. officinalis	50	41–50	300
Diospyros virginiana	50	32–50	60
Fraxinus lanceolata	41	32–50	30
F. ornus	53	32–58	90

* After stratification gave only 5-10 per cent seedling production. Planting in coldframes covered with board covers in February gave between 30 and 40 per cent seedling production the second spring following planting. Open coldframes gave only 15-32 per cent. Mulched coldframes gave 30 to 36 per cent seedlings. When stratified for 90 days at 59 degrees followed by 90 days at 34 degrees, seeds gave about 30 per cent germination.

Among farm crops that suffer because the seeds are of low vitality are clover, blue grass, corn and wheat; among garden crops; cabbage, cauliflower, onion, turnip, parsnip, lima bean and celery. Hence, they are high priced.

41. Seed corn drying experiments have shown that corn dried down to 10% did not have its germination impaired. The rate of drying has little effect on germination while drying temperature has. A temperature of 104° to 113° F. does not damage the seed. At 122° F. considerable damage results. At 140° F. in an experiment nearly all seeds were killed.

42. Seeds in the tropics.—Many kinds of seed deteriorate rapidly in tropical climates—instances of 90% germination immediately on gathering with only 50% a month later and zero at three months.

Powdered charcoal is recommended as packing for such seeds as lose their vitality when shipped long distances.

43. Vitality of buried seeds.

Experiments started by W. J. Beal in 1879 at the Michigan State College with twenty-two species of weed seeds buried in inverted bottles in the soil to test vitality showed the following percentages of germination at the end of fifty years (in 1929); Common smartweed or water pepper (*Polygonum hydropiper*), 4; black mustard (*Brassica nigra*), 8; common evening primrose (*Œnothera biennis*), 38; curled dock (*Rumex crispus*), 52; moth mullein (*Verbascum blattaria*), 62.

Many nuts and acorns quickly lose their vitality when dried; therefore, they should be either planted soon after maturing or stratified in moist but not wet sand, soil or moss kept in a cool place. Dr. T. H. Hoskins reports perfect germination of butternuts after storage in a loft four or five years!

The longevity of seeds is well illustrated by the following instance: At Columbia, Mo., white clover seed which had been buried about six feet deep under a race track for 35 years, was found, upon being uncovered, to germinate freely.

Table 7 gives the length of time seeds may be expected to retain their vitality under average storage conditions.

44. Effect of green manures on germination.

In New South Wales, C. Hoffman found that decomposition of clover used as green manure sometimes interfered with the germination of cotton and flax seed but had no material effect on corn, wheat or clover. He attributed the cause to reduction of the oxygen supply and an increase of the carbon dioxide in the soil air. This change, he considers, prevents flax and cotton germination because these seeds are rich in oil and so require more oxygen than such seeds as corn, wheat and clover which are deficient in oil but rich in carbohydrates.

At the Wisconsin Experiment Station, E. B. Fred, who conducted experiments along the same lines, believes the failure of "certain seeds" to be due to parasitic fungi, the development of which is favored by the decomposition of the green manures. As a rule, oil seeds are easily damaged, whereas starchy ones are resistant. Cotton and soy bean seeds seem extremely sensitive to conditions resulting from green manuring. The germination of peanuts, hemp, mustard and clover was reduced somewhat by the presence of decomposing vegetable matter in the soil. Damage to oil seeds from green manuring seems to be confined largely to the first stages of decomposition. Experimental evidence seems to indicate that two weeks after green manure is added, injury to the seeds does not occur. Small applications of calcium carbonate seem to increase the injury to germination.

*TABLE 7—AGE AND VITALITY OF CROP AND VEGETABLE SEED

Seed	Years	Seed	Years
Alfalfa	6–8	Oats	3
Alsike clover	2	Okra	5
Asparagus	5	Onions	2–7
Beans	3	Orchard grass	2–3
Beets (garden)	6–10	Parsley	3–9
Beets (sugar)	6	Parsnip	2–4
Brome grass	5	Peas	3–8
Cabbage	5–10	Pumpkin	5–9
Carrots	4–5	Pepper	4–7
Cauliflower	5–10	Radish	5–10
Celery	8	Rape	5
Corn, field	2	Red clover	6–8
Corn, sweet	2	Red top	6
Cress	5	Rhubarb	3
Crimson clover	1–2	Salsify	2–8
Cucumbers	10	Soy bean	2
Egg plant	6	Spinach	5–7
Endive	10	Squash	6–10
Kale	5	Timothy	6
Kentucky bluegrass	1–2	Tomato	4–7
Kohl-rabi	5–8	Turnip	5–10
Leeks	3–9	Vetch	3
Lettuce	5	Watermelon	6–10
Millet	6	Wheat, barley, rye and other small	
Muskmelon	5	grains	1–2
Mustard	4–9	White clover	2

* Col. Agr. Col. Bul. 238.

44A. Time Seeds Need to Germinate. It is important to know the approximate time needed by seeds for germination in order to sow them with satisfaction and success. Many seeds are condemned and neglected before they have had sufficient time to start. Always divide the packages and sow at different times. You can then give them a second or a third trial. Sow together those seeds that start about the same time. Keep the seed-box or bed moist, but not wet, and do not let the soil dry out until the seeds have had ample time to germinate. Seeds are influenced by conditions and the plants may appear 25% earlier or 25% later, according to circumstances.

45. Rest period of seeds.—Many seeds will not germinate for considerable periods although mature, even when placed under conditions favorable for germination. Such seeds are said to be "dormant," "resting" or having an "after ripening" development. The length of the rest period varies considerably in different seeds. It may be broken in various cases by drying, freezing, treatment with chemicals, or by alternate freezing and thawing. Most garden seeds will sprout within a month after maturing, a few with almost no delay. Should wet weather occur for long at harvest time seeds of cereals often sprout while still in the head. The mangrove normally sprouts its seeds while still attached to the parent plant.

46. After ripening is the term applied to the period between the maturing of the fruit of certain plants and the time when the seeds will germinate. Seeds of every genus of Rosaceæ studied in detail at The Boyce Thompson Institute (Pomeæ, Pruneæ and Roseæ) all need such a period in germinative conditions.

Fig. 27.—Germination of bald cypress seed. X, Check (dry seeds); 1, stratified one month at one degree centigrade; 5, stratified one month at 5°; 10, stratified one month at 10°. Photographed 37 days after planting in greenhouse.

The old practice of stratifying certain seeds at low temperature in moist condition preparatory to planting, furnished this condition in a general way. It often failed, in part, because it was not realized that the process of after-ripening in these seeds has a rather definite temperature optimum. Work at the Institute has established beyond doubt the existence of such temperature optima and that the optima may vary somewhat with different species, although it is more generally in the region of 5° C. (41° F.) In some cases the optima are distinct or involve a narrow range of temperature. In others they are not so distinct or represent a rather wide range of temperatures. The work has also established that the various species have a distinct after-ripening time at their respective temperature optima, that a good oxygen and water supply is important in the stratification beds and that in some cases it is important to regulate the acidity of the stratification medium. In the experiments the seeds are mixed with the stratification medium instead of in successive layers of seeds and stratification medium.

The accompanying figure (29) on seeds of Rosa rubiginosa shows the existence of the optimum. The after-ripening occurs at 0°C. (32°F.) and less readily at 10°C., (50°F.) but the process requires a much longer time at either temperature than at 5°C. At temperatures much above 10°C. the seeds tend to go back into the dormant condition so a period at higher temperatures prolongs the necessary time for after-ripening. Periods at temperatures below freezing have no effect on after-ripening provided they are not low enough to give freezing injuries. (Figs. 27, 28, 29).

Contrary to the general view,[1] freezing any of the rosaceous seeds of the three sub-families mentioned does not aid after-ripening in any way so far as our studies indicate. It does not even assist in cracking the stone coats. The stone coats of plum, for instance, crack quickest at 10°C. (50°F.) or a little above, although the after-ripening occurs quickest at lower temperatures. There is no doubt that some seeds are much aided in germination by freezing or repeated freezing, but so far as now certainly known, these are not seeds that demand an after-ripening of the embryos.

Rosa multiflora requires only a little over two months at 5°C. for after-ripening while Rosa canina shows considerable germination under this condition only after nearly a year of favorable stratification at this temperature.

FIG. 28.—Germination of Pinus insignis (P. radiata) seed. x, Check (dry seeds); 1, stratified two months at one degree centigrade; 5, stratified two months at 5°; 10, stratified two months at 10°. Photo made 19 days after planting in greenhouse.

The study of these and many other species of roses of the cold temperate zone indicate that the various species demand various periods of cold stratification for after-ripening but in general the optimum is near 5°C.

Studies of the after-ripening of about 250 different crosses of roses indicates that hybrids containing largely cold temperate blood respond to low temperature stratification as do the seeds of the species with about 5°C. the optimum, and with a great variation in the time required. Apparently with hybrids of warm climate forms, the low temperature stratification is not so important, if at all necessary. It is probable that the low temperature stratification is merely an imitation of Nature's method for temperate zone forms. One can improve on Nature, however, for his purpose by giving the most favorable conditions as to temperature, time and stratification medium.

Bittersweet plants from seed. After satisfactory methods of handling bittersweet (*Celastrus scandens*) seed, prolonged tests at the Boyce Thompson Institute have been formulated by H. C. Joseph who writes in part as follows: [2]

[1] William Crocker, Professional Papers No. 6, 1927. *Dormancy in Hybrid Seeds,* Reprint Memoirs Hort. Soc. of N. Y. Vol. 3, July, 1927.
[2] *Florists' Exchange and Hort. Trade World,* June 9, 1928.

Seeds may be harvested any time after fully ripened from mid-October as long as they hang on the vines. They do not suffer frost injury until after they have fallen to the ground and absorbed additional water. It is advisable to dry the material in thin layers of either the fruits or the washed-out seeds at room temperature for two or three weeks after harvesting. Undried seeds mold when stratified and germinate poorly or not at all. Seeds dried artificially at 113°F. or higher shrivel and germinate poorly after being stratified. Seedsmen often ship freshly harvested seeds in the berries, but the pulp ferments, heat is developed and seeds arrive shriveled and often moldy.

After being dried as advised, seeds require a period of after-ripening in moist condition at low temperature before they will grow. The after-ripening may be brought about by late fall sowing or stratification outdoors or by mixing with a moist medium and storing at 32 to 50° in an ice chest, cellar or refrigeration chamber (Fig. 30).

Fig. 29.—Rosa rubiginosa seeds. Check stored dry, others in moist sand for six months at temperatures designated, then planted in flat in greenhouse. Picture shows effect of temperature for stratification; that is 5°c. (41° F.).

Seeds never after-ripen in the pulp alone outside of a stratification medium like moist sand, soil or peat. Samples stored in cloth bags in cool and humid chambers while the berries were still fleshy failed to grow, possibly because of lack of aëration, the presence of some substance in the pulp that inhibits germination or some other deterrent cause. The following points are considered of special interest:

1. Freshly harvested seeds need to be dried carefully at least two weeks at room temperatures before stratifying or sowing.

2. Before planting in seed beds or outdoors, the seeds should be stratified in sand, soil or peat, or in a mixture of sand and soil or peat and sand. The time needed for stratification is three months if an ice box is used, and five months if coldframes are employed.

3. If stratified in frames outdoors, the seeds should be covered with boards or a light layer of mulch.

4. In order to avoid damping-off the planting of after-ripened seeds should

be so arranged that young seedlings appear early in the spring when the weather is still cool.

In physiological studies of germination, E. Heilpern of Germany discovered that certain seeds which have a period of dormancy appear to be uninfluenced by snow, ice, water or air at zero degrees Centigrade, regardless of rest period. Plants reported upon are Norway maple (*Acer platanoides*), *Geranium pyrenacium, Ranunculus acer* (*acris*, of most authors), common evening primrose *Œnothera biennis*, and moss campion (*Silene acaulis*). The period differs in different plants, apparently in some degree as an individual property, but not depending upon locality and date of harvesting in a given species.

FIG. 30.—Methods of handling bittersweet seed. Also shows importance of after-ripening seeds in right way to obtain good germination. A, Twenty-five seeds after-ripened out of fruits in moist peat and sand at 41° F. for three months; then planted in flat. Good germination. B, Twenty-five seeds stored in cloth bag in fruits at same temperature and for same time; then planted. No germination.

Howard and Wiggans of Missouri planted about 200 species of seeds representing 51 genera to determine whether seeds in general are capable of germinating immediately after ripening if placed in favorable conditions. Seeds of grass, lily, pink, mallow, legume and composite families seem to have no rest period, while rose, cashew and vine families have a pronounced one. In general seeds of woody plants have a more characteristic rest period and are more difficult to force into growth than seeds of vegetable and other herbaceous plants. Variation in length and intensity of the rest period is greater between species than within species. Etherization tends to stimulate seeds into early growth and to increase the percentage of total germination. Soaked and stratified seeds are more strongly affected by ether than are dry seeds. A 12-hour exposure to ether seems the most favorable dose to force seeds to germinate.

In garden practice, advantage is often taken of differences in time of sprouting by sowing quick-germinating and slow-sprouting seeds of some unlike genus or family in the same rows, the former to mark the positions of the rows so cultivation may start as soon as the seedlings appear. The markers must always be sown thinly. Radish of forcing varieties is a favorite for this purpose, because it sprouts and matures early. Mustard is better because it has a smaller root.

The cold treatment of lettuce seed to break the rest has given excellent results. H. A. Borthwick's and W. W. Robbins' discussion and summarization of this work are condensed from *Hilgardia* as follows:

The requirements for germination of lettuce seed are an adequate moisture, temperature below 25° C. (77° F.), and good aëration. Seeds absorb sufficient for germination in four to six hours. High percentages of germination are secured from 31° to 77° F. Between 77° and 86° F. most varieties fall off rapidly in percentage germination; at 86° F. in most varieties, germination is almost inhibited.

Varieties grown under similar conditions and of the same age vary, however, in their response to high temperatures. Some attain fairly high percentage germination; at 85° F., others have low germination. Although a varietal difference occurs in the response of lettuce seed to high temperatures, these differences disappear when the seed is germinated at low temperatures.

Generally speaking, freshly harvested seed is inferior in germinating power to that several months old. With many varieties germination at ordinary temperatures improves noticeably in the first few weeks after harvest. Seed stored dry, at low temperatures for 7 to 37 days did not improve in germination, as compared with seed stored at laboratory temperatures.

Lettuce seed may be kept at 86° F., either dry or moist, without altering its ability to germinate at lower temperatures. Davis "kept lettuce seed upon absorbent cotton continuously for eight months at a temperature from 80° to 86° F. without perceptible loss of seed."

Within the limits of the experiments the longer the exposure of seed (moist) at 86°, the longer the time required to germinate when placed at a lower temperature.

Failure of seed to germinate at temperatures of approximately 86° and above is ascribed to the inhibiting influence exerted by a structure which closely invests the embryo. This includes the endosperm (two layers in cells) and a semi-permeable integumentary membrane. Evidence indicates that this structure retards gas exchange. Oxygen requirements at high temperatures are greater than at low ones. Increased oxygen pressure increased germination percentage. There is also the possibility that products of metabolism arise and probably accumulate in the endosperm or the embryo at high temperatures and that these products inhibit initial germination stages.

If the early stages of germination are initiated at low temperatures, growth is uninterrupted by the transference of the seed to high temperatures.

If seed is to be planted in a soil which during many hours daily has a temperature of 86° F. or above, a treatment as follows is recommended as a practical measure: Store moist, with good aëration at approximately 40° F. for four to six days. Soaking the seed in water at this temperature is ineffective, because the seeds do not have sufficient aëration. Practically, aëration is accomplished by placing the seed between folds of moist burlap and storing on ice.

Seed treated as recommended may be thoroughly dried at room temperature with no appreciable loss in viability. One lot of treated seed gave a germination of 32% after 14 days drying at room temperature, whereas the untreated check gave a germination of 0.5%. These experiments suggest the probability that various changes initiated at these low temperatures, when moisture and oxygen are adequate, are irreversible.

47. The seed counter[1] (Fig. 31) developed by the Bureau of Plant Industry eliminates the personal element, selects seed indiscriminately, aids accuracy, saves time and places the seeds in the sprouting medium evenly spaced. Essentially it consists of a brass

---

[1] *U. S. Dept. of Agr. Circ. 53.* 1928.

plate (pierced by 100 holes) as the top of a vacuum box connected with a vacuum pump through a hand operated valve and a heavy, flexible tube 3/8″ in diameter. Three plates with holes respectively 0.008, 0.013 and 0.02″ in diameter will serve for seeds ranging in size from timothy to wheat.

To operate the counter satisfactorily a pump which furnishes a vacuum of at least 27″ of mercury is desirable. It should have a capacity of six cubic feet of free air per minute for the smaller and more regular seeds such as clovers, brassicas and even hairy vetch, but be of larger capacity for irregular seeds that *do not cover the holes* well.

In use, hold the counter plate up, open the valve, pour on an excess of seed, shake gently until a seed is held over each hole, pour off the surplus seeds, remove with tweezers one of any two seeds that lodge over any one hole, invert the plate, place on the seed bed and close the valve to release the vacuum so the seeds will be placed evenly.

The counter is adapted to all seeds with somewhat regular outlines but not to such as oats, orchard grass, or those with loose and irregular glumes and such small seeds as agrostis.

A modification of this counter, 10″ long with 100 holes in three rows one inch apart, is convenient for planting seeds in soil flats for greenhouse tests.

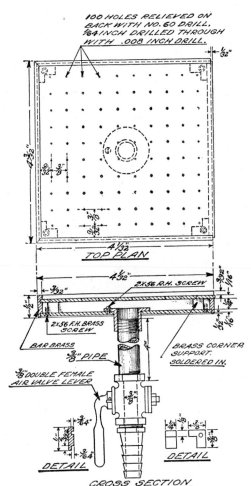

Fig. 31.—Seed counter for germination tests.

Moist storage and germination of apple seed. Dry apple seeds often fail to germinate. Experiments have shown that apple seeds kept in moist storage at a temperature of 34° to 37.5° F. for several weeks (4 to 6) gave 91% germination. Quicker germination results were obtained when the treated seeds were planted after January first, than when planted before that time. Mechanical injury to the apple seed coats have failed to influence germination. Cold treatment results appear to be associated with breaking the rest period of the seed.

Germination temperatures for orange seeds taken direct from fruits by H. S. Fawcett of California, planted in jars of sand, kept uniformly moist and maintained at various temperatures with light supplied artificially after germination, led to the discovery of an optimum temperature range for sweet orange seed germination and early growth between 75° and 85° F. and for sour orange 75° to 80°. *Calif. Citrogr. 14.*

48. Aids to germination.—Most seeds properly handled germinate freely; but seeds of certain families, the Umbelliferæ (especially parsley, carrot, celery, parsnip), are slow. These and hard,

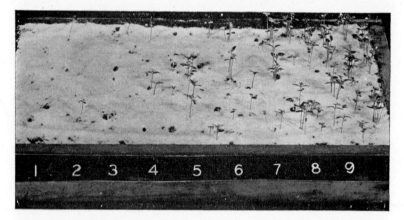

Fig. 32.—Germination of Scotch broom seed. 1, Check (no treatment); 2, soaked 2 minutes in concentrated sulphuric acid; 3, 3 minutes; 4, 5 minutes; 5, 10 minutes; 6, 15 minutes; 7, 30 minutes; 8, 45 minutes; 9, 1 hour. All seeds treated with bicarbonate of soda solution after removal from acid. Photographed 23 days after planting.

bony seeds (below) allowed to dry out too much may fail entirely unless treated prior to sowing. Treatments are given to soften or break the seed coats so the embryos can emerge.

Enzymes used in solution increased the percentage of germination when seeds were soaked several hours. The vigor of the young seedlings was also often enhanced. Within limits these good effects increase with the strength of the solution; diastase seems to be the most useful especially with tomato seeds.

Many fruits soften their seeds by their own acids, also the acids in the stomachs and intestines of birds and animals that eat the fruits act similarly (barberry, cedar, cherry, mulberry).

FIG. 32x.—Olive seedlings potted, A, when 4″ to 5″ tall and B, when 1′ to 2′ high and cut back to 6″ or 8″, C, Algerian Seedlings (left), Redding (right). Five months from seed.

Chemicals (weak acids or alkalies) are sometimes used for seeds with hard, bony coats affected neither by soaking nor freezing. They soften the shells so water may enter. Vinegar aids the seeds of bramble fruits (blackberry, raspberry).

Sulphuric acid,[1] 50% or full strength, is sometimes used (cotton, alfalfa, clover). The seed is soaked in the acid two or three to 20 minutes (Fig. 32). Sweet pea seeds which do not germinate readily may be treated with sulphuric acid (one half commercial strength)

[1] Great care must be exercised in diluting. The acid must be poured slowly into the full volume of water. If the reverse order is followed the acid will "fly." It must not touch skin or fabrics, because it burns.

for 30 minutes but must be thoroughly washed. Old seeds which would not otherwise germinate often do after this treatment.

Germinating dormant seeds such as sweet clover with sulphuric acid for 10 to 20 minutes immersion in a solution of 1.78 specific gravity increased germination from 11% to 84%.

Fig. 33.—Olive seed clipper. A, Front view; B, side view; C, Redding seeds clipped at their apices.

49. Chlorine water treatment of seeds.—Add two drops of saturated chlorine solution to 60 cubic centimeters of water after which add the seed and stand them in the sun a few minutes. Some of the seed will germinate completely in six hours. However, the seeds must be removed from the chemical and washed in water immediately after the radicle appears. Chlorine has a decomposing effect in the presence of light, breaking up water into hydrogen and oxygen. The rapid germination is due to the action of the nascent oxygen liberated by the chlorine. Hard seeds need a preliminary soaking in water before the chlorine treatment. Ammonia and soda in highly dilute solutions, also aid germination.

50. Formic acid.—Another curious method of aiding germination consists in watering the seeds with formic acid (1 in 5,000) at a temperature of 25° to 30° centigrade (77° to 86° F.). This treatment dissolves the integument so seeds which normally require eight or ten days will germinate in as many hours.

Olive seeds may be treated by feeding the ripe olives to turkeys. The seeds are recovered after passing through the digestive tract of the turkey where they receive a treatment which hastens germination.

51. Olive propagation.—A simple and rapid method of raising Redding seedlings for grafting stock follows: (Fig. 32x).

The fruit must be gathered when ripe and pulp removed by immersing the olives in a 3% or 4% soda lye for several hours to soften the skins. After washing off the lye, the pulp can be removed by rubbing through a wire sieve of

3/16″ mesh. The cleaned seed is then placed in 25% brine (two pounds common salt to one gallon water) and all floating seed rejected.[1] Each seed is then clipped at its pointed end and (Fig. 33) sown in porous soil (sand three parts, leaf mold one part) one-eighth to one-quarter inch deep and the surface of the soil covered with one-eighth of an inch of sifted moss or similar material.

The planted flats are then placed in a greenhouse, coldframe or ordinary seed-bed and watered only enough to prevent complete drying of the layer around the seed. The warmer they are kept, the more rapidly they will germinate and grow. (Fig. 34).

The seedlings will commence to come up in four or five weeks and continue for two, three or more months. At the end of about five months from planting, though of many sizes from a few inches to two or more feet (Figs. 34 and 32x), they may all be transplanted to small pots. It is probably best to pot them as soon as they reach 4″ or 5″. This will necessitate going over the seed-beds several times, but the plants will probably make larger trees for grafting in the spring than if stunted by transplanting when large.

The potted seedlings are kept in a greenhouse, lathhouse or other protected place until the following spring. When the weather and the soil warm up, about April, they may be planted in the nursery. The following autumn and spring they will be ready for budding or grafting.

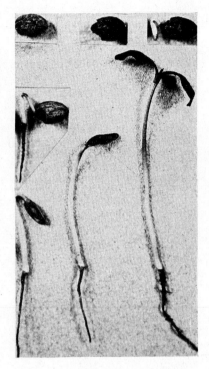

Fig. 34.—Olive seeds and seedlings of various stages development.

52. Soaking of farm and garden seeds (peas, beans, celery, corn) is common, but good results are less usual than is popularly supposed, for the soil should be decidedly moist and the soaking discontinued as soon as the seeds have swelled. When kept in water longer, and when placed in soil too wet, decay is almost sure to occur; and if placed in soil too dry they may dry out and fail to grow in consequence. With strong seeds sown outdoors in cold or unfavorable soil the time the seeds would be under such conditions may be shortened by half a day or a day and thus be a help.

Soaking of seed is often employed as a substitute for stratification, the dry seed (locust, apple) being covered with water for half a day to two or three days before sowing. This is of special use in cases where the seeds have become unusually dry. Many nurseries

---

[1] Wash seed to remove salt before planting.

now store their peach pits dry from harvest time through winter. About two weeks before planting the seeds are placed in water and allowed to soak until planting time. The authors have enjoyed good results by stratifying peach pits in fall for spring planting. Since imported apple seeds do not reach the United States before mid-winter, they are generally soaked two or three days, and then placed in stout cotton bags between cakes of ice and kept thus until planting time. Due to the impracticability and uncertainty of the latter process, many American nurserymen prefer to buy dormant apple, cherry and other seedling trees, (421) plant them in nursery rows, and later bud to desired varieties.

Soaking beet seed experimentally shortened the time of germination; soaked seed germinated in four, five and six days after sowing, while dry seed required two weeks. Soaking the seed was done for 12 to 14 days at a temperature of 43 to 48 in 35 to 40 pounds water to 40 pounds seed. All seeds must be equally dampened but not wet and must be frequently stirred.

53. Scalding Seeds.

53. Scalding Seeds.—Pouring boiling water over seeds and letting it cool gradually is often done to dry and hard-shelled seeds which are little, if at all, affected by cold water or by freezing. For instance, the seeds of Kentucky coffee tree are covered with boiling water, which cools rapidly enough to prevent injury. The seeds of the nearly related honey locust are usually soaked in very warm water for two or three days before planting. In nature only a small proportion of these seeds sprout. The reason that even these do so is probably that the seed coats are softened by the fermentation of the pulp around them in the seed pod. The acid treatment, probably, will give quicker and better results.

Hot water used by Wernicke, a German investigator, in germination experiments with *Acacia mollissima* and *Lathyrus* gave 60% when soaked six hours at 122°, 72% when soaked three hours at 167° and 92% when heated from 204° to 212° for an hour. Untreated seed handled in flower pots of sand the same as the treated seed gave 50%.

54. Mechanical helps are used for seeds whose coats are too hard to be affected by ordinary methods. Filing, clipping or boring holes (Abyssinian banana, moonflower, canna) is often done. The object is to let water in to the embryo. Lotus seeds not kept in water from time of ripening must also be treated thus, but if kept immersed as in nature they will sprout readily.

Clipping of olive seeds may hasten germination nearly a year by clipping the apex end, taking care to avoid injuring the embryo. A specially designed pincher (Fig. 33) does the work rapidly and without harming the seed.

Scarification is accomplished by passing hard coated seeds through a machine that scratches the surface (Fig. 35). Hard seed coats are thus made permeable to water. The seed may be blown by an air current against sandpaper, emery cloth or garnet paper. The germination of sweet clover has been increased from 36% with untreated seeds to 87% with those scarified. Authorities do not agree on the desirability of scarifying alfala seeds.

55. Azaleas and rhododendrons have long been reputed difficult to grow from seed. This is due to misunderstanding the needs of the plants. As the result of experiments with fifteen species, B. Y. Morrison makes the following recommendations:[1]

Seed should be fresh because it germinates quickly and strongly, though when properly stored it retains viability for several years. Soil should be one-third sharp sand and two-thirds decayed oak leaves rubbed through a quarter-inch screen. In collecting this material the upper layers of leaves and the lower, completely decayed layers of leaf mold should be discarded for seed pans but the latter may be used for nursery beds. The reason for this selection is that the half decayed parts prevent packing and water-soaking of the soil—conditions fatal to the seedlings. Intimate mixing of sand and leaf debris is essential to assure uniformity, for pockets of the latter are hard to keep moist and to re-moisten when once dried, except by complete immersion.

Fig. 35.—Wooden block faced with fine sand paper for scarifying hard seed.

Flats are filled with the mixture nearly to their brims, pressed firm and level with a board, watered thoroughly and left to drain until the next day. Seed is then sown sparsely on the surface, covered thinly with dry sphagnum dust obtained by rubbing through mosquito screening. The flats are finally covered with panes of glass and set nearly rim deep in pans of water. No watering is given from above until after the seedlings have been twice transplanted. Even then none is allowed to touch the leaves for fear of damping off but allowed to flow gently on the surface and soak in.

Under ideal conditions germination takes two to four weeks. If sown too early in unheated quarters the seed will lie dormant until moderately warm weather. In Washington, D. C., April is a favorable time for outdoor sowing. May has given fair results but later sowing is undesirable because seedlings should develop several true leaves before summer arrives. Further care of the plants is presented in Morrison's own words as follows:

While the seedlings are small and apparently fragile, with roots as slender as the most delicate threads, the plants are easily moved, even before the development of the first true leaf, if the operator has ample patience and a light touch. The transplant flats are prepared as for seed flats, but no sphagnum moss is used on the surface. The flats when filled with plants 1″ apart each way are set in the water pans for several days. They can then be moved to benches where the earthworms cannot work up into the soil, as these soon bury the tiny plants with piles of earth from their borings. Slugs are very harmful at this time and should be trapped on leaves of lettuce or cabbage set about the house.

The best tool for transplanting is a small knife. The seedlings can almost be lifted from the sphagnum moss of the seed flat with the fingers, as they are not deeply rooted at this stage, and can be carried between the fingers of the left hand and slipped into the hole made by the knife held in the right hand. The opening is then closed by the finger tips. This is tedious to one not interested in the work. The sooner it is done the better, as seedlings with several leaves are checked in later moving.

---

[1] Condensed from *U. S. Dept. of Agr. Circ. 68,* 1929.

In the writer's work the seedlings in some cases have been carried through the first summer and winter in the pit house, which has probably delayed the development of the plants. Here they are frozen lightly during the coldest months, but are protected from harm by lath shade, which tempers the rapidity of thawing. Injury usually comes from splitting of the bark and the subsequent loss of the top. If the plants are valuable they should not be immediately discarded, as they will often start again from the base.

The following spring all the seedlings are transplanted into nursery beds either before growth starts or in late July or early August as the second period of growth is beginning. Transplanting during the spring season of growth seems to check that growth in the case of deciduous American and oriental species so that they do not make the total height that is obtained by a midsummer transplanting, but they often make a desirable branching growth in late summer and early fall.

The soil in the transplant beds must be of the same acid nature as that in the seed flats, but need not have so carefully prepared a texture. It must have greater depth, however, and adequate drainage.

In transplanting for the second and third times, the operation is simpler than it is the first time. With a sharp knife cut between the rows of seedlings, whether in flats or in nursery rows, and then between the individuals in the rows. By a careful manipulation it is then possible to lift out each plant with a rectangular mass of earth attached to its roots which penetrate the fibrous soil throughout the mass. Of course some of the roots are cut for each plant, and occasionally a large root running out from a seedling in a horizontal plant is severed to the harm of that individual, but usually there is as little damage as would be done in moving a potted plant.

In a nursery where quantity production is the aim, it is probable that an area with overhead shading and watering would be the ideal nursery site for growing the seedlings to flowering size.

56. Germination of Orchid Seeds [1] was formerly recognized as difficult and uncertain. Practical orchid growers made attempts to find a method which would give better percentages of growth. Sometimes they succeeded but more often failed. Those commercial growers who were reputed to be successful naturally would not publish or divulge their methods. From the scientific standpoint it is doubtful whether they could explain the cause of their success.

About a decade ago Lewis Knudson published a method which has removed these difficulties and simplified propagation so that commercial growers throughout the world now produce plants with ease and certainty.

The method consists in sowing the sterilized seeds under aseptic conditions on the surfaces of agar slopes in test tubes (or large containers) which are kept then in moist chambers under greenhouse conditions at 15° to 35° C. (57° to 95° F.), shaded with cheesecloth and supplied with a sugar solution. When roots are produced the plants are moved individually to pots in the open or to sterile cultures in larger flasks, the latter preferred because insect and disease attack is under better control and because more rapid growth is obtained thereby. After a year or two under these conditions the little plants may be potted.

57. Hard Seeds of legumes.—At the end of a germination test of alfalfa, sweet clover or other small legume seeds some, though viable, retain their former size and color but do not sprout. They are popularly called "hard seeds" because their impervious coats do not allow water to enter. It is not always practical to treat these

---

[1] *Bot. Gaz.* 73, 77, 79, 89 and *New Phytol.* 26.

seeds chemically if their percentage is not high for the lot. However this percentage should be ascertained by a germination test and
the difference made up by sowing a greater quantity of seed to the
acre. The sulphuric acid treatment (48) is effective with these but
is apparently difficult to use commercially.

58. Longevity of flower seeds.—Accurate knowledge of the
longevity of flower seeds would be invaluable to many particular
seedsmen. As yet no published table has been accepted as standard.
The numbers of years that such seeds retain their vitality vary with
the species, the locality in which grown and the seasonal conditions,
especially during and following seed development, harvesting and
curing, as well as with the conditions under which stored and handled by the grower and the seedsmen. Because of all these conditions lists compiled by diverse seedsmen would necessarily vary.
Henry A. Dreer of Philadelphia, has supplied most of the above
comments and also Table 9.

59. Garden annuals, a popular term for flowering plants which
develop from seed to maturity in one growing season or less, but do
not live over winter (marigold, portulaca). The term is also broad-
ened in northern gardens to include many tropical and semi-tropical
plants which in their native homes are biennials, perennials or even
shrubs (snapdragon, jasmine) and which when started early enough
reach the flowering stage but are killed by frost in fall or winter
(castor bean, cobæa).

Conspicuous among the "winter annuals" are crimson clover and
some of the chickweeds whose seeds normally germinate between mid-
summer and midautumn, attain more or less development before the
ground freezes deeply, pass the winter safely, blossom in the spring,
mature their seed before hot weather and die, thus completing their
cycle "from seed to maturity in one growing season or less" though
this "season" consists of parts of two different years interrupted by
winter.

Among vegetables which man often treats as winter annuals are
spinach and fetticus (corn salad or lamb's lettuce) the seed of which
is sown in August or September and the seedlings (usually) lightly
protected by mulches over winter for use in the spring, earlier than
plants grown from spring-sown seed could be had.

Far more important and conspicuous than these, however, are rye
and fall wheat whose seed is sown in the autumn. The mature grain
is harvested by midsummer of the following year.

Then, too, there are the so called plur-annuals—those hardy herbaceous perennials (snapdragon, pinks) which, when started in a
greenhouse, will blossom the first season but which though they may

survive the following winter become scraggly, bloom poorly or otherwise are less attractive than during their first season.

Among the biennials are some species that when started early enough in a hotbed or even a coldframe and coddled more or less will bloom during the same season, though later than the normal biennial

TABLE 9.—LONGEVITY OF FLOWER SEEDS

	Years		Years
Abutilon	3-4	Cineraria hybrida	3-4
Achillea	2-3	" maritima candidissima	5
Aconitum	4	Clarkia	2-3
Acroclinium	2-3	Clematis paniculata	1
Adlumia cirrhosa	2-3	Cleome gigantea	2-3
Ageratum	2-3	Cobæa	2
Agrostemma coronaria	3-4	Coleus	5
Alyssum	3	Convolvulus major	3-5
Amaranthus	4-5	Cosmos	3-4
Ampelopsis	2	Cyclamen	2-3
Anchusa capensis	3	Cypress vine	4-5
Anemone coronaria	3	Cyperus alternifolius	1-2
Anthemis	3	Dahlia	5
Antirrhinum	3-5	Delphinium	1-2
Aquilegia	2	Dianthus, annual	3-5
Arabis	2-3	" perennial	3-5
Arctotis	3	Digitalis	2-3
Argemone	4-5	Dimorphotheca	2
Armeria	2-3	Dolichos	3-4
Asparagus plumosus	1	Dracæna	1
" sprengeri	1	Echinocystis lobata	4-5
Aster chinensis	2-3	Echinops	2
Aster, perennial	1-3	Eryngium	2-3
Auricula	2-3	Erysimum	3-4
Balloon vine	3-4	Eschscholtzia	2-3
Balsam	5-8	Eupatorium	2
Baptisia	3-4	Euphorbia	3-4
Begonia semperflorens	2-3	Ferns	3-4
Bellis perennis	2-3	Gaillardia	2-3
Bocconia cordata	1-3	Geranium	3
Boltonia	3	Gerbera months	3-6
Brachycome	3-4	Geum	2-3
Browallia	2-3	Globe amaranth	3-5
Cacalia	2-3	Gloxinia	2-3
Calceolaria	2-3	Godetia	3-4
Calendula	3-4	Gourds	5-6
Calliopsis (annual)	3-4	Grass: Agrostis nebulosa	2-3
" (perennial)	2-3	Coix lachrymæ	2-3
Campanula (perennial)	3	Eulalia japonica	2
" medium	3-5	Gynerium argenteum	2-3
Candytuft annual (Iberis)	2-3	Pennisetum longistylum	2-3
Canna	3-4	" ruppeli	2-3
Carnation	4-5	Stipa pennata	2-3
Celosia	4-5	Uniola latifolia	2-3
Centaurea	2-5	Grevillea robusta	4
Canary bird vine	3-4	Gypsophila elegans	5
Cerastium	2-4	" paniculata	5
Cheiranthus	5	Helenium	3-4
Chrysanthemum	3-5		

TABLE 9.—LONGEVITY OF FLOWER SEEDS—*Continued*

	Years		Years
Helianthus cucumerifolius	3-5	Pansy *(Viola tricolor)*	2-3
" dbl. chrysanthemum		Pentstemon	2-5
flowered	4-5	Petunia	3-5
Helianthus globosus fistulosus	4-5	Phlox	1-2
Helichrysum	2-3	Physalis	4-5
Heliopsis	2-3	Platycodon	2-3
Heliotrope	1-3	Primula veris	2-5
Heuchera	3	" sinensis	2-3
Hibiscus	3-4	" vulgaris	2
Hollyhock	3-5	" obconica	1-2
Hunnemannia	2	" malacoides	2
Impatiens sultani	2-6	Poppy	3-5
Ipomœa grandiflora	3-4	Portulaca	3-4
" imperial Japanese	3-4	Pueraria	3-4
Iris germanica	2	Pyrethrum aureum	3-5
" kæmpferi	2	" hybridum	4
Kochia	2	Rhodanthe	2-4
Lantana	1-2	Ricinus	3
Larkspur, annual	3-4	Rudbeckia	3-5
Lathyrus latifolius	3-4	Salpiglossis	4-5
Lavandula vera	2-3	Salvia azurea	4-5
Lavatera	3-4	" farinacea	4-5
Liatris	2	" patens	2-3
Lilium	1-3	" splendens	1-2
Linaria	2-5	Sanvitalia	2-4
Linum grandiflorum	5-6	Saponaria ocymoides	3-5
" perenne	5	" vaccaria	2-3
Lobelia erinus	4-5	Scabiosa	3
" cardinalis	2-3	Smilax	2-3
Lunaria biennis (honesty)	3-4	Solanum	4-5
Lupinus, annual	4-5	Statice, annual	1-2
" polyphyllus	5	" latifolia	2-3
Lychnis	3-4	Stevia	2-3
Lythrum	2	Stocks	4
Marigold	4-5	Stokesia	2
Marvel of Peru	3-5	Sweet peas	2
Matricaria capensis	2-3	Sweet rocket	3-4
Matthiola bicornis	4-5	Sweet william	5
Maurandia	2-3	Thunbergia	2-3
Mesembryanthemum tricolor	3-5	Torenia	2-5
" crystallinum	3-5	Tritoma	1-2
Mignonette *(reseda)*	3-4	Tunica saxifraga	2-3
Mimosa	2-3	Valeriana	3-4
Mimulus moschatus	3-6	Verbena	2-3
" tigrinus	6	Veronica	2-3
Momordica	3-4	Vinca	2-3
Musa ensete	1-2	Viola	1-2
Myosotis	2-3	Wallflowers	5
Nasturtium	3-5	Xeranthemum	2-3
Nemesia	2-3	Zea japonica (rainbow corn)	2-3
Nicotiana affinis	4-5	Zinnia	3-4
Nigella	3-5		

time of blossoming of the same species. They may thus be considered as annuals because they die after blossoming. Among them are canterbury bell and some species of evening primrose.

Some annuals begin to bloom in only a few weeks (stock, candy-tuft), others require several months (chrysanthemum, China aster); some have a short season of bloom (poppy, lupine), others a long one (nasturtium, verbena); some are tall (cosmos, Japanese varie-gated corn), others are dwarf (ageratum, edging lobelia); some are bushy (treemallow, scarlet sage), some are vines (morning-glory, hyacinth bean), and so on.

Gardeners classify annuals as *tender*—those killed by even light frost (nemophila, balsam); *half-hardy*—those which resist even the rather hard frosts of late fall (sweet alyssum, calendula) and con-tinue to bloom until just before winter.

In cold climates annuals are usually started during winter or early spring in greenhouses, hotbeds or on sunny window sills and the plants transplanted once or oftener before being set in the open ground, but only when danger of frost injury has passed. Half hardy annuals are usually treated in the same ways but later, often in coldframes, sometimes in the open after the soil becomes warm; hardy annuals are also started in all these ways but also outdoors, fully exposed to the weather. The main, general advantages gained by sowing under glass are protection against frost damage, develop-ment of plants to blooming stage earlier than from outdoor sowings, lengthening of the blossoming period and establishment of plants before hot, dry weather arrives.

Some annuals are difficult to transplant (nigella, mignonette) so their seed is generally sown where the plants are to remain, any excess being weeded out; others do so well without transplanting (sweet pea, godetia) that they are usually treated in like manner.

Various species have so short a period of bloom but adapt them-selves so well to varied conditions that they are often sown succes-sionally at intervals of two to four weeks so as to have their flowers from early until late in the season (calliopsis, babysbreath).

Outdoor sowing before soil and weather conditions are favorable often means loss of time and money, though the hardy species may be sown much earlier than the half-hardy ones and these earlier than the tender kinds.

60. Herbaceous perennials or perennial herbs or "perennials" may be propagated by seeds, cuttings or division, under glass or outdoors. When started in spring the plants are usually superior to those started in June or July, though these latter under favorable conditions should bloom, but not so freely, the following season. Choice varieties (phlox, iris, peony) are better propagated by cut-tings or division rather than by seeds.

Other desirable herbaceous perennials for garden and class work are: Delphinium, foxglove, campanula, sweet-william, hollyhock, columbine, hardy chrysanthemum, gaillardia, lupine, lemonlily,

Fig. 36.—Effective means of hastening germination. 1, Seedlings under inverted flower pot; 2, under pane of glass.

babysbreath, gayfeather, oriental poppy, speedwell, monkshood, goldentuft, boltonia, bleedingheart, daylily, alumroot, perennial pea, perennial flax, cardinalflower, evening-primrose, mosspink, false dragonhead, polemonium, balloonflower, cowslip, showy sedum, meadowrue, globeflower, viola, yucca.

Mushrooms. Among the many species of "cap fungi" popularly known by the synonymous terms *toadstool* and *mushroom* the only species propagated and cultivated extensively in Europe and America are the "common" or "field" mushrooms which consist of several nearly related species generally grouped as *Agaricus campestris,* but distinguished by mycologists by at least five different specific names. Though perhaps many other more distantly related kinds of cap fungi and also other species of fleshy fungi of different formation (for instance, morels and puffballs) may be "encouraged to grow," none have so far been propagated in more than an experimental way.

When the spores, which correspond to the seeds of higher plants, germinate, a thread-like "mycelium" develops. This is the vegetative stage or "spawn" of the plant. It grows freely in compost, manure and rich earth and by pure culture may be easily increased from small pieces to form the so called "mushroom bricks" from which commercial supplies are grown. As it develops, by the absorption of food and water from the soil or the manure, it stores the surplus as a reserve for the fruiting stage which follows. It becomes matted, corded and more or less abundantly supplied with "pinheads" which develop into "buttons" that, when conditions are favorable, are said to "grow in a single night" and become mushrooms.

Though mushrooms grow naturally in pastures, meadows, lawns and many other places well lighted, if not fully exposed to the sun, their production under such conditions is unreliable in the extreme because weather conditions, food supply and other factors are uncontrollable; hence the development of commercial mushroom culture in caves, cellars and special mushroom houses.

Stable manure with ample straw develops into the most satisfactory compost for commercial propagation, after being carefully fermented or composted. When ready, fresh spawn is placed in it, kept moist but not wet and the temperature maintained between 50° and 55° F. so as both to develop large, fleshy caps and to prevent trouble from insects which become pests at temperatures only a few degrees higher. Good ventilation is also necessary. Consult Duggar, B. M., *Mushroom Growing.*

III

SEED TESTING

Specialists divide seeds into two classes—those whose botanical purity can be determined from the specimens themselves and those which can be judged only by the plants they produce. Most farm seeds (oats, corn) belong to the first class; most garden seeds (bean, cosmos) to the second. Hence, the former are the more easily tested and their value for sowing more accurately judged beforehand. With the latter the point of most importance is trueness to name and strain. Of course, they must germinate, but gardeners would rather have low vitality seed of good stock than high vitality seed of poor stock; for though they might get only 25% of plants from a sowing of the former these would be of the type they desire; but even 90% in the other case might mean no sale for the product. Modern reputable seedsmen, therefore, test their stock (Fig. 25).

The importance of this was recently told the Senior author by a prominent seedsman whose firm took a contract to furnish a canning factory with a large quantity of best seed. The seed firm was obliged to buy the seed to fill the order. No test was, therefore, possible prior to filling the contract. The seed proved to be so inferior that the seed firm promptly met the loss of $1,200 when the canning company made complaint.

61. Purposes of seed testing may be outlined as follows: 1, To discover whether the seed is true to name, except as to variety. 2, To ascertain whether it has been intentionally adulterated. (Adulteration, except with seed of some variety of lower vitality is no longer a common practice.) 3, To discern the relative proportions of inert material and of foreign seed. 4, To disclose the presence of noxious or other weed seeds (Fig. 38). 5, To learn by the nature of its impurities the probable source of the seed. 6, To determine the amount of viable seed and (in the case of legumes) the amount of hard seed present.

The value of seeds can be determined in only one way; testing of *purity* and *germination*. Casual inspection is not enough. A carefully conducted *purity* test will detect adulterants, weed seeds and inert matter. For example, in alfalfa seed containing large-seeded dodder seed, not one buyer in ten will detect this pernicious

Fig. 37.—Forest tree seed beds. A, Raking surface smooth for seeding. B, Marking rows. C, Rolling to firm seeds in soil.

Fig. 38.—Mixture of weed seeds commonly found in low grade alsike clover seed. a, alsike clover; b. white clover; c, red clover; d, yellow trefoil; e, Canada thistle; f, dock; g, sorrel; h, buckhorn; i, rat-tail plantain; k, lamb's quarters; 1, shepherd's purse; m, mayweed; n, scentless camomile; o, white campion; p, night-flowering catchfly; q, oxeye daisy; r, small-fruited false flax; s, cinquefoil; t, peppergrass, two kinds; u, catmint; v, chickweed; y, Canada bluegrass; z, clover dodder; 1, mouse-ear chickweed; 2, knot-grass; 3, tumbling amaranth; 4, rough amaranth; 5, healall; 6, lady's-thumb. Enlarged.

parasite without testing, because it closely resembles alfalfa seed in size and color.

Seed testing is an aid to agriculture in avoiding one hazard of crop production. It gives definite information as to the potential ability of the seed to produce a good, bad or indifferent crop of desired plants, information that aids in controlling the quality of seed offered for sale.

The possibility of introducing weeds to the farm through "weedy" seed may be avoided by acting upon the information gained by a purity test. Seeds of various weeds will lie dormant in the ground for years (43). Hence the importance of the purity test.

62. Purity test of seeds.—Two tests are necessary to determine the viability and value of seeds; viz, purity analysis to detect impurities, and a germination test to discover vitality. In making the purity test the idea is to calculate the percentages of pure seed and the impurities. Seed impurities are classified as *inert material* and *foreign seed,* including both other crop seeds and weed seed (Fig. 39).

Inert matter includes seeds broken one-half or less, decorticated seeds of legumes, dirt, stones, chaff, fungous bodies, ergot, (other sclerotia and smut balls) and any other matter not seeds. In grasses

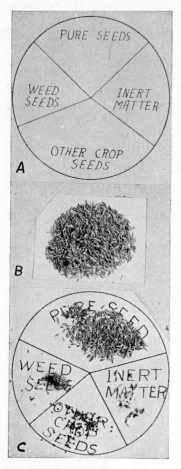

Fig. 39.—Counting chart used to make purity test. A, How chart is made. B, Sample of seed. C, In use.

empty glumes are considered inert matter. Attached sterile glumes of grasses should also be so rated and separated from fertile glumes.

With some grasses (Rhodes grass) where separation of sterile glumes would involve excessive work this procedure may be omitted, but the report should indicate such variations from the rules. The presence or absence of grass grains may be determined by pressing each glume between forceps, or between the finger nail and the table, or by the aid of transmitted light as with a mirror box.

Weed seeds. Whoever makes seed tests must be familiar with the seeds of injurious weeds. Most weed seeds found in tests are of comparatively harmless plants so their recognition as to kind is more of interest than practical importance. However, seeds of noxious weeds are often present, so the worker should be able to recognize them, especially those of plants designated by law or official regulation, or by general usage as such.

Individual seeds of rushes *(Juncus)* and other plants that grow in wet ground, may be included with inert matter, except where they occur in bunches large enough to be removed readily with forceps. Universally accepted distinctions are not possible between weed and crop seeds, since a plant species may be harmful weed under certain conditions and a useful crop plant in another (Bermuda grass, a weed among intertilled crops but a valuable pasture and lawn grass otherwise). Those plants considered crop plants should be listed by each seed laboratory.

Other crop seeds. Seeds of various farm crops sometimes constitute a part of foreign seeds (Figs. 38, 41). Their proportions as compared with the desired seed should be noted in making the purity test. The importance to be attached to their occurrence depends on the nature of the crop. For instance, timothy seed is detrimental to alsike clover seed used to produce seed but for hay it is often desirable.

Pure seed. Whether shriveled, cracked or otherwise injured all seeds of the kind under consideration should be considered pure, provided, (a) that broken pieces smaller than one-half, and (b) decorticated seeds of legumes be considered inert matter.

63. Sample for the purity test.—The first step in conducting a purity test is to secure the sample from the seed to be tested. To have this represent the bulk of the seed in question it should be drawn by taking small quantities from top, middle and bottom of the bag with a trier (Fig. 40) and from several bags of a lot. Bulk

Fig. 40.—Seed trier or sampler. Five or 6″ size costs about $1.50. If carefully used it will not injure a cotton bag. Trier is inserted full length in bag with large open end inclined downward so seed will run out. When enough seed has been obtained for sample trier is pulled out and small opening in bag closed easily by drawing point of trier lightly several times across opening.

seeds in bins, cars or other large containers are to be sampled with a long trier extended through the bulk in several places. In the case of packet seeds, an entire packet is taken. Any portion of seed exposed for sale should be considered as liable to contamination so should be sampled with special care.

Dividing the sample. It is important to mix the various small samples before taking the amount to be analyzed and if possible to use a mechanical divider. The sample should be larger than practical to use in the actual determination. Great care must be taken to have the working sample represent the material sent for analysis.

TABLE 10.—APPROXIMATE WEIGHTS OF CROP SEEDS TO BE USED IN PURITY ANALYSES

For kinds not listed use a quantity that will give approximately 3,000 seeds *

(a) One gram: Agrostis spp., Poa spp., Rhodes grass, Bermuda grass
(b) Two grams: Timothy, orchard grass, fescues (excepting meadow fescue), meadow foxtail, alsike, white clover, carrot
(c) Five grams: Rye grasses *(Lolium)*, meadow fescue, foxtail, millet, alfalfa, red clover, sweet clovers
(d) Ten grams: Awnless brome grass, crimson clover, *Brassica* spp., flax
(e) Twenty-five grams: Proso, millet, sudan grass
(f) Fifty grams: Sorghums, buckwheat, beet
(g) One hundred grams: Vetches, cereals
(h) Five hundred grams: Corn, beans, peas, cowpeas, soybeans

* *U. S. Department of Agr. Dept. Circ. 406.*

The minimum weight of various seeds for the purity analysis is indicated in Table 10. It may be desirable to take two working samples of one-half the size given and make the purity analysis on each part separately.

Noxious weeds. If noxious weeds are present the determination of the number of each kind per unit weight should be made on the entire sample, or at least on the following minimum quantities for the various classes listed in Table 10: (a) 25 grams; (b) 50 grams; (c) 50 grams; (d) 50 grams; (e) 150 grams; (f) 300 grams; (g) 500 grams.

Identity of sample. Whenever determination is possible the sample should be examined to uncover a correct name. Any discrepancy should be noted and reported. It must be recognized that varietal identity can usually be determined only by growing the plants; for often differences cannot be detected until the plants are several weeks old. Perhaps the most conspicuous examples occur with kale, cauliflower and other relatives of cabbage.

Origin of seed, to the farmer, may be fully as important as a statement of impurities or vitality; therefore, any definite indica-

TABLE 11.—NUMBER OF WEED SEEDS REQUIRED TO MAKE 1% OF SAMPLE IN SLIGHTLY ROUNDING TEASPOONFUL OF ALFALFA *

Black bindweed, *Polygonum convolvulus*	11
Black medick, *Medicago lupulina*	34
Black mustard, *Brassica nigra*	64
Brown pigeon grass, *Setaria glauca*	20
Bull thistle, *Circium lanceolatum*	23
Catchfly, *Silene* sp.	45
Crab grass, *Digitaria sanguinalis*	182
Curled dock, *Rumex crispus*	36
Dodder, *Cuscuta arvensis*	84
Dodder, *Cuscuta trifolia*	192
Green pigeon grass, *Setaria viridis*	40
Lady's thumb, *Polygonum persicaria*	36
Mayweed, *Anthemis cotula*	210
Morning-glory, *Convolvulus arvensis*	2
Nut grass, *Cyperus esculentus*	27
Peppergrass, *Lepidium* sp.	126
Pigweed, *Chenopodium album*	72
Prickly pigweed, *Amaranthus retroflexus*	134
Ragweed, *Ambrosia artemisiæfolia*	18
Rib grass, *Plantago lanceolata*	57
Rugel's plantain, *P. rugeli*	85
Sorrel, *Rumex acetosella*	100
Sweet clover, *Melilotus alba*	24
Water grass, *Echinochloa crus-galli*	70
White mustard, *Brassica arvensis*	25
Wild carrot, *Daucus carota*	62
Wild oats, *Avena fatua*	2

* *U. S. Department of Agr. Dept. Circ. 406.*

tions as to source should be reported. Since any conclusion about the origin usually can be based only on the agreement of various indications obtained by the critical study of the incidental matter in a large sample, no statement concerning the actual place of production should go beyond the evidence secured.

Duplicate analyses. When a purity analysis indicates that a law has been violated or that a label is incorrect, one or more additional analyses should be made and the average of all analyses used.

Purity test without a balance. A slightly rounded teaspoonful of alfalfa, clover and other small seeded legumes weighs approximately five grams. On this basis a table has been compiled whereby the approximate percentage of many common weed seeds may be determined by counting (Tables 11 and 12).

TABLE 12.—NUMBER OF CROP SEEDS PER UNIT OF WEIGHT

Kind of seed	Approximate number of seeds per gram [1]	Minimum weight for purity analyses (grams)	Approximate number of seeds in working sample
Alfalfa	500	5	2,500
Barley	30	100	3,000
Beet	54	50	2,700
Bent grass	18,000	1	18,000
Bermuda grass	3,940	1	3,940
Blue grass, Canada	5,500	1	5,500
Blue grass, Kentucky	4,800	1	4,800
Brome grass, awnless	300	10	3,000
Buckwheat	45	50	2,250
Carrot	900	2	1,800
Clover, alsike	1,500	2	3,000
Clover, crimson	330	10	3,300
Clover, red	600	5	3,000
Clover, sweet	570	5	2,850
Clover, white	1,500	2	3,000
Crested dog's-tail	1,900	2	3,800
Fescue, meadow	500	5	2,500
Fescue, red	1,200	2	2,400
Fescue, sheep	1,500	2	3,000
Fescue, hard	1,250	2	2,500
Flax	300	10	3,000
Meadow foxtail	1,200	2	2,400
Meadow grass, rough-stalked	5,600	1	5,600
Millet, foxtail	470	5	2,350
Millet, proso	180	25	4,500
Oats	28	100	2,800
Orchard grass	1,150	2	2,300
Rape, winter	230	10	2,300
Redtop	11,000	1	11,000
Rye	40	100	4,000
Rye grass, Italian	500	5	2,500
Rye grass, English	500	5	2,500
Rye grass, short-seeded	700	5	3,500
Sorghum, amber	55	50	2,750
Sorghum, kafir	50	50	2,500
Sudan grass	120	25	3,000
Sweet vernal grass	1,600	2	3,200
Tall oat grass	330	10	3,300
Timothy	2,500	2	5,000
Turnip	340	10	3,400
Velvet grass	2,500	2	5,000
Vetch, hairy	36	100	3,600
Vetch, spring	19	100	1,900
Western rye grass (Agropyron)	330	10	3,300
Wheat	25	100	2,500

66. Home or school purity tests are not presumed to be made in highly equipped laboratories so it may be necessary to make substitutes for laboratory technique. (Practicum IX.) Lacking scales or balances the counting table (Table 12) may be used.

67. Questions to consider in testing seed.—1. Is the seed to be purchased truly named? If not, should it be refused? Seed purporting to be *Trifolium repens* (white clover) but really *T. parviflorum* (a worthless clover species) should be refused and the seller perhaps sued for fraud.

Fig. 41.—Sterilized vs. unsterilized soil. A, Sterilized by heating before sowing. B, Unsterilized. Notice weed growth.

2. Is the seed fresh or old? Old seeds that have become dead may be treated to make them look fresh, but that won't put life in them. When mixed with new seed they reduce the value. This trick is practiced much less now than formerly. It constitutes a fraud and is punishable by law. Mere number of years does not necessarily make seed "old." Some seeds (Table 7) retain vitality ten or more years. If they germinate well they properly deserve still to be called "fresh." Reputable seedsmen, after testing their "returned" seeds offer the good samples for sale again. This is perfectly legitimate.

3. Has a cheaper seed been mixed with the desired kind? Yellow trefoil seed superficially resembles and is sometimes used to adulterate red and alsike clovers and alfalfa. Cock's-foot grass seed may be adulterated with meadow fescue or perennial rye grass. Similarly charlock seed (perhaps baked to kill it so its seedlings will not betray the fraud) may be mixed with cabbage, rape and similar seeds.

4. How pure is the sample? The percentage of seeds true to name is of great importance. The impurities should be identified—weeds and their species, seeds of other cultivated plants, chaff, bits of stem, leaf and pods, dirt, etc. Bad weed seeds should be named. "Rubbish" impurities are of small consequence compared with weed seeds, especially if bad; for instance, a sample of clover 99% pure and with 99% germination, would be unsatisfactory if it contained dodder.

5. What does the seed weigh? Generally heavy seeds within the limits of the species are best.

6. Are the seeds dry? Well-dried seeds keep best and give best results.

7. Where did the seeds originate? Seeds from some countries or even localities may be better than from others.

8. What percentage will germinate and at what rate or "strength?"

9. What percentage are "hard" seeds? Perhaps this will not be considered as serious a question as formerly, when the sulphuric acid method (48) comes into more general use.

68. Germination vs. guesswork.—Germination is the only accurate way to determine vitality and viability. Appearance and general condition often are not an index of vitality. When subjected to an actual test only a few seeds may show strong germination. Old seeds may have been oiled or polished to improve their appearance but a germination test will reveal the fact. On the other hand, seeds not of excellent appearance may test high as to their germination.

69. Conditions which affect viability.—*Maturity.* Although seeds often germinate when not fully ripe, plants from such are usually weak and cannot withstand unfavorable conditions. Yields from immature seeds are always lower than from properly matured ones. *Age* (Table 7). In time all seeds gradually lose viability. The rate depends upon species and condition of storage. As a rule, seeds retain their viability longest under low and equable temperature and moisture conditions. Ordinary crop seeds lose their viability rather quickly when stored in moist air and high temperature. Seeds containing oil (corn, flax) lose viability more quickly than do starch-bearing seeds (wheat, buckwheat). Seeds of legumes are noted for their great longevity (some for 150 to 250 years).

If only 10,000,000 seeds are sown to the acre, Sample 1 in (Table 1) would provide over 20 weed seeds to the square yard, whereas Sample No. 3 would distribute 240. But notice also the number of good seeds obtained for a cent and figure out how much is being paid for inferior and weed seeds in each case; then judge the help that pure seed will be in preventing weed growth on the farm.

The Canadian Department of Agriculture found that "red clover" seed sold in Ontario contained 6,000 to 15,000 weed seeds to the pound and in alsike as high as 23,550 to 49,830. An American sample of alfalfa gave 6.8% or about 32,500 weed seeds in a pound, including 5,490 of dodder.

In certain parts of the United States, it is stated, clover seed tailings are sometimes used on the farm, the clean seed being sold. Such tailings have been found to contain over 272,000 weed seeds to the pound. Sowing it will soon make any farm a weed paradise!

Losses due to low grade seeds are evident from the examples cited. These may be grouped under the following heads: a, Direct loss on the purchase. b, Loss of crop due to insufficient good seed sown to the acre, with possible total loss in worst cases. c, Loss due to direct destruction of crop because of introduced parasites such as dodder and broom rape. d, Necessary cost of extra cleaning the seed crop, perhaps even for several years, due to the introduction of weeds. e, Damage caused by introduction of new weeds, which may spread over the farm or the district. f, Loss due to insect and fungous pests introduced with the seed.

a. Direct loss following the purchase of low-grade seeds may be due to one or both of two factors: (1) reduced quantity of seed true to name, and (2) poor germinating capacity of the seeds. Usually low quality seeds are poor in both ways.

b. When truly high class samples of seed are bought, less seed is needed for a given area than when low grade samples are used. When a low grade sample is sown unwittingly, the result may be a poor stand, which may be overcome by strong growing weeds, many of which may have been introduced with the seed. Sometimes the whole field may have to be plowed, and re-sown, thus causing loss of cultivation, one lot of seed and much time, the last, perhaps, most serious, except the equivalent loss of money.

c. The loss due to parasites may be calculated from the statement by M. Marre that a single dodder stem may spread so rapidly in three months as to kill clover or alfalfa on an area of about 30 square yards! By experiment, dodder seed has been found to germinate when only half ripe! The seeds of dodder and broom rape lie dormant in the soil for several years.

d. Introduced weeds may necessitate extra cultivation and extra cleaning of the seed crop.

e. Weeds take from the soil moisture and mineral nutrients which could otherwise be utilized by the crop plants. Certain weed plants use as high as 850 pounds of water to produce one pound of dry matter and some to take as high as 18 pounds of nitrogen and

5 pounds of phosphoric acid from the soil in one ton of weeds produced.

On every count, therefore, low grade seeds are undesirable at any price. Low price is almost surely an index of low quality.

70. True value of seed.—To calculate the true value of seed, multiply percentage of purity by percentage of germination and divide by 100. For instance, suppose a sample to be 90% pure. This would mean that it contains 90 pounds of pure seed in 100. Suppose then that the germination test showed 80% pure seed. Then $90 \times 80 \div 100 = 72\%$ total good seed. That is 100 pounds of this seed would contain 10 pounds of dirt, weed seeds, other crop seeds, etc. and 18 pounds of seed not viable, giving a total of 28 pounds of dead seed, weed seeds, other crop seeds, dirt, etc. What man in his right senses would pay for this worthless and perhaps also largely noxious stuff?

71. The longevity of seeds, the percentage of germination and the purity of the sample have much to do with the resulting crop.[1] In Table 14 the percentages of purity and germination are high averages in high-grade seed.

72. Does it pay to test seed for germination?—C. E. Myers has furnished the following figures on tests of crimson and sweet clover seed made prior to purchase. From three and two seedsmen respectively, he received samples and prices (Table 13).

TABLE 13.—GERMINATION TEST OF CRIMSON AND SWEET CLOVER SEED

Seed Samples	Price	Percentage
Crimson Clover, Sample 1	$ 6	92
" " " 2	6.70	78
" " " 3	5	94
Sweet " " 1	15	82
" " " 2	17	66

In these two series of tests it happened that the lowest priced seed gave the highest germination and the most expensive the lowest. Since the amount of time required to make the tests was scarcely more than an hour and the cost certainly not more than 50 cents for each series, it is evident that a saving of $1 to $1.70 on the crimson clover and $2 on the sweet clover was made on each bushel of seed bought, even without considering the higher percentage of plants likely to follow sowing these seeds. One interesting point in these tests is that the seedsman who quoted the lower price on sweet clover also quoted the highest on crimson clover.

It must not be inferred from these instances that cheap seed is

---

[1] Frank, Haack and others have claimed that power to produce seedlings in the soil falls much faster than power to germinate in germination tests. According to Crocker, this is true for three to five year old seeds of delphinium stored under poor conditions but not true of seeds stored under nearly optimum conditions.

TABLE 14.—GERMINATION AND LONGEVITY OF SEEDS

[Purity and Germination figures from Duval; Longevity from Vilmorin.]

Kind of Seed	Per Cent			Kind of Seed	Per Cent		
	Purity	Germination	Average Longevity		Purity	Germination	Average Longevity
Alfalfa	99	95	—	Grass, Timothy	99	96	2
Asparagus	99	85	—	" Velvet	97	85	—
Barley	99	98	3	Hemp	99	90	—
Beans	99	98	3	Kafir Corn	99	97	—
Beet, Garden	99	150*	6	Leek	—	—	3
" Sugar	99	150-175*	6	Lettuce	99	98	5
Buckwheat	99	96	2	Mustard	99	95	4
Cabbage	99	95†	5	Oats	99	96	3
Carrot	98	85	4 or 5	Okra	99	80	5
Celery	98	85	8	Onion	99	96	2
Clover, Alsike	98	95	—	Parsley	99	80	3
" Crimson	98	97	—	Parsnip	98	85	2
" Red	98	95	3	Pea	99	98	3
" Sweet	98	90	—	Radish	99	97	5
" White	95	90	—	Rape	99	96	5
Corn, Field	99	99	2	Rice	99	95	—
" Sweet	99	94	2	Rye	99	96	2
Cotton	99	90	—	Salsify	98	85	2
Cowpea	99	95	—	Sorghum	98	95	—
Cucumber	99	96‡	—	Soy Bean	99	95	2
Eggplant	99	90	6	Spinach	99	90	5
Endive	99	85	10	Sunflower	99	90	—
Flax	99	95	2	Sweet Pea	99	90	—
Grass, Blue	95	85	—	Teosinte	99	90	—
" Brome	90	90	—	Tomato	99	94	4
" Fescue Meadow	98	90	—	Tobacco	99	90	—
" " Sheep's	96	85	—	Turnip	99	98	5
" Millet	99	90	2	Velvet Bean	99	90	—
" Orchard	95	90	2	Vetch	99	93	—
" Red top	96	90	—	Wheat	99	98	2
" Rye	98	90	—				

* Beet "balls" usually contain two to six seeds—the figures are for 100 balls tested.
† Kale, cauliflower, collard, kohl-rabi, etc., have same figures.
‡ Other vine crops—pumpkin, melon, squash, etc.—have same figures.

always or necessarily the better to buy. On the contrary, low priced seed is perhaps more often the more expensive because of its probable dirtiness and low percentage of germination. *Nothing but an actual test can determine this point.*

73. **Damping-off** is a nurseryman's and gardener's term for the decay of cuttings and seedlings, more especially just above the surface of the ground. The conditions that favor it are excess of moisture in both soil and air, poor light and higher temperature than necessary for normal plant development. The weak plants that develop under these conditions succumb to tiny fungi which live upon decaying vegetable matter in the soil, and which continue to exist in spite of drouth or of frost.

Should damping-off be noticed the healthy plants should be pricked out (198) or transplanted into fresh soil to save them if possible. So rapidly does the trouble spread that thousands of cuttings or of seedlings may be lost in a single night. Perfect drainage in open soil with ample watering and fresh air are partial safeguards.

Steam sterilization (Fig. 320) of the sand for several hours is often done with good results. Damping-off often follows copious watering of a bed which has been very dry longer than advisable.

The fungi usually believed to cause damping-off are *Phytophthora omnivora* (*Fusarium* sp.), *Pythium debaryanum;* but V. Peglion, an Italian investigator, has identified several others—*Botrytis cinerea, Thielavia basicola* and *Phoma beticola.* By experimenting with soil infested with *Pythium debaryanum,* heating to 130 to 212 degrees and treating with 20 to 30% solutions of formalin and various quantities of carbon disulphide, he found that camelina, a plant highly susceptible to attacks of this fungus made good growths, the action of this fungus being reduced even to nothing.

Damping-off of seedlings in plant beds, according to the Minnesota station, is commonly caused by *Pythium debaryanum* or rhizoctonia which attack a large variety of plants as well as live upon dead organic matter in the soil. Little can be done to check the disease when such conditions prevail. Therefore, methods which kill fungi are needed to prevent the disease. The preventive methods must be applied before sowing the seed, otherwise the seed will be killed also.

Chemical agents as fungicides have been tested against damping-off. Of these formalin alone has proved of value. Treatment of the soil with it (one part to 100 of water and lesser strengths), as frequently recommended, does not kill the fungus. Although it may check the disease for some time it will allow damping-off to develop later when weather conditions permit. The value of formalin at these strengths, therefore, depends largely on the time weather conditions favorable to damping-off appear.

74. Seeds as Carriers of Disease.[1]—

For years seeds have been known to disseminate disease germs, thereby initiating veritable epiphytotics, as epidemics of plant diseases are called. Often the seeds themselves are destroyed in storage and germination. Hence, preventives are important. Study of the problems involved has discovered a preliminary list of more than 200 parasites known to be carried by seeds. Doubtless many hundreds of others exist.

Losses of crops due to these causes would be national calamities if they were exceptional and occurred only at rare intervals, but because they are present every year they have come to be taken more or less as matters of course, so little thought is given to them.

The seed-borne organisms that produce seedling diseases, blights, etc., apparently belong to four general groups, all microscopic in the germ; namely, bacteria, fungi, nematodes (eel worms) and a few (mosaic, yellows) whose etiology (causes) are in doubt. The first two groups may be carried as spores on the surface of seeds classed as *external* (stinking smut of wheat, covered smut of sorghum); or their vegetative growth (mycelium) may penetrate the seed coat or even the embryo, classed as *internal,* (bean anthracnose, fusarium

---

[1] C. R. Orton, *Jour. N. Y. Bot. Gar.,* March, 1926.

and diplodia of corn). Nematodes are sometimes carried on the surface of seeds but more generally in gall tissues along with the seeds. The method of transmission of mosaic and similar organisms is unknown, but by analogy presumably may be classed as internal.

All these parasites may remain alive in or upon the seed for long periods; certainly over-wintering and in many cases probably as long as the seeds are viable. When such infested or infected seed is planted and germinates, these accompanying parasites start growth and attack the seedling in various ways, often as blights (damping-off); probably as often the sprout never reaches the light, being killed in the early stages. This accounts for poor stands, or poor germination under field conditions. Sometimes no marked effect is to be noted until the plants are nearing maturity (cantaloupe wilt).

Seed treatments have been in more or less successful use for many years but the materials have been too restricted in application to meet the problem. Copper sulphate has been more or less used for bunt of wheat since 1789; but it often injures the seed. Copper carbonate has taken its place since about 1915 and is today the chief wheat disinfectant. However, its utility is obviously restricted to surface-carried types of diseases. It cannot be generally used on all kinds of seeds because of its toxicity. Much the same situation exists with formaldehyde and mercury (corrosive sublimate). Both are powerful disinfectants but their action on many seeds is toxic.

Certain organic mercury compounds possess the following properties which make them nearly ideal seed and plant disinfectants:

(1) High bacteriocidal and fungicidal properties. (2) Slow toxicity to plant tissues, thus eliminating largely the injurious effects which make the older disinfectants objectionable. For this reason they can be used at varying strengths and periods of exposure without danger of serious injury. This is particularly true of the chlor-phenol groups. (3) They do not corrode ordinary metals, which makes them more adaptable to field operations than inorganic mercury. (4) They possess a selective action upon the growing tissues of higher plants and the lower types of life such as bacteria and fungi. This makes them especially valuable in the control of "damping-off" and other diseases produced by soil organisms which attack plants on the roots or stems near the soil. If the work is properly done, tender seedlings may be sprayed and the soil about them disinfected without injury. (5) They also possess insecticidal properties and are effective in ridding the soil of maggots and similar root pests. Certain of them may be applied to the soil without injury to the plants in situ. (6) They are available in both dust and liquid form and so are readily adapted to various purposes. It is thus obvious why they are superior to the old standard disinfectants. A much greater latitude of application, safety and a greater efficiency render them especially valuable.

They have also been found of great value in the preservation of seeds requiring long periods of dormancy in the soil or stratification medium prior to germination and where such seeds untreated may be nearly or entirely killed by bacterial and fungous parasites.

75. Seed Treatment to Increase Stands of Plants.*—In field and greenhouse experiments supposedly healthy seed of cabbage, lettuce, radish, spinach, pea, corn, cucumber, tomato and string bean were treated with organic mercury preparations (semesan, uspulun, and Bayer dipdust) at the New York Experiment Station (Geneva) to determine the effect on stand of plants. In the cases of peas, beans and corn the effect on yield were also noted.

Counted lots of treated and untreated seed were sown at intervals from

---

* E. E. Clayton, *N. Y. Exp. Sta. Bul. 554* (Abstract and summary combined and condensed).

early spring to midsummer and records taken of germination periods, percentage germination. With seed sown early the germination periods were long and the percentages of germination for untreated seed low, owing chiefly to the decay of many seeds, some before sprouting and some soon after. Seed treatment with the organic mercury preparations gave considerable protection against this decay and thereby increased stands. With seed sown after the soil had become warm, the germination periods were shorter and the percentage of germination secured with untreated seed were much higher. Decay of seed was not a serious problem so seed treatment with the organic preparations proved of little benefit.

The yields recorded in a limited number of cases indicate increases somewhat greater than would be expected from the gains in germination only.

It is concluded that vegetable growers can profitably treat seed to be sown early. With midsummer sowings there is less need for this protection.

In greenhouse tests seed treatment greatly increased stands from seeds sown in midwinter, during which seed and seedling decay is a serious problem. Comparative sowings of the same treated and untreated seeds late in spring, however, showed little benefit from seed treatment.

76. Sterilization of coniferous seed beds* at The University of Washington, reported by T. C. Scheffer, proved that low pressure steam is a satisfactory means of sterilizing soil when temperatures of 95° to 100° C. (202° to 212° F.) are maintained for 60 minutes at the soil surface. Stronger root and crown development resulted. A delay of two or three days following sterilization before planting removed any hazard from toxic substances. At 100° C. (212° F.) the mycelium and spores of damping-off fungi were killed in not exceeding five minutes. Weed seeds were destroyed in five to eight minutes, resulting in a marked reduction in weeding costs.

77. Formalin soil treatment.—Treating the soil with formalin (441) will kill damping-off fungi, and will hence effectually prevent the malady under the most favorable weather conditions for fungous growth. Formalin soil treatment is also somewhat beneficial in stimulating plant growth and in killing some weed seeds. The chief objections are the cost, the time required for it to act, and for the soil to dry out.

If the fungus gets into the cutting or seed bed it may be checked more or less by withholding water and allowing the sun to reach the sand or soil in the bed.

78. Sterilization of the soil by heat (441) has proved most satisfactory from all standpoints, except that under certain conditions it may be more expensive than formalin. Aside from preventing damping-off several secondary beneficial effects may follow; for instance, killing of weed seeds and insect pests, and greatly increased size and vigor of plant growth. As a cultural control growers should avoid infected, poorly drained soils and thick sowing of seed. The only means of checking the disease after it has started is to remove the covers in order to reduce the temperature and the moisture of the soil and of the air immediately above the plants.

---

* *Jour. Forestry, 28.*

The United States Department of Agriculture secured best results in treat ing soil for damping-off of coniferous seedlings by drenching with dilute sul phuric acid (one ounce to one gallon) several days before seed sowing and a week after the seedlings appeared. In December there was a fine stand of healthy seedlings on the treated plot and the soil was free from algæ and moss while the check plot was green with algæ and moss and there were practically no seedlings left. Only Norway spruce seemed to suffer. For this plant a weaker solution (1 part to 500) is recommended.

According to another source damping-off may be prevented by "treating the soil with dilute iron or copper sulphate."

78A. Fifty worst weeds of the United States are shown in Table 15 in alphabetical order with information to enable the reader: (1) to identify them, (2) determine the nature and place of their greatest injuriousness, and (3) ascertain their duration or natural length of life—whether annual, biennial, or perennial. With this knowledge he will be able to attack most troublesome weeds intelligently.

TABLE 15.—DESCRIPTIVE LIST OF FIFTY WORST WEEDS OF THE UNITED STATES

(A = annual, B = biennial, P = perennial)

Common name, botanical name, and duration of life.	Color, size, and arrangement of flowers.	Sections where injurious.	Method of seed distribution; vegetative propagation of perennials.	Place of growth and products injured.
Bermuda a grass (*Capriola dactylon*), P.	Purple; $1/12$ inch; spikes.	Maryland to Missouri and southward.	Seeds sparingly; rootstocks.	Fields and lawns; hoed crops.
Bindweed, field bindweed (*Convolvulus arvensis*), P.	White or pink; 1 inch; solitary.	Entire United States, especially California.	Grain and flax seeds; creeping roots.	Rich, moist soils; grain and hoed crops.
Bindweed, or morning glory, hedge bindweed (*Convolvulus sepium*), P.	White or rose; 2 inches; solitary.	Mississippi Valley region.	Grain and flax seeds; rootstocks.	Rich prairie and river bottoms; corn and small grain.
Bitterweed, yellow dogfennel (*Helenium tenuifolium*), A.	Yellow; ¾ inch; head.	Virginia to Kansas and southward.	Wind, hay, animals.	Meadows and pastures; injures live stock and taints milk.
Bracken, brake (*Pteridium aquilinum*), P.	No flowers	Northwestern States and the Pacific coast.	Spores scattered by wind; running roots.	Logged-off land, meadows, and pastures.
Broom-sedge (*Andropogon virginicus*), P.	Green; ¼ inch; racemes.	Massachusetts to Michigan, Florida and Texas.	Wind; short rootstocks, plants in tufts.	Fields and waste lands; pastures and meadows.
Buffalo-bur (*Solanum rostratum*), A.	Yellow; ½ inch; solitary.	Illinois and Colorado to Texas.	Plants rolled by wind; seeds in hay and by animals.	Fields; grain and hoed crops, wool.
Chess, cheat (*Bromus secalinus*), A.	Green; spikelets in panicles.	All grain sections.	Grain seed; especially wheat.	Everywhere; grain fields.
Chickweed, common chickweed (*Alsine media*), A.	White; ⅛ inch; cymes.	Entire United States	Grass and clover seed, animals; has a long seeding period.	Meadows, lawns, winter crops.

TABLE 15.—DESCRIPTIVE LIST OF FIFTY WORST WEEDS OF THE
UNITED STATES—*Continued*

Common name, botanical name, and duration of life.	Color, size, and arrangement of flowers.	Sections where injurious.	Method of seed distribution; vegetative propagation of the perennials.	Place of growth and products injured.
Cocklebur, clotbur (*Xanthium* spp.), A.	Green; ¼ inch; head.	...... do	Carried by animals.	Cultivated fields and waste places; hoed crops and wool.
Crabgrass (*Syntherisma sanguinalis*), A.	Green; spikes...	Entire United States, especially the South.	Clover and grass seed, hay, animals.	Cultivated fields, gardens, lawns, hoed crops.
Daisy, oxeye daisy (*Chrysanthemum leucanthemum*), P.	White with yellow center; 1 inch; heads.	Maine to Virginia and Kentucky.	Clover seed, hay; woody, rather short rootstocks, but largely by seed.	Pastures, meadows, roadsides; hay, pasturage.
Dandelion (*Leontodon taraxacum*), P.	Yellow; 1¼ inch; head.	Entire United States.	Wind; taproot, which spreads but little.	Lawns, meadows, waste places; hay and lawns.
Dock, yellow dock (*Rumex crispus*), P.	Green; ¼ inch; panicle.	...... do	Hay and straw, clover and grass seed; taproot, which spreads but little.	Hay, small grain and hoed crops.
Dodder, alfalfa dodder, field dodder (*Cuscuta arvensis*), A.	Yellow; ⅛ inch clusters.	All clover and alfalfa regions.	Hay, clover, and alfalfa seed.	Clover and alfalfa fields.
Dogbane, Indian - hemp (*Apocynum cannabinum*), P.	Greenish white; ¼ inch; terminal clusters.	Upper Mississippi Valley.	Wind; creeping root.	Fields with sandy soil; pasture, grain and hoed crops.
Foxtail, yellow foxtail, pigeon grass (*Chaetochloa lutescens*), A.	Green; spikes.	...... do	Animals, hay, grain, and grass seeds.	Land cultivated in early part of season; young grass and clover seedlings.
Garlic, field garlic (*Allium vineale*), P.	Flowers rare; umbels with bulblets.	Rhode Island to Georgia and west to Missouri.	Seeds rare; bulblets carried in wheat; underground bulbs.	Everywhere; wheat and dairy products.
Hawkweed, orange hawkweed, devils-paintbrush (*Hieracium aurantiacum*), P.	Orange; 1 inch; heads.	Maine to Ohio.	Wind, grass and clover seeds; runners similar to strawberry.	Untillable pastures and meadows.
Horsenettle (*Solanum carolinense*), P.	Purple; 1 inch; solitary.	Entire United States.	Plants rolled by wind; running roots.	Everywhere; grain and hoed crops, pastures.
Horseweed (*Erigeron canadensis*), A.	White; ¼ inch; heads in cymes.	...... do	Hay, grass, and clover seeds.	Meadows, pastures, and grain fields.
Ironweed (*Vernonia noveboracensis*), P.	Purple; ⅓ inch; heads.	Maine to Maryland and Iowa to Kansas.	Wind; short thick rootstocks, making plant grow in bunches.	Pastures and meadows.
Jimsonweed (*Datura stramonium*), A.	Purple; 3 inches; solitary.	Maine to Minnesota and Texas.	Pods and plants blown by wind.	Pastures, barnyards and waste lands; seeds, flowers and leaves poisonous.
Johnson grass (*Holcus halepensis*), P.	Green; ⅛ inch; panicle.	Virginia to Texas and California.	In hay, grain, and grass seed; running rootstocks.	All crops except hay.
Lambs-quarters (*Chenopodium album*), A.	Green; very small; panicle.	Entire United States.	Grain and grass seed.	Grain fields and hoed crops.
Lettuce, prickly lettuce (*Lactuca scariola*), A.	Yellow; ¼ inch; heads in panicles.	Ohio to Iowa, Utah to California.	Wind	Everywhere; all crops.
Milkweed, common milkweed (*Asclepias syriaca*), P.	Purple; ½ inch; umbels.	New York to Minnesota.	Wind; creeping roots.	All crops and in pastures.

Table 15.—DESCRIPTIVE LIST OF FIFTY WORST WEEDS OF THE UNITED STATES—*Continued*

Common name, botanical name, and duration of life.	Color, size, and arrangement of flowers.	Sections where injurious.	Method of seed distribution; vegetative propagation of the perennials.	Place of growth and products injured.
Morning-glory (*Ipomœa hederacea*), A.	White, purple, or blue; 1½ inches; solitary.	New York to Missouri.	Cornstover, straw, and wind.	Cultivated fields, especially corn and small grain.
Mustard, wild mustard, charlock (*Brassica arvensis*), A.	Yellow; ½ inch; racemes.	Maine to Washington.	Grain, grass, clover, and rape seeds.	Small-grain fields and meadows; grains.
Nutgrass, coco (*Cyperus rotundus*), P.	Brown; 1/16 inch; spikelets.	Maryland to Florida and Texas.	Wind, nursery stock, hay, and grass seed; tubers.	All soils; hoed crops.
Pennycress, Frenchweed (*Thlaspi arvense*), A.	White; ⅛ inch; racemes.	North Dakota and Minnesota.	Wind	Grain fields and pastures; grain and dairy products.
Pigweed, redroot, careless weed (*Amaranthus retroflexus*), A.	Green; very small; spikes in panicles.	Entire United States.	In grain and grass seeds; plants blown by wind.	Plowed land; hoed crops.
Plantain, buckthorn, ribgrass (*Plantago lanceolata*), P.	White; 1/16 inch; spike.	...... do	Hay, clover and grass seed; spreads but slowly from a crown.	Everywhere; meadows, pastures, and lawns.
Poison-ivy (*Rhus toxicodendron*), P.	Greenish white; ⅛ inch; panicles.	Entire United States.	Does not spread fast by seeds; running rootstocks.	Moist rich land, along fences; poisonous by contact.
Purslane, pusley (*Portulaca oleracea*), A.	Yellow; ¼ inch; solitary.	...... do	Tillage implements; has a long seeding period.	Rich cultivated land, especially gardens; hoed crops.
Quackgrass, witchgrass (*Agropyron repens*), P.	Green; spike....	Maine to Pennsylvania and Minnesota.	Seeds of grain and coarse grasses; creeping rootstocks.	All crops on the better soils; hold crops.
Ragweed, smaller ragweed (*Ambrosia elatior*), A.	Yellow; ¼ inch; small heads on spikes.	Entire United States.	Wind carrying matured plants; in grain and red-clover seeds.	Everywhere, especially grain stubble; hoed crops and young grass seeding.
Russian thistle (*Salsola pestifer*), A.	Purplish; ¼ inch; solitary.	Minnesota to Washington and southward.	Wind rolling matured plants.	Everywhere; small grain and hoed crops.
St. Johnswort (*Hypericum perforatum*), P.	Yellow; ¾ inch; cymes.	Maine to North Carolina and Iowa.	In hay and grass seed; rootstocks.	Meadows, pastures. and waste places.
Sandbur (*Cenchrus pauciflorus*), A.	Green; 1/3 inch; bur.	Maine to Florida and westward to Colorado.	Animals, especially sheep.	Sandy land pastures and waste places; pastures and wool.
Smartweed (*Polygonum pennsylvanicum*), A.	Light rose; 1/16 inch; racemes.	Maine to Minnesota, Florida, and Texas.	Wind carrying matured plants.	Moist, rich soils; hoed crops and young grass seedings.
Smartweed, marsh smartweed, devils-shoestring (*Polygonum muhlenbergii*), A.	Rose color; 1/16 inch; spikes.	Indiana to Iowa.	Wind and farm machinery; rootstocks.	Wet land, prairie, and muck soils; hoed crops, hay, pasture.
Sorrel, sheep sorrel (*Rumex acetosella*), P.	Red; ⅛ inch; panicles.	Entire United States.	In clover seed; creeping roots.	Meadows and pastures.
Sowthistle, perennial sowthistle (*Sonchus arvensis*), P.	Yellow; ¾ inch; heads.	Maine to Minnesota.	Wind; running rootstocks.	Grain fields and hoed crops.
Squirreltail grass, squirrel grass, foxtail, wild barley (*Hordeum jubatum*), A.	Green; spike with long bristly glumes.	Minnesota to Texas and California.	Hay, animals, wind.	Meadows and pastures; barbed seeds produce sores on live stock.

TABLE 15.—DESCRIPTIVE LIST OF FIFTY WORST WEEDS OF THE
UNITED STATES—*Continued*

Common name, botanical name, and duration of life.	Color, size, and arrangement of flowers.	Sections where injurious.	Method of seed distribution; vegetative propagation of the perennials.	Place of growth and products injured.
Thistle, Canada thistle (*Cirsium arvense*), P.	Purple; ¾ inch; heads.	Maine to Pennsylvania and Washington.	Wind, in hay and straw and in clover and grass seeds; creeping roots.	All crops.
Thistle, common thistle, bull thistle (*Cirsium lanceolatum*), B.	Reddish purple; 1 inch; heads.	Maine to Virginia and Washington.	Wind, in alfalfa, clover, and grass seeds.	Pastures, meadows, and winter wheat.
Wild carrot (*Daucus carota*), B.	White; very small; umbels.	Maine and Virginia to the Mississippi.	In foreign clover and alfalfa seed; carried by animals and wind.	Meadows and pastures.
Wild oats (*Avena fatua*), A.	Green; panicles; similar to oats.	Wisconsin to Washington.	In seed oats....	Oat fields; awns injurious to stock.
Wintercress, yellowrocket (*Campe barbarea*), P.	Yellow; ¼ inch; racemes.	Maine to Virginia and westward.	In grain, clover, and grass seeds.	Grain fields, pastures, and meadows.

a. The fact that Bermuda grass is often a troublesome weed where it is not desired does not contradict the fact that it is the most valuable pasture grass in the South. With proper rotations it is rarely a serious weed. Where only intertilled crops are grown, such as cotton, it greatly increases cultivation. For its valuable features see *Farmer's Bulletin 814.*
U. S. Dept. of Agr. Far. Bul. 660.

IV

VEGETATIVE PROPAGATION

79. Vegetative propagation with seed plants is the production of a complete plant from a bud. This definition includes all asexual methods (layerage, division, separation and graftage) but its most specific application is to cuttage, to which the following paragraphs are mainly limited.

As presented in Chapter One, a seedling develops from a single fertilized cell in the ovary of a flower. Stated in its lowest terms, therefore, a seedling consists of a root and a shoot. Its growth by enlargement and differentiation of its cells is limited only by conditions unfavorable to development. Hence, theoretically, so long as conditions continue favorable, cell multiplication typical of the species will maintain plant growth without limit and supply parts suitable for vegetative reproduction.

Theoretically, any one living cell is capable of producing a complete new plant. However, practical application of this hypothesis has not so far been found feasible. Yet under exact control methods new plant individuals have been developed from surprisingly small numbers of living cells. When larger numbers of such cells are employed as in ordinary cuttings, grafts, etc., the processes of vegetative reproduction become the foundation upon which rests the standardization of most horticultural products—the commercial growing of named varieties of nearly all fruit and ornamental plants and some vegetables (potato, sweet potato, tarragon, horseradish).

From all this it is evident that vegetative reproduction is associated with cell multiplication. Among monocotyledonous plants (palm, pineapple, dracena, bamboo) it is almost wholly limited to the growing tips of shoots and the latent buds at the nodes of the stems. Among dicotyledonous plants (carnation, strawberry, grape) and gymnosperms (yew, pine, juniper) regenerative possibilities are far greater because of the almost ever-present cambium. Hence, we realize the basic importance of the structural nature of the plant in vegetative reproduction—the development of new roots and new shoots from and upon pieces of roots, or shoots or other plant parts removed from their original sources, or "parent" plants. These parts are highly complex groups of living cells though it is known

that from them originate new roots, shoots, leaves and the reproductive organs which may develop fruits and seeds to perpetuate the
species.

In practice the aim in vegetative reproduction is usually to stimulate the development of adventitious buds and of roots from
primordial tissue.

When new monocotyledonous plants are to be developed asexually, almost the only method is to arouse the normal but latent or
dormant axillary buds, because once the cambial tissues [1] in the
stems become inactive they rarely resume activity.   Almost invariably the only points at which these tissues can be reawakened
are at the nodes and the basal parts of the leaves.[2]   Hence when
stem parts of monocots are to be used for vegetative propagation
they must almost without exception include normal axillary buds.
Under favorable conditions these develop new shoots and roots
while still connected with the "parent" cutting, from which when
sufficiently developed, they may be severed.   A typical case in point
is dracena, whose cane-like stems, laid horizontally on a cutting
bench, partly buried in moist sand and given bottom heat often
produce a new plant from every axillary bud.

There is more latitude in the propagation of dicots than of monocots, because in the former the cambial tissues are far more widely
distributed and much more active.   Hence, methods of vegetative
reproduction are more numerous and easy of application.   The parts
which most frequently develop new shoots are axillary buds.   When
no such buds occur upon a cutting, growth will often start either
from the minute dormant apices of shoots, from the axils of bud
scales or from accessory buds at the bases of axillary buds.   Even
when none of these rudiments are present new buds or roots may
still be formed, as proved by W. Plett [3] who out of 401 species
tested, produced roots from internodal cuttings upon 67 species,
shoots from internodal tissues on 38 species and both shoots and
roots on 27 species.   These results suggest the greater likelihood of
root than bud formation on cuttings.   Therefore, in making cuttings

[1] According to Strassburger and Hillhouse (*Practical Botany*, p. 96): "Closed fibro-
vasal bundles are not capable of increase in thickness, and therefore where such
occurs in the monocotyledons, it cannot be brought about through the medium of
the fibro-vasal bundles. ' This increase of thickness results from the action of a cambium ring which is found outside the fibro-vasal bundles, and is confined to the
families of Dracæneæ and Aloineæ i.e., the so-called 'Arborescent Liliaceæ' and the
Dioscoreæ."

[2] Except under the influence of chemicals. See Chapter VIA.

[3] Untersuchungen uber die regenerationserschein ungen an internodien. 46 p., illus.
Hamburg, 1921. (Unpublished *Inaug. Diss. Auszug* published 1921.)   Cited by J. H.
Priestly and C. F. Swingle in *Tech. Bul. 151, U. S. Dept. of Agr.*, 1929.

care should be exercised in having at least one visible bud near the top of the cutting for shoot growth to form the top of the new plant. No bud need be present at the base of the cutting since root development is not from visible buds there, but from inner primordial tissue.

80. Cuttage is propagation by plant parts—roots, rhizomes, tubers, stems, or leaves—cut in pieces with or without buds. These pieces take root and asexually produce new plants of the same variety and species as the parent plant. In general it is a cheap, quick and handy way to secure large numbers of plants in a given time. But though all plants may perhaps be multiplied by cuttage, there are some which may be more economically handled by other means such as grafting, seedage, budding, division, etc.

For instance, certain varieties of apples, pears, plums and peaches readily strike root from cuttings, but the great majority do not; therefore, the pome fruits are largely grafted and the stone fruits budded, the most satisfactory method being chosen in each case. In other words, species differ in the facility with which they may be propagated by cutting, grafting or other method. Nothing but experience with the actual plant can decide the matter.

In popular parlance when the term "cuttage" is used it is supposed to refer to cuttings of the stem, except when qualified by the name of some other part used; as tuber cutting, leaf cutting, root cutting. By amateurs stem cuttings are often called "slips."

Propagation by cuttings is a cheap, convenient and therefore popular way to secure new plants. Probably all species of plants may be propagated by one or more methods of cuttage, using one or another part, but with annuals, biennials and many perennials some other method (layerage, graftage, seedage, etc.) is often easier and cheaper. Even varieties differ in ability to root.

For instance, when Clotilde Soupert rose was a novelty a certain seedsman bought stock from which to grow new plants for sale and gave orders to his propagators to secure a certain number of plants, if possible. These men, acting upon their experience with roses of the same class, calculated upon what appeared to them a reasonable percentage of loss and made provision for the required space on that basis. But the variety rooted so much easier than they had thought that thousands more plants were grown than the seedsman had ordered. However, as the demand created by good advertising was greater than had been counted upon, practically all were sold and a big profit made. Reverse cases are probably more common.

The principal advantages of cutting over seed propagation are (1) that a fully developed and often stronger plant is obtained in considerably less time than when seed is sown and (2) the character of the variety is preserved in the new plant. The latter is not always the case with propagation by seed.

Climate has a noticeable effect upon the rooting of cuttings. In parts of southern Europe and South America, many plants which can hardly be made to strike root elsewhere readily do so. In some of the Gulf States sweet potato vines may be cut in pieces a foot long and thrust into the sand with certainty that they will grow. In Texas hard wood cuttings of quince and persimmon readily take root. Probably in such cases the condition of the soil

FIG. 43.—Effect of shade on rooting of cuttings. Lilac in ten-cutting sets grown in varying amounts of shade. 1, Open; 2, slats; 3, gauze; 4, cheesecloth; 5, muslin; 6, double muslin; 7, sash plus slats. B, Philadelphus coronarius (same arrangement as above, except 8, cheese cloth placed directly on the cuttings). C, Baccharis (same arrangement as B.)

also has an influence, but since similar soil in similar conditions in northern localities does not produce similar results the credit for success must be given to climate.

81. Value of shade for cuttings.—It is an old established practice to shade cuttings while in the rooting medium. Figure 43 shows the variation in response to various amounts of shade. At a glance one can see that for the average plant some protection is beneficial, but that the results vary with the species. In experiments where 50 species were tested at the Boyce Thompson Institute, it was found that shade furnished by cheesecloth or muslin was generally best. In some cases, however, for example Baccharis, there was no value in shading. In general the results also show a variation from season to season. Results in June and July of 1931 were not exactly like those of 1930, due to the dark and humid weather of 1931 compared with 1930. The practical propagator must always reserve judgment and vary his practice according to the weather at hand. (Fig. 43).

82. Summer propagation of hardy plants in Minnesota and other western states is difficult because of the dry air. S. B. Green successfully propagated hydrangea, spirea, barberry, Tartarian honeysuckle, and eleven varieties of roses by stretching burlap over the beds. The strips were not laid horizontally but inclined to the south so the northern edge was at least 1' above the bench, while the southern edge rested directly on the bench. By applying this shade at about nine o'clock and leaving it on till about five the cuttings were kept from wilting in the driest weather. It was also found that syringing the burlap with water increased the cooling effect and that comparatively little attention was necessary in watering.

83. Rooting cuttings in dry climates.—Because the relative humidity in dry climates is low, as in parts of the Pacific Coast states, special methods are necessary to make cuttings of certain plants (roses) take root. Florists have had good success with the following method: Hotbeds with 18" of fresh manure and 3" of sand are covered with glass beneath a burlap frame to provide shade and reduce air circulation. Only one daily watering is usually necessary. At this time, the sashes are raised only one at a time to reduce loss of humidity.

Cuttings often require a moist air of proper temperature and sometimes bottom heat.[1] This general statement applies with special force to cuttings of growing parts. Heat and humidity must be carefully regulated to suit the species or variety of plant being propagated, because the demands of each vary more or less. Many

---

[1] To date the necessity of bottom heat has not been proved—when other factors are under control.

devices, some of them simple, have been adopted for regulating both heat and moisture.

Moisture regulation is usually accomplished by propagating frames and boxes of various forms, the commonest being similar to a hotbed but smaller (Figs. 44, 45). The principle in all is confining

Fig. 44.—"Sweat-box" propagator. Humidity and temperature controled by raising and lowering lid and bottom heat by lowering burlap curtains beneath bench.

the air. In a small way a pane of glass (Fig. 45) may be inverted over the cuttings (Fig. 36) or a bell jar placed above them. By tilting these more or less, humidity and air circulation may be regulated.

84. Callus, new formation of cells upon an injured tissue. It appears most conspicuously at the lower end of a stem cutting, the cut surface of a layer or of a root graft, but also at the apical ends of cuttings where these are cut.

85. Stock plants are grown in greenhouses and nurseries merely to supply cuttings, layers, buds or scions for propagation.

86. "Blind eyes" are shoots which do not produce flowers. They are common on roses and some other plants grown under glass. Many propagators think they will produce flowerless plants.

Blind vs flowering wood, L. C. Corbett tested this belief that "blind wood," is inferior to "flower wood" in the propagation of roses. Each year for five years wood was selected respectively from these two classes of shoots to test the cumulative effect of propagation through a series of years. As to rooting ability and growth, little difference was noticed. During the first year the flowering wood plants produced 156% more flowers than plants propagated from blind wood, but during the next two years the percentage decreased instead of increased. The percentage of flowers on the latter also decreased, but not in so great proportion. As a result of these experiments the author concludes that where bloom rather than stock plants is desired, the flowering wood is decidedly the better, but the cumulative effect of propagating roses from one or the other year after year is not marked.

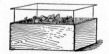

FIG. 45.—Small glass covered propagating box for germinating seeds and rooting cuttings.

Suckers are leafy shoots produced from adventitious buds on the underground parts of plants. The term is sometimes applied 1, to aërial roots or holdfasts of orchids and other epiphytal plants and 2, to shoots which sprout from the trunk. Properly, however, these last are water-sprouts. Plants that produce them usually may be propagated by cuttings of the producing parts.

For instance, certain kinds of plum and cherry stocks must be carefully handled to prevent sucker formation; but for plant propagation the stools of blackberries, red raspberries, etc., are often severely root pruned by thrusting a sharp spade vertically full depth of the blade into the soil around the plant so as to cut the roots 6″ or 8″ from the stool and again farther out. Theoretically every cut piece may produce a plant. Instead of using a spade the stools are often removed and the ground deeply cut with a disk harrow run in two directions at right angles across the field. See Root Cuttings.

Water-sprouts are shoots or limbs of one season's growth produced from latent or adventitious buds on trunks and branches of well-established trees, mainly near where limbs have been removed. See Suckers above.

Both water sprouts and suckers commonly follow over-pruning. They show an excessive loss of balance between root system and top. In cold climates they often winter-kill. They are best removed by promptly pulling or rubbing them off while still soft and green. Wounds so made soon heal and other sprouts seldom follow. When allowed to become woody they must be cut, in which case other sprouts often develop around the wounds. Where practical, careful root pruning will tend to overcome this condition.

87. Buds are of two general kinds, true (or normal) and adventitious. A true bud, sometimes called a "brood body" is a growing point in normal position on a stem. It may develop into leaf, flower, branch, clus-

FIG. 45A.—Double Pot of cuttings.

ter of leaves, or of flowers, or of both leaves and flowers (apple).

Adventitious buds are developed at unexpected points from certain cells in the meristematic tissue in roots, stems or leaves. Under favorable conditions any of these cells may develop buds which may form either roots or sprouts, according to their position or the necessity of the case. Familiar examples on roots are red raspberry and blackberry; on stems, pome and stone fruits; on leaves, bryophyllum.

88. Origin of roots on cuttings.—In making stem cuttings the usual practice is to "cut to a node"; i.e., stems are cut just below buds. The reason given for this is that with most plants, as believed by many propagators, a larger proportion of cuttings will "strike root" than if the cuts are made farther away from the nodes, but in most cases experimental evidence has not sustained this theory. True buds of themselves, however, exercise no influence in the production of roots, for if buried in the earth or other medium, they rarely grow. The reason roots form best near the nodes is believed to be that stem tissues at such points are richer in plant food stored there than between nodes to assist the bud should it start growth. (See Chapter VI-A).

Propagation as influenced by girdling with knife or wire was reported by G. Hostermann with fruit stocks, fruit varieties, nuts, ornamentals, etc. Doucin and Paradise apples, quince, Mariana plum, golden currant and poplar rooted without any treatment. Compared with ringing, a tight wire band gave more favorable results, making possible the vegetative propagation of 31 of the 43 species, including apple, pear, sour cherry, Mahaleb cherry and Damson plum. *Behr. Lehr. u. Forschun gsanst. Gartenbau Berlin-Dahlem, 1926.*

89. New root formation on transplanted trees, according to experiments conducted at Woburn, England, showed that apple trees originated less than half the new roots within the last half inch of the old roots which had been trimmed for planting; whereas with currants and gooseberries more than half were produced from this half inch. Roots originating from the stems were usually 20% stouter than those formed elsewhere. This result explains why deeply planted, free-rooting stocks flourish better after a time than similar stocks planted at ordinary depth. As to the effect of trimming the roots at the time of transplanting on the subsequent formation of new roots, results showed considerable variation in different seasons and with different plants. The general conclusion reached is that trimming is of no importance.

Wood or branch buds are undeveloped branches bearing rudimentary leaves (scales) modified for protection. Under favorable conditions of growth they develop into branches which mature other buds in the axils of the leaves and usually one or more at the ex-

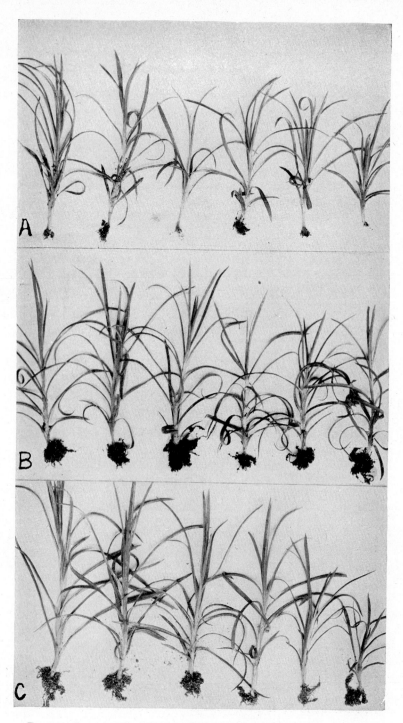

Fig. 46.—Carnation Cuttings in various media. A, Sand; B, peat; C, slag.

tremities. Flower buds develop one flower or several, with or without leaves. As to position, buds are lateral, axillary, terminal, etc.

In experiments at the Edinburgh Botanical Garden, as reported in *The Florists Exchange*, it was discovered that internodal cuttings of clematis root readily, but nodal cuttings develop only large calluses which fail to make roots. The Phelia rose and its sports also act in this way.

Adventitious roots usually develop from tissues known as the pericycle or cambium, beneath the outer bark, but sometimes they may arise from phloëm tissue. They may develop from meristematic tissue in any part of a plant or in some rare cases where older mature tissues again become meristematic. The change which leads to their

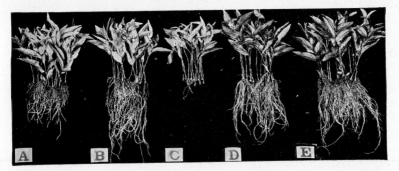

Fig. 47.—Prunus glandulosa cuttings, June 25 to August 10 rooted in: A, Bay sand. B, half sand, half peat moss (by volume); C, peat moss neutralized with lime; D, E, Mixture of peat moss and sand neutralized with lime.

formation always follows an unusual condition of plant growth such as insufficient assimilation of elaborated food by the plant or an injury of some kind.

Adventitious buds may be called emergency buds, because they seek to preserve the plant when endangered. This provision of nature has given rise to many of the asexual methods of plant propagation (cuttings, layers, etc.). Buds formed at the bases of stem cuttings readily push through the callus, but often roots push through the epidermis, even high above this point.

90. **Latent buds** are normal buds in normal positions but dormant beyond the usual time (a month, a year or more). They are called into growth by some peculiar stimulus. Many of the buds on the lower third or more of the annual growth of trees and shrubs become latent during the second year but start growing if the upper part is cut off.

90A. **Lateral buds** are situated on the sides of branches, usually in leaf axils. A terminal bud is situated at the extremity of a branch or stem. Usually only one is in this position, but sometimes (lilac) there are normally two or even more. Axillary buds are produced in the axils of leaves.

91. **Roots on stem cuttings and polarity.**—Roots form on the end normally nearest the root of the parent plant. Stems appear on the other end. Botanists call this phenomenon polarity. With root cuttings the plan holds good; the end normally nearest the top of

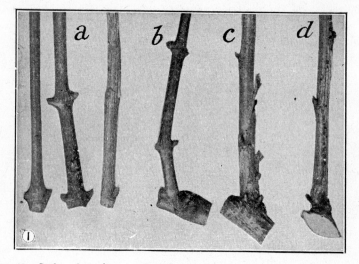

FIG. 48.—Styles of cuttings: a, Straight; b, c, mallet; d, neel. All styles (and "single eye") are used in grape and shrub propagation, but straight style is most popular.

the plant will produce a stem, and that farthest away, roots. Some species may be compelled to take root when reversed but growth is puny and of short duration.

If horseradish cuttings are inverted, they will start late, make roots from the "root" end and stems from the "stem" end, but the resulting roots will be small, irregular and unsalable. Hence horseradish growers generally cut the upper ends of their cuttings square across, and the lower ends oblique so the planters may see which end should be placed uppermost.

The Florists Exchange reports that at the Edinburgh Botanic Garden cuttings, especially of hard wooded plants, rooted most readily in acid media. It was also discovered that quartz sand compared with river sand in unheated frames reduced the necessary time to form roots even as much as one-third. Where bottom heat is used, British propagators favor cocoanut fiber as a rooting medium. The Edinburgh investigators advocate the old practice of placing cuttings around the margins of flower pots. Old school gardeners attributed success of this method to good aëration but Bernard Field explains it as due to radioactivity of the pot itself.

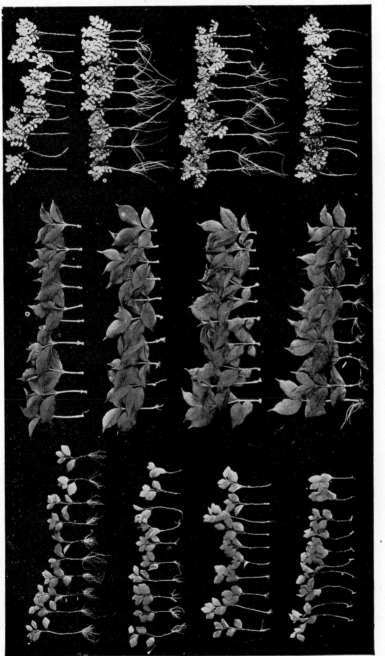

FIG. 49.—Comparison of rooting between cuttings of various types of bases. See text page 98.

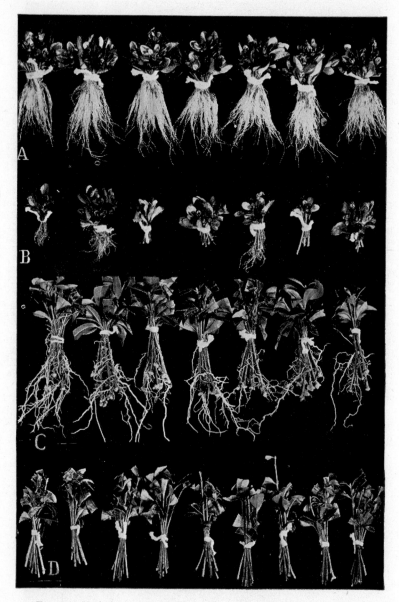

FIG. 50.—Variations of rooting between cuttings in acid peat moss and neutral sand. See text, page 99.

92. Rooting media must be relatively cheap, easily obtained, capable of holding sufficient moisture for the cuttings, produce high percentages of root growth and be as free of decay-producing fungi and bacteria as may be economically feasible.

Experiments conducted during the past decade or more show advantages for various media with certain kinds of cuttings. Peat moss is used in many greenhouses and nurseries; slag (a by-product of the steel industry) has been advertised and sold extensively near steel-producing centers; sphagnum moss is also used to some extent; but sand is more widely employed than perhaps all other media combined. These individually and in combination have been tested

A   B

Fig. 51.—Salvia cuttings in 2″, 4″ and 8″ of water. A, not aërated; B, aërated with oxygen.

experimentally by many scientists, with a large assortment of plants. In general it may be said: "Cuttings root satisfactorily [1] in a wide range of media if they are properly handled as to water and shade. The medium apparently serves more as a control of moisture than any other service or effect it may have on the cuttings in it." (Fig. 46.)

93. Rooting Response of Cuttings.—Contrary to the general belief that sand is the most suitable medium in which to root most kinds of cuttings, A. E. Hitchcock,[2] of the Boyce Thompson Institute, found that this held true under the conditions of his tests for only six out of 96 varieties (included in 46 genera), but that 90 varieties rooted readily in a peat moss and sand mixture which proved far superior to sand alone or peat alone. These results are of special interest, since the advice in text books on propagation and in a recent paper by Stewart [3] is to the effect that "clean sharp sand" be used for rooting most kinds of cuttings. (Figs. 47, 50, 51.)

[1] W. W. Wiggin, *Ohio Sta. Bul.* 487.
[2] *Bot. Gaz.* LXXXVI, 2, 1928.
[3] L. B. Stewart, *Methods of Propagation,* Jour. Roy. Hort. Soc., London, 52, 33-39, 1927.

Because of the marked contrast in their physical and chemical properties (Table 16) peat moss and sand afford unusually good means of obtaining widely divergent conditions without at the same time introducing more than two sets of substratum complexes.

TABLE 16.—PROPERTIES OF PEAT MOSS COMPARED WITH THOSE OF BUILDING SAND

Property	Peat Moss	Sand
Reaction (pH value)[1]	3.6	7.0+
Wt. of water in gm. held by 100 gm. dry weight peat moss	1000[2]	20
Origin	Sphagnum bogs	Rock strata
Organic matter content	99%	Negligible
Texture	Finely fibrous	Coarse crystalline
Weight in gm. of 100 cc. (air-dry)	15[3]	162

Other phases of the work showed that the capacity of cuttings to form roots is dependent to some extent upon the age of the wood, season taken, activity of growth and the amount of leaf surface left on the cutting. These factors were accordingly taken into consideration when selecting material for the experiments.

According to their rooting response in peat moss and in sand the cuttings were classified in three groups: Those which rooted readily in peat moss but poorly in sand; those which rooted readily in sand but poorly in peat moss (Figs. 47, 50); and those which rooted readily in either peat moss or in sand. (Table 17.)

Hitchcock concludes: The fact that cuttings in all three groups rooted readily in a mixture composed of equal parts of peat moss and sand (with the exception of five varieties in Group II) indicates that this mixture is superior to sand as a general medium in which to root cuttings. Although the pH value of the medium was an important factor in determining the type of rooting response of some varieties of cuttings, it was not the single limiting factor. The critical acid value, at which injury to the cuttings listed in Group II occurred, was found to lie between pH 3.6 and 4.1. For the same

---

[1] "pH value" is the generally accepted symbolical means of specifying the electrically measured degree of free acidity or free alkalinity of soils. Technically it "designates an electrical determination of hydrogen ions in solution; the capital H designating hydrogen, and the small p being a symbol denoting that hydrogen has been determined by electrical measurement. Non-technically, pH value provides a simple and easily understood measure for stating free acidity or free alkalinity, where the scale of measure and not the technical meaning is wanted; upon this scale, seven is neutral, with acidity ranging from seven to one, and alkalinity ranging from seven to nine.

[2] DACHNOWSKI gives a value of 1635.5.

[3] The moisture content of peat moss in the bale will vary greatly according to the humidity conditions under which it is stored.

TABLE 17.—CLASSIFICATION OF VARIETIES OF CUTTINGS ACCORDING TO ROOTING RESPONSE IN PEAT MOSS AND SAND

Group I — Cuttings Rooted Readily in Peat Moss but Poorly in Sand	Group II — Cuttings Rooted Readily in Sand but Poorly in Peat Moss	Group III — Cuttings Rooted Readily in Either Peat Moss or in Sand	
Azalea amœna * (6-12)†	Asclepias nivea (1-4)	Buddleia davidii (8)	Ribes alpinum (6-8)
Azalea ledifolia* (8)	Berberis thunbergi (8)	Buxus sempervirens (7, 11)	Ribes nigra (6-8)
Azalea (hardy mollis hybrids) (7)	Carnation (7)	Callicarpa purpurea (6-8)	Rosa (American Pillar) (6-9)
Blue spruce (2-4)	Cotoneaster horizontalis (7)	Capsicum grossum (4)	Rosa (Dorothy Perkins) (6-9)
Delaware grape (7)	Daphne cneorum (7)	Coleus blumei (4 var.)* (1-12)	Rosa setigera (5)
Enkianthus campanulatus (9)	Datura stramonium (1)	Cornus florida (pink) (6, 7)	Rosa (Silver Moon) (7)
Ilex crenata (3)	Deutzia gracilis* (6-8)	Cornus florida (white) (6, 7)	Salix alba (5, 6, 11)
Vaccinium corymbosum (6-8)	Heliotrope (10)	Cornus kousa (6)	Salvia splendens (5, 8)
	Lagerstræmia indica (8)	Cornus mas (6)	Sambucus canadensis (6-8)
	Ligustrum ibota (var. regelianum)* (8)	Dahlia (6 var.) (4, 5, 8-11)	Spiraea (Anthony Waterer) (6-8)
	Ligustrum japonicum (9)	Evonymus radicans (7, 8)	Spiraea arguta (6-8)
	Ligustrum ovalifolium* (, 8, 11)	Evonymus (variegated) (7)	Spiraea nipponica rotundifolia (6-8)
	Ligustrum vulgare * (8)	Forsythia intermedia (5-9)	Spiraea reevesiana (6-8)
	Mentha piperita* (7-10)	Forsythia viridissima (5-9)	Spiraea thunbergii (6-8)
	Osmanthus aquifolium (white variegated) (8)	Fuchsia speciosa (3 var.) (6-9)	Spiraea van houttei (6-8)
	Prunus glandulosa (pink variety)* (6-8)	Gardenia florida (2, 7)	Symphoricarpos racemosus (6-8)
	Prunus tomentosa* (6)	Geranium (4, 6, 10-12)	Symphoricarpos vulgaris (6-9)
	Prunus triloba (12)	Hydrangea opuloides (8)	Taxus cuspidata (1, 6, 11)
	Rosa hugonis (6)	Hydrangea petiolaris (6)	Taxus (weeping variety) (1)
	Syringa vulgaris* (6, 7)	Ilex aquifolium (8-10)	Tsuga canadensis (6-8)
		Ilex cornuta (1)	Ulmus parvifolia (6)
		Ilex glabra (8-12)	Ulmus pumila* (5, 6)
		Ilex opaca (6, 8-12, 1)	Viburnum carlesii (7)
		Lonicera fragrantissima (7, 8)	Viburnum opulus americanum (6-8)
		Lonicera morrowi (7, 8)	Viburnum opulus sterile (6-8)
		Lonicera tatarica (7, 8)	Viburnum tomentosum plicatum (1-3, 12)
		Philadelphus coronarius (6-8)	Weigela floribunda (6-9)
		Philadelphus falconeri (6-8)	Weigela rosea (7)
		Philadelphus gordonianus (6-8)	
		Philadelphus grandiflorus (6-8)	
		Philadelphus lewisi (6-8)	

* Cuttings tested in neutral peat moss.

† Numerals in parenthesis indicate months during which cuttings were taken; for example, (6) refers to June.

Note: Cuttings in all three groups rooted readily in a mixture of equal parts of peat moss and sand with the exception of the five varieties.

varieties of cuttings callus formation was inhibited at pH values more acid that pH 4.1.

Whether peat moss was furnished in its natural acid state, neutralized, or mixed with sand, a more rapid rate of growth occurred in a medium containing it than in one containing only sand. Good rooting occurred for most varieties of cuttings over an acid range of pH 4.5-7.0.

Uniformity of rooting response of Azalea amœna cuttings in peat moss is attributed to the efficient moisture-retaining capacity of this medium. An increased moisture content of sand, as furnished by auto-irrigation, showed that in many cases, but especially under conditions of high light intensity, a more favorable rooting response was obtained.

For coleus cuttings the conditions in the medium influenced the rate of root growth rather than the time of root protrusion. Cuttings of Ligustrum japonicum which failed to root during two months in peat moss, rooted in two weeks when transferred to sand, indicating that root initiation had probably taken place, but that unfavorable conditions provided by peat moss prevented root protrusion.

The efficient buffer capacity of peat moss was found to be due principally to solid material, and not to the solutes in an extract. Methods for preparing samples and for making pH determinations are described in detail. Extracts of peat moss were found to give higher pH values than heavy suspensions.

94. Cutting type influence.[1]—At the Boyce Thompson Institute comparisons were made of similar shoots having different aged wood at the base only. Mallet cuttings of Spiræa vanhouttei root poorly but the presence of a mallet heel does not retard the rooting of Spiræa salicifolia. Diervilla hybrida roots best in May from shoots with a piece of last season's wood attached, but when made during the summer all four types of cuttings root badly. This is not true, however, for Spiræa vanhouttei, Rosa hugonis and many other shrubs. Figure 48 shows examples of styles.

Apparently no one type of cutting will give best rooting for all kinds of plants. So no generalization can be made as to type of cutting to use for a specific species unless such information has resulted from tests similar to those just described. Where, however, the best type of cutting is selected for any individual species it may mean the saving of several days to several weeks, even for plants which are regarded as easy or certain to root.

In Figure 49 the arrangement corresponds to that used in *Contributions from the Boyce Thompson Institute,* 1932. In the experi-

---

[1] A. E. Hitchcock.

ments the shoots of all four types were of approximately the same length and age so *the essential difference is on the age of the wood at the base of the cutting.* IT IS NOT A COMPARISON OF DIFFERENT AGED SHOOTS.

The order of arrangement in the figure is as follows: Top row, cut made ¼" to ¾" above the base of the shoot; second row, cut made exactly at the base of the shoot; third row, a heel of last season's wood; fourth row, a mallet of last season's wood. The cuttings were placed deeply in sand so that only one-fourth was exposed. Some or all of the leaves were left on the portion of stem buried. A, Spiræa vanhouttei cuttings in the bed from May 10 to June 2; B, Diervilla hybrida, May 12 to May 29; C, Rosa hugonis, June 11 to July 7.

95. Variation in rooting.—*Azalea amœna* and European privet *(Ligustrum vulgare)* were placed in the same 6" pots containing acid peat moss (Fig. 50, rows A and C) and neutral sand (rows B and D). Azalea shows uniformly good rooting and privet uniformly poor rooting in the acid peat moss. The variation in rooting of similar lots of cuttings placed in sand is attributed to fluctuations in moisture during the hottest part of the summer. Due to its efficient moisture retaining capacity, peat moss does not dry out as sand will.

96. Stem cuttings of fruit trees.—If fruit tree varieties could be propagated by stem cuttings and thus be established on their own roots two great benefits would result: Variable and incompatible stocks would be eliminated and cost of propagation would probably be lowered. In commercial work plum stocks are often multiplied by replanted suckers but the method is uncertain and the numbers of suckers obtainable are dependent upon the facility with which the "parent" plant produces them.

Root cuttings and stool layers (quince and Doucin apple) are often used but these methods are cumbersome and variable in their application to specific varieties. Doubtless the most convenient and least costly method would be by hardwood stem cuttings but nurserymen have experienced difficulties in making these take root. Because of this many of them and many scientists, especially during the past decade, have tried to discover reliable means of rooting and establishing such cuttings, but their efforts in toto, as reported, have resulted in probably 95% or greater failure. (See Chapter VI-A.)

97. Aëration factor in rooting cuttings.[1]—Figure 51 shows variation of root growth of salvia in shallow versus deep water and aërated versus non-aërated deep water. The results are rather conclusive that oxygen is necessary for root growth. They also verify the old recommendation that cuttings be placed in shallow water so absorption of oxygen from the air will supply the needs. In studying these results one must be careful not to overestimate the need for

---

[1] P. W. Zimmerman.

oxygen in the average rooting medium. Unless the sand medium is over-saturated with water it will have far more oxygen available than the roots can use. The air normally has 20% oxygen in it; but the average plant can make normal growth with 5% to 8%. Generally bad results in rooting can be accounted for in some way other than poor aëration.

98. Method of "Striking" Greenwood Cuttings.[1]—Greenwood cuttings are susceptible to rapid drying due to limited water

Fig. 52.—How removal of leaves affects rooting of greenwood cuttings.

absorption and continued loss of water from the leaves. When the exit is greater than the intake of water wilting results. Under such conditions the chances for root production decrease. The problem then is to keep the cuttings fresh in light for a long enough period to permit of root formation. The method is, therefore, important.

The rate of transpiration from the leaves varies with the relative humidity of the air on the under sides of the leaves. Leaves close to the rooting medium transpire less than those farther away because the relative humidity is higher near the moist surface. This suggests planting in such a way as to permit the leaves to rest on or near the medium. Often the method calls for slanting the stems so the leaves will naturally parallel the surface of the medium. On bright, sunny days additional protection may be given by covering the cuttings with cheesecloth. This is superior to newspapers be-

[1] P. W. Zimmerman.

cause it is more readily applied, lasts longer and does not absorb moisture to nearly the same degree. When the weather is not too humid the cloth may be left on day and night.

99. Removal of leaves from greenwood cuttings is so commonly practiced that many propagators claim it is essential to success in root formation. This is a mistake. The real reason for removal is convenience in placing in the cutting medium. Entire stripping of leaves as compared with reduction of leaf surface must be avoided as the assistance of some leaf area is necessary to root formation, provided proper moisture control is practiced. Doubtless reduction checks transpiration of water and therefore wilting of leaves unless these are placed close to the surface of the medium. These statements are well supported by experiments at the Boyce Thompson Institute, concerning which P. W. Zimmerman writes as follows: [1]

The importance of leaves on greenwood cuttings is demonstrated by two sets taken from the same bush of black currant (Fig. 52). Where the cuttings had the support given by a leaf (A) they went ahead to root in two weeks; without leaves (B) they were unable to form roots. As autumn approaches, a time is reached when leaves can be dispensed with.

In young cuttings of Prunus tomentosa, when all leaves are removed they do not root. A small leaf might pull them through but it would take much time. Three leaves can bring out the roots in four weeks. The larger the number of leaves that can be kept in good condition, the better will be the root growth.

In corroboration of these statements the senior author vividly recalls the appearance of a propagating bench in the winter of 1892—3 at Downer's Grove, Illinois, where the leaves of rose cuttings were laid flat on the sand like shingles on a roof and where the success in rooting was strikingly greater than in the greenhouse where he was then employed.

---

[1] *Florists Exchange,* August 14, 1926.

V

PROPAGATION BY LAYERAGE, DIVISION, SEPARATION

100. Layerage, division, separation are asexual reproductive processes which merge into one another so that lines of demarkation are not well defined. With layerage the new plants take root while still attached to the "parent" upon which they depend for food until they can care for themselves. The parts are not necessarily specialized for that purpose (stems of grape, rose, forsythia). In *division* they do not naturally break apart but may be cut or torn, often before rooting, from the parent (rhizomes of canna, crowns of lily-of-the-valley). In *separation* the rooted parts, or parts not yet rooted usually detach themselves at the close of the growing season and become, or develop into, new plants (bulbs—hyacinth; corms—crocus). Many species that do not naturally propagate by separation may be divided (rhubarb, achillea) and many that do not naturally multiply by either of these methods may be made to do so by layering (Figs. 53, 54).

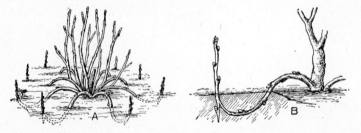

Fig. 53.—Common layerage. A, Branches bent down and buried. B, Layer enlarged to show wound to hasten root development.

Layering is one of the easiest and most popular methods of propagation. In outdoor practice it is best performed in fall or early spring (Practicum XI). It is essential to propagate Cory Thornless blackberries by layerage since plants coming from the root are not true to type. They bear thorns whereas tip layers make thornless plants. As far as the authors know no satisfactory explanation has been published.

ORNAMENTAL PLANTS PROPAGATED BY LAYERS

Akebia	Cornus	Hoya	Nerium
Aubrietia	Cotoneaster	Laburnum	Parthenocissus
Berberis	Daphne	Lonicera	Philadelphus
Cantua	Echium	Magnolia	Pyracantha
Cistus	Euonymus	Mandevilla	Robinia

ORNAMENTAL PLANTS PROPAGATED BY DIVISION

Agave	Gypsophila
Aloe	Helenium
Amaryllis	Helianthemum
Anchusa	Helleborus
Anemone	Heuchera
Aquilegia	Hydrocleis
Arabis	Hypericum
Armeria	calycinum
Aster	Iris
Astilbe	Kerria
Aubrietia	Laburnum
Bauhinia	Leucothöe
Berberis	Linum
Campanula	Mahonia
Canna	Musa
Chrysanthemum	Nymphæa
Cornus	Paeonia
Cotyledon	Paulownia
Cyperus	Philadelphus
Dahlia	Phlox
Delphinium	Potentilla
Dianthus	Primula
Dicentra	Rudbeckia
Doronicum	Scabiosa
Echinops	Sedum
Eremurus	Sempervivum
Erigeron	Statice
Erythrina	Strelitzia
Gaillardia	Thalictrum
Gazania	Zantedeschia
Geum	

Fig. 54.—Various steps in simple layering. A, Notches near nodes of stem to hasten rooting. B, Pegging branch in hollow. C, Branch covered with earth, except tip.

The chief styles of layering are: Tip, simple, compound (or serpentine), continuous, mound (or stool) (Fig. 55) and Chinese or pot (Fig. 58).

Tip layerage is a simple form in which the tip of a shoot naturally bends downward (or is made to do so) and takes root. Black raspberry and loganberry are perhaps the best known examples (Figs. 56 and 57). The canes do not form roots readily at other points, though several buds near the tips often develop into shoots and form roots after the tip has rooted.

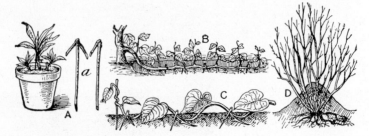

Fig. 55—Styles of layering. A, ordinary, a, layering pegs; B, continuous; C, serpentine (alternate nodes pegged down); D, mound or stool.

When the tips are about ready to take root they may be buried or anchored with pebbles or clods of earth to prevent being shifted about by the wind. This is especially important where the ground is hard and dry. Dewberries and some varieties of purple fruited raspberries may also be propagated by this method (Practicum XI).

Fig. 55x.—Filbert layering. A, pegging down; B, bending down; C, young plants; D, dormant plants ready to be cut apart from trench layered stem.

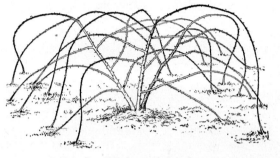

FIG. 56.—Black raspberry layers.

In the following spring, or the same fall, the rooted tips are severed for planting with about 6″ of the original stems to serve as handles. Plants of black raspberry ready for planting are shown in Fig. 57. These were propagated by tip layerage then grown a year in the nursery.

101. Simple or common layers (Figs. 53, 54, 55) are made by bending and covering the branches with more or less soil. In general, a shallow and short trench or a small hole is made in the earth and the branch pegged or weighted down in it prior to being covered with soil to the depth of 2″ or 3″ but with 6″ to 12″ of the extremity of the shoot uncovered to draw sap and elaborate plant food. To hasten root formation the stems are often wounded at the points to be covered. Wounding may be done by scraping the bark or cutting through the cambium layer on the lower side of the branch below the bud or shoot to grow, or it may be by severely twisting the

FIG. 57.—Black raspberry layerage. A. Newly buried; B, Rooted, arrow po'nts to bud from which new cane will develop.

FIG. 58.—Chinese layering of croton.

branch at this point. Hacking with a knife near the node is also often done. These woundings tend to form adventitious buds on which root growth in asexual propagation depends.

So many species and varieties of shrubs may be propagated by simple layering that it seems probable any woody plant capable of being bent to the earth can be thus propagated (Currant, gooseberry, forsythia).

102. Compound or serpentine layers (Fig. 55) are made by covering the stems at several points alternating with other points not covered. The method is most frequently used for propagating vines and other long supply stems (grape). Management is the same as for simple layers.

103. Continuous layers (Fig. 55) are made from plants which root readily when the whole branch except the tip is buried with 3″ or 4″ of earth. Since the buds on most plants will not develop into shoots if buried, only a few plants are adapted to this form of layering (red-osier, willow, American cranberry bush, snowball, filbert).

104. Chinese or pot layers (Fig. 58 to 60), used almost wholly in greenhouse practice, are made on upright stems which cannot be readily bent as in simple layering or covered at their bases and treated by the mound method. It is of special use for re-rooting plants with stems that have become "leggy" (dracæna, oleander, croton, rhododendron, rubber plant, pandanus). It is also of service in making the branches of such plants take root.

While still growing in their natural position, the stems are wounded, usually by girdling or notching, and bound with earth, moss or some other moisture-holding material held in place with raffia or cloth bands. Until roots have developed, the bandage and its contents are kept moist by watering when necessary—an easy matter in a greenhouse. Roots push out from the upper side of the girdle or notch. As soon as they have filled the ball of moss the stem is severed below the

FIG. 59. — Home made Chinese layerage pot.

wound and planted usually in a flower pot. Sometimes the leafage
is reduced as in transplanting. Often special flower pots with open
sides (Fig. 59, 60) are used in this method; but as good results are
secured with moss alone.

**105. Mound or stool layer-
ing** (Fig. 55, 55x, 61), which
consists of burying the bases of
shrub stems deeply with earth,
thus forcing roots to strike, is of
special utility in propagating
short-stemmed and stiff-branched
shrubs.   Quince,   gooseberries,
Paradise and Doucin apple stocks
are so grown. When many plants
are desired it is common to cut
down the shrubs the previous sea-

FIG. 60.—Types of Chinese layerage
utensils. a, stout waxed paper cone;
b, slit pot; c, d, slide pot; e, hinged pot.

son to produce new shoots close to the ground and the center of the
shrub.   Preparatory to covering, these shoots are often wounded
near the ground so roots will be produced quickly in abundance.
One season's growth is usually enough to make plants suitable for
setting out.   The advantage of the method is that strong, stocky
plants are thus produced.

106. Runners (Fig. 62), special, usually creeping, branches
formed by strawberry and some other plants, produce little clusters
of leaves at each second node which, under favorable conditions
develop roots and thus form new plants.   All that is necessary to
have the roots develop is to anchor the rosettes of leaves for a few
days with clods of earth or pebbles.   With strawberries the runners
root naturally.

Often the runners are made to root in 2" or 2½" flower pots
filled with good soil and plunged full depth in the strawberry bed.
Such plants usually give better results than those allowed to grow
without this restriction, because there is little or no loss of roots
when the potted plants are transplanted.

One to nine plants may be produced in succession by one runner; but since the later ones are usually inferior and weak because
they have less time in which to grow before the close of the season,
only the first one or perhaps two rosettes on any one runner are
allowed to grow either for transplanting or fruiting.   In field practice no such care as this is taken, the plants being allowed to root
freely within the limits of the matted or hedgerow width.   As in
other asexual propagation methods runners produce the same variety
as the parent plants from which they are formed.

107. Laying down the whole stem and treating it as a layer
is a new method of propagating ("trench layering") deciduous fruits

perfected by Knight, Amos, Hatton and Witt at the East Malling Research Station in England. One-year-old trees are planted at an angle of 30° to 45° with the ground (Fig. 63), allowed to attain one season's growth, then laid prone in 2″ or 3″ trenches and held in position by means of notched stakes or U-shaped pieces of stiff galvanized wire (Fig. 64). The main stems and strong laterals are tipped lightly to remove soft wood. Weak laterals are pruned back to two or three buds.

FIG. 61.—Doucin apple layers. A, trench. B, mound or stool.

Apples, pears, cherries and quinces are left uncovered until the sprouts arising from the buds have unfolded a few leaves, before beginning to bank earth around them. Plums should be covered about 1″ deep with fine soil just before or as the buds are opening. If the layer is too deep the buds will fail to develop at all. The new shoots are thus forced to push their way through a layer of soil which prevents the bark from coloring and favors quick root formation. With all species when the sprouts have reached an average height of 2″ or 3″ fine soil is shovelled around them and the process repeated every few days, as the shoots elongate until covered 5″ to 8″, depending upon whether the soil is heavy or light. After this they require no further attention than cultivation or irrigation until the end of the season.

In late fall when the leaves are off and the wood is thoroughly dormant the soil is drawn away from the layers and the rooted

FIG. 62.—Strawberry runners. A, node which, when anchored in soil, will form roots as shown in B. C, characteristic node which does not normally produce plant.

shoots detached from the parent plant. They should be clipped off with sharp pruning shears or a sharp knife, being careful not to lift the layers out of position. The rooted shoots are used for bench grafting, lined out in the nursery row or heeled-in until spring, according to local practice and climatic conditions.

The old layers must be completely uncovered and left that way until the following spring when the program of the previous year is repeated. Care must be taken to have the layered plants flat on the ground as they were originally. If some parts have been raised this will result in some of the shoots being covered to a greater depth than others. The trouble is not so much in the difference in covering as the handicap

FIG. 63.—Fruit trees laid obliquely as first step in layerage.

some will suffer in emerging through the first thin layer of soil. If covered too deeply in the first place the shoots may fail to get through and if the final covering is too shallow the stems will not be kept white and roots will not form.

108. Rhizomes or rootstocks, subterranean stems, especially if uniformly thick, for storage of plant food (German iris, Bermuda grass, canna, arrowroot—Figs. 65, 66). These parts are divided and planted.

109. Stolon, a slender branch which naturally takes root and bears a bud at its extremity where it forms a new plant (redosier). It may be produced below or above the ground.

110. Root tips sometimes send up shoots which produce new plants. Red raspberry often does this as well as forms similar plants on other parts of the roots, especially those wounded by insects or injured by tillage tools.

111. Offsets, short, lateral branches or stolons produced near the bases of plants to serve in natural propagation. They usually take root and become new plants (houseleek—Fig. 67).

Fig. 64.—Further steps in fruit tree layerage. A, laying stems in trench; B, wiring stems in place; C, stems ready for development of new shoots. (See text.)

112. Date palm propagation.—Like the seedlings of most other fruit trees date palm seedlings do not produce fruit true to variety and as it is a monocotyledonous plant and therefore lacks the cambium ring which assures asexual propagation of dicotyledons, it cannot be grown by cuttings, budding or grafting. Fortunately, however, it produces offsets from a few to sometimes 50,

FIG. 65.—Division of iris. 1, individual rhizome. 2, 3, pieces of rhizome after "eyes" or buds have developed roots; 4, 6, pieces of rhizome ready for planting. 5, more advanced rhizome—highly desirable for planting.

FIG. 66.—Rhizomes (rootstocks) of Bermuda grass. Each
joint will produce new plant.

developed in the leaf axils usually at or near the bases of the trunks though
sometimes 25′ or more from the ground. Generally these offsets begin to grow
when the trees are only two or three years old and still attached to the parent
plant. Advantage is taken of this characteristic to produce varieties true to
name.

In order to determine the effect 1, of size, 2, the absence or presence of
roots, 3, spring and fall planting, and 4, of poor cutting on the number of offsets
grown, the Arizona Experiment Station has conducted experiments concerning
which D. W. Albert has summarized the results as follows:[1]

The growing of date offshoots has passed the experimental stage. When
properly cared for new plants can be grown almost as successfully as can the
more common fruit trees. The essential factors for growing them successfully
are: Proper size and maturity before removing them from the parent palm; a
well developed root system before they are cut from the parent plant; extreme
care in cutting and handling them; correct preparation of holes in which they
are to be planted; planting them to the depth of their greatest diameter; correct pruning, tying together and protecting their foliage; frequent but light irri-

[1] *Ariz. Exp. Sta. Bull. 119*, Dec. 1926.

FIG. 67.—Houseleek offset production. A, parent plant with
offsets developing. B, rooted offset.

gations, thus keeping the soil uniformly moist; mulching them as soon as planted; winter protection; careful supervision of newly planted offshoots.

113. **Crowns** are rooted buds usually formed at the tips of rhizomes or underground stems and at the close of the growing season of the individual species. Each season they push forward and also develop flowering stems and leaves (Mayapple, achillea, Solomon's seal, Johnson grass, asparagus (Fig. 67x), Bermuda grass, etc., Fig. 66). Lily-of-the-valley is one of the commercially most important crown-producing plants. Its "pips" are annually imported from Europe by the million to supply the demands of florists. Until needed for forcing, they are generally cold stored.

114. **Rosette,** a cluster of leaves or other organs arranged somewhat like the petals of a double rose; (radical leaves of dandelion, stolons of houseleek).

115. **Rough division** is often practiced when herbaceous perennials grow too thick (phlox, rhubarb, peony, iris) by digging up and cutting the clumps in pieces with a sharp spade. The best pieces are re-planted. Many shrubs (snowball, lilac, barberry) are so

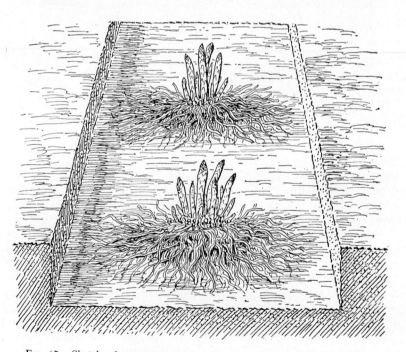

Fig. 67x. Sketch of asparagus crown with roots spread ready for covering with soil.

treated. This, the crudest form of division, is little practiced in a commercial way, more in home gardens.

116. Tubers are short, thickened parts of subterranean branches (Irish potato, Fig. 68) stored with plant food, largely starch, to start new plants at the beginning of the next growing season or other period of activity. Another view is that parent

Fig. 68.—Irish potatoes sprouting. *Left,* in cellar; *middle,* in sunlight; *right,* in soil.

tubers serve as water reservoirs, since experiment has shown that they are heavier after the plant has grown several weeks than before growth starts, due to accumulation of water during plant growth.

Often thickened roots (sweet potato, dahlia) are popularly classed with tubers. Botanically the distinction is: True, or stem tubers have "eyes" or buds, whereas thickened roots or root-tubers do not. In practice, true tubers (Irish potato) are often used for making cuttings, whereas thickened roots (sweet potato) are generally planted whole (119).

When tubers are planted whole, just as broken from the parent plant, the process is called separation; but when cut in pieces, each bearing one or more eyes, it is called cuttage or division. From the eyes shoots are developed, and at the bases of these roots form, seldom from the tuber itself. As growth progresses special stems develop above the roots and swell into new tubers.

Tubers are most frequently found in arid climates but are by no means rare in moist ones. Like bulbs, some are hardy, some tender. Hardy species (Jerusalem artichoke) do best left in the open ground until spring; tender ones (potato) must be dug in fall and stored in a cool place not too dry nor too moist, otherwise they will either shrivel or mold.

Hastening growth of potatoes may be done in three ways, summarized by the Rhode Island Station thus: a, by planting sets in pots in greenhouses and transplanting to open ground; b, by "sprout-

FIG. 69.—Dahlia clump as dug.

ing"—that is, planting sets thickly in coldframes and when ready to "break ground" transplanting them to the field, etc.; c, by "budding"—that is, subjecting seed tubers the size of hen's eggs from four to six or more weeks to the action of moderate heat and light so one or more strong, dark colored buds ready to develop leaves and roots are formed on each tuber, but all other buds remain practically dormant. They may be "greened" by exposure to light on ground free from vegetation, directly after digging and placed in trays at any convenient time during winter. This process has produced 30 to 50 bushels more potatoes an acre than similar tubers not so treated.

"Germinating" seed potatoes in boxes in Scotland has given an average of nearly 1,100 pounds an acre gain in crop. Potato tubers partially dried are also said to make more productive plants than those not dried.

117. **Dahlia tubers** develop in clumps firmly attached to the

parent stems (Figs. 69, 70). As a rule they have no buds on their bodies—only on their necks. When entire clumps are planted they develop thickets of weak stalks which produce poor flowers, but when cut from the clump and planted separately at ample distances they develop stout stalks and good blossoms. Care must be taken

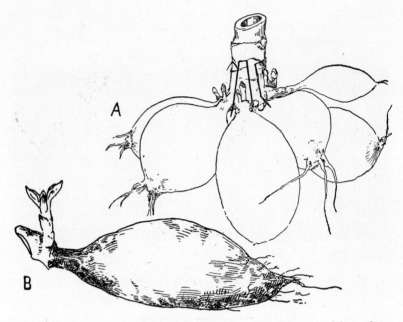

FIG. 70.—Dahlia clump showing bulbs and buds. B, bulb separated from clump with developing stem.

in the cutting to include the neck with each tuber and at least one bud, otherwise no growth may result. To make sure of success it is advisable to cover the clumps with damp earth, sand, or peat moss and put them in a moist, warm place for a week or longer before cutting the tubers apart. During this time buds will show themselves and thus serve as guides. It is not advisable to have long sprouts when the clumps are cut apart because of danger of breakage. When desired the sprouts may be treated as soft wood cuttings.

118. Dahlia storage experiments[1] at various temperatures showed that some roots and their accompanying buds lived over winter when stored at high temperatures (70° to 80° F.), but that excessive drying occurred; that a much higher percentage kept in good condition when stored at 35° to 50°; that little drying occurred at these low temperatures, even immature roots being preserved

---

[1] P. W. Zimmerman and A. E. Hitchcock, *Dahlia Root Storage at Different Temperatures*, Boyce Thompson Institute, Professional Paper, Vol. I, No. 21, reprinted from the American Dahlia Society Bul., Series XIII, No. 59., Jan. 1932.

in good condition; that tubers stored in a fluctuating low temperature (cold glasshouse) were as well preserved as those at a constant low temperature; that freezing temperatures are probably detrimental; that imported peat moss used direct from the bale is satisfactory storage material, being dry enough to take care of excess moisture from the roots and yet not cause excessive drying; and that field tests indicated that previous storage temperatures for tubers did not affect the vigor of surviving plants, but that those stored at high temperatures developed fewer plants than preliminary examination indicated (Fig. 71).

Among other methods and materials tried for the storage of dahlias, cannas, gloxinias, and tuberous begonias by J. A. Nielson of Michigan State College, paraffin has given best results. By the method outlined below Nielson reports

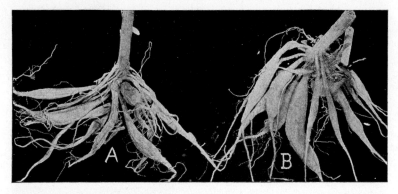

FIG. 71.—Dahlia clump after storage from November first to May 12. A, At 73° F. constant temperature; B, at 50° F.

that J. E. Carter of Guelph, Ontario, held waxed gloxinias in dry storage from October to August, then shipped them to Australia where they arrived in first class condition. He was as successful with a similar shipment of tuberous begonias to New Zealand.

Plant material intended for treatment should be washed free of soil and thoroughly dried. When ready to treat the tubers fill a deep pail about two-thirds with water at a temperature of 170° to 180° F. Melt the wax on a heater and pour into the pail to within a few inches of the top where it will float. The tubers should then be quickly immersed and withdrawn immediately. If one immersion does not leave a good coating then immerse again. After all the tubers have been treated, place in a crate or a tray and set in a cellar or a room where the temperature is above freezing.

The most important factor in this treatment is that of temperature of the wax; if too cool it will form a thick coating, flake off and thus be ineffective; if too hot it will injure or kill the tuber. The optimum temperature is not definitely known, but it is believed 160° to 170° F. is safe.

119. Sweet potatoes develop new stems from adventitious buds which appear anywhere on the surfaces of the storage roots. In the Southern States these roots are often planted whole, either in the field or in beds. In the cooler sections within their cultural range (southeastern New York) they are usually propagated by being split lengthwise in early spring and laid flat side downward in mild hotbeds filled with light soil or sand. The hotbeds may be either manure heated or, where considerable quantities of plants are required annually, in permanent flue heated beds (Figs. 72, 73).

Where fresh stable manure cannot be obtained the flue heated bed is well suited for growing the plants. A pit is located at one end, a furnace installed and the smoke, fumes and heat conducted beneath the plant bed through flues to a chimney at the far end.

When the "slips" or sprouts have grown 4″ to 6″ and developed leaves they are carefully pulled individually and transplanted in the field (Figs. 74, 75). Roots almost never grow from the tubers themselves but from the bases of the sprouts. Other shoots soon develop so the process may be repeated several times. New varieties of Irish potato are often propagated in this way and also by stem cuttings. Pseudobulbs of orchids are similarly handled.

For best results seed stock should be selected during or before harvest. The *plant* rather than the roots should be the basis of selection which is carried on from the standpoint of freedom from disease. Probably there is no appreciable advantage in selecting seed stock of desirable type because the sweet potato is propagated vegetatively and little if any variation is likely to occur among individual plants. "Seed roots" should be disinfected with corrosive sublimate

Fɪɢ. 72.—Sweet potato propagation. Above, left, slips as pulled from buried potatoes; above, right, dropping and planting; below, flue heated hotbed.

(mercuric chloride) in water—one ounce to eight gallons—for ten minutes. The dipping must be done in wooden or earthenware containers.

120. Bulb, a specialized, usually subterranean, bud whose leaf bases are thickened and filled with stored food and whose stem is reduced to a disc from the lower side of which roots develop (Fig.

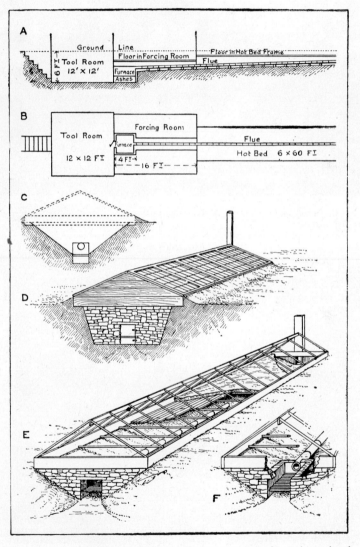

Fig. 73.—Fire heated hotbed for sweet potato propagation. A, sectional view through side; B, ground plan; C, cross section; D, general outside view; E, construction; F. detail.

FIG. 74.—Hand transplanters. Young plants are dropped through small tube (at left of center machine), jaws open at bottom, make hole in loose soil and set plant in place, then water from tank (large cylinder) wets soil and insures growth.

FIG. 75.—Machine transplanting. Boys alternately place small plants between jaws which open at regular intervals, close, set them in loose soil and when necessary water them all at one operation as machine proceeds across field.

76). Its function is to tide over a period unfavorable to growth, usually winter or a dry season.

Bulblet, bulbel, bulbil, bulbule, are terms concerning which authors do not agree. For instance, one defines "bulbels" as borne attached to the mother bulb, and bulblets as borne above ground, generally in a leaf axil. Another applies "bulbel" to the latter definition and says that bulblet is synonymous with "bulbil." In this book no distinction is made; "bulblet" is most used.

Some plants develop bulblets by transforming their flower buds (garlic, top onion) some from transformed axillary leaf buds (tiger lily, Fig. 77); and below ground around the bases of "mother" bulbs (hyacinth, tulip, Fig. 81). Sooner or later these bulblets grow to normal flowering size. The larger ones may be separated after the plants are dug. However, unless they readily separate from the parent bulb it is usually better to leave the small ones attached to the main bulbs. The same rule applies to cormels (129).

121. Bulbs are of two classes: A, scaly (lily, Figs. 76, 87); B, tunicate, or laminate (onion, hyacinth).

Scaly bulbs are composed of loose, thickened scales which, after the bulb has flowered, may separate in the soil and form new, but little bulbs (Fig. 78). Advantage is taken of this in propagation.

Tunicate bulbs are produced at the bases of the stems, though

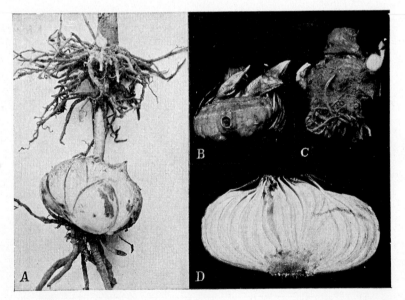

Fig. 76. Bulbs of various types. A, scaly bulb of lily; B, solid bulbs (corms) of gladiolus and tuberose; C, tunicate bulb of onion showing sheathing of bulb leaves.

often from buds inside the parent bulb, frequently in the axil or a bud scale. They are common among plants which have a long resting period, as in arid regions, though they also occur among plants of other districts.

Garlic is normally propagated by breaking the "cloves" from one another and planting them separately. In Germany, P. Vogler proved that strains can be propagated by selecting plants which have a definite number of cloves to the bulb but that selection based on the mere weight of the bulb is of no value and that modified characters are not propagated asexually.

122. "Dutch bulbs," a term used by the trade to designate those species produced most extensively in Holland (hyacinth, tulip, narcissus, etc.), that blossom in early spring and after their leaves die down remain dormant until autumn, when they develop roots for the following season's flowers. Hence the importance 1, of planting them in early fall so root growth will be strong before winter sets in, 2, setting them at proper depth (Fig. 79) and 3, allowing the leaves to die naturally so they will store ample food for the succeeding season's flowers.

123. Tunicate or laminate bulbs.—By ordinary, natural increase only two to half a dozen bulblets are reproduced each year.

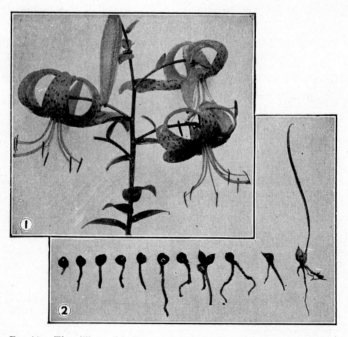

FIG. 77.—Tiger lily and bulblets. 1. Bulblets in leaf axils. 2. Bulblets rooting soon after falling to the ground.

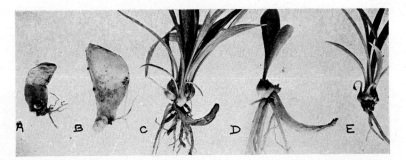

FIG. 78.—Bulb formation from lily scales. A, B, scale with bulblet forming; C, D, scale with well developed bulbs, top and roots; E, independent plant, scale having rotted away.

These ordinarily require one to three or four years to attain salable size. For rapid propagation the bulbs are handled as described by Fred De Meulder in the *Florists Exchange,* condensed as follows:

124. Hyacinth propagation.—Nature has an easy method of increasing tulips, narcissus, crocus and other bulbous plants. These bulbs, divided into several parts, multiply themselves without the aid of human skill. Not so the hyacinth, which if left to its own devices, multiplies in such a way that each succeeding generation of young bulbs is more dwarfed than the former, making it impossible to get anything like fair specimens.

It was observed that the hyacinth generally forms bulblets where the old bulbs have been injured. This useful hint has led to purposely wounding the bulbs. Repeated experiments have developed two distinct methods; "scooping" and "notching." In the first (Fig. 80) the hard base of the bulb is cut away (Figs. 82, 84), leaving the bottom scooped out; every section or layer of the bulb is thus cut through. In the second method the cutting is done transversely

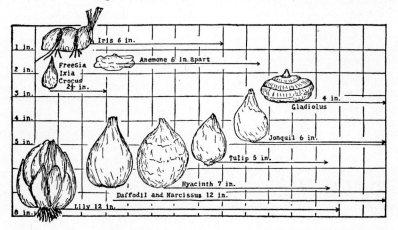

FIG. 79.—Bulb planting chart. Depth to plant bulbs indicated by figures at left; distance apart by line at right of each bulb. Squares 1″ in diameter.

to a depth which the cultivator has learned from experience to estimate (Figs. 81, 83).

Each treatment has advantages and drawbacks. Bulbs scooped leave three times the number of bulblets and of much greater vitality, as appears from the preference shown them in the selection of material for forcing. Those notched give less returns, but in a much shorter time, producing flowering bulbs in three to four years, while the others require four to five. More skill is required in scooping than in notching, though a casual observer might say that both are delicate operations. Perhaps the cultivator bases his estimate of the skill needed on the comparative value and number of bulblets endangered, so that operation would be the more critical which is to bring about the better and more numerous bulblets. If gouged out too much, wounding the bulb to

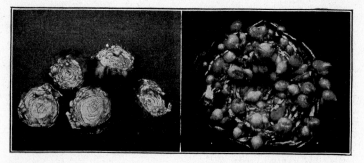

FIG. 80 Scooped hyacinth bulbs, early and later stages. Bulblets require two to five years to reach salable sizes.

the extent of seriously weakening it, a limited amount of feeble young bulbs is the result; if scooped not enough, the remaining solid matter at the base effec tually impedes or even frustrates the formation of bulblets.

The second method seems to entail as much risk to the mother bulb and her offspring. Transvere cutting looks simple enough; and so it is. But long experience and careful attention have taught the workman just how deeply to cut. Here again there is danger of seriously damaging the bulb. Cut too deeply, and the whole bulb is lost; not deeply enough, a very limited and dwarfish progeny. Planters differ in their use of the two methods; dividing the annual stock between the two is common.

Both classes of bulbs undergo practically the same treatment in the "nurse-room," a place in the bulb house reserved for them and kept at a high temperature. Here they remain until—after a fortnight or so—about 100 bulblets in the case of scooped bulbs, and 30 in that of notched ones are formed upon them. They are left until after all the other bulbs are planted so as to give them the care of the nursery as long as possible. Then, usually the last week in October or the first in November, they are deeply planted.

The ground has been carefully prepared for them; dug and liberally dressed with well-rotted cow manure earlier in the year. This kind of fertilizer is preferred to others, both because it is cheaper (in Holland) and because it is less harmful to the hyacinth, whose extremely sensitive bulb would be burned by commercial fertilizers. Hyacinths cannot be set in the same ground except at two-year intervals, or at one-year intervals if the soil is turned up from a much greater depth than usual. Tulips and hyacinths thrive on ground used for each other alternately.

Taken to the field, the bulbs are set in the ground about 5″ deep and an area of about 5″ square is allowed for each. The flower beds are 3′ wide and a path 1′ wide is left between them. When all is ready, the whole field is covered with about 10″ of hay or straw; a necessary precaution, for the hyacinth is susceptible to cold. The fields lie thus till spring, when tops develop. The flower stems are cut about 10 days after flowers appear to strengthen the bulbs.

Fig. 81.—Hyacinth propagation in Holland. Reading down, *left, top,* natural method; notched bulbs, early stages—largest of these (*bottom*) may reach salable size in two years; *right, top,* cutting bulbs, nursery storage house, interior of house showing shelves for storing cut bulbs, planting bulbs after storing.

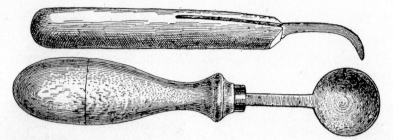

Fig. 82.—Tools for cutting hyacinth bulbs. Above, scooping knife; below, scooping spoon.

The bulbs now begin to enlarge and are left to grow during April and May. About the middle of May, with fair, warm weather, the leaves turn yellow, a sign that the bulbs are matured and can be taken out.

When the bulbs are dug, the new bulblets are the size of acorns; and the mother bulb has almost entirely disappeared, having served as food for her numerous progeny. These are taken to the warehouses and placed on lath frames to dry, merely a matter of plenty of air and ordinary summer temperature. This is also the case with the old bulbs of the "notched" class. The opinion prevalent in some quarters that it is necessary to apply absorbent material to all bulbs after treatment, experience has proved to be without foundation. Only in the case of scooped bulbs is it found necessary to apply an absorbent.

Cleaning the bulbs, a process always attended with danger of damage, is deferred until fall when an injury will be speedily healed by the earth in which the bulbs are soon after placed. Set in the ground again in October, the new bulbs bear leaves the following spring. The second year those of the notched class flower, while the others need still another season. The flowering bulbs ready for shipment are carefully sorted, packed with chaff in large paper bags or in boxes according to the quantity.

The propagation of some species of tulips must be left entirely to nature; no scientific cutting of the bulb can be done. Left to itself this plant yields

Fig. 83. Hyacinths propagated at British Columbia Experiment Station.

three or four bulblets, only one or two of which survive and mature. The process of growing the young bulbs is simple. The bulblets appear attached to the mother bulb after the blooming period, the old bulb being "eaten up." The following spring the little ones are removed, cleaned and re-planted, the bulblet thus having taken two years to mature.

125. Bulb growing in America.

—Tuberoses have long been grown extensively in North Carolina; gladioli in many states, especially New York, California and Illinois; and other summer-blooming bulbs in various parts of America; but so far we have no tunicate or scaly bulb industry comparable with that of Japan, Bermuda or Holland. Probably this is because until recently little attention has been devoted to the work. But good bulbs can be grown in this country, as proved by growers in Washington state, where narcissus, tulips and various other bulbs have been grown to some extent for several years (Fig. 85).

Fig. 84.—Bulb scooping machine used by United States Department of Agriculture in Washington (state) bulb growing.

126. Lily growing.—In practice many scales are accidentally broken from the lily bulbs in digging and handling. These often take root without any care and produce bulbs. Growers take small advantage of this method of propagation with common varieties because enough bulblets are produced to supply the needs of planting. Where the plan is employed as with rare or costly species and varieties, from a dozen to two dozen of the looser, thicker outside scales are gently cut between mid-autumn and mid-winter from the base of the bulb (which thus does not cease to be useful for replanting) and thrust an inch deep in light, sandy loam in a propagating frame or flats or pots and treated like cuttings.

Damp sphagnum is sometimes used instead of soil. If the soil is kept slightly moist and the temperature under 60° F. but not below 45°, some hardy and half hardy species will form bulblets in a month or even less; others require three months or more. Tender species often seem to need a little bottom heat.

If conditions have been favorable and the scales fully "ripe," when planted one or more bulblets should have developed at the base of each scale. If the planting has been done late, the flats or pots may be placed in a shaded frame outdoors in spring and left there during summer, or the bulblets may be potted as soon as they have rooted and later transplanted in nursery beds. The scales

FIG. 85.—Tulip planting in Washington (state). 1, making furrows;
2, placing bulbs.

of hardy species are usually left in flats or outdoor frames all summer and
mulched over the following winter. In the second spring they are transferred to
nursery beds. At the close of the second season the majority should be large
enough for sale (Fig. 86).

Lily bulbs are best dug soon after their tops have died. The shorter time
they remain out of the ground and the cooler they are kept the better. Small
bulblets should be allowed to remain but those ½″ or more across, may be
separated and grown in nursery beds another season (Fig. 87).

127. Lily bulb disease is caused by a parasitic fungus *(Rhizopus necans)*
which apparently cannot penetrate unbroken tissues, but gains entrance to the

FIG. 86.—Lily propagation from scales. A, Lilium testaceum: Row across 3′
bed in place at end of first season at Bellingham Experiment Station, Washington. B, candidum development under bench in cool greenhouse between
November and June, Arlington Experiment Farm, D. C.

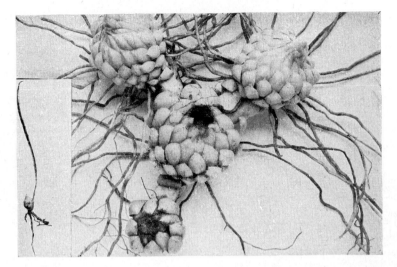

FIG. 87. Underground parts of turkscap lily (*L. superbum*). Dark spots show where flower stems were produced in previous years. Other bulbs will produce stems next year.

bulbs through broken roots; for bulbs experimented with were not diseased when dug. A brief immersion is salicylic acid or dilute corrosive sublimate solution (1 to 100) will destroy all spores on the bulbs. Daffodils are subject to the same disease. Precautionary measures, such as rotation of crops, avoidance of injury to roots and destruction of refuse, are recommended. When exported the bulbs should first be dipped in the fungicide and allowed to sweat thoroughly before shipment.

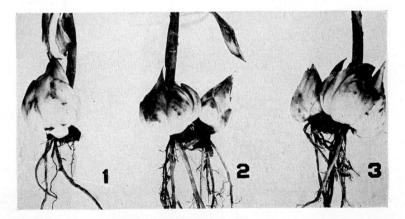

FIG. 88.—Lilium candidum. 1, Bulb which has produced flower stem but no bulbs. 2, Flowering bulb which has produced one new bulb. 3, Natural production of two bulbs.

To avoid lily disease, Oliver advocates growing Easter lilies from seed rather than from bulbs. He has thus produced plants which bloomed within seven months. On the Pacific Coast seed has been found to be quicker than scales or even small bulbs. Under favorable but exceptional conditions plants will give salable bulbs the first year. The usual sizes secured are 5″ to 7″, but a considerable percentage of 7″ to 9″ is common where good attention is given. The crop ripens in early August.

TABLE 18.—LILY SPECIES WITH METHODS OF PROPAGATION [1]

Name of species	Pronunciation	Seed	Scales	Heeled or layered stems	Underground bulblets	Aërial bulbils	Common name
Auratum	Au-rä'-tum	××	×		×		Goldband
Batemanniæ	Bäte-man'-ni-ī		×		××		Batemann
Bolanderi	Bo-lan'-der-ī	××	×				Thimble
Browni	Brown'-ī	××	××				Browns
Bulbiferum	Bul-bif'-er-um	×	××			××	Bulbiferous
Canadense (fig. 31)	Can-a-den'-sē	××	×				Canada
Candidum	Can'-dī-dum		××	××			Madonna[2]
Cernuum	Cer'-nu-um	××	×				Nodding
Chalcedonicum	Chal-ce-don'-ī-cum	×	××	×			Chalcedonian
Columbianum	Co-lum-bī-ā'-num	××	×				Columbia
Concolor	Con'-col-or	××					Redstar
Croceum (fig. 32)	Cro'-ce-um	×	××	×	×		Orange
Dauricum	Dau'-rī-cum	×	××	×	×		Candlestick
Delavayi	De-la-vä'-ī	×					Delavay
Elegans	El'-e-gans		××	×	×		Thunberg
Giganteum	Gī-gan'-tē-um	××					Giant
Grayi	Gray'-ī	××	×				Grays
Hansoni	Han'-son-ī	×	××				Hanson
Henryi	Hen'-ry-ī	××	××		×		Henry
Humboldti	Hum-böldt'-ī	×	××				Humboldt
Japonicum	Ja-pon'-ī-cum	××					Japanese
Kelloggi	Kel'-log-ī	××	×				Kellogg
Leichtlini	Licht'-lin-ī		××	×	×		Leichtlin
Leucanthum	Lu-can'-thum	××	××		×		
Longiflorum	Lon-gī-flō'-rum	×	×		××		Easter
Maritimum	Ma-rit'-ī-mum	××	×				Coast
Martagon	Mar'-ta-gon	××	×				Martagon
Michauxi (Carolinianum)	Mī-shō'-ī	××	××				Carolina
Monadelphum	Mon-a-del'-phum	××	×				Caucasian
Pardalinum	Par-da-lī'num	××	××				Leopard
Parryi	Par'-rȳ-ī	××	××				Lemon
Parvum	Par'-vum	××	××				Sierra
Philadelphicum	Phil-a-del'-phi-cum	××					Orangecup
Philippinense	Phil'-ip-pin-en'-sē	××					Glade
Pomponium	Pom-pō'-nī-um	×	××				Little Turkscap
Pseudotigrinum	Su'-do-tī-grī'-num	?	××				Thayer
Pyrenaicum	Pī'-re-nī'-cum	×	××				Pyrenan
Regale	Re-gä'-le	××	×				Regal
Roezli	Rē'-zel-ī	××	××				Roezl
Rubellum	Rū-bel'-lum	××	×				Rubellum

[1] The methods that have been found worth while and applicable to each species are indicated by crosses (×). Those that have given the best results are indicated by two crosses (××).
[2] Also called St. Joseph, St. Andrew, Annunciation, etc.

128. Lilies are propagated [3] by seed, scales, bulbils, axillary bulblets (Fig. 89) division or separation (Fig. 88) and by stem cuttings. Table 18 gives the methods of propagation applicable to each species.

Propagation of lilies from axillary buds or bulb scales may be either natural or artificial. Both methods result in small bulb formation. Natural reproduction by stem bulblets produced in the lower parts of the stems, mostly below ground, can be accelerated by artificial means. If the lower parts of the stems

[3] Condensed from *U. S. Dept. of Agr. Circ.* 102.

are in moist and shaded atmosphere similar bulblets will be produced above ground to a height of 2″ or more.

This form of propagation occurs in Lilium leichtlini, umbellatum, elegans, dauricum and others. In these, under cultural conditions, this form of reproduction is much more copious in young than in old bulbs, largely because the young ones are strewn along the row in any position in which they happen to fall, thus causing the stems to travel through the soil before reaching the surface. Large sizes are set upright so their stems go directly upward leaving only short lengths of stem below ground. A crook in the stem induces formation of bulblets.

In another group (Longiflorum, speciosum, auratum) considerable bulblet formation occurs in large stems. Deep planting, banking earth about the stems at or near blossoming time, application of mulch, or disbudding will accelerate and enhance bulb formation. In some cases (umbellatum, candidum, testaceum) if conditions are favorable some of these artificial accelerants may induce formation of bulblets in the axils of the upper leaves of the decapitated inflorescence.

In many of these lilies that form stem bulblets, possibly in all of them, cultural conditions play important parts in the extent of bulb formation. Often conditions inimical to the best natural development of the plant tend to increase bulblet reproduction (regale)—almost a sure indication of either a poor development or imperfection in the main bulb.

These stem bulblets are an excellent source of planting stock. They are usually set thickly in their permanent quarters in the field when the bulbs are dug (longiflorum, regale, henryi, speciosum, auratum). When digging must occur while the stems are still green and before the bulblets are fully grown the stems with bulblets attached may be heeled-in in the field for the bulblets to double in size in a few weeks. They may be removed and planted singly, or the section of stem bearing the bulblets may be laid in the ground at proper depth. Late disturbance of the bulbs is usually unsafe because they fail to make root in cold weather.

Fig. 89.—About two dozen bulblets developed on stem of Lilium testaceum heeled in field from July 15 to October 15. Owing to late handling no tops were formed until following summer.

Some lilies naturally produce few or no stem bulblets but may be induced to do so by artificial means (candidum, testaceum, Fig. 89). Under normal field conditions the large bulbs of umbellatum produce almost no bulblets, but phenomenal reproduction may be readily induced.

The favorite time for artificial stem-bulblet reproduction is at or near blossoming period. Climatic conditions may influence the time. In the Eastern States it may be advisable to delay propagation a few weeks, but on Puget Sound the shortness of the season requires that little or no time be lost after the plants bloom.

When large numbers of stems are to be handled it is usually best to cut off the inflorescences with a sickle to facilitate handling. Each stem is firmly gripped about two-thirds way down with both hands, given a slight twist and a sharp, quick jerk to one side to pull it up. The stems are laid in uniform piles for convenient handling or, if many, are tied in bundles to facilitate transportation to the heeling-in ground.

Much time and space may be saved by heeling-in according (Figs. 90, 91) to a plan. A favorite one is to dig a trench 4″ deep across a 3′ bed, one side vertical, the other sloping at 45° or less. The stems are laid in this trench with their lower ends against the vertical side. When the row is complete another trench is opened 8″ to 12″ away, the earth thrown over the stem bases and the process repeated.

The thickness of setting the stems will vary with the grower's ideas of economy and time, space and other factors. In cases of leafy stems (umbella-

Fig. 90.—Lily propagation. In foreground is trench prepared for stem bases. Position of next row is shown by shovel. Stems are placed in first trench and covered with soil from second.

tum) sloughing down of foliage must be avoided by thin placing. The object should be to keep the stems functioning as long as they would if still attached to the plant. Twenty-five stems to the row in rows 1′ apart seems to be best spacing.

It is imperative that stems be taken out of the heeling-in ground early. If heeled in about July 8 to 10 (normal time), August 15 to 20 would be about the right time to remove them to permanent quarters. The bulblets will scarcely make root in this time unless kept wet, but will start soon after.

If the stems are left in the heeling-in ground undisturbed for a month longer much finer bulbs will develop but disappointment will come the next season when the late-disturbed ones fail to make top growth and lie dormant for another year without benefit of leafage the first summer. No growth beyond absorption of substance from the old stem will occur. Therefore, to succeed with stem propagation, especially with testaceum and candidum on Puget Sound, stems should be heeled-in before July 10. In a longer season conditions are not so exacting. The main requisite seems to be to allow sufficient time for the young bulbs to get rooted in permanent quarters before winter.

When stems are dug bulblets will be on about 6″ of their bases. It is advisable to cut off and plant the bases as they are. The amount of reproduction to expect will vary with size of stems, climatic conditions, technic employed in handling and variety of lily; in candidum not less than 20, in testaceum 12 to 15, but in umbellatum 50.

Instead of being heeled-in in the field, the stems may be laid in dry earth, preferably on an earthen floor, under cover, so no rain may affect them but where slight capillarity prevents too great drying. When stems are thus buried it is advisable to strip off the leaves, because they slough quickly when thus smothered and rots and molds are likely to occur.

Another method of handling the stems may be used by growers who have greenhouses or frames with glass where the temperature and moisture are under control. Stems in moist atmosphere do not need burial to propagate. Good

Fig. 91.—Heeling-in Lilium testaceum stems after blooming. *Left*, Stems laid flat in rows after having developed bulblets by method in Figure 90.

propagation may be had under the benches of a greenhouse on wire trays, the space closed in with canvas or burlap and the atmosphere kept saturated by liberal use of water on the soil beneath.

Propagation thus or in warm situations under sand is much more rapid than under ordinary conditions outside. No more bulblets may be produced, but they develop more rapidly. The bulblets are planted in the field as already advised.

Large numbers of lilies may be produced by stem cuttings. The principle does not differ from that in heeled-in or layered stems. The technic is a little different, however. Cuttings may be prepared at almost any time until several weeks after the flowering period. For economy of material they are best made with three or more leaves, all but the upper one being cut off within $\frac{1}{4}''$ of the stem, then buried in sand up to the last leaf. As many bulblets may result as there are leaf axils in the cutting.

Instead of making cuttings the grower may remove the leaves from the stems with good heels attached and set them in sand just deep enough to cover the heels. Bulblets will be formed in the leaf axils.

In propagation by cuttings the cutting itself does not callus or form roots. Development is of the latent axillary buds into bulblets These form roots

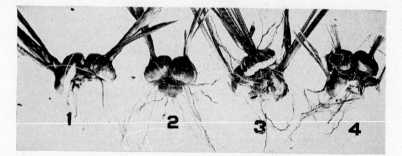

Fig. 92.—Gladiolus corms. 1, two corms and several cormels developed from one planted; 2, old, shriveled corm beneath two new, large ones; 3, three new corms and several cormels from one planted; 4, four from one. All large ones are of blooming sizes.

young, thus maintaining the cutting through its progeny rather than through its own root system.

129. A corm is the enlarged base of an herbaceous stem (gladiolus, jack-in-the-pulpit, crocus). It consists of one or several short internodes and serves as a storage of food materials. It differs from a bulb (120) in being solid instead of bud-like and from a tuber (116) mainly in being upright (or more nearly so) and in rarely being produced upon an elongated subterranean stem.

Corms (Fig. 92) usually produce one to three new ones above the old ones, the latter shrivelling and dying. Between the old and the new several little ones, "cormels," (called "spawn") are often

Fig. 93. Seed and bulb drying shed. Temporary poles and racks are placed on permanent ones.

developed. These may be separated and grown a year or two to form large corms. Besides the central bud often one or two others develop into flower stems. Often also a corm bears, near its apex, several little buds, which may be artificially made to form new corms (or cormels) by cutting through the substance of the bulb around them. After the original corm has borne its flower stem and leaves, it gradually shrivels and dies and a new corm forms around the base of the stem above the old corm.

Fig. 94.—Storage cellar on hillside. Shelves are used for cannas, dahlias, gladiolus in boxes. Potatoes and roots are generally stored in bins.

129A. Care of bulbs and corms.—From the garden standpoint bulbs and corms are of two classes: A, spring blooming, b, summer blooming. The former, all hardy, are planted in fall for outdoor blooming and mulched with leaves or litter during winter. For best results over a series of years their tops must be allowed to mature before being cut or dug. When dug they must be dried in the shade, cleaned and stored (Fig. 93) in bags or trays in an airy, dry, cool place till fall.

Summer-blooming bulbs (gladiolus, tuberose, zephyranthes, etc.) are mostly tender to frost. They are planted in spring, usually after the soil has become warm. Because of their tenderness they must be dug before the ground freezes hard, and after drying in an airy shed (Fig. 93) or other shelter, stored in a dry, warm place such as a cellar with a furnace in it or on boards under greenhouse benches. Before resetting in spring they must be cleaned (Fig. 94).

Temperatures for bulb storing. Lilly-of-the-valley pips are cold stored at 25° to 30° F. and hardy bulbs at 17° for the first two weeks, after which the temperature is raised and kept at 24° till the bulbs are needed for forcing in greenhouses.

VI

CLASSES OF CUTTINGS

130. Plant parts used.—Cuttings may be made from any plant part that has a primary tissue (meristem) and may be divided into five groups, dependent upon the parts used: (1) *roots*, (2) *rootstocks or rhizomes*, (3) *tubers*, (4) *stems*, (5) *leaves* (Fig. 95). As in all other kinds of asexual propagation, cuttings reproduce the same variety as the parent plants from which taken, bud variations or "sports" excepted.

131. Root cuttings may be made from true roots of any plant species which naturally produces suckers (persimmon, orange, red raspberry, trumpet creeper, horseradish, plumbago, bouvardia). There being no true buds upon roots, growth must come from adventitious buds. The resulting shoots are, therefore, called adventitious shoots. Such buds develop after the cutting is planted.

The roots are cut in pieces usually 2″ or 3″ long and the cuttings either stored in moist moss or hardwood sawdust or placed directly in the propagating beds. With most cool climate plants the rooting is done outdoors without artificial heat; warm climate subjects usually require bottom heat in greenhouse or hotbed, but plants in the former group are also often handled with bottom heat to secure best results or shorten time (Practicum XV).

Blackberries and red raspberries, especially when stock is scarce, are often increased commercially by root cuttings (Fig. 96, 97) made in fall, packed in green sawdust, moist sand, or moss, stored in a cold but frost proof cellar till spring and the callused ones then planted like peas, not closer than 1″ asunder in furrows wide enough apart for horse cultivation. They make salable plants by the following fall. When an extra demand is expected the cuttings are sometimes started in heated propagating beds in fall so plants may be ready for sale in spring. In the South they are often made in spring and planted outdoors.

Pear, apple (Fig. 98), cherry and peach root cuttings may be grown in frames with bottom heat, but this method has never been popular with nurserymen because few varieties root readily and because graftage is more economical. As the advantages are obvious much experimenting has been done by both nurserymen and scien-

Fig. 95.—Propagation by cuttings. A, rubber plants ready for potting; B, sansevieria cuttings in foreground, rubber plants in middle distance; C, dracena cuttings grown from canes laid on sand bed; D. cutting bench of miscellaneous stock.

Fig. 96.—Heeled-in blackberry plants to keep roots moist until planting. Tops
cut back to 6″ to facilitate handling.

tists but success has been too small to warrant its adoption, as the
following cases illustrate.

Marked difficulty was experienced by Upshall and Gardener in attempts to
secure own rooted apple trees of some 50 varieties by root cuttings. Of 4,079
cuttings only 3.28% rooted as compared with 81% of French crab seedling roots.
Unfavorable results were also obtained when commercial variety roots were used
in bench grafting. Of the few varietal root cuttings that did grow, some produced sufficient roots for further propagation and in these cases 42.9% of successful rooting was secured, indicating the possibility of developing vigorous
rooting strains. The authors believe that the difference in behavior of seedling
and scion roots lies in the difference of anatomical origin, the seedling roots coming from the true root tissue of the seed and the scion roots presumably arising
from the cambium.[1]

Root cuttings are open to the objection that they do not always
transmit variegation though they do perpetuate the variety otherwise; except, of course, that roots of grafted plants below the union
will produce "seedling-stock" plants.

132. A sport or bud variation is a plant or plant part, as a
twig, which unexpectedly shows a character different from that of
the variety or species or the balance of the plant. Usually this

[1] *Amer. Soc. Hort. Sci. Proc. 25.*

Fig. 97.—Root cuttings planted with tops just above sand surface. More common
method is to bury horizontally.

character cannot be reproduced by seed but is almost always propagated asexually. Even then it is still called a sport. The term is not commonly applied to monstrosities or deformities, but to more or less attractive and apparently normal characters, as doubling of flowers on single-flowered plants, solid red color on a normally streaked variety (Red Northern Spy apple), variegation *(Vinca major)* and other changes of the color on green plants, etc. But variations may be the starting point of new varieties or of reversions to earlier forms.

FIG. 98.—Root cuttings of apple about one month after planting.

Root cuttings are sometimes classed as: 1, Cuttings of roots proper (sweet potato) and 2, tuber cuttings (Irish potato), the latter properly as cuttings because tubers are thickened, specialized stems.

Stem cuttings of certain tuber-bearing plants (potato) do not develop new plants, but tubers either at the bases of cuttings or in the axils of leaves above ground. New plants will develop from these tubers. Leaf cuttings of some kinds also do this.

Rhizome cuttings, made from underground stems (achillea, canna, iris, rhubarb), are treated like tuber cuttings. Two bad weeds accidentally propagated in this way by hoeing and harrowing are quack grass and perennial morning-glory (bindweed), every joint of which is capable of producing a new plant.

133. Stem cuttings are of three general classes. First, those known as ripe, mature or hardwood cuttings; second, cuttings of green, succulent, immature, or softwood; and third, an intermediate stage between these two classes designated semi-hardwood cuttings.

134. Hardwood Stem Cuttings.—(Figs. 99 to 103). Nearly all soft and loose wooded plants grow readily from hardwood cuttings but plants with denser wood are propagated more easily from soft or growing wood. Oak and nut trees are difficult to propagate from cuttings although some are made to grow from tip cuttings of roots. If properly treated probably all dicotyledonous plants can be multiplied by cuttings of some form.

Hardwood stem cuttings are made from the ripe wood of the past season's growth or older wood, which in the case of deciduous plants will make no more length growth for the present season. The leaves may or may not still be retained (Fig. 103). Some plants may be propagated from wood two to three years of age, (tamarix, willow, maple, olive). Many plants (see list) are propagated by hardwood stem cuttings.

FIG. 99. Tamping soaked sand for planting cuttings.

RIPENED WOOD CUTTINGS ROOTED IN THE OPEN

Azalea	Lonicera
Berberis	Lotus
Chænomeles	Philadelphus
Diervilla	Polygonum
Duranta	auberti
Fuchsia	Punica
Hydrangea	Rhododendron
Kerria	Rosa
Kolkwitzia	Salix
Lagerstrœmia	Spiræa
Leptospermum	Tamarix
Ligustrum	

135. **Mature or hardwood cuttings** may be made at any time in fall, winter or early spring. With plants growing in the open the great majority are made for spring planting. Many of these are cut only a short time before being planted; many more in fall and stored over winter in bundles buried in a well-drained sandy knoll, under cover in moist soil, sand, saw-dust, sphagnum moss, or peat moss.

The chief advantages of storing are that the bases callus (Fig. 104) before planting time, possible winter injury is avoided and the cuttings may be held for favorable outdoor weather. Occasion-ally (currant, gooseberry) cuttings are made as soon as the wood is mature and the leaves begin to fall. They are then callused and fall planted, thus gaining time. In localities where the ground freezes, winter mulching of fall set cutting beds is essential to suc-cess because heaving and settling of soil will break the tender roots and perhaps throw the cuttings out of the ground.

On the University of California Farm at Davis results were far more favorable with cuttings not stored than with stored cuttings. It appears that the less a cutting is disturbed from the time of making to the time of rooting the better the results. The non-stored cuttings were made from mid-November to March first and planted directly in medium fine sand. Many plants gave as high as 90% stand of rooted cuttings. Under Eastern conditions results might not be the same.

136. Hardwood stem cuttings of deciduous fruits (apple, pear, peach, cherry, plum) will often root if grown in such manner that a small length of the bark (1″ to 2″) is kept white by excluding the light. Trees and shrubs from which cuttings are to be made are cut back to within 1″ or 2″ of the ground. When the sprouts are 2″ or 3″ high fine soil is shovelled around them, care being taken not to cover the growing tips. The process is repeated every few days until they are mounded 4″ to 5″ deep. This depth should insure having sprouts with at least 2″ of the base of each with white

Fig. 100.—Making trench for cuttings. A, sheet metal thrust almost to bottom of bed; B, trench ready for cuttings.

FIG. 101.—Tamping between rows of cuttings. Board (1″ x 4″) is placed on soaked sand on each side of each row and struck with mallet. Test of good job is firmness of cutting in sand.

or almost colorless bark. When these sprouts are treated as cuttings the following season they should root readily.

If the trees are mounded deeply enough to keep the covered parts moist throughout the season many of them will take root that same season (Mound layering 105). All the sprouts are carefully cut away from the parent plant in late fall. Those that are rooted, if to be used as stocks, may be bench grafted or lined out in the nursery row for budding. Those that are not rooted may be propagated by the special mounding process, set 2′ apart in wide nursery rows and allowed to grow for one season before being cut back for sprout production.

137. **Preparation of Stem Cuttings.**—No general rule governs the length of hardwood cuttings. For convenience of handling cuttings of ornamental shrubbery, mariana plum, etc., are usually made from 3½″ to 8″ long. The authors prefer 3½″ to 5″. Whatever the kind of stem cutting it should have at least two buds or nodes, one for the region of rooting and one for the top shoot or new plant above ground. Some plants (oleander, butterflybush, grape) have internodes often 8″ long thus making 5″ two node cuttings impossible.

In case of the grape, particularly long jointed varieties, the cuttings

A

B

FIG. 102.—A, well planted flat of hardwood cuttings. Rows slightly farther apart than necessary; B, poorly planted flat—spaced irregularly and rows too far apart.

may be much longer than the length mentioned. The average length of three or four node grape cuttings is 14″. Formerly it was thought necessary to make grape cuttings 18″ to 24″ long. Though many grape cuttings of the proper length—14″ to 16″—may contain only two or four buds, currant, plum, spirea, deutzia, etc., will usually contain 4 to 10.

Number of buds does not determine whether a cutting will make satisfactory growth. In most cases it is not customary to take pains to "cut to a bud" (to have a bud at the base of the cutting) particularly with short pointed plants. In the grape the buds are not only far apart but experience proves that roots rarely form except near the nodes. Hence, in making grape cuttings propagators always cut to a node (See Chapter VI-A).

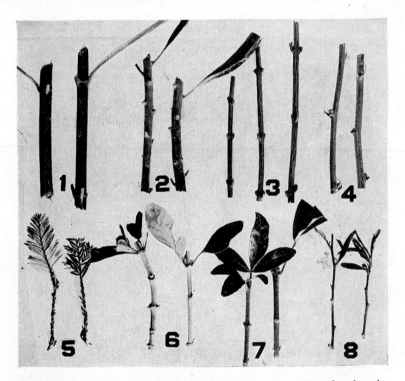

Fig. 103.—Hardwood and semi-hardwood cuttings. 1, evergreen oleander, single and double nodes; 2, hardwood evergreen Pittosporum cuttings. Note closeness of nodes. Such cuttings need not be cut to node. 3, California privet (right one too long, otherwise good); 4, hardwood hibiscus cuttings; 5, coniferous evergreen cuttings with heels; 6, coprosmia cuttings showing amount of leaf surface to retain; 7, semi-hardwood cuttings of Choisya ternata; 8, pyracantha crenulata, semi-hardwood *right*, tip taken in August, *left*, in early summer, just below tip which would then be soft wood.

In planting hardwood cuttings, even though they bear many buds, only one or two are left above ground. Sometimes all the buds below ground are rubbed off in order to prevent sprouting. When mariana plum cuttings are grown to supply budding stocks, this is a desirable practice because any sprout except the desired one would be regarded as a seedling. Hardwood cuttings, if long, are often planted at an angle in the soil to prevent their being buried too deeply.

If the soil is poorly drained or the season wet and cold, cuttings are likely to root poorly. In such soils grape cuttings with two nodes under ground stand a much better show of making good plants than those with only one, for if the bottom node cannot throw out roots because too cold or wet the node above may do so in a warmer or better drained stratum. (Practicum XXII.)

138. Callus pits are excavations in which cuttings are buried for a few weeks or months prior to planting (Fig. 105). They must be made on well-drained knolls fully exposed to the sun so the great-

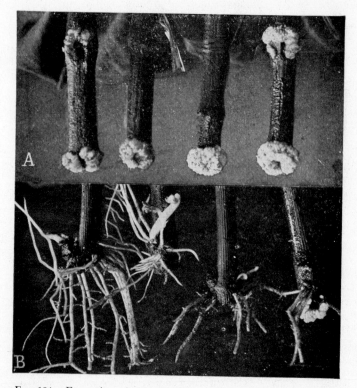

Fig. 104.—Formation of callus and roots. A, grape cuttings showing callus; B, others showing roots.

est possible use may be made of natural bottom heat. For short
periods in fall and spring, bundles of cuttings are buried upright
with their butt ends upward to hasten callusing. Depth will be
governed by length of cuttings and season; a covering of 2″ to 6″
of sand or friable soil is enough. Because the upper ends of cuttings
are placed downward the buds are kept cooler than the butt ends

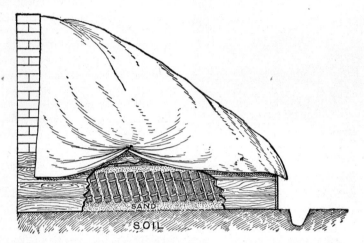

Fig. 105.—Callusing bed. Bundles set upright with butts upward. Best
position for rooting.

and, therefore, do not sprout under fairly favorable conditions for
starting growth.

139. Fall-callused cuttings may be dug and stored in cellars
over winter. Fresh hardwood sawdust from green wood is considered the best material in which to store mature wood cuttings because it has just the right humidity and retains moisture well; watering is rarely necessary. The storage room must be kept cold but
above freezing. If warm the packing material may dry out rapidly.
Watering may cause cuttings to heat and sprout long before they
could be planted in spring. Hence there would be loss.

140. Burying hardwood cuttings bottom end upward from a
few days to a few weeks in spring before setting in the outdoor cutting bed takes advantage of heat in the upper layers of soil. It is
of particular advantage with slow rooting cuttings of certain varieties
of grapes, (Norton, Delaware). Usually, for convenience in handling, the cuttings are tied in bundles of 100 and buried tops downward in a sandy knoll fully exposed to the sun and only 2″ to 3″
deep. Often frames are used. Sometimes cuttings are so treated
in fall and taken up for cellar storage when the ground begins to

Fig. 105x.—Carnation cuttings. A, newly made; B, rooted.

freeze hard; sometimes they are stored without this previous treatment, but buried in spring for a few weeks before planting. Hardwood cuttings grown out doors do best when 6″ or 8″ long rather than extreme length.

In some cases cuttings may be taken as early as August or as soon as the wood is matured, but when taken this early they should be stored and allowed to callus and complete the rest period under cool conditions before planting. It may even be necessary to strip the leaves two weeks previous to making the cuttings in order to hasten maturity (currants). When made early, callusing should develop in time to allow for fall planting.

141. Cutting tests[1] throughout the year with lilac showed that only those cuttings made in June and July while growth is active rooted freely. Those made from mid-September to mid-December developed no activity whatever, thus leading to the conclusion that this is the true dormant period of lilac. This period is followed by continued dormancy, apparently caused by low temperature and other conditions unfavorable to growth. Cuttings taken during this period showed active bud development in the early part and bud callus development in the latter part of the period.

A definite correlation was indicated between growth and callus formation. Calluses formed only when buds were present and active. In general the location of the callus was immediately below the most active bud. Bud growth, however, was not necessarily accompanied by callusing. It is suggested that rooting did not occur in cuttings of resting material because reserve foods were insufficient to provide for the metabolism of dormancy, bud growth, callusing and rooting. The roots arose entirely from the cambium within the callus. Silver sand (pH. 6.9) proved the most successful rooting medium.

Most of the cone bearing trees probably can be propagated from cuttings but with the pines and spruces it is not profitable as they are grown cheaply from seed. Choice varieties, however, especially of the latter are grafted upon seedling stock (Koster's Blue Spruce on seedlings of Norway or white spruce— *Picea excelsa* or *P. canadensis*). Spruce cuttings require 12 to 18 months to take root, under ordinary methods. (See Chapter VI-A.)

142. Broad-leaf evergreen cuttings, are not stored but planted directly after being prepared. All leaves except the one or two at the top buds of each cutting are removed and these leaves are reduced a half or more by cutting with a knife or shears. The cuttings

---

[1] W. L. S. Kemp. *Sci. Agr. 9.*

are then planted in the usual manner, preferably in a flat and placed in a greenhouse or a frame (Fig. 107).

142A. Coniferous Hardwood Stem Cuttings.—Many evergreen varieties, especially of coniferous plants (retinospora, juniper, cypress) are propagated commercially by cuttings since they do not come true from seed. The cuttings, 3″ to 5″ long, are made in October (or later) of well ripened wood and are not stored, but

FIG. 106.—Evergreen cuttings. A, arborvitæ; B,
hemlock; C, box.

planted directly in flats of sand and kept in a cool greenhouse, a lath house or a cold frame. Most species root slowly, often remaining in the original flats or benches a year or more, but their treatment is simple. Arborvitæ and retinospora can usually be depended upon to root in six or seven months after planting. After rooting they are either transplanted or left in the flats another season when they are removed to nursery rows (Fig. 106). (See Chapter VI-A.)

In making the cuttings (preferably with a heel) it is often necessary to use three or even four year old wood (younger wood is preferred) but they are usually made of the required length regardless of this fact. The usual practice is to trim off the needles with a sharp knife for 2″ or 3″, none of the leaflets being buried in planting but the necessity of this procedure is questioned by some investigators (Fig. 48).

143. Vegetative Propagation of hollies[1] has been considered an important subject in recent years because of extensive ravages made upon these plants at Christmas time and also because of their growing popularity as ornamentals for home planting. Nurserymen have not been able to supply the

FIG. 107.—Evergreen cuttings grown in steam heated bed now open for summer.

demand for plants since seeds have germinated poorly and cuttings have not responded well. Occasionally some grower has rooted a cutting but success has been far too infrequent to be of any commercial importance.

Hollies are diœcious, so due to the fact that berried types can not be selected from seedlings until the plants are several years old, vegetative reproduction is of particular value. There is also much variation in leaves, berries and size among seedlings, so if a good method for vegetative propagation can be found, new plants which would grow true to type could be made from selected trees (Fig. 108).

In efforts to discover such methods Zimmerman and Hitchcock, of the Boyce Thompson Institute, worked during two years with cuttings of one deciduous holly *(Ilex verticillata)* and five evergreen species *(I. opaca, I. crenata, I. glabra, I. cornuta* and *I. aquifolium)* obtained at various seasons from several trees, each lot studied separately. Their slightly condensed conclusions follow:

1. In the case of Ilex opaca, the percentage of rooting varied according to the source of cutting material. Of four lots taken at the same time from different trees in Massachusetts the percentage was approximately 40, 60, 80 and 80%, respectively. Even though three types of cuttings were made from each lot the percentage of rooting remained fairly consistent for each tree. Similar results were obtained with material from Maryland and New Jersey (Fig. 108).

2. Rooting was equally good from August 1 to January 1. Results were generally unsatisfactory after January 15 because of frost injury.

3. Three types of cuttings were tried. Cuttings made of current year stems were slightly better than where old stems remained attached. A 4″ or 5″ cutting of current growth plus a portion of two-year-old stems gave satisfactory results. Culls or material 4″ to 6″ long taken at random from stems

---

[1] P. W. Zimmerman and A. E. Hitchcock, *Vegetative Propagation of Holly,* Am. *Jour. Bot.* XVI. 556-570, July, 1929

FIG. 108.—Holly propagation. *Ilex cornuta* from cutting, photographed about nine months after being made. This species produces no pollen and does not require pollen to form berries; B, *I. opaca* seedling photographed about three years after berry was collected at close of growing season; C, *I. opaca* from cutting about 12 months after being taken from growing tree.

two to five years old gave a greater variation and a lower percentage of rooting than other types.

4. Of the five media used, a mixture of 50% sand with 50% peat moss by volume was generally the best. Rooting was obtained, however, over a pH range of 3.6 to 8 in the various media.

5. Cuttings of evergreen hollies did not root when all leaves had been removed. Ilex verticillata, a deciduous species, rooted when no leaves were present.

6. Ilex opaca cuttings started rooting in 21 days, but to obtain a high percentage of rooting it was necessary to leave the material in the medium for three to four months.

7. Holly cuttings rooted at various temperatures from 59° to 80° F., but for practical purposes 65° to 75° F. was considered a satisfactory range.

8. Stems of Ilex opaca increased in starch and decreased in reducing substances while in the rooting medium. Ilex crenata cuttings kept in the dark lost starch regularly for six weeks and did not root. Comparable sets in light increased in starch and formed roots.

9. Dormant cuttings taken in October produced roots but few shoots when kept continuously in a warm place. The buds did not develop until after being stored two or more months in a cool place. Many plants lay without top growth throughout the summer of 1928 but having been stored in a cool place the following winter, they made normal growth in the spring of 1929.

10. Potted holly plants *(I. opaca)* when properly selected and pollinated produced crops of berries during the first season.

144. Softwood cuttings are made not only from plants whose tissues are always relatively soft (chrysanthemum, carnation, pachysandra) but from the soft tissue of those which become woody and which may also be propagated by hardwood and semi-hardwood cuttings (weigela, deutzia). What characterizes them is not the type of parent plant but the immaturity of the part used. These are usually the tips of branches still actively making or just having completed growth. (Fig. 105X).

Most soft wood plants may be increased by greenwood cuttings. Bedding plants are universally propagated thus (see list). Tender growing tips of ornamental shrubbery and other hardwood plants may be also used for propagation, provided that cuttings are taken in early summer when growth is most rapid and planted immediately in well-drained, well-shaded sand beds under glass.

SOFT GREEN CUTTINGS

Abutilon	Felicia	Mahernia	Scabiosa
Arabis	Forsythia	Malvaviscus	Sedum
Aubrietia	Fuchsia	Mesembryanthe-	Sophora
Boronia	Gerbera	mum	Sparmannia
Cactus	Helianthemum	Pentstemon	Streptosolen
Calceolaria	Hibiscus	Petunia	Tecoma
Chrysanthemum	Hypericum	Phlox	Verbena
Cytisus	Kerria	Pimelea	Veronica
Dahlia	Lantana	Rehmannia	Viburnum
Dianthus	Leptospermum	Rochea	Viola
Erica	Linum	Salvia	

HARDENED GREEN CUTTINGS

Abelia	Deutzia	Ipomœa	Nerium
Azalea	Diervilla	Jacaranda	Pelargonium
Boronia	Escallonia	Jasminum	Pernettia
Bougainvillea	Eugenia	Lavandula	Rosa
Camellia	Forsythia	Lavatera	Solandra
Cassia	Grevillea	Leonotis	Solanum
Chorizema	Hibiscus	Mahonia	Spiræa
Cistus	Hoya	Mahernia	Stephanotis
Clerodendron	Hydrangea	Mandevilla	Syringa
Cytisus	Ilex	Myrtus	Tibouchina
Daphne			Trachelospermum

145. **Condition of Plant.**—One necessary condition of softwood cutting propagation is that the plant from which they are taken must be in vigorous health. If weak or diseased failure is almost certain. One of the best guides is that the shoot will *snap clean across* instead of bend or only partially break; if it bends, it is too old. Though it may root, it will do so much slower and make a weaker plant than the one that snaps off cleanly (Fig. 109).

The old parts of even softwooded plants are slow to root, make poor plants and are handled with difficulty. Softwood cuttings must be planted in moist sand to sufficient depth to prevent wilting.

146. Length of Softwood Cuttings.—Greenwood cuttings are made 2″ to 4″ long with at least one green leaf each. In most cases it is customary to cut to a node, although this is not always necessary. In fact, many softwooded plants are capable of forming roots from almost any point below ground. As a rule the roots have a tendency to emerge near the base of the cutting regardless of whether or not a node is at that point. In many instances roots are formed from various parts of the stem at the same time.

Fig. 109.—Choice of parts for greenwood cuttings; a, just right—snaps; b, too old—crushes.

147. Shading and Watering Softwood Cuttings require great care (Fig. 112). Intense sunlight is disastrous to newly planted softwood cuttings. On this account it is necessary to shade the plants until they form roots. If the soil is pressed firmly around them at the time of planting and there is a moderate amount of bottom heat, many species will begin to root in ten days or less and in two weeks most of them should be started.

148. Parts Used for Softwood Cuttings.—The terminal cutting of a main stem or a strong branch usually makes more satisfactory growth than any made lower down the stem because the

Fig. 110.—Croton plants grown for stock. New plants are secured largely by Chinese layers.

terminal wood is sure to be full of vitality and in good growing condition—not because it carries the terminal bud. Where cutting material is abundant and all of it cannot be used it is customary to

Fig. 111.—
Ventilated cutting pot—small
flower pot inverted in "azalea" pot with
sand around it.

gather only the tips of the plants. This is particularly true of plants growing outdoors and from which it is desired to propagate in the fall. The branches will then have become more or less woody toward the base. On the other hand, where the same species and varieties are grown as stock plants in the greenhouse (merely for the purpose of producing "cutting wood") during winter cuttings in February will be 6″ to 10″ long, turgid, crisp, full of life and therefore in the best of condition to make good cuttings. (Fig. 110).

149. Rooting Medium for Softwood Cuttings.—Some propagators prefer as a medium an inch of broken stone or coarse gravel overlaid with 1½″ to 3″ of sand, but clean sand of a texture fine enough to retain moisture around the cuttings but coarse enough to allow water to drain through it freely is the rooting medium most generally used. Sand such as builders use for plastering often is suitable. It should be free from organic matter and foreign material such as clay. If necessary it should be passed through a screen to remove coarse gravel and then washed to free it from sediment.

Many pronounced hardwooded plants, when growing, are propagated by means of semi-hardwood cuttings (see list). Naturally these must be made in June or July when length growth is most rapid. Hydrangea, weigela, oleander, etc., are readily propagated in this manner. Privet, in particular, which is annually propagated extensively for hedge making is increased almost exclusively in this way. New growths are often long enough to make several 4″ cuttings.

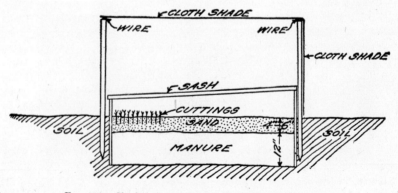

Fig. 112.—Shaded frame for outdoor softwood cuttings.

150. Water as a Medium for Softwood Cuttings.—Not all softwood cuttings root readily in water, but if a nasturtium stem with a leaf attached or an oleander stem is placed in water, it will form roots. The stem has the ability to absorb water; the leaf carries on the photosynthetic process of food manufacturing; this food is translocated to where the roots should be although roots are not present. Growing points of roots soon form, however, and a rooted cutting results.

Good plants may thus be grown, plants which after wintering in coldframes, may be set in the open the following spring. This is

Fig. 113.—Rose cuttings. A, first made; B, partially callused; C, callused; D, roots starting.

a quick method of increasing stock, since cuttings of green wood may be made from the plants in the latter part of the season and grown indoors during the winter.

151. Transplanting outdoor grown cuttings should be done at the close of the growing season, provided there is time for them to become established between the ripening of their wood and the approach of winter. Winter mulching is necessary. When maturity is late, planting in the spring is advisable. Always liberal space must be given so the plants will have ample food and develop symmetrically. In some cases, plants may be sold at one year old; in others at two years. Cutting plants must never be allowed to remain in the nursery rows more than one growing season otherwise serious loss of roots will occur when they are dug.

Greenwood or softwood cuttings are widely used because they strike root easily, are readily rooted under glass and the great majority of plants, whether soft- or hardwooded, can be propagated by them. In amateur window gardening they are often called "slips," because they are the side shoots pulled or "slipped" off the main stems and branches of plants. The term is not used in commercial practice since "cutting" covers the whole idea. Bedding plants (alternanthera, coleus, geranium) are so propagated. Greenwood cuttings are also made of dahlia, sweet and Irish potato sprouts when stock is costly or scarce, tubers being started in the usual way, the stems cut when large enough and placed in a cutting bed.

152. Roses may be propagated by seeds, suckers, layers, cuttings and by graftage.—Seeds are used to obtain new varieties and to increase the number of plants of species (*rugosa, spinosissima, carolina, nitida, blanda, lucida*) and also of several groups of varieties (*moss, alba, damask, gallica*). Suckers which spring from rootstocks of grafted or budded roses will not reproduce the varieties which constitute their tops so must be destroyed, the earlier the better.

Layering may be practiced by amateurs who desire only a few plants of some varieties or types of garden roses already growing on their places, especially of those not readily propagated under amateur conditions from cuttings. *Rosa wichuraiana* produces natural layers. Dorothy Perkins and others of its class root easily when layered. Persian Yellow and *Rosa hugonis* are often layered. Most other species and varieties grow readily from cuttings (Fig. 113 and 114).

Cuttings may be of hardwood or semi-hardwood under both amateur and commercial conditions and of softwood when greenhouse conditions are supplied. Climbing varieties are propagated mostly by hardwood cuttings; cut flower varieties from all these kinds and also by budding and grafting. (Practicums XXIX to XXXIV.)

153. Rose stocks from softwood cuttings.[1]—Most roses propagated in New York [2] are field grown, the desired variety being budded on stocks particularly grown for this purpose. Many species and types of rose have been used as understocks, one particularly in demand for budding to hybrid tea varieties being *Rosa multiflora japonica*.

Understocks of "multiflora" may be propagated by seed, hardwood and softwood cuttings. Until recently, seedlings have been largely used, but the difficulty of finding smooth places upon which to bud has been a serious fault. Plants grown from cuttings, particularly if disbudded, branch higher on the canes and so offer good, easily reached places to bud. Hardwood cuttings root readily in some parts of the country, providing a suitable source of lining-out stock at reasonable expense. In New York, however, the rooting of hardwood cuttings is not always successful, so other methods have been tried.

Cuttings were taken from field grown multiflora stock, made 6" or 7" long and struck with the lower ends 3" deep in the rooting medium in a cold frame, covered with sash, shaded with cheesecloth immediately and kept covered for 10 days, by which time the cuttings had usually rooted. Spraying with water three times a day kept the leaves from wilting and drooping. As soon as new growth indicated rooting, air was given gradually to harden them. In 7 to 10 days from the time they were made all protection was removed.

Cuttings made the first week in August rooted and made good growth but the plants failed to mature properly so late in the season and were either severely winter injured or failed to make vigorous growth the following season when lined out for budding.

Cuttings made July 1 and 17 show clearly the better size of plant and bet-

[1] H. B. Tukey and K. D. Brase, Bul. 598, N. Y. Exp. Sta., 1931. Condensed.
[2] And California—Authors.

ter developed root system of plants from cuttings struck July 1 as compared with those made at later dates (Fig. 114x).

Cuttings taken from tips of growing canes rooted more quickly than those from the bases and middle portions yet the difference is so slight as to be of no great practical significance since base and middle cane cuttings were well rooted in 10 to 14 days. Tip cuttings were slower to mature than base and middle cane cuttings, so they were more affected by low temperatures, but with early made cuttings this was of no significance.

Rooting media were German granulated peat, bank sand and a mixture of equal parts of these. Sand gave best results as regards both root formation and maturity of plant. Peat alone resulted in less mature plants than those rooted in sand alone.

It is well known that rooting of greenwood cuttings is improved by leaving the leaf surface unreduced, provided the cuttings can be adequately protected from wilting and excessive water loss during the rooting period. With cuttings in closed frames this is not difficult, since spraying with water and shading from direct sunlight are not difficult.

Each year of the tests the lower leaves were removed from some cuttings and the rooting response compared with that of cuttings with no lower leaves removed. Removal markedly reduced the percentage of plants rooted so this factor is not so important as might at first be interpreted. On the other hand, it is easier to handle and strike cuttings which have the lower leaves removed, so from the practical standpoint the value of removal of lower leaves may outweigh the value of less rapid rooting.

Fig. 114.—Rooting hardwood rose cuttings under fruit jar. This protection is even more necessary for greenwood than for hardwood cuttings.

From the experiences of three seasons, it is recommended that greenwood cuttings of *Rosa multiflora japonica* be made as early as maturity of the new wood will permit, about July 1 in western New York.

154. Rose cuttings of dormant wood are largely used both outdoors and under glass. When to be grown outdoors the cuttings are made 6″ long from mature wood in the fall before severe freezing weather comes. Bundles are stored in sand over winter and planted in spring in V-shaped trenches with only one bud showing. Rich soil produces strong plants in one season. When grown under glass the cuttings are made in November or December and planted in sand in coldframes or cool greenhouses. By February or March they may be potted. When warm weather arrives they are planted in rich soil.

155. Ringing roses to facilitate cuttings propagation was done experimentally by Greiner, a French investigator, who found that such cuttings take root more readily than do ordinary ones. The stems of the parent plants were ringed in July or August. By November the wounds had callused. The method is recommended for varieties difficult to propagate by ordinary cuttings. Several rings made at proper distances apart to get right-sized cuttings may be made on the same branch.

156. Cuttings from grafted grapes.—F. Baco, a French investigator, has proved that with certain varieties of grapes used as scions, grafting not only causes specific variations but that these variations may be perpetuated by cuttings. Variations in the vegetative parts also seem to be accompanied by variations in the root system.

157. Dwarf plants from cuttings.—In France cuttings taken from the tips of branches of plants which have reached full development but have not produced flowers, will take root under proper conditions and produce flowers without much further growth. If the plants to be dwarfed produce both terminal and axillary flowers the cuttings should be taken from the least developed flower branches. The cuttings should be made about an inch under a node in each case. Chrysanthemums, asters, roses and several greenhouse plants have been thus dwarfed.

158. Tomato cuttings grown experimentally outdoors have given more, earlier but smaller fruits than seedlings; indoors, seedlings were decidedly superior.

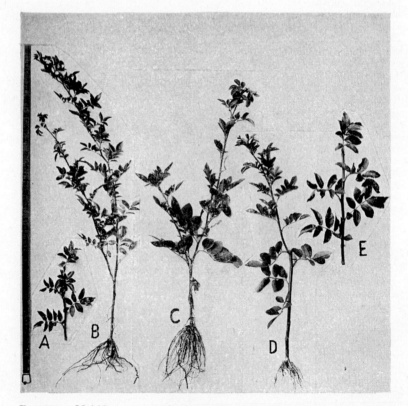

Fig. 114x.—Multiflora rose stocks from softwood cuttings struck in sand and grown outdoors. A, type of cutting used; B, cutting struck July 1; C, struck July 15; D, struck August 12. Photos made September 15.

159. Keeping soft cuttings alive for long periods.—G. W. Oliver has successfully transported herbaceous cuttings from distant places as follows: A layer of cuttings is arranged, upper leaf surface down, without crowding, on a pane of glass and covered with 2″ or 3″ of fine, damp sphagnum moss evenly distributed. A second layer of cuttings is placed on the moss with the upper surfaces of the leaves facing upward and covered with a second pane of glass. The two panes are pressed firmly and made into a package by tying. By keeping the moss moist and giving plenty of light, the cuttings carry well, provided

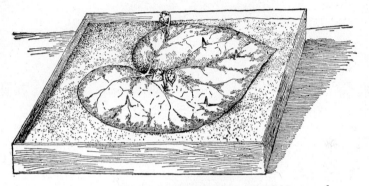

Fig. 115.—Propagating *Begonia rex* by leaf laid on sand.

the material is healthy. When the journey is long the cuttings are often rooted on arrival. With the moss only slightly dampened, scions and bud-sticks of rare plants have kept well under the same treatment.

160. Sugar cane cuttings have been shipped long distances when treated with bordeaux and then packed in damp charcoal.

161. Cuttings of Coleus blumei placed in water cultures of various pH values[1] rooted most readily in a pH 6.5 medium. The condition of the reserve foods in the cutting had a marked influence on rooting. Cuttings taken from plants grown in full sunlight and with high starch content rooted more readily and more profusely than others from plants in darkness of the various pH values were independent of carbohydrates.

162. Leaf cuttings.—Leaves of certain plants may be made to produce new plants. Some of these are planted whole (Fig. 115), others cut in various ways. In certain cases (rex begonia) the new growth arises from adventitious buds, but in others (various ferns) it comes from true buds which originate in the stems. True buds may form on the leaves before being cut from the parent plant (*Bryophyllum calycinum*, Fig. 116) or afterwards (rex begonia); normal in the former case, adventitious in the latter.

Temperature and moisture conditions are the same for leaf cuttings as for softwood cuttings. Though many plants may be made to reproduce by leaf cuttings (lemon, cabbage) few can be profitably so propagated. The process, in some cases, destroys variegation in the progeny; e.g., though certain varie-

[1] E. P. Smith. *Bot. Soc. Edinb. Trans. and Proc.*, 30.

gated ivy geraniums may be reproduced by softwood cuttings they become plain green when leaf cuttings are used.

In some cases whole leaves are used as cuttings, in others the leaves are cut in pieces. A whole leaf of *Begonia rex* is placed flat on the propagating bench with a short piece of its stem buried in the sand. Cuts are then made across the main veins in various places and the leaf either pegged down or held in posi-

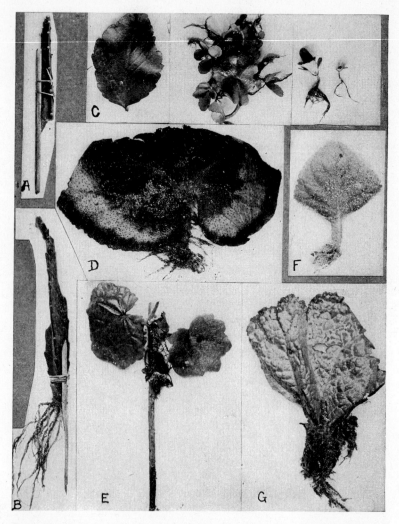

FIG. 116.—Various types of propagation. A, cactus stem cutting fastened to toothpick to steady it in medium; B, similar cutting rooted; C, bryophyllum plantlets developing in notches of leaf margin, plantlet separated; D, *Begonia rex* leaf with part of stem rooted in sand; E, geranium cutting too short to be firm without toothpick; F, gloxinia leaf stem rooted; G, sectional leaf of *Begonia rex* rooted by its main veins.

tion with a little sand. If contact with the sand is good and if moisture and temperate conditions are right, little plants will be produced at the wounds and also where the veins start to branch at the leaf base. When large enough to handle conveniently, they may be potted.

With costly or scarce stock rex begonia leaves are often cut from their bases outward to the margins, thus forming somewhat fan-shaped or triangular pieces 2″ or 3″ long and 1″ or more wide. In this case the stalk is cut off close to the leaf blade and the basal third of the blade also cut from one edge to the other by a straight slash. This base is then cut into wedge-shaped pieces with a rib in the middle of each and a small part of the stem at the lower end. The triangular pieces thus formed are placed stem end down in a cutting bench. Soon young plants form at the lower points (Fig. 116).

In greenhouse practice, bryophyllum leaves are laid flat on the propagating bench. Soon they form little plants from most of the notches on their margins (Fig. 116). In Bermuda and other moist climates, such small plants will form even when the parent plants or the mature leaves are hung on the walls of a room. The same thing often occurs in greenhouses.

Whole gloxinia leaves are used, the stems being placed in sand. Unlike the other cases cited, neither stems nor leaves usually take root, but a little tuber forms at the base of each leaf stem. Such tubers are then dried and after a "rest" planted like other tubers.

Hyacinth scales placed in a propagating bed soon develop bulblets at their bases. Treatment of these is the same as for those grown by other methods.

163. Tubers and tuber cuttings, because of their food content, can live long after growth starts before the new plants may be able

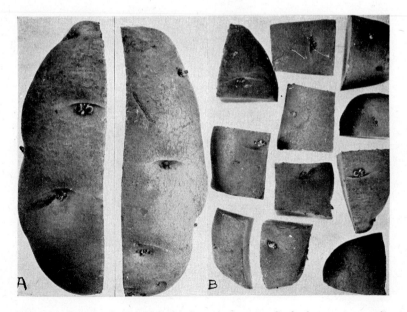

FIG. 117.—Potato tuber cut for planting. A, first cut; B, final stage—as nearly as possible single eye pieces.

to take food from the soil. In potato plant formation the eye sends a shoot through the soil to air and light. Then roots begin to form near the base of the shoot. These roots secure food though the plantlet continues to draw upon the food stored in the tuber. In time special shoots emerge from the stems, extend short distances and later thicken to form tubers.

For commercial planting, Irish potato tubers are usually cut in pieces, each containing at least one eye or bud. If cut through an eye each half eye may produce a shoot and be somewhat earlier than

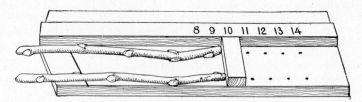

FIG. 118.—Grape cutting and scion gauge. Base of cutting, stock or scion is placed against adjustable cross piece and moved back and forth until bud comes to right of guide line when it is cut off flush with edge of board. Thus 1½″ of internode above top bud and maximum of only this amount variation in total length is secured.

the other eyes in the same piece. Cuttings are often slightly dried and allowed to sprout in the light, which produces short purple shoots (Fig. 68) that develop more rapidly than do unsprouted eyes. They apparently do not rob the tubers of plant food as do the white shoots formed in the dark.

Irish potato tuber cuttings (Fig. 117) each piece including at least one "eye" are dropped in the ground and allowed to take their course. Much discussion has arisen as to the proper size of piece. Experiment in many states and under numerous soil and other cultural conditions seems to favor moderate-sized tubers and cuttings rather than over-sized ones and single eye pieces.

164. Broccoli vegetative propagation from pieces of sterile inflorescence with attached scale leaves has been successfully done by R. J. D. Graham and L. B. Stewart in Scotland. The cuttings rooted readily when placed in a satisfactory environment. This method is of value in increasing rare breeding stock.

165. Grape hardwood cuttings are made of well matured canes from any parts of the vine that meet the specifications, preferably from vines examined while still in fruit to make sure they are healthy and true to name. Vines which have suffered from drouth, disease or defoliation yield poor cuttings and canes on young vines that have not fruited are often ill nourished and likely to make poor cuttings.

Best cuttings are made from canes with joints of normal length for the variety. When much shorter than this average they suggest disease; when much longer they hint at immaturity. In California, preferred cane diameters are ⅓″ to ½″; in the East, ¼″ to ⅓″. The bark should be typical of the variety in health—clear yellow for some, purple-brown for others. When cut with a sharp knife the inner bark should be green and full of sap; the wood hard, free from dark spots and streaks, the pith clear, firm, light colored and of moderate size.

Cuttings which fail to meet these specifications may still be good enough to grow in nursery rows where a reasonable proportion may make vines suitable for planting the following season. They are not suitable for planting as cuttings where they are to grow permanently.

Cutting lengths favored in California for direct vineyard planting are 14″ to 18″; for nursery rows, 10″ to 18″, though in good soil and with special care 8″ cuttings do well. In the East maximum lengths rarely exceed 12″ (Fig. 118).

Best results are gained when cuttings are made with the lower cut below and as close as possible to a bud without injuring the partition of wood (diaphragm) across the joint. When this condition is met callus forms quickly and well; whereas when pithy wood is left below the bud decay is likely to follow. Above the uppermost bud about an inch of internode should be left (Fig. 119).

Cuttings made within two weeks after leaf fall are supposed to be best, but if the vines are healthy and the wood well matured they may be made until within a week of bud-swelling time in spring. When made on a large scale they are placed, 100 in a frame (Fig. 120, 121) with butts even, a label in the center, wired securely at each end (Fig. 121) and a second label fastened near the top on the outside for quick reading. On the painted side of each label should be written the number of cuttings and the name of the variety; on the reverse side, the maker's name. All writing on labels should be with greased pencil because this is more permanent than plain lead. Ink and indelible lead are unsuitable because they quickly become illegible.

The amount of growth cuttings will make the first year depends on kind of soil, regularity and sufficiency of water supply, temperature and length of growing season. In the Imperial Valley

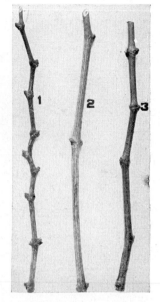

FIG. 119.—Grape cuttings. 1, with short internodes—often indication of diseased canes, except in naturally short jointed varieties; 2, long internodes—also undesirable because of probable immaturity and lack of nourishment; 3, internodes of moderate length —indicating healthy, vigorous canes.

of California a properly handled cutting in suitable soil will make as much growth the first season as a similar cutting equally well handled in a cool locality will in three. In New York many varieties (notably Concord) will make a goodly proportion of Number One grade vines in a single season. These are preferred by many vineyardists because they are generally robust, start quicker, grow more vigorously and cost less than two year Number One vines.

In order fully to utilize the growing season in any region, the cuttings should start growth as early as reasonably safe from frost or prolonged, cold, wet weather. The chief danger in the cooler regions is planting too early. Several weeks of cold weather may cause rot, especially in low places and in heavy soils. Under such conditions April is perhaps the best month for planting. In the hottest regions the chief dangers are drying of the cuttings before rooting and sunburn of the young growth before the roots are developed enough to supply water.

Root and bud formation may be delayed by keeping the cuttings dry and cool or hastened by keeping them moist and warm. Too much heat or too much water will cause decay. Dryness is less dangerous, especially at low temperatures. There is little danger from cold, even freezing, if the cuttings are mature.

Cuttings made at planting time should be planted at once, with care to prevent drying. If made several weeks or months before planting, their success will depend much on their handling. They may be stored in a pit on well

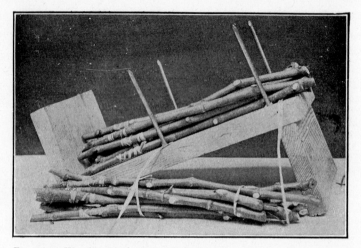

FIG. 120.—Wooden block and wire nail stand for bundling cuttings and grafts. Lengths of raffia, tape or cord are laid on block to be tied around bundles.

drained soil, butt ends up. The best way, however, is to bury them in moderately dry sand in a cool place until two or three weeks before planting, then to moisten the sand and increase its temperature until planting begins. A good way to do this is to place a pile of sand in a sunny spot early in the season and protect it from surface water by a shallow surrounding trench. Moisture may be controlled by sprinkling if necessary or by covering with boards or canvas in case of too much rain.

In spring when the ground has become warm enough the cuttings may be planted in the nursery. Spades, shovels, plows or other means may be used according to character of soil, number to plant and means available. If kept in dry sand they must be soaked for 24 to 48 hours before planting. Clean, five-gallon oil cans filled with water are convenient receptacles. The soil should be fairly rich; its texture is less important. Excessively sandy and heavy soils are not suitable. Unless naturally loose it should be well plowed or subsoiled at least 12″ deep and where irrigation is necessary be well graded to aid irrigation.

If the cuttings have been properly callused they should be removd from the sand just before planting, carefully protected from drying with wet burlap and not exposed to sun or dry air even when planting. A taut line or a long batten should be used to insure straightness of row and thus aid cultivation. When the trench is about a third full the soil must be firmed around the butts and settled with water unless it is already moist.

If water has been run in while planting, no irrigation will be needed for about two weeks. Otherwise the nursery should be irrigated a day or two after planting. Subsequent irrigation will depend on soil and climate, but should be relatively frequent during the first part of the season to start growth early and keep it going until the vines have made tops of 12″ or more and have developed good root systems that will make them less sensitive to drying. Irrigation should stop usually in late August. Between early and mid September the tips should cease growth and the canes become dark at their bases.

Fɪɢ. 121.—Bundles of grape cuttings. A, irregular length, undesirable; B, end view of well made bundle; C, side view.

In commercial planting a plowed furrow may be followed by a subsoiler at least 15″ below the surface, then the trench cleaned with spades or shovels and 8″ of loose soil thrown in. The cuttings, spaced 2″ or 3″ apart with a planting board are thrust deeply in the loose soil at a slight angle toward the straight side of the trench so one full joint projects above the surface. The soil is then packed around them, the planter standing in the trench and planting ahead of him. When the planting is complete the trench is nearly filled with soil and tramped well. To facilitate irrigation, which is often necessary the soil must be mounded around the cuttings almost to the top bud by hand or a suitable implement so the cuttings will be in the middle of a slight ridge. The first good rain will settle this soil down and expose the tops.

Vines may be dug as soon as they have dropped their leaves or may be left in the ground until needed for planting in spring. The ground should be moist down to the roots, but not wet when the vines are dug. All fit to plant should be sorted into two classes, No. 1 and No. 2. In California, to be No. 1, vines must have well ripened tops at least 6″, have healthy roots at least ⅛″ diameter at the bottom and show no dead areas or mechanical injuries on what was the original cutting. No. 2 vines have a smaller growth but well matured wood and no serious defects. Vines showing black knot, nematodes, serious mechanical injuries, or little or no mature wood roots should be rejected. In the East the roots are much smaller than in the West. One year vines carry several main roots usually less than ⅛″ in diameter at their bases, with many fibrous roots.

The roots are tied in bundles of 50 or 100, according to size and after tying the tops and roots shortened with a broad axe to 4″ or 5″. Each bundle should be furnished with a good label showing variety, number and grade. Vines should not be exposed to the sun. In eastern nurseries vines are usually dug in the fall, bundled and stored over winter in storage houses without packing material, earth or sand. Low temperature and relatively high humidity of the air maintain them in health and dormancy until spring. During winter they are graded and made ready for shipment.

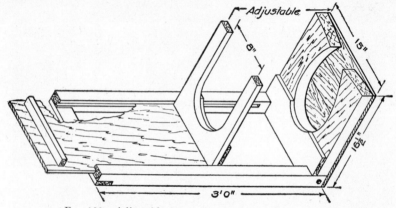

Fig. 122.—Adjustable frame for bundling grape cuttings.

Small lots are shipped in bales—moist packing, oiled paper, tough paper and finally burlap either pinned snugly with wire nails or sewed with stout cord. Large shipments are made in paper-lined boxes with ample moist packing around the roots but little over the tops. The bundles are packed snugly, often with battens, to prevent shifting. In the absence of storage houses if the vines are to be kept long they should be buried in a shady place or a shed, kept as cool as possible until planted and be planted then before buds or roots have started to swell or grow. In hauling or shipping they should be well protected with wet sacks from drying. If to be left out of the ground for more than two days wet straw is better.

166. Blueberry propagation.[1]—One of the outstanding horticultural achievements of the current century is the "taming" of the blueberry *(Vaccinium corymbosum)*. Until within the past two decades its many failures and few successes in gardens were without explanation. Almost no commercial planting had been done, mainly because wild bushes supplied the demand and no attempts to propagate it had been reported successful.

In 1906 Dr. F. V. Coville, botanist of the United States Department of Agriculture, began experiments from which both cultural and propagating methods have been developed. As to cultural requirements let is suffice here that the blueberry must have acid soil (Fig. 124), preferably one composed of

[1] Synopsized from *U. S. Dept. of Agr. Buls. 334* and *974;* and *Bureau of Pl. Ind. Bul. 193* and brought up to date by Dr. Coville.

peat and sand; good drainage; thorough soil aëration; and permanent but moderate soil moisture. It is also believed to require a beneficial, symbiotic root fungus *(mycorrhiza)* which is always attached to wild blueberry plants. Coville's recommended methods of propagation include stumping, tubering, winter cuttage and budding.

Stumping is the easiest way to propagate the swamp blueberry. (Fig. 125). In late fall, winter or early spring (but always before the buds start) cut the bushes or individual stems at the ground surface. These may be used as stock for tubering or winter cuttings. Pile mixed sand and sifted, rotted upland peat

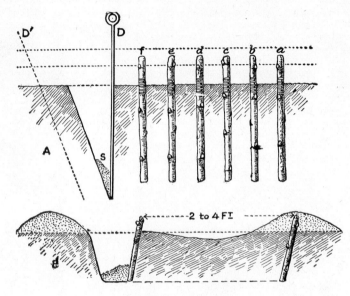

FIG. 123.—Methods of planting grape cuttings and grafts. A, with dibble. D, dibble pushing soil against graft, f; D', position of dibble for next thrust of soil; S, loose soil in bottom of hole. B, planting in trench. Mound of earth at right will flatten with tillage.

(2 to 4 of sand, 1 of peat) about 3″ deep on the stumps. Keep the bed in place by boards and maintain moisture in it during dry weather. Mulch heavily with leaves (preferably of red oak) to prevent soil heaving and maintain acidity.

In early spring of the following year before the buds start, carefully remove the mulch and sand mixture, sever each well rooted shoot from the stump and replace the mixture around the others. Cut the selected shoots back to about three buds above the former level of the sand and trim any injured bases with a keen edged knife. Use the discarded tops for cutting if desired. Set the trimmed shoots in a coldframe or a cool greenhouse in mixed upland peat and sand (2 to 1). Shade from direct sunlight and if possible for two or three months keep the temperature just below 65° F. in the daytime and above freezing at night. Water as little as practicable but keep the soil moist, well aërated but not soggy. Ventilate amply but not enough to make new growth droop. When new twigs stop growing and wood becomes hard, new roots are formed and secondary twig growth follows. Until this occurs the plants' lives are not assured.

"Tubering," (Fig. 126) the novel method of propagating the blueberry is as

follows: In midwinter or very early spring on a warm day when the plants are not frozen make 3″ or 4″ cuttings of old hard, unbranched pieces of stem ½″, 1″ or more in diameter. Avoid injuring the bark, splitting or straining the wood or having rough ends.

Lay the cuttings horizontally in a cutting bed or a clean box about 8″ deep and cover about ¾″ with mixed, sifted, rotted upland peat and clean sand (2 to 1). Wet the bed with water free from lime—rain or bog water preferred. Pack firmly. Cover with glass and provide holes for excess water to drain away through pieces of broken pots. Have the bed in a shaded place or shade it from direct sunlight. Keep the air over the bed saturated with moisture—as evidenced by condensation on the glass. Water as seldom as possible—just enough to keep the bed moist, but well aërated and the air saturated. Shoots appear in a few weeks, grow 1″ to 3″ and the bud at the tip dies. Roots develop after the leaves mature.

In working upward through the cutting bed the shoots become scaly, like rootstocks. During spring and summer they form abundant roots and usually make secondary growths the same season from the axils of the uppermost buds. The rooted shoots may remain in the original cutting bed until the following spring, being exposed to winter temperatures but mulched with oak leaves. In spring they may be transplanted to nursery beds spaced 1′ apart each way and grown for a year before being transplanted to the field.

Winter cuttings when started early enough in spring in a shaded greenhouse

Fig. 124. Importance of peaty, acid soil for blueberry. Small plant in little pot is same age as large ones. It was planted in rich garden soil, others in peaty, acid soil.

make roots before warm weather. A coldframe so located and sheltered as to maintain low temperatures as late as possible in the season is also good. Other essentials to success are abundant indirect light and ample cool air circulation between the frames and the shade.

Cuttings are made about 4″ long in mid winter from well matured, unbranched wood of the current season, using a sharp knife to make a short, diagonal cut at the base, just below a sound bud and about ⅛″ above the topmost one. Keep the knife clean or wipe it often with alcohol to avoid infection. Wrap the cuttings in a moist, clean towel to prevent drying. Set them vertically 3″ deep in holes made with a small dibble in the cutting medium and press them firmly in. The cutting bed, which must be well drained with broken flower pots or gravel at the bottom, may be 3½″ of coarse, fresh basswood sawdust or imported peat mull, or old rotted fine oak sawdust, or acid bank sand, or a mixture of such peat or sawdust with sand and should be wetted with lime-free water.

Manage the bed as described for tubered blueberries at temperatures about 60° to 65° F. during the day and not below 35° at night. After new twigs develop from the upper buds and the tips have become brown and the new leaves have reached full size, roots begin to form and ventilation may start—little at first and increasing slowly during several weeks.

When the secondary tips become brown and their leaves mature the plants may be fully ventilated. Dying cuttings should be removed promptly. Cuttings that are about to die usually turn brown at their lower ends. Afterwards their leaves begin to turn yellow and drop off. The plants are best left in the cutting bed all winter either indoors at slightly above freezing or outdoors mulched with oak leaves. In spring before their buds swell they must be carefully lifted with their mats of roots intact and planted in clean

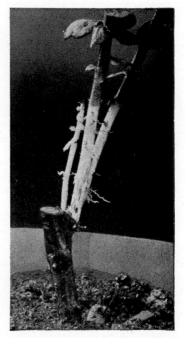

Fig. 125.—Blueberry shoots grew after original plant had been cut to stump and buried with peaty, acid soil as deep as white parts of stems. Through this they forced their way and started to develop roots.

flower pots of standard blueberry soil or 1′ apart each way in nursery sand-peat beds.

When blueberry plants are grown in porous pots the surface of the pots must never become dry because the rootlets around the balls of earth would thus be killed. Bedding the pots rim deep in moist sand is the simplest way to prevent this danger. Burning of the leaves and young tips in summer may be prevented by partial shade. In winter the plants should be kept outdoors exposed to freezing temperatures but mulched with leaves, preferably of oak.

167. Southern blueberry propagation[1]—L. M. Ware has proved that plants may be increased readily by cuttings taken just before or just at the cyclic period characterized by cessation of shoot growth and the initiation of

---

[1] *Miss. Sta. Bul.* 280.

root growth in the parent plants. Small shoots made the best cuttings and an
increase in leaf area up to two square inches each gave a corresponding increase
in root development and secondary top growth. A rooting medium of equal
volumes of peat and sand proved satisfactory with some suggestion that the
proportion of sand be increased after June first. Although cuttings were rooted
readily in various environments such as solar frames, lath-covered benches and

FIG. 126.—Tubered blueberry stems. A, stout plant developing from piece of old stem buried in cutting bed;
B, younger sprouts emerging from sand.

coldframes the last was most successful because of low cost and easy construction coupled with good rooting.

In Michigan, S. Johnson[1] tried various outdoor frames (cold, solar, box
and open) during the growing season. With German peat as a medium more
than 80% of both hardwood and softwood cuttings rooted in the solar frame;
good results also were obtained in the box frame which is recommended because
of its lower cost and easier operation. This medium gave better results with
both hardwood and softwood cuttings than did American peat, German peat
and sand or sand alone. Varietal differences were noted in rooting capacity with
little difference in the case of hardwood cuttings whether taken in February or
April.

[1] *Mich. Sta. Spec. Bul. 202.*

With softwood cuttings, approximately the middle of July proved the best time for taking cuttings. Evidence suggested that moderately high temperature and aëration are important factors in the rooting process. Seed taken from ripe berries and sown in German peat grew readily and the seedlings were successfully carried over winter.

168. Rhododendrons and other acid-soil plants.[1]—Nature provides plants with acid nourishment by the accumulation of half-rotted leaves, twigs and rootlets. When this occurs in a sphagnum bog it is called bog peat, or simply peat; on well-drained sandy or gravelly soils, upland peat. Under good conditions upland peat is laced into a tenacious mat by the roots of the eric‑

Fig. 127.—Effect of soil on rhododendron. A, plant potted for 13 months in fertile garden soil mixture; B, similar plant in same soil mixture but treated with ⅓ gram of aluminum sulphate in 10 cubic centimeters of water only once; C, plant in neutral garden soil (equal parts by bulk of loam, sand and well rotted cow manure) made no growth in about 13 months; D, similar plant in strongly acid soil (two parts upland peat to one of sand). Whenever practicable it is better to plant in acid soil than in neutral soil to be acidified artificially.

aceous plants. This mat continually renews itself through annual leaf-fall and the penetration of new roots. Upland peat is normally brown, but is often blackened by ground fires.

On limestone and other soils with alkaline reaction upland peat does not form. The alkaline substances hasten the decomposition of the leaves, much of it passing in liquid form into the underlying soil, prior to the leaf-fall of the following year. Fully decomposed leaves form a true, black leafmold, neutral or alkaline, in reaction. Rhododendrons and other acid-soil plants will not grow in this (Figs. 127, 128, 129). In soils derived from granite, sandstone, sand and gravel, acid conditions are usually maintained with ease by adding upland peat, half-rotted oak leaves, decayed wood or bark.

Sawdust and spent tanbark are acid materials useful as mulch for acid-soil plants. They should be applied experimentally at first, however, to test the

[1] F. V. Coville, *The Effect of Aluminum Sulphate on Rhododendrons and Other Acid-soil Plants. Smithsonian Report for 1926*, pp. 369-382.

safety and suitability of the particular kind available. Some kinds of sawdust, (redcedar, pitch pine) contain fresh substances directly injurious. Other kinds (basswood, maple, birch) are free from these substances. In general it is best to use weathered, decayed sawdust.

When an attempt is to be made to grow acid-soil plants where the soil is neutral or alkaline, such as limestone soil, bottom land, river valley, ordinary fertile garden, a prairie or arid-region soil, it is necessary to prepare holes or trenches and make up a special soil mixture. This should consist of 1 part

FIG. 128.—Aluminum sulphate effect on blueberry plants. Healthy seedlings of equal development were potted in garden soil known to be injurious to them. Plant A was given heavy dose of aluminum sulphate. Photo taken seven months later shows effect.

clean sand to 1 or 2, or even 4 parts of upland peat or its equivalent. To keep earthworms from bringing up the underlying soil the bottom of the hole should be lined with a 2″ layer of soft-coal cinders. The depth of the peat and sand mixture need not be more than 8″ to 12″. If the materials for the mixture are available in quantity a bed may be laid down over the whole surface of the ground. A permanent mulch of oak leaves will help maintain moisture and by decomposition will add to the peat supply.

In choosing peat for the culture of acid-soil plants two mistakes should be avoided; First, the use of the deposit that looks like peat in certain swamps but which is neutral or alkaline in reaction; Second, the much decomposed peat in the submerged lower layers of deep bogs, such as is used for fuel in Europe, or the lighter kinds for stable bedding. This is not suitable, by itself, for acid-soil plants. It may furnish the needed acidity but it is deficient in plant food.

Fig. 129.—Soil experiments with Franklinia plants. A, typically healthy plant grown in standard acid soil; B, similar plant in neutral garden soil— almost dead after five months; C, similar plant in same soil for eight weeks became as sickly as B. Soil was then acidified with aluminum sulphate and plant recovered as shown three months later when photo was taken.

When such a peat is used, nourishment for the plant must be supplied in some other material. The light peat imported from Europe, much used in the United States as a mulch, as an ingredient of potting mixtures, and in cutting beds, for acid-soil plants, is well suited to these purposes, but being deficient in plant food it should not be used alone or with sand only as a potting soil.

A sharp distinction should be made between half-rotted oak leaves and ordinary compost of leaves with manure, garden soil and garden trash. Such a compost is neutral or alkaline and should not be used on acid-soil plants. Sugar maple, elm and linden leaves rot rapidly and so soon become alkaline that they also are not desirable. Oak leaves, especially red oak leaves, rot slowly. In two or three years, if the pile is turned over several times, they make a good substitute for upland peat.[1]

No manure, lime, or wood ashes should be applied to plants that require acid soil, for all these substances tend to neutralize the necessary acidity. Cottonseed meal, ground soybeans and spent malt, all of which contain a large amount of nitrogen in organic and acid form, are excellent fertilizers for acid-soil plants. In very sandy soils for which so little peat is available that the plants suffer for nourishment the following special acid fertilizer devised for blueberries and cranberries will probably do well for rhododendrons, applied at the rate of an eighth to a fourth of a pound to the square yard: Cottonseed meal, 10 pounds, acid phosphate, 4; sulphate of potash, 2.

Hard water (alkaline in reaction) will ultimately injure an acid-soil planting. Rainwater or some other neutral or even acid water should be used if practicable. If only alkaline water is available it can be made neutral or slightly acid by dissolving it in a suitable amount of aluminum sulphate. The proper amount can be determined by adding to a teaspoonful of the treated water in a white dish a fraction of a drop of the dye, bromthymol blue. If the amount of aluminum sulphate added to the water is just sufficient to make it neutral its color under this test will be green; if it has become acid, yellow; if it is still alkaline, blue.

---

[1] For a more extended discussion of the decay of leaves and its relation to acid soils see "The Formation of Leafmold," *Smithsonian Report for 1913*, pp. 333 to 343.

ROOT INITIATION ON CUTTINGS BY "GROWTH SUBSTANCES"

Within the past several years, but especially since 1929 (as noted further on), many reports have been published concerning the effects of "growth substances" on plants. Though it is true that under specific conditions, some of the results are more or less spectacular, the unofficial publicity given these phenomena has fostered sensationalism which doubtless is responsible for misconceptions as to the use that may be made of these materials. Therefore, the following sketch is given to set forth the main facts concerning the history, the application of the knowledge so far verified, and the prospective results that may be expected.

History of Plant "Growth Substances."—About a decade before his death in 1897, Julius Sachs, German pioneer physiological botanist, announced that growth in plants is probably influenced by extremely small quantities of specific substances that cannot be designated as foodstuffs but which direct the activities of cells. However, he was unable to prove his conjecture.

The idea that plants contain such growth regulators has also been surmised by horticulturists; for the dominance of the terminal bud over lateral buds has been common observation in the development of plants from cuttings, of shoots from grafts and in other similar cases. This phenomenon is supposed to be due to an inhibitor formed by the apical bud during development.

In general, so far as plants are concerned the term "growth substance" is used for any material—organic or inorganic—that induces specific types of formative response in plants, such as retardation or stimulation of growth of various tissues, initiation of cell division such as excessive development of cells or other parts (proliferation), downward bending of stems or leaves (epinasty), or development of roots—characteristic responses that permit tracing the movement of these materials through the plant and the capacity to modify normal growth activities.

For many years it has been well recognized that organic manures, such as stable manure, cause accelerated growth increments even greater than those produced by the application of equivalent chemical fertilizers. These results are credited to *auximones*, which are defined as "certain substances considered necessary, though only in small quantities, for the vigorous growth of plants, and occurring especially in sphagnum peat decomposed by nitrogen bacteria."

1906, E. H. Starling first used the word *hormone* (from the Greek, to arouse, excite or set in motion) and defined it as "any substance produced in the cells of some part of the [animal] body and carried to distant parts which it affects for the good of the body as a whole." To this may be added Tincker's comment that "in animals where differentiation into glands is highly developed, physiologists have for many years known of these relations, in plants where there is comparatively less differentiation of the tissues the study of such relations is of more recent date."

The term *hormone,* as applied to plants, was first used by H. Fitting in 1910. Other names since used synonymously are growth hormone, growth regulator and Wuchsstoffe. The term, therefore, applies to substances naturally produced by the plants themselves without artificial influence.

Boysen-Jansen (1913) showed that "restoration of the decapitated *Avena* coleoptile tips retained the power to respond to light. He was thus the first to *demonstrate* hormone-like effects in plants— his predecessors having only postulated the existence of such effects."

Probably there are many natural hormones, though they have not as yet been definitely isolated and pinned down to formulæ, though Doctor Kögl, formerly believed that he had succeeded.

Several hundred scientific papers and a few books have been published on the general subject, 85 of them listed by Tincker in the *Journal of the Royal Horticultural Society* (Vol. LXI, Pt. 9, 1936).

F. A. F. C. Went and his son, F. W. Went, have proved that a root-forming material, which they called *rhyzocaline,* is formed by the leaves; for defoliated greenwood cuttings fail to form roots. In 1934 Thimann and Went reported on the chemical nature of this hormone.

Bouilenne and Went found a root-forming substance in cotyledons, evidently stored in the seed. Their work indicates that photosynthetic action in the leaves is necessary to produce it. This is also apparent from the fact that leafy cuttings root more freely than do those stripped of leaves. It has been found in buds, also in old, and even dying leaves—which latter often yield relatively large quantities. For horticultural practice, this suggests that greenwood cuttings should be taken while bearing leaves.

Zimmerman and Hitchcock, of the Boyce Thompson Institute, became prominent in these investigations when their reports of the effects of certain gases on plants were published. The report (1933) of the effect of carbon monoxide initiating roots on plants is the first case of a known chemical substance to initiate any organ on a plant.

FIG. 129A.—Rooting of cuttings after treatment with Hormodin A (Indolebutyric acid). The usual practise is to treat the basal end of the cuttings in the proper strength of a solution of the chemical for 24 hours, then plant in the rooting medium and handle in the custom- ary way. *Top,* dahlia; *second,* carnation; *third,* bittersweet; *bottom,* Souvenir de Claudius Pernet. Groups on the left, untreated; on the right, treated.

Since then they have found "32 growth-promoting substances. Among them are 14 acids, 11 esters, and 4 unsaturated carbon-containing gases. Also salts of the various acids are effective." These are known to initiate effects similar to those developed by the plants themselves.

Several of the substances with which these scientists have experimented have been patented for the protection of the Institute and the public. The right to place one of them upon the market has been officially granted by the Boyce Thompson Research Foundation, Inc., to Merck and Company, Inc., of Rahway, N. J., under the trade name of "Hormodin A." Other growth substances are also being officially sanctioned by this Foundation under different letters.

Scientists, on the one hand, are interested in all phenomena produced by these various substances as helping to reveal and explain plant functions; on the other hand, plant propagators see that the formation of roots has a practical application, primarily because of the use they may make of growth substances to produce plants from cuttings, perhaps secondarily also in the apparent promise that this method may enable them to discard more cumbersome, costly, risky or otherwise faulty methods.

Origin of Hormones.—Light apparently fosters hormone formation in seedlings, opening buds and in rapidly growing young leaves. Observation and experiment support the belief that they form in the generating tissue (meristem) of older plants. From these parts of the plants they move to other parts where they exercise more or less control over the centers which initiate growth.

Apparently they initiate cell division in the cambium layer and, therefore, in cotyledonous plants, stimulate cambial activity. Under favorable conditions they may foster callus and root formation; however, they are not peculiar in these respects; many substances (as already noted) have been proved equally effective.

In spite of countless experiments, the mechanism by which these materials promote plant growth has not yet been discovered, though it seems probable that they cause the inception of cell activity rather than become materials used to form cells. Since numerous experiments have proved that when they are absent no shoot growth occurs in higher plants, it is evident that even though not the sole important agents that influence, they are essential to plant development.

Inorganic Plant "Growth Substances."—After natural growth substances had been discovered and their effects proved by many scientists, inorganic substances were discovered that produced the same effects, as already noted. Let it here suffice that when applied to cuttings, either in solution or in various other ways, they initiate root production. Thus they promise to be of particular value in the propagation of plants, especially of woody species which are normally either difficult to make form roots or are slow to do so.

Experiments conducted by Zimmerman and Hitchcock have proved that, by means of these materials, roots will form upon any part of the stem and, in many cases, even upon the leaves.

For developing roots upon cuttings, the materials are best applied when dissolved in water, but the effectiveness of the treatment in growing roots on parts which develop above ground—either upon the plants themselves or upon cuttings—is dependent upon various factors, especially the plant species, the method of application, the age of the "wood" from which the cuttings are made, and the concentration (dilution) of the growth material. "For practical plant propagation," these scientists announce, "naphthaleneacetic acid and indolebutyric acid are the most important. . . . Water solutions of growth substances are effective over a wide range of concentrations from one part in 5,000 to 1 part in 1,000,000. The dilutions must be varied according to the substances and the uses to which they are put."

Propagation of plants by cuttings of both herbaceous and woody species, especially the latter, have proved highly satisfactory. For example, in experiments with American holly (*Ilex opaca*)—a slow and difficult species to make form roots—cuttings were taken in late December and January (one of the worst periods for propagation). They were chemically treated for 24 hours, placed in a 50-50 mixture of sand and peat moss with the result that roots in abundance developed in five weeks! Similar results were secured with various other difficult, as well as easy rooting species (Fig. 129A). Check experiments show that when cuttings were immersed in tap water few or no roots were formed during equal times.

According to Dr. Zimmerman,* "Approximately eighty-five genera, involving several hundred species and varieties, have been found to make satisfactory response when given the chemical treatment. . . . In general, leafy cuttings of all species respond better than leafless, hardwood types. The difficulty may be that the leafless cuttings do not take up the material from solution. However, it has been encouraging to find that many species respond when both hardwood and green cuttings are used."

Among species hitherto considered difficult the following have given excellent percentages of rooting: Apple, blueberry, chestnut hybrids, American elm, gardenia, American and Japanese holly, junipers of various species, lavender, magnolia, maple, plum, peach, poplar, rhododendron hybrids, Paul's Scarlet and Claudius de Pernet roses, Japanese yew, and viburnum species.

---

* *Ohio Journal of Science,* Vol. XXXVII, No. 6, November 1937.

The effectiveness of the treatments for root formation is more or less proportional to the concentration (or dilution) of the growth substance and the time during which the cuttings are treated.

Because the effectiveness of the solutions increases with the increase of concentration the temptation will be to use solutions that approach, if not reach, toxic strengths and thus destroy the life forces in the cuttings, also that for any specific, effective solution lengthening the duration of treatment is likely to have a similar effect.

Doubtless no one solution or duration of treatment will prove equally effective for all plant species and varieties or for cuttings of different ages of the same species. Therefore, for safety's sake, the experimenters recommend preliminary tests with five to ten cuttings of each species to determine the effective range of concentration and duration before treating large numbers of cuttings according to general directions.

Preparation of Cuttings for Treatment.—Though cuttings of many plant species root well at any time of year, best results are usually obtained during the normal, outdoor growing months. Any "wood" suitable for making cuttings by ordinary methods will give better and quicker results when treated with a growth substance, but with shrubs and trees best results may be gained with comparatively young shoots. In the northeast quarter of the United States cuttings may be made of such subjects in late May or early June; greenwood cuttings from mid June to mid July.

Convenient sizes for cuttings are from 3 to 6 in. long. When possible, cuts should be made where one year wood starts from two year old parts, but long shoots may be made into two or three cuttings.

Generally it is not necessary to remove the leaves from more than the lowest inch or two of leafy stems; never from the upper parts. Removal is merely for convenience or placing in the solution and the cutting medium.

When cuttings are to be treated with a growth substance it is not necessary to make the cuts either slanting or close to a bud as in ordinary methods. A sharp knife is not essential for making the cuts; sharp pruning shears can be used in most cases.

Cuttings, especially those which bear leaves, should be kept turgid until treated. It is best to place them in water or to cover them with a wet cloth as soon as made. Unless this is done the leaves may fall off prematurely. This will be a disadvantage to the performance of the cutting.

Treatment of Cuttings.—No one treatment can be used for all species of plants or for cuttings of both green and mature wood. After the cuttings have been prepared as just outlined they are to be stood with their lower ends from ¾ to 2 in. deep in the solution and left there for a predetermined time. This time cannot be specified here because it is influenced by the species and variety of plant, age of the cuttings, tempeɪ. ture, strength of light (never in direct sunshine), humidity of the aiɪ, number of cuttings in the receptacle, number and size of leaves, etc. In general, more solution will be taken up when the temperature is high, the air dry, and the light strong than when the air is cold and humid and the light weak. Cuttings which wilt or shrivel readily must not be exposed to direct sunshine until about ten days after they have been planted.

When taken from the solution the cuttings must have their immersed parts rinsed in water. After their removal from the solution they should be set in a rooting medium and treated according to ordinary established methods. During the growing season the rooting material should be a 50-50 mixture of clean, fairly coarse sand and granulated peat moss; during the colder months, two-thirds sand and one of peat moss. These proportions assure good drainage, aëration and retentiveness of moisture during their respective seasons.

Best results, especially with leafy herbaceous and evergreen cuttings (except geranium), are secured when the cuttings are placed in the rooting medium at an angle of about 45° with the surface so that half to two-thirds of their stems are covered. As nearly as possible, the leaves should rest on the surface of the rooting medium, even though the petioles of the lower remaining leaves may thus be more or less covered. This position encourages the development of roots, not only at the bases but relatively high up on the stems, thus assuring greater success in planting than under old processes.

Outdoors in sunny, summer weather shading, preferably with cheesecloth, for ten days or longer is advisable. Otherwise treatment ˙s the same as with ordinary methods. After roots have formed, the cuttings may be planted and treated like other rooted cuttings.

Present and Prospective Results of Treatment.—Among the advantages of treating cuttings with growth substances the following are already proved:

The necessity for bottom heat is obviated; callus forms quickly but not excessively; roots develop more quickly and over a larger area—along the stem as well as the base—than by old methods, so that smaller numbers of cuttings need be made to secure desired numbers of plants, thus saving time both in making and handling, also reducing necessary propagating and other bench space; larger numbers of roots are formed—often 20 to 40 as against 3 to 5 by old style treatments; many slow, difficult and "impossible" species are easily rooted by growth substance treatment; larger percentages of success follow treatment than from old methods.

Still further, it is possible to transplant the rooted cuttings earlier from the cutting bench to flower-pots, flats, hotbeds, coldframes and the field. Hence there are smaller losses of transplanted plants because of stronger root systems and greater resistance of the plants to outdoor conditions. As general consequences, the method reduces cost, both of overhead and of plants.

Though all this is ample reason why plant propagators should test the new method, there are prospective possibilities that promise still greater advantages. Since difficult, slow and "impossible" species root readily under the new treatment, the method suggests that in the future these subjects may thus be propagated by cuttings instead of by layering, inarching, budding and grafting. Among the advantages that seem probable of attainment in these directions are the following:

The difficulties that accompany these methods may be avoided; plants of salable size may be developed in much less time than by old methods; as the plants will be "own-rooted," shoots that spring from the bases of those whose tops have been killed back to the ground level by frost or otherwise may be allowed to grow to replace the dead tops because they will be of the same variety and not of a nondescript seedling stock; should grafting or budding be preferred, the work can be done on cutting-propagated stocks, thus assuring uniformity of stock-influence upon scion which will also assure evenness of stand, quality, yield, harvesting and grading of the plants, the flowers or the fruits.

Should the new method prove as satisfactory in these directions as seems probable it will throw into the discard all such perennial moot questions as grafting *vs.* budding, own-roots *vs.* grafted or budded stock, whole-roots *vs.* piece-roots, desirable and undesirable stocks, effects of stock upon scion, and others of their ilk. But the process of graftage will still be essential in specific cases where resistance to cold and to disease are critical problems.

FIG. 130.—Propagation in greenhouses. *Top,* cyclamen ready for sale; *middle,* geraniums by thousand in large commercial house; *bottom,* orchids on benches and in hanging pots.

VII

PROPAGATING STRUCTURES

The essential factors to consider when constructing and operating forcing structures are: (1) *light;* (2) *heat;* (3) *humidity,* (4) *water,* (5) *air,* and (6) *soil* or *other growing medium,* (7) *shade.*

Light is essential for the photosynthesis carried on by the leaves and other green parts of plants in the manufacture of food. Though means of reducing it are often necessary, the nearer its maximum is capable of being reached the better. There is such a thing as excess of light. This is overcome by various types of shading—newspapers spread over cutting benches, screens of diverse sorts, whitewash on greenhouse roofs, especially in summer. (Figs. 141 to 145X, 150)

Heat cannot be used as a substitute for light. Temperature requirements of plants vary even for the same plants at different stages of development. Soil and air temperatures should be approximately the same in most cases. The heat should be uniform. It may be supplied by the sun, by fermenting materials, or by fire and distributed by flues (warm air or the products of combustion) or by pipes (hot water and steam). Because of its cost, precautions must be taken to lose as little heat as possible.

Humidity must be controlled in the air to meet individual plant requirements.

Water is essential to all plant life, therefore adequate, controlled application is necessary, either below the surface by sub-irrigation or on the surface by watering-pot or hose. Hence the source of supply must be conveniently located. In recent years overhead irrigation by various systems has met with favor. Water should not be applied in the evening since this encourages damping-off; only in the mornings.

Air, because of its content of oxygen and carbon dioxide, is essential to all plant life so some method of ventilation should be provided. Special devices for changing and circulating air are often used. (Figs. 153, 196).

169. **Coldframes** are enclosed plots of earth usually covered with glass but without artificial heat (Figs. 132, 133). They are used: 1, as beds in which to harden off early plants started in hotbeds; 2, to start medium early and grow late vegetable and flowering plants in spring; 3, as a means by which early spring and late

FIG. 131.—Curved eave lean-to greenhouse and hotbeds attached to garage. One fire supplies heat for all.

fall crops of lettuce, radish, scallions, etc. may be brought to edible maturity; 4, for carrying over winter hardy plants like cabbage, kale and cauliflower; 5, for flowering pansies, violets, and English daisies; 6, for storing half hardy plants over winter. If not used during the winter for any of the above, they may be utilized as storage pits for celery, cauliflower, Brussels sprouts or root crops.

The coldframe is an excellent place to grow cuttings in flats to make growth previous to setting outdoors. Sand is put in shallow

FIG. 132.—Small knock-down frame for hotbed or coldframe. Larger sizes are built on same principle.

boxes or flats placed in the frames, care being taken to set them level and fit them close against one another. One advantage of flats so used is that if the cuttings do not root during summer they can be transferred to a greenhouse bench in the fall.

Ventilation for the coldframe is not as urgent as for the hotbed; but it must not be neglected. In seasonable weather seedlings must

FIG. 133.—Two styles of coldframes. 1, concrete walls around beds covered with sash on wooden frame; 2, board frames on ground for temporary use. Notice block method of ventilation.

be given as much air as possible without danger of drafts or frosts.

The plants will then gradually become hardened to outside conditions and will suffer little from transplanting. In ventilation the aim should be to keep the temperature as uniform as possible by proper manipulation of the sash.

Hotbeds differ from coldframes only in having some artificial means of heating (fermenting stable manure, fallen leaves, brewers' grains, flues, steam or hot water pipes or electric current). They are used primarily for growing plants out of season, either for transplanting or to maturity. They must be located on well drained soil, protected from north and west winds (Fig. 134). It is essential to

Fig. 134.—Hotbeds sheltered from north wind. Important in spring. Beans far in advance of season at rear.

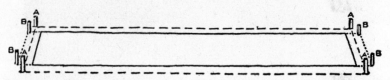

FIG. 135.—Laying out ground for hotbed. AAAA, area to be excavated; BBBB, lines between 2″ x 4″ posts, or back and front of bed.

have full southern exposure, conveniently located and near a water supply. No school that teaches agriculture should be without one, if only for demonstration of construction principles and uses. Hotbeds may be used as coldframes after fermentive heat has subsided, or by cutting off the heat from other sources.

Watering must be carefully looked after. Thorough watering at intervals gives far better results than merely moistening the plants several times daily. In the latter way only the top soil and the plants become wet and an insufficient quantity reaches the roots.

170. Transplanting.—Plants started in flats in hotbeds should be transplanted to other flats or pots or, if desired, directly into the bed. This gives each plant ample space for development and promotes stocky growth. When coldframes are used in connection with hotbeds, seedlings may be transferred to them before setting in the field. Transplanted seedlings may be checked slightly by the operation but they soon become established and produce far better plants than those left in the original seed bed.

Hotbeds in the South, and to some extent also in the North, are often made wholly above ground; i.e., without any pit. The quantity of manure must be greater for a given locality than when a pit is used because of loss of heat at the sides of the pile. Depth of pit,

FIG. 136.—Making permanent hotbed frame. Concrete to be poured in trenches without forms below ground, except on inside, but raised to proper height above surface. After concrete sets earth will be removed, mostly by power scoop but finished by hand and concrete end walls and wooden superstructure added.

manure and whether a pit shall or shall not be used depend upon the climate and the season when the bed is made.

Although the hotbed may not be required until February or March, it is advisable to have the pit made and the sash in position well ahead of time. The depth of the pit may vary with the climate from 1½′ to 3″ deep.

171. Hotbed making. (Figs. 135 to 139.) In making a hotbed a pit 1′ to 2′ deep, 6′ wide and any desired length (preferably a mul-

Fig. 137.—Wooden frame, four-sash hotbed set on cedar posts.

tiple of 3′, because standard hotbed sashes are 3′ X 6′) is excavated and filled with the freshest possible horse manure that has not been exposed to the weather. For most satisfactory results it requires careful handling. It must be neither too compact nor too loose Two parts of solid excrement to one of litter is a good proportion. Manure which contains shavings should not be used.

The manure is taken fresh from the stable during winter or early spring and placed in a flat-topped pile 5′ high of any length and width desired. If dry, it should be moistened so as to start fermentation. Ordinarily it will begin to steam in two or three days. When fermentation is well under way it should be turned so the interior will form the exterior of the new pile to insure uniform heating. After three or four days more the entire mass will be ready for the pit. The time between piling and pitting is usually 10 or 12 days, so preparation should begin about two weeks before time for making the bed.

It is desirable to cover the bottom of the pit with several inches of straw or litter before putting in the manure to save heat (Figs. 138,

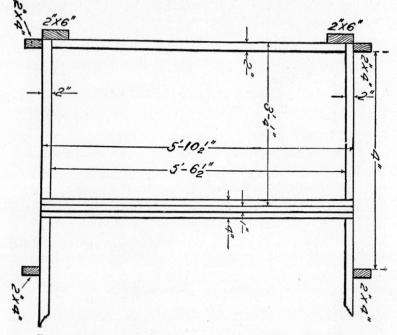

FIG. 138.—Cross section construction details of wooden frame hotbed.

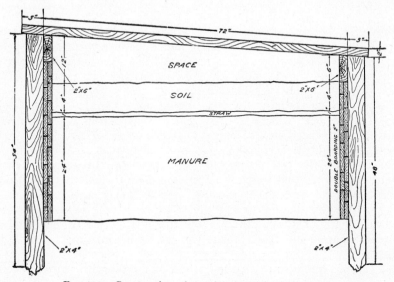

FIG. 139.—Construction of wooden frame hotbed corner.

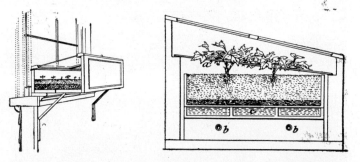

Fig. 140.—Propagation beds. A, pipe-warmed hotbed; B, window frame
bed for cuttings and seedlings.

139). The manure is then thrown in successive layers of 5″ to 6″
and tramped firmly especially in the corners and around the edges.
Allowance must be made for settling 3″ to 5″ or 6″.

A layer of less than 6″ in the bed will usually give poor results;
12″ to 18″ are the usual depths. Then a layer of say 4″ of good
friable soil, (sand if for cuttings), is placed on the manure and lastly
a surface inch or so of fibrous compost, which because of its content
of thoroughly rotted manure, grass roots, etc., will bake but little
after watering. Sifted loam or compost should be used for the seed
bed. After the sash are put on the frames the temperature should
be allowed to rise high. When this heat subsides seeds may be sown.
During the violent heating period ventilation should be given. Banking around the outside aids in retaining heat.

The pit well filled and packed is then ready for the soil. If the
bed is to be used for flats or pots, 2″ of soil will be sufficient, but if
to be used for a seed bed, 4″ to 6″ will be necessary. In the latter

Fig. 141.—Frames for homemaking straw mats. Nursery and greenhouse supply houses make mats by machine.

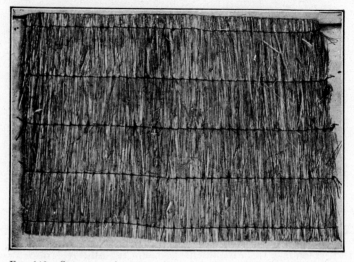

FIG. 142.—Straw mat for protecting coldframes and hotbeds from cold.

case, good soil consisting of one-third well-rotted manure and two-thirds good garden loam should be used.

The hotbed will heat vigorously for about three days and the temperature may rise to 125° F. After this it will gradually cool to about 90° after which seed sowing may start. Seed should be sown thinly in drills 4″ to 6″ apart, across the bed from front to back. Plants which do not transplant easily should be sown in flats or seed boxes. Whether sown directly in the hotbed or in flats, the seed should be sown in soil sufficiently moist to germinate them.

After sowing small seeds, flats or beds, cheesecloth should be laid on them and water sprinkled through it to prevent washing out the seed and also to provide favorable conditions for prompt germination. It is important, however, to remove the cloth promptly when germination begins and to repeat when necessary until the plants are growing well.

FIG. 143.—Shutters for placing over mats on hotbeds and coldframes. Positions of cleats favor easy piling, good ventilation and quick drying.

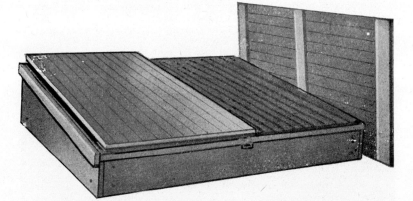

FIG. 144. Hotbed protected from cold by burlap pad mats and shutters.

172. Substitutes for glass.[1]—Paraffin cloth and celluloid as substitutes for glass in hotbed and coldframe sash have been on the market for several years with many claims for their durability, strength, resistance to weather, economy and effect upon plant growth. To test the various materials six manufacturers supplied their product for comparison with glass. Ten vegetable crops of various types were grown during the seedling stage by Donald Comin and Walter Sherman who summarize the results of two year's work as follows:

Glass, as a hotbed sash material, was superior to its substitutes for the raising of most vegetable plants, parsley being an exception. The stunting effect of the substitutes was overcome after the plants were set in the field in the case

[1] *The Bimonthly Bulletin*, Ohio Exp. Sta., 144, May-June, 1930.

FIG. 145.—Machine-made lath shade for reducing light over coldframes and hot beds.

of tomatoes and peppers. Cabbage produced greater early, as well as total, yields when the seedlings were grown under glass.

The screen-base materials were far superior to the cloth-base materials in growing seedlings for outdoor planting.

Temperature under the various materials used in the test was rather uniform and was not considered an important factor in this comparison.

The glass substitutes are lighter, thus easier to handle; this is their only proved advantage over glass. The cloth-base materials are somewhat cheaper than glass or screen-base materials but are inferior in all other respects. Their

FIG. 145x.—Permanent lath shade to reduce sunlight on plants that grow best in partial shadow.

short life makes them actually less economical than any of the other materials. The screen-base substitutes are far superior to the cloth-base materials for growing seedlings. At present their cost is prohibitive. There is evidence that the manufacturers of screen-base materials have greatly improved their product of late. With a further reduction in their cost, these materials may replace glass to a greater extent than is warranted at present.

At present the glass substitutes can only be recommended where ease of handling is of first importance, although in the case of the screen-base materials, their resistance to breakage and heat-insulation properties may further justify their use.

173. Ventilation is one of the most important items in hotbed management. If not properly ventilated poor results are sure to follow. Oxygen supply and temperature are largely controlled by ventilation. Experience alone can teach the times when ventilation is necessary. However, general principles will help to guide. Plants that require warmth (tomato, pepper, cucumber) do best at about 75° F. during the day; lettuce, radish, onion, cauliflower and others do better at 55° to 65°. Though it is not satisfactory to grow both

FIG. 146.—Electric heat. A, *left*, double wired hotbed with cable 6″ apart directly on subsoil; *right*, cable covered with galvanized hardware cloth to protect it from digging tools; thermostat at back; B, similarly heated cutting bench, thermostat outside; C, heating cable supported on screw hooks on side walls of coldframe.

kinds of plants in the same bed it can be done by having partitions.

Ventilation may be obtained by sliding the sash up or down or by propping them up at one end or side. The plants should be kept out of drafts by lifting the end or side of the sash away from the direction the wind is blowing. Drafts are detrimental to plant growth. As the weather moderates more ventilation may be given (Fig. 146 to 148, 153, 200).

173A. Electricity [1] is being used by annually increasing numbers of plant producers to heat propagating benches, hotbeds, coldframes, and even greenhouses. Merits claimed for it in propagating benches are: 1, Automatic control of heat for each bed; 2, labor saving; 3, 10% to 50% increase in rooting of cuttings; 4, increase of percentage of seeds germinated; 5, 10% to 25% reduction of time necessary to root cuttings or start seedlings; 6, more vigorous plants due to continuous natural growth; 7, feasibility of summer and autumn propagation; 8, saving in cost as compared with that of steam or hot water; 9, convenience.

It is not possible to maintain uniform heat in the soil or the air of a cutting bench or a hotbed during the daytime when the sun is shining, though the minimum temperature can be regulated and uniform temperatures can also be maintained where the bed is not influenced by a surrounding atmosphere or the sun's rays, which heat the bed higher than the point at which the thermostat is set.

When compared with manure as a source of heat for hotbeds electricity obviates the necessity of making new beds each year, insures propagation during autumn when maximum heat is needed at the end of the growing season, (whereas manure loses its value in four to six weeks) and it eliminates the trouble, expense and labor of procuring and handling manure.

In coldframes its chief use has been to protect plants from possible injury during cold snaps, more especially at night, but it also permits early sowing and development of plants.

In greenhouses not otherwise heated experimental installations in New York and California have been used to raise the temperature 17° to 22° F. above that of the outside air during occasional cold spells. In these cases the cost of installation was much less than that for steam or hot water, operating costs compared favorably, labor of firing was eliminated and control was automatic when desired.

Installation in propagating benches and hotbeds (Figs. 146, 147, 185) is with flexible, lead covered heating wires made specially to protect the heating elements from contact with the soil. The wires are usually protected from damage from digging tools by galvanized

---

[1] Paragraphs *in re* electricity are compiled from Reports 5 and 6 of the *National Rural Electric Project*, College Park, Maryland.

hardware cloth (wire netting) placed in the soil (or other cutting medium) above them. Control of the temperature may be manual but preferably automatic by thermostat because this eliminates labor and responsibility, assures uniform temperature and probably considerable saving of current, particularly in mild weather.

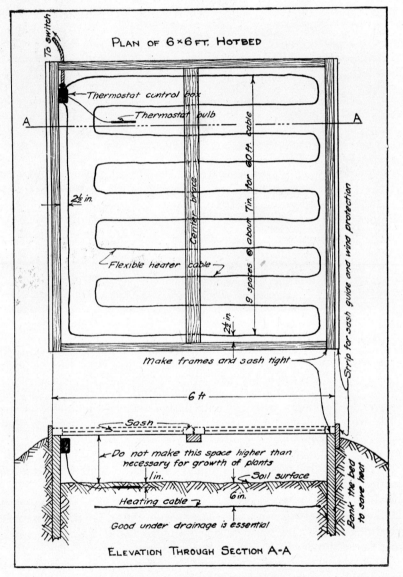

Fig. 147.—Layout of electrically heated hotbed.

Another method extensively used is to place an oven type of heater in a housed-in compartment immediately beneath the bench (Fig. 148). Heaters of this type consist of uninsulated resistance wire supported on insulators on a metal framework.

A third system is through the use of flat plate heaters about 30″

Fig. 148.—Heating element being placed in compartment beneath cutting bench. Hinged doors make it easily accessible. Heavy corrugated galvanized iron bottoms in benches support sand well and transmit heat better than boards. Ends of corrugations left open for drainage. Operating costs are reduced by tightly built heating compartments beneath benches.

square and covered with galvanized sheet steel (Fig. 149). Complete with a thermostat for heat control these heaters are especially adapted for placing on a bench under flats in which plants are grown.

Heat may be controlled automatically by placing a thermostat in the heating circuit with the bulb in the sand or the soil. Once installed and set the minimum temperature is held automatically at the point desired without further attention. Thermostats most used at present turn the heat on and off within a 5° range; others may be secured which will regulate more accurately.

174. Horizontal brick or tile flues which carry the gases of fires beneath a hotbed are used for propagating sweet potato plants

(Fig. 73) in Delaware, Maryland and more southern states but are obsolete in greenhouse heating.

Hot water and steam in iron pipes are by far the most popular commercial methods of heating because of their ready adaptability to any sized greenhouse. (Figs. 140, 155).

Air and heat are often confined above the cutting bed by means of glass sash over hotbed-like frames on the greenhouse benches (Fig. 44). When necessary to intensify the heat the space beneath

Fig. 149.—Galvanized iron unit placed on top of bench, thermostat inclosed in it.

the bench is walled in tightly to confine it. In a small way bell glasses and similar utensils (Fig. 45) are placed over seeds, seedlings or cuttings on the benches or merely over a soup plate or a saucer filled with sand which covers the cuttings. Sun heat alone is often used in such cases.

174A. Propagating ovens are sometimes used for small lots of seeds or cuttings, as in schools where teaching the principles of plant culture rather than commercial work is the aim, where the room temperature falls low at night and where there are no greenhouse facilities (Fig. 17x).

They are generally heated by lamps and are usually more or less insulated boxes with only three to five cubic feet content. In the bottom is a chamber for a kerosene lamp reached by a door for filling and other attention. Above the lamp is a galvanized iron water tray and above this a perforated floor. Next above is the sand tray in which the cuttings are placed for propagation. The cover is of glass. By means of the lamp the water is made to give off vapor which keeps sand and air above it warm and moist. Regulation of the size of flame and ventilators controls both temperature and humidity.

175. Bottom and air heat effects.—All growth in plants results from a stimulus of some kind. Various agents may bring it about; for instance, ether vapor. However, so far as the commercial plant propagator is concerned heat is the most important one. For though

Fig. 149x. Work in propagating frames. *Top,* forking soil by hand is usually necessary because beds are too narrow for horses or garden tractors; *middle,* right and wrong method of weeding, man on right has his foot in bed; *bottom,* potted plants in cold frame being weeded.

Fig. 150. Types of temporary shade. A, cheesecloth supported on framework and held down by cords; B, lath sections laid on framework; C, newspapers (inferior to cheesecloth) laid on propagating beds in greenhouse. Notice burlap curtains beneath bed to provide bottom heat.

all these agents produce the same effect (arousing the activity of enzymes or ferments, chemically or physically, to change and make available the stored plant food, especially that near the buds) heat is the most active, most normal and most easily and economically applied.   Therefore, the plant grower, while interested in the ab-normal agents, applies heat under proper control to secure a healthy growth where he knows it is needed first of all—the parts where roots are expected to form.

Fig. 151. General purpose type greenhouse for amateur place.

Cuttings after being set in the propagating bed always begin to grow at the part most favorably placed as to temperature.   That is, if a stem cutting be placed so its upper end is in an air temperature appreciably higher than that of the soil, growth will begin in the upper buds.   With no cuttings is this so apparent as with those of immature wood grown in a greenhouse.   When bottom heat is lacking and the air warmed, even only by sun heat, the buds expand into new stems and leaves; but few or usually no roots are produced.   Such conditions must be avoided, because the reverse is necessary to root making, which should always, except perhaps with tuber and root cuttings, precede growth of stem and leaf.

The philosophy of this is apparent; for when growth starts, the foods stored in the plant are moved rapidly to the part that has become active.   Hence if the part be above ground all the food goes there; in fact, is removed from the part that should form roots. Result, breakdown and death.   Conversely, if the air be cool and the soil sufficiently warm from start to finish the cuttings soon develop calluses and roots upon which top growth normally depends. Hence such conditions should be maintained, because if cuttings are properly planted growth will occur only below ground, where it should be.

When once the roots have begun to grow below ground plant food materials can be taken up by the roots and transferred to the parts above ground. As soon as green matter has been developed

FIG. 152. Small greenhouse suited to beginners and small places.

by the expanding buds (already present in greenwood and leaf cuttings) it can work over the crude food in the presence of sunlight and the full functions of plant growth will have started properly above and below ground.

Mature wood cuttings can stand greater hardships in propagating before making roots than can immature wood cuttings, because they contain considerable stored food, but even they should not be started in warm air and cool soil. With greenwood cuttings, root growth must always precede leaf and stem growth or death will almost always result.

176. A greenhouse is a glass house devoted to the protection and cultivation of plants. In America the term is used for any glass house irrespective of its temperature; in England it is restricted to a house containing plants that require little or no artificial heat. In America a greenhouse is thought of as heated unless otherwise stated (Figs. 131, 151, 152).

Locations for greenhouses should be such that south, east, and west sun rays are not cut off, not shaded, because sunshine is essential for growth of plants. The house should be protected from winds as much as is possible without shading. If a lean-to type is erected against another structure or a wall, the wall or building should run east and west. An even span house in the same case should run north and south, with its north end against the other structure. Level but well drained ground is usually most desirable but extra hours of sunlight at both ends of the day may be secured by having the house on a south, southeast or southwest slope.

Factors to consider in locating commercial greenhouses are: 1, Fuel supply; 2, labor; 3, marketing facilities; 4, soil and 5, water. Large amounts of coal or oil are necessary to maintain heat, so greenhouses located where cheap fuel can be obtained have a distinct advantage over those less fortunately situated. A large plant should be situated either on a canal or a railroad so fuel can be placed in the boiler room without expensive handling. The weight of fuel used to produce a crop is often greater than the crop itself; therefore it may be advisable to ship the product some distance rather than ship the fuel an equal or greater distance.

In the greenhouse industry an abundance of specially trained labor is essential since every square foot of greenhouse soil must be intensively worked and the amount of waste space reduced to a minimum. Each acre of glass will readily furnish employment throughout the year for at least two men, usually more. Help can soon be trained to perform work satisfactorily.

Nearness to market is desirable in many ways but this need not be a deciding factor. It may be better to build the greenhouses where cheap land, and plenty of labor can be had, provided good shipping facilities are available; but it is essential that the crop be placed on the market in the shortest practicable time so the location must be where the product can be moved by truck, fast express or other means to meet this end. It is desirable but not essential to locate on good soil since such soil can soon be developed. A loam is preferred for most purposes.

Large quantities of water are required for greenhouse plants so an ample supply must be assured at all times. City water is usually best for small enterprises; for large ones maintaining one's own pumping plant may be more economical.

177. **Types of greenhouses and construction materials.**— Greenhouses of many types are adapted for various purposes. The more standard types are : 1, Lean-to, 2, uneven span, 3, even span, 4, curvilinear, 5, curved eave, and 6, attached or ridge and furrow houses (Figs. 131, 151, 152, 153, 154, 155, 156x).

Construction and Device. The frame construction of greenhouses varies from all wood, semi-iron, to all iron frame and from home construction to contract built.

Pitch of Roof. The degree of slant should be theoretically to allow the greatest amount of sunlight to enter through the glass during the shortest day of the year, December 21. This is not practical for construction reasons. It would require the roof to be set at a pitch of 65° for the sun rays to strike the glass at an angle of 90°. This would make the roof too high for practical purposes. Even though there is a loss of 15% of total possible light, 35° is

Fig. 153.—Side ventilators hung from eaves and operated by wheel, worm-screw gear and shafting.

more practical. For houses 25′ wide a pitch of 32° to 35° is recommended; for wider houses the angle must be reduced even more to economize construction costs.

The long span of an uneven span house should face south and have a pitch of 26° to 35°. The short span facing the north should have a pitch of 40° to 50°. For a 32° pitch the rise should be 7½″ to the horizontal foot; For 26° a 6″ rise.

Partitions. Since it will be found necessary to provide various conditions of humidity, temperature and moisture for different plants, it may be advisable to make separate compartments. A better plan is to grow plants that require different growing conditions in houses of their own.

Ventilation is essential to provide a fresh supply of air and move the air to the various parts of the house. But plants suffer from drafts as well as lack of air so ventilators must aid in equalizing temperature as well as air circulation. They may be opened wide on hot days of summer and raised or lowered as the case may be on days of alternating cloudiness and sunshine.

Ridge ventilators are essential because warm air rises. To facilitate circulation they should open at the top. Cold air entering the house through chinks between glass panes, doors, etc., and without making drafts, goes to the floor, is heated and then rises to the top of the house.

Hinged sash ventilators placed across the sash bars can be opened to any desired degree (Figs. 200, 201). The ventilators should be on both sides of the ridge in houses 30' wide or wider so the one on the lee side of the wind may be opened. On smaller houses, one ridge ventilator placed on the south side is sufficient. Only ridge ventilators are used during the winter.

Ventilators hinged to the eaves plates (Fig. 153) are desirable in the side walls as well as at the ridge even though commercial houses often lack them and though they are best in houses with no side benches. They should be used during warm weather of spring, summer and fall.

Glass. Clear American window glass strength B is usually used, the standard size glass being 16″ wide and either 18″ or 24″ long. The joints are lapped $\frac{1}{8}$″ and spaced the 16″ way between bars. A claim is made that 16″ by 18″ glass breaks less easily than glass 16″ by 24″; but such a roof is not as tight due to more laps.

Sash bars allow for the glass being 1-16″ between glassing channels. Before glazing those panes slightly curved should be sorted into rights and lefts so the glass may be placed with the curves up and thus make the joints tight at the laps. Thus the condensation of water on the inside will run to the bars and be carried to the eaves in the drip grooves in the roof bars.

In glazing, the putty is rolled out in the rabbet of the sash bars and the glass is pressed down upon it, thus sealing the glass to the bars. Then the excess putty is scraped off. Glazing nails ($\frac{5}{8}$″) are used to secure the glass in place. One is placed directly below the lower edge on each side to keep the pane from slipping down, one on each side about 2″ from the lower end of the pane and one on each side at about the middle, six nails for each pane.

Painting. Before the woodwork leaves the factory it should be given a primary coat of pure linseed oil with a little white lead. As soon as erected and before glazing the entire frame should be painted inside and out. A good painting combination is a mixture of pure white lead, linseed oil and zinc oxide with a little turpentine drier. Another coat should be applied after glazing, taking care to seal all openings in the wood and cracks between the glass and the sash bars and to avoid painting more than $\frac{1}{8}$″ of the edges of the glass.

Wooden greenhouses require painting of the inside because conditions there favor decay and because of the excessive contraction and expansion outside due to differences in temperature.

On iron work, red lead paint is best for the first coat. This should be put on at the factory before shipment. White lead may be used over this as the second coat after the frame is up. One or two coats of white lead may be applied over the red lead.

Fig. 154.—Tile bottomed greenhouse bench, one of the best styles because so well drained and so durable. The flat, thin, hollow unglazed tile rest on T-iron supports.

Side walls are best made of concrete although boards may be used. Considerable strength is required because a heavy structure is to be supported.

Greenhouse benches are expensive to install, so unless the best materials are used they are short lived. Those of durable construction with pipe legs and cast-iron supports and bottoms, with iron frame and tile bottom (Fig. 154) or of concrete, are durable but their cost is high. Wooden benches are fairly satisfactory if made of cypress, redwood or other wood that resists decay when wet. Even so they must be replaced every three to five years. Wooden bench legs should not touch the soil but rest on stone, concrete or brick piers.

Benches are usually placed around the side walls. At present the tendency is to dispense with them. Growers find it possible to raise many crops in ground beds, so in modern greenhouses, especially vegetable houses, only enough space is given to walks to facilitate handling crops.

For such crops as roses and carnations, it is desirable to have the plants above the walks so they may be easily handled. This is often accomplished by either depressing the walks or by putting concrete curbs 2′ or 3′ high along the sides of the walks and filling the beds with soil. The same results can be obtained by using boards along the walks, but such an arrangement is more or less temporary.

Greenhouse walks may be of any suitable material (cinders, brick, or earth). Concrete walks, often used, serve as satisfactory

Fig. 155.—Ideal propagating house with 30″ center and 24″ side walks. Beds are 4′ wide and 3′ from ground. Heating pipes being closed to maintain any desired temperatures.

tracks for trucks and wheelbarrows used in handling material. As little space as convenience permits should be devoted to walks, since it costs as much to heat walk areas as that of crops. (Fig. 156.)

Shading. Whitewash applied with a brush is one method of shading greenhouses during summer. Much of this will be removed by the weather before winter. If not, it must be scrubbed off. White lead or whiting in gasoline in a thin preparation is perhaps the best shading material. It is put on with a tree spray outfit or a hand operated spray barrel, hose and nozzle. Usually it is desirable to apply a thin coating early in spring and add a second in May or June. Any remnants may be rubbed off with a stiff brush while applying water from a hose.

178. Plants grown in greenhouses may be divided into three groups: 1, Fruits—strawberry, grape, peach, plum, fig, pineapple, loquat, pear, nectarine, none of which are of commercial importance in America but are almost wholly amateur; 2, vegetables—tomato, cucumber, lettuce, parsley, cauliflower, rhubarb, cantaloupe, asparagus, radish, pepper, bean, eggplant, spinach, onion sets, carrot, beet —the first three of which are grown extensively for market, one tomato establishment of which the authors know having forty acres

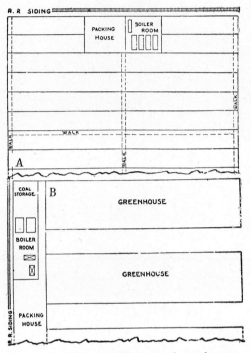

Fig. 156.—Good lay-out of greenhouses.

under glass; 3, ornamentals—rose, carnation, chrysanthemum, violet, cyclamen, tulip, narcissus, hyacinth, smilax, fern and sprenger asparagus, stevia, palms, begonia, vinca, azalea, primula, poinsettia, impatiens, ferns, orchids, cacti and many others of commercial importance during winter also a great variety of bedding and other ornamental plants for summer use; for instance, geranium, coleus, celosia, "achyranthes" (*Iresine*), acalypha, alternanthera, fuchsia, petunia, verbena, zinnia, and countless others.

179. **Unheated or cold greenhouses** may combine the joy of the open garden and to some extent the pleasure of the hothouse. They have no fixed heating apparatus but are intended to prevent the temperature falling below 35°F. The principle is to keep them cool enough for plants of the temperate regions. Since the mere

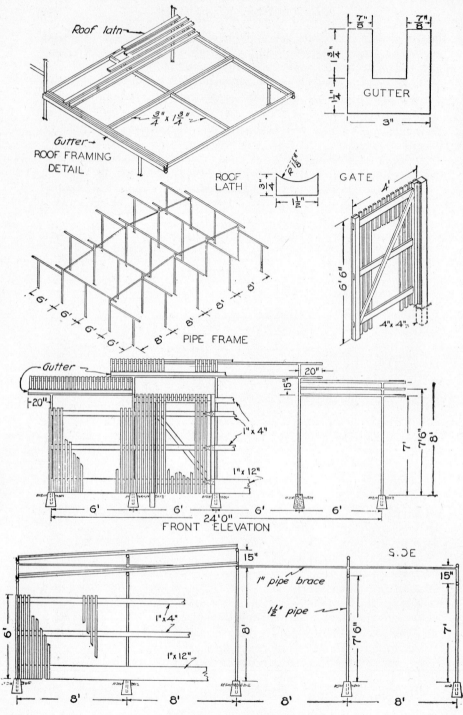

Roof lath

ROOF FRAMING DETAIL

$\frac{3}{4}'' \times 1\frac{3}{4}''$

Gutter

GUTTER

$\frac{7}{8}''$ $\frac{7}{8}''$

$1\frac{3}{4}''$

$1\frac{1}{4}''$

3''

ROOF LATH

$R 1\frac{1}{8}''$

$\frac{3}{4}''$

$1\frac{1}{2}''$

GATE

4'

6' 6'

4'' x 4''

PIPE FRAME

6'   6'   6'   6'   6'

8'   8'   8'

Gutter

20''

15''

20''

1'' x 4''

1'' x 12''

7'

7' 6''

8'

6'   6'   6'   6'

24' 0''

FRONT ELEVATION

SIDE

15''

1'' pipe brace

1½' pipe

15''

1'' x 4''

1'' x 12''

6'

8'

7' 6''

7'

8'   8'   8'   8'

Fig. 156x.—Lath house.

shelter of glass will not keep out severe frost, some means of raising the temperature are not forbidden; but in a general way, artificial heat is undesirable.

Such greenhouses are too slow for the professional gardener who is interested in turning out plants wholesale. But for the man who operates for pleasure and who is not interested in profits they have their place. Pests do not thrive in them to the same extent as in heated houses.

Types of cold houses may be classed as 1, glass gardens; 2, garden corridors; 3, conservatories; 4, even span and lean-to.

The glass garden is really a place adapted to permanent planting of shrubs and climbers. It usually contains plants which make a

Fig. 157.—Vegetables grown under glass. A, cucumbers inter-cropped with lettuce; B, tomatoes trained on light stakes attached to roof bars.

garden under glass, largely for the winter protection of flowering shrubs which live and flower in sheltered positions and favored climates. If conditions are such that the temperature falls below 35° only hardy forms must be used.

The conservatory often adjoins the dwelling and is a place where plants, usually developed elsewhere, are placed when in flower to be seen and admired.

The garden corridor may take the form of a lean-to passageway connecting garden structures or it may be an outlying room of a dwelling. Here should be specimens of the rarer flowering shrubs which do best trained against walls. Hardy climbers such as the finer kinds of clematis and jasmine, ivy and other vines, tea roses, agapanthus, crinum and others which lend themselves to tub and large pottery receptacles.

The working greenhouse may be placed in some corner of the garden. It should have a front bench and some sort of stage. It is a nursery for young plants, a recruiting place or one of storage, not a show place but a work house. In it may be germinating seeds, spores in process of fern production, flowering plants on the way to the conservatory, etc. (Fig. 151).

VIII

POTTING

180. Growth requirements of plants.—To make best development, plants need proper texture of soil as well as moisture, warmth and food. Fundamentally texture depends upon the size of the inorganic soil particles (sand, clay). Most plants grow poorly in a mixture of pure sand and pure clay. The former usually is infertile, the latter is hard to handle. They both become valuable by the addition of vegetable matter. In nature both light (sandy) and heavy (clay) loams occur, often near together.

For potting and bench work in greenhouses and nurseries texture must be varied to meet the needs of specific plants. Soil must be light and friable so as to handle easily, drain readily and without crusting and baking after being wetted. It should also be fertile in proportion to the needs of the plants to be grown in it—rich for some, poor for others. Also its friability must vary; for ferns looser than for roses.

When pure sand or sifted coal ashes are added to pure clay the resulting mixture will be "lighter" but less fertile than the clay alone because these materials are deficient in plant food and therefore dilute the quantity contained in the clay. When sandy and clayey loams are mixed the resulting blend is better than either of its components; the sandy loam becomes richer and holds more moisture and the clay loam becomes more open and penetrable and its plant food more available in consequence.

Mixing natural light and heavy loams is often not sufficient for indoor work. The water-holding capacity of the soil must be increased, especially for use in small flower pots. Sifted coal ashes accomplish this. They also lighten the texture and admit more air, which in reasonable amount is necessary to roots as well as foliage. But they add inconsequential quantities of plant food. More satisfactory ways to lighten heavy soils are to apply lime, manure, leaf mold or peat. Lime flocculates the clay particles combining several small particles into one larger particle thus giving a desirable crumb structure, and keeping them apart. It also sets free plant food held in humus (or organic matter—animal and vegetable remains in the soil). The particles of manure, leaf mold and peat in these potting soils hold an appreciable amount of water and when they decay yield

Fig. 158.—Potting soil mixed and sifted by machine under cover ready for use.

their plant food to the new plants. Decaying sod is another important source of vegetable matter in potting soil. Mixing these materials thoroughly and screening are essential (Figs. 159, 160).

181. Soil Mixing.—The two most popular ways of mixing soil are by means of the soil shredder and the compost pile. The shredder is either a hand or power machine (Figs. 158 to 163) which more quickly and efficiently breaks up, mixes and sifts soil and manure than can be done in large quantity by shovel alone. The rough materials are shoveled or forked into the hopper whence they pass to and are thrust against a revolving cylinder whose teeth tear it apart and dump it out in a loose pile or sift it ready for use.

The compost pile is made as follows: In spring after grass has begun to grow well, remove sod from an old grass pasture or greenhouse sodding field where the soil itself is rich and deep. For convenience in handling, cut the sod in strips a foot or so wide, 3" thick and as long as can be easily handled either in rectangles or in rolls,

Fig. 159.—Mason's seive with ½" mesh to remove stones and other debris.

the latter perhaps preferred. Spread the sods close together on the ground in a layer, grass side down, on a well-drained space adjacent to the greenhouse. Convenient widths are 6' to 10'. On this layer place 2" or 3" of well-rotted manure and sprinkle pulverized lime on it—say, about a pound to the square yard. Repeat alternate layers of sod, manure and lime dust until a pile 3' to 5' or 6' high with sloping sides and of any desired length has been

made. It is an advantage to make
the top concave, so it will hold
water when needed in dry weather.

The pile should stand thus for
two years or longer before being
used. Then it may be treated in
either of two ways: In a small way
sliced with a sharp spade vertically from top to bottom and mixed
thoroughly by throwing in a heap
as slicing proceeds, at the same

FIG. 160.—Hand seives with ¼″ or
finer mesh for fine work with seedlings.

time, adding enough sand to be plainly visible on the pile, then
screened. On a commercial scale a soil shredder is more satisfactory.

Commercial greenhouse men cannot usually afford so expensive
a soil as this because of the cost of the turf and the loam—often
$100 to $200 an acre for the surface 3″ or 4″. They, therefore, use
a rich garden loam with liberal quantities of compost and sand
(Practicum XXIV).

For houses where little of the earth is sold with the plants the
soil is returned to the field after being used in the greenhouse and
there liberally fertilized and made to grow crops of clover, rye, buckwheat and grass, each crop plowed under to put vegetable matter
back in the soil for its next journey to the greenhouse. In such cases
the soil is generally run through a soil shredder before it is used.

FIG. 161.—Hand operated soil shredder.

Thus the soil area actually becomes richer and more friable
from year to year.

182. Flower pots are of
three principal kinds; those with
and those without rims. (Third
style described in 182A). They
range in ½″ sizes between 2″
and 7″, and in 1″ sizes between
7″ and 12″. Between 2″ and
2½″ is a 2¼″ size. There are
also 14″, 16″, and 18″ sizes, but
tubs and boxes are usually more
satisfactory and less expensive in
these and larger ones. Sizes below 16″ are machine made in
"standard" form. Below the 2″
size are "thumbs" used for tiny
plants.

Azalea or "three-fourth" pots (as to height) are most useful for growing ferns, azaleas and other house plants, lilies and many other bulbs. They afford ample soil and root room, are not as unsightly as full-sized flower pots of the same width. Their "low down" effect is more pleasing to the eye than is that of the tall pot.

"Seed pans" are earthenware trays usually 1" to 2" deep. They are most largely used for growing ferns, seedlings of small-seeded plants, etc. For this purpose they excel pots.

The rimmed or "standard" pots (Fig. 164), though easier to grasp are harder on the hands than are those without collars when large numbers must be handled in a day, yet they are so popular that the old style collarless ones are almost a curiosity. When to be first used, unglazed pots should be soaked in water for an hour or more and the surface water then allowed to evaporate. The pores of the pottery must be filled with water but the surface must not be wet when plants are set in them.

182A. New style flower pot. In 1931, A. H. Hews and Company, originators of the standard flower pot, introduced a new style

Fig. 162.—Gasolene or electrically operated soil shredder. Wheelbarrow may be placed beneath hopper.

Fig. 163.—Large capacity gasolene or electrically operated soil shredder with double screen attachment.

of pot (Fig. 164) which is a great improvement over its predecessors. Instead of the shoulder which characterizes the standard style and which becomes rough from chipping the new pot has a thicker edge which increases strength. The bottom is also reinforced by an "inside shoulder" which prevents wedging and reduces breakage when the pots are struck on the bench as in potting. In addition to the increased strength and handling without wounding the fingers is the feasibility of molding the pots in beautiful forms thus making them help in the retail sales of plants because of their attractiveness. Sizes are listed as numbers, 5, 6, 7, 8, and 9 which correspond to standard 4″, 5″, 6″, 7″ and 8″ but are shallower and wider; a number 6, for instance corresponding to a 5″ standard.

FIG. 164.—*Left,* Standard Pot; *Right,* "Hews" New Style Pot.

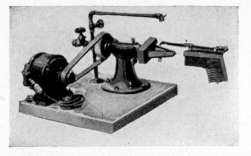

FIG. 165.—Pot washing machine operated by electric motor.

183. Pot washing in the past with stiff brushes was a job assigned to apprentices. It was costly because of the time required and the breakage due to rough handling. Later the work was lightened by soaking the pots in dilute sulphuric acid over night, but even so it was still tedious and expensive for the same reasons. Hence in many greenhouses and nurseries old and dirty pots were either worked off in sales or discarded because the cost of washing was too near that of new pots to make washing pay.

Since the introduction of the electrically operated pot washer (Fig. 165) these wasteful practices have been largely abandoned because unskilled labor can thoroughly clean as many as 1,000 pots an hour without risk of breakage. As the machine revolves, streams of water inside and outside carry away the dirt, fungus and algæ and leave the pots clean.

184. Containers other than pottery.—A direct relationship exists between plant growth and the container material as proved by Knott and Jeffries.[1] Pulp and paper are attacked by decomposing organisms thus causing inferior growth. New clay pots are inferior to used pots apparently because of absorption of nitrates. As remedies or preventives the authors suggest treating paper and pulp pots with asphalt, wax, or other chemicals not harmful to plant growth so as to reduce the rate of decomposition. They also suggest that when plants in any container turn yellow or become stunted, liquid manure or dissolved nitrates will correct the trouble.

Peat flower pots failed to show any advantage as measured in growth[2] of tomato plants over the old fashioned clay pot; in

FIG. 165x. Tomato plants in paper and earthenware pots. Former readily rot so may be left around plants when transplanted.

[1] *Penn. Sta. Bul.* 244.
[2] *Market Growers' Jl.*, 42.

fact, under comparable treatments the clay pots were significantly superior. Since peat pots cost nearly as much as clay pots of the same sizes and are good for but one season, J. E. Knott, who conducted the test, questions their value in plant propagation.

Fibre pots *vs.* clay pots for growing vegetable plants showed but little difference where both were plunged into soil. With tomatoes more early fruit was harvested from clay pot plants suggesting that these become re-established more readily than the others.[1]

FIG. 166.—Proof of non-porosity to air in moist clay flower pot. A, rubber suction disc fell from dry pot in a few seconds; B, disc adhered to moist pot for weeks.

185. Standard porous pots,[2] with drainage holes in the bottoms, are generally used for plants grown in containers. With a good potting soil, proper temperature, water and sufficient light, the attendant in the greenhouse knows he can produce good plants in such pots. When these same plants with their containers are removed to the rooms where man works and dwells, experience indicates that they will lose their luxuriance and may even die.

Among the excuses for failure to grow house plants may be mentioned the dryness of the air, the presence of coal gas, and a natural lack of sympathetic understanding with the plants. The paramount picture of household plants is the success of the poor people with their tin-can containers. To all appearances these people have disobeyed all the rules of culture in that the non-porous containers with

---

[1] *Ia. Sta. Rpt., 1930.*
[2] Linus H. Jones, *Mass. Exp. Sta. Bul. 277, October, 1931.*

inadequate drainage are in kitchens with a great range of temperature, where coal gas is frequently present, and where the sunlight is often of short duration. At the conclusion of experiments to test the merits of several types of plant containers, the investigator writes:

An investigation has been made of the effect of flower pot composition on plant growth. Flower pots are either porous or nonporous. This character of porosity in any pot determines the cultural practice to be followed for good growth. The porous pot,

FIG. 167.—Outdoor pot bins convenient to coldframes and hotbeds.

because of its evaporating surface, allows soil to dry out unless a means is provided for the pot itself to take up moisture from some outside source.

The porous pot, when dry, can absorb one-half the normal daily application of water given to 3″, 4″, 5″, and 6″ sizes, and one-third the amount given to a 7″ pot. The evaporation of moisture from the outside surface of the pot has a cooling effect on the soil; but this cooling has no effect on plant growth. About twice as much water is lost from a porous pot by evaporation as from a non-porous pot in the same time. (Fig. 166.)

The relative humidity of houses and offices is so low during the heating months that the evaporating power of the air frequently dries out the lower half of the mass of soil in a clay or porous pot. The roots in this section, therefore, are killed, weakening the plant so that it gradually dies. The moisture deficit caused by the excessive evaporation is seldom made up by the daily watering of plants.

Paper pots properly protected from the activities of microorganisms, will produce as good growth as can be obtained in glass or clay pots. However, if decomposition is in progress, the organisms make use of the available nitrogen in the soil and the plant suffers from nitrogen starvation.   This nitrogen deficiency may be overcome by the addition of available nitrogen to the soil in excess of what can be utilized by the micro-organisms.

A disc placed in the bottom of the paper pots used in the experiments served to prevent the leaching of nutrients and also aided in the retention of the root system within the pot.

The most practical paper pot was one in which the fibers were impregnated and bound together with asphalt.   These produced plants equal to those grown in glass and clay pots.

Glass containers may be used successfully for plants.   With a

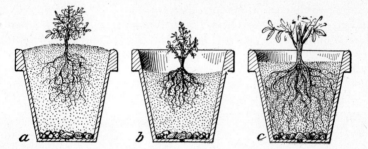

FIG. 168.—Good and bad potting. A, too full; B, not full enough and plant too low; C, right—space at top of pot half depth of pot rim.

glass pot, or any non-porous pot, care must be taken not to overwater the soil.   Compared with the watering of porous pots, the frequency for watering a non-porous pot may be cut in half.   There should be more soil in a non-porous pot than in a porous pot to prevent excessive applications of water.   Glass containers are particularly valuable for home and office, or in atmospheres of low humidity.   They conserve the moisture, which is evenly distributed in the soil of the container.

Rubber flower pots represent a type of non-porous pot moulded from a synthetic substance.   These pots produced good plants and are more permanent and less breakable than glass or clay pots.

186. Care needed in potting.—Simple though potting is, it must be properly done to get good results.   Many losses of potted plants are due solely to carelessness.   The potting soil must be neither too dry nor too wet, just the condition that when squeezed firmly in the hand it leaves the impress of the fingers and shows several little cracks in it, but does not break down (too dry) nor remain as a gob of mud (too wet).

The plants must be set at just the right depth (Fig. 168C), otherwise they will fail.   Seedlings and cuttings must not be placed in pots too large for them. The almost universal size to start with is 2″, though many ferns and other little plants are set at first in "thumb" pots, a still smaller size. The roots of cuttings must neither be too large nor too small because in the first case there would be breakage, in the latter refusal to grow; ⅛″ to ½″ is about the usual range for speedy work.

A 2″ pot should always have a vacant space ¼″ to 1/3″ deep at the top for water. Drainage should be provided in pots larger than 4″ size (Fig. 168). The pots, when placed on the greenhouse bench, must be set level so as to avoid loss of water over the rims. At first the plants need shade. Lath shutters (Fig. 150), in general use, are placed on inverted pots large enough to raise them above the plants. Sometimes these are made in rolls (Fig. 141 to 145). In hot, sunny weather, newspaper or cheesecloth is used for additional shade for three days to a week at first, being placed early and removed late in the day, but the time shaded gradually shortened. Sand to the depth of ½″ to 1″ on the bench aids greatly in the retention of moisture as well as in placing the pots level.

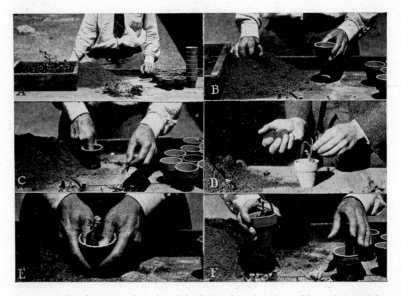

Fig. 169.—Potting operations by right handed man. A, position of materials; B, *first*, empty pot seized by left hand, placed in front of operator and partly filled with soil by right; C, *second*, left hand picks rooted cutting, right index finger makes hole in soil; D, *third*, left hand places cutting roots in hole, right adds more soil; E, *fourth*, pot grasped by both hands, thumbs parallel to body press soil firmly once; pot is then given quarter turn and thumbs press once again; F, *fifth*, loose soil is placed on packed soil barely to pot rim. Lastly, pot is given sharp rap on bench with right hand and placed in flat at right while left hand reaches for another pot.

FIG. 170.—Potting operations by left handed man. A, right hand held in pot scoops up soil while left picks up rooted cutting; B, right hand is withdrawn from pot and left places plant in hole thus left; C, right hand adds more soil while left holds plant in place; D, thumbs at right angles to body press soil once, hands give pot quarter turn, thumbs press once again, left hand raps pot on bench once, gives shake to distribute loose soil and places pot in flat while right hand gets another pot.

187. The operation of potting (Figs. 168 to 170) is capable of a high degree of skill and speed. It is no unusual feat for a man to pot 5,000 rooted cuttings in 10 hours. The highest record which has come to the authors' attention is 11,500 verbena cuttings in 10 hours. This was made in the greenhouse of Peter Henderson and Co. of New York by "Jim" Markey, who did only the potting, two boys keeping him supplied with soil, pots and cuttings and taking away the potted plants. Elimination of waste motion is the secret of such speed. (Practicum XXVII.)

188. Labels.—Pot labels (Fig. 170x) should be used to identify the plants potted.

189. "Shifting" is the trade name for transferring potted plants to larger-sized pots. At a glance the trained man can tell when shifting is needed; the novice may "knock out" the plants to examine the roots. To do this the pot is inverted and its top is rapped smartly on the edge of the bench, the ball of earth being caught by the hand. If the roots form a network around the earth, especially if they are dark colored, the plant must be shifted to avoid becoming "potbound."

190. In knocking out plants for shifting (Fig. 171) only one rap is usually needed; more waste time. Plants should never be shifted while the soil in the pots is either soppy wet or powdery dry; only when dry enough to crumble between thumb and fingers. Pot-

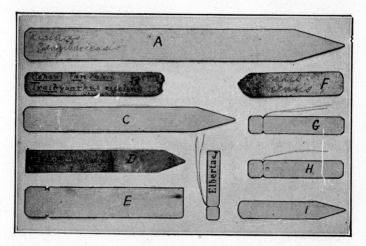

Fig. 170x.—Labels and methods of marking. A, C, I, various sizes of pot labels; B, old label rotted at bottom without losing name; D, zinc label with writing almost illegible after year of use; E, G, H, tree labels; F, old label showing wrong way to write name, thus losing important first syllable or two by decay; centre, tree label printed on both sides to speed handling in large establishments.

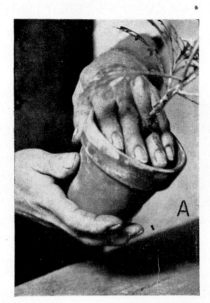

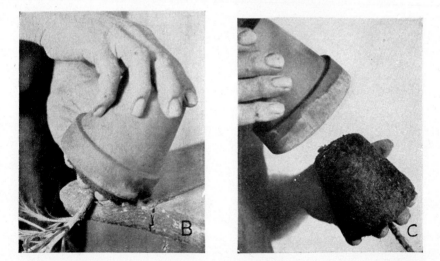

Fig. 171. Knocking plants out of pots to examine roots or preparatory to repotting. A, fingers placed on soil with plant stem between middle two; B, pot inverted and its rim rapped smartly on bench to separate ball of soil from pot; C, pot and soil separated.

bound plants need special attention. Pots should be free from caked dirt and fairly clean. After removal from the small pots, each plant is "shouldered"; i.e., part of the surface soil is rubbed off so fresh soil may take its place in the larger pot in which it is to be placed.

Plants, soil, pots and flat being ready, the workman puts enough soil in the bottom of the pot to have the top of the ball of earth around the plant on a level with the rim of the pot. The plant being so placed by the right hand, the left hand fills in soil; the pot is then grasped, raised slightly and rapped twice on the bench, the thumbs pressing the soil as in motion 5, first in one position then in the other. The unpressed earth is then firmed in the same way and the shifted plant set in the flat.

Shifts should be from small pots to the next size larger. Never skip a size in the fall, though sometimes with quick-growing subjects in spring a size may be skipped; that is, a plant in a 3″ pot may be placed in a 5″ size, or a 4″ in a 6″. Usually a size at a time is best, particularly in commercial establishments, where the aim is

Fig. 172.—Repotting. A, broken pots ("crocks") placed in 5″ and larger pots for drainage; B, plant removed from pot and with outer soil removed; C, soil being firmed in new pot.

shipping. When pots become larger than 4″ and even in that size for shrubby plants, drainage is necessary. "Crocks"; (broken flower pots) are the orthodox things. A large piece is placed over the drainage hole and smaller pieces above to the depth of an inch in 5″ and 6″ pots and twice as much in larger sizes. Pots larger than 3″ should be set on gravel, cinders or other loose material to insure drainage (Fig. 172).

191. Pot-bound plants, those which have been checked by remaining too long in the same pots and have been thus stunted in

FIG. 173.—Shifting plants to larger pots must be done regularly; *left,* plant pot-bound with brown and worthless roots; *right,* plant just right to shift.

growth, need special attention (Fig. 173). Before knocking out, the surface soil should be scraped clean to remove "moss" and some of the sour soil. After knocking out, the hard ball of earth should be crushed between the palms of the hands, perhaps broken by raps of the closed hand. The plants may then be replaced in the same pots with additional fresh soil. In most cases, however, it is better to stand the plants, pots and all, in water, say half an hour, and then wash and work out the earth in water either in a tub or in a gentle stream. After washing, the plants should be placed in pots one or two sizes smaller than those they have been in. Shrubby plants should be pruned back. Plenty of shade but little water is needed until the roots "take hold" and danger of wilting has passed. The appearance of new growth is the favorable sign. Leggy plants should be pruned back severely to make them develop stockily (Fig. 174).

Flat, a shallow box in which seeds are started and seedlings grown until large enough for pricking out (198) or transplanting, usually of a size easy to handle when filled with 2″ to 4″ of soil. It is convenient to have flats of some standard size that will fit the bench or the hotbed space without waste.

192. Feeding.—If the plant is already in as large a pot as convenient, or if one desires to bring it into heavier flowering, additional plant food should be given by direct application. Frequently plants

FIG. 174.—Effect of pruning. A, unpruned plant; B, well pruned and trained.

can be carried for a considerable time without changing or making additions to the soil, if they are properly fed.

Steamed bone meal seems to be the most popular feeding material—one quart to a bushel of soil, or 2 or 3 tablespoonfuls for soil enough to fill an 8″ pot. Pulverized sheep manure may also be used at the rate of one quart to a bushel of soil.

193. Paper cones for small plants.—Great claims are made for the Hallna method of plant propagation awarded gold medal at the Nice Horticultural Exposition in 1931 (Fig. 175). Its aims are: 1, to supplement bench area in greenhouses by utilizing waste space above the benches and thus increase the capacity of the houses—10 to 20%; 2, to reduce the cost of plant containers; due to initial price and breakage of earthenware pots; 3, to substitute a receptacle—a cone—of better shape than ordinary flower pots, paper pots or dirt bands; 4, to favor root development by the cone shape, the roots descending deeper than in other shaped receptacles of equal capacity; 5, to avoid root losses when plants are taken from flats; 6, to facilitate transplanting by this shape, one move of the trowel in properly prepared soil sufficing to make the hole; 7, to save time and labor in transplanting, the cone and its contents being planted intact, not "knocked out"; 8, to avoid risk of root losses when plants are knocked out of earthen pots or when paper pots fall apart; 9, to save time needed to fit complicated bottoms in paper pots; 10, to save transportation

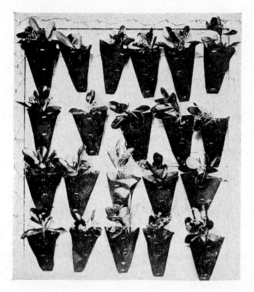

Fig. 175.—Small plants grown in paper cones on woven wire rack.

charges and storage space needed by earthen pots, the cones being light, shipped and stored flat or nested.

It is also claimed that the paper, being impregnated with fish oil, is repellant to insects; that being tough it will support considerable weight of soil even when wet; that the bottoms being reinforced increase this capacity, especially when two or three are nested; that as the cones hang by "lips" held in place by clips they do not break from their supports; that wooden frames fitted with woven wire fencing are best supports; that they can be raised or lowered by pulleys attached to the greenhouse roof frame; and that when the plants are transplanted in their containers to the open ground the paper decays and becomes humus. At present writing the authors do not know of this method having been tested in America.

194. Repotting is the process of removing a plant from the pot it is growing in, breaking up the ball of soil (Figs. 176, 177), removing it, reducing the root system of the plant, cutting back the top and setting the plant in a smaller pot or one of the same size from which it was removed.

Fig. 176.—Repotting. A, "shouldering" to remove "moss-infested" surface soil; B, soil is filled around otherwise undisturbed soil ball.

In case the plant is already in as large a pot as convenient or if one desires to bring it into heavier flowering, additional plant food should be given by direct application, or the plant should be repotted. When the plant has become too large, the branches scraggly and bare of leaves, the roots badly matted and decayed, the soil puddled by the work of angle worms, the time for repotting has arrived.

Fig. 177.—Repotting old and over-sized plants. A, old plant removed from pot; B, root and top pruned ready for potting; C, repotted. In a few weeks plant will be thrifty again.

Repotting dangers. It seems to be a rule that plants grown in the open ground attain larger size than those grown in flower pots; also that those grown in large pots grow larger than those grown in smaller and smaller ones. Experiments have proved that the greater the number of repottings the smaller the plants so treated.

195. Clean foliage is important not only for repotted plants but especially all house plants because dust is detrimental to plant

Fig. 178.—Sponging house plants is slower than syringing but often more practical.

growth (Fig. 178). Its removal is comparatively easy by means of spraying or syringing rather forcefully or by standing the plants in a rain shower.

196. Tomato propagation.—In Maryland, 83 varieties of tomatoes were grown experimentally, some in the usual way of transplanting, some from seed sown direct in 4″ pots imbedded in earth and the seedlings thinned. There was loss by damping-off among the transplanted plants, but none among the pot grown. These latter suffered no loss or check when moved to the field; the transplanted plants were slower to start and to bloom. With 72 of the 83 varieties the pot plants yielded more than the others, and among the 10 greatest yielders nine were potted. The average yield on an acre basis was 12¾ tons, against 10¾, an increase more than enough to pay for the labor. The potted plants, as a whole, produced about twice as much fruit prior to August 15 as the others—59 bushels, against 30. (This is of special interest from a market standpoint, because of high prices early in the season.) Each of the 20 best early producers gave greatest yield from the potted plants.

197. Transplanting lettuce and other plants experimentally in Wisconsin in the greenhouse seems to warrant the general conclusion that transplanting does not promote earliness nor increased yield. Once transplanting, as of cabbage plants, from seed bed to field, or "pricking off" as commonly practiced in the greenhouse, is necessary to economize room, but repeated transplanting of vegetable plants is not advisable.

IX

PRICKING OUT AND TRANSPLANTING

198. Pricking out (or off) is a gardener's term for transplanting seedlings while yet so small they can easily be lifted on a stick scarcely wider than a toothpick at its sharpened end, or they may be flooded out with water if growing in sand. A better form for the stick is two points which form a blunt *V*. The seedlings are thus moved from the seed pans and placed in other flats at greater distances apart, say 1″, until better rooted. Pricking out is done also to avoid risk of damping-off (73).

Holes for receiving somewhat larger seedlings may be made with the knife blade or a pot label, but a better method is to use one of the two types of markers (Figs. 179 to 181). The plants are usually planted in flats and the marker or "spotting board" is made to fit the flat exactly.

199. Transplanting is the removal of living plants from one place and planting them in new quarters. Plants under proper care may be transplanted at almost any time, either while dormant or when actively growing. Small herbaceous plants are usually the only ones transplanted while active and only when they may have the best attention of watering and shading.

Transplanting is a severe shock to plants even under best conditions. Many of the roots are destroyed, the attachment to the soil is loosened and normal activities interfered with. The top continues to transpire moisture and produces a drying effect on the plant. To overcome this setback the soil into which the plant is transplanted should be made firm and well supplied with moisture so the plant may soon re-establish its root system. The operation is more successful on an overcast, cool, cloudy or foggy, damp day and in humid regions.

The younger the plant, the better are the chances for success as it can withstand the operation much better than when older. A short, stocky, compact plant transplants better than a long, "leggy," weak one when transferred from a protected place to the open air.

The appearance of the first or second true leaves is an indication (Fig. 184) that seedlings should be "pricked out" into other flats, another part of the frame or to other frames. By so doing the individual plants will have more space than if left in the original seed bed, so stocky and healthy plants will result. They should be shaded for a couple of days to become established. One should always water thoroughly after transplanting. When older trees are dug for transplanting as much of the root system as is possible should be saved.

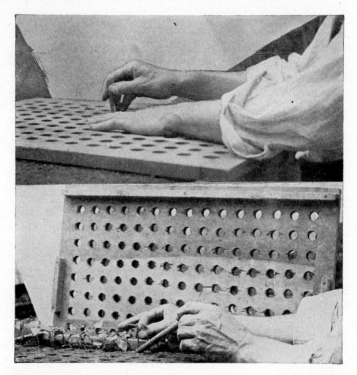

Fig. 179.—Spotting board. A, dibble punching holes in soil of flat through holes in board; B, putting seedlings in place. Dibble used to firm them in soil.

200. Hardening off.—Before transplanting to the open ground young plants grown in greenhouses, hotbeds or coldframes must gradually become acclimated to outside conditions. This can be done by admitting more air daily until the sash is removed entirely during the day and later at night until the plants are thoroughly hardened.

201. Bottom heat is the heat applied beneath growing plants by means of fermenting material (manure, spent tan bark, brewer's grains, etc.), by warm flues, hot water, steam or electricity. It is used more or less for all kinds of seeds started in advance of the outdoor season, especially for those of warm climate plants. Only seeds of certain tropical plants require high heat to germinate. Most garden seeds do not need bottom heat, though many sprout quicker if warmed from below. Always when bottom heat is used the seed-

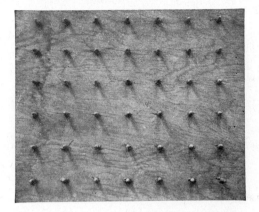

FIG. 180.—Peg style of spotting board for locating positions of seedlings.

lings should be removed to cooler places soon or they will become tall, spindling, and weak ("leggy"). Good ventilation will help make them "stocky" and strong (Fig. 174).

The expression "ten degrees of bottom heat" means that the bed should be that many degrees warmer than the air just above the bed or in the propagating house. Usually, however, the temperature of the bed is indicated, as 60, 70° F. or some other degree.

202. Natural bottom heat obtained from the sun during the day is of importance at all times, but is scarcely considered in green-

FIG. 181.—Steps in growing seedlings. *Left*, flat with holes punched for seedlings through spotting board; *middle, above*, peg style spotting board; *middle, below*, newly pricked out seedlings; *right*, seedlings ready for transplanting.

house winter work, except as something to offset heat from the pipes in the propagating house. In hotbeds, coldframes (and other structures not usually heated artificially) it is of great importance, especially in spring. During the day the sun penetrates the surface layer of soil, which becomes warm. During the night this heat is given

Fig. 182.—Lotus (*Nelumbo*) propagation. *Top, outdoor pond; left, below,* pots in which seeds are sown; *right, below,* seedlings of various ages.

off slowly and checked by mats (Fig. 142) and shutters (Fig. 143) so the fullest use may be made of it. The depth to which the soil may thus be warmed depends upon the intensity of the light, the color and other characters of the soil; for instance, dark soils absorb heat more rapidly than light ones.

It is a good and common practice to "harden off plants" gradually rather than expose them immediately to the heat and cold of outdoors. This can be done by placing them first in a cooler part of the greenhouse for a few days, then in the coldframe, then the lath house and finally outdoors. Or if propagated in the coldframe

FIG. 183.—Planting evergreens for reforestation. A, man and boy or two men form crew, mattock man digs holes, planter carries plants in pail with roots in inch of water; B, planter spreads roots in normal position before covering with soil; C, fine soil is pressed around roots; D, soil is tamped firmly around roots with stone or E, packed firmly by tramping with heel to get rid of air spaces; F, planted tree should stand erect and be so firm it cannot be easily pulled up These steps apply equally to other planting.

FIG. 184.—Apple seedling of right size for transplanting.

the sash may be left open for longer periods each day, finally at night except in cold weather.

Usually the more times a plant is transplanted the better does it withstand the shock of transplanting, since the root system becomes compact and is disturbed less than when transplanted fewer times or not at all.

The soil into which the plant is transplanted should be freshly turned because of the greater amount of moisture present in the upturned surface. A mulch is beneficial to prevent baking, cracking and undue loss of moisture. It may be leaves, straw, litter, sawdust, peat moss, buckwheat hulls or loose earth. If the ground has a tendency to dry out it will be necessary to water the plants at frequent intervals. When transplanting is done on a small scale apply the water in holes alongside the plants and cultivate when the weeds appear.

Plants transplant more readily when grown in flats or pots than when grown in the open soil. When pot grown plants are transplanted the roots are maintained in the ball formed by the pot and all the earth is taken with them. In this way the roots are disturbed little and the plant may continue its growth with little or no shock. Soaking the soil well should follow transplanting. A good sprinkling can, with a fine nozzle, is useful on a small scale (Fig. 186).

Winter and spring are usually the times chosen to transplant

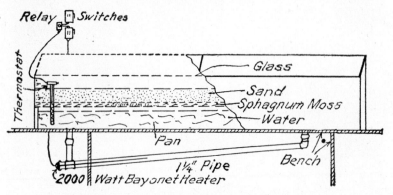

FIG. 185.—Electrically heated propagating bed.

Fig. 185x.—Pricking out plants in shaded coldframe. Men must bend nearly double to do this work.

trees and shrubs with balls of earth around the roots. Large trees are not often successfully transplanted by the novice so the job should be given to an expert.

A dibble is a handy implement (Figs. 188, 189) to use in transplanting small plants. A hole is made with it, the plant roots placed in the hole, the dibble inserted at the side and the earth moved against the plant (Fig. 190).

Transplanting usually destroys the primary root. This is why seeds of carrot, beet and similar edible root plants are generally sown directly in the garden or the field. On the other hand, cabbages and tomatoes are started in the hotbed or the window box and when the seedlings are high enough are transplanted. With the latter any injury to the tap root is compensated for by the plant developing a shallower and more compact root system, which will better utilize plant food in the soil (Fig. 190x).

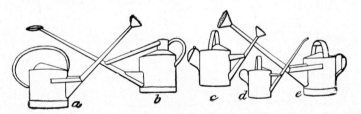

Fig. 186.—Watering pots. a, adjustable by tilting handle to any position; b, long reach; c, common style; d, long neck without rose: e, common style but with long neck.

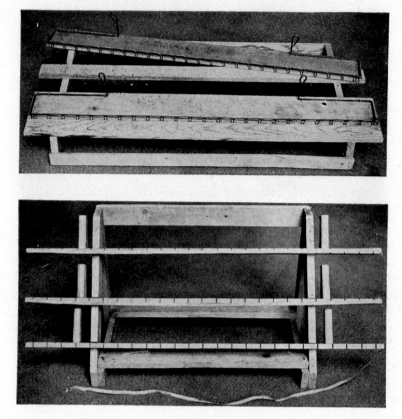

FIG. 187.—Styles of transplanting boards. See text.

203. Transplanting apple and cherry seedlings.[1]—Three methods have been used in transplanting; namely, by hand with dibbles, with transplanting boards and with automatic machinery. When dibbled by hand many "gooseneck" seedlings have been produced, due to the planters not taking care to trim the tap roots and placing the plants crooked in the soil. With proper supervision this could be overcome but American labor does not take kindly to this work.

The planting board method has proved best under present conditions. Several boards are available but those used in evergreen seedling nurseries are too heavy for handling soft succulent plants, such as fruit tree stock seedlings. The type used in these tests (Fig. 187) has the advantages of being light to handle and offering protection to the seedlings. As a general statement, the board must be relatively short so as to adapt itself to unevenness of the soil and the planting edge must be as narrow as possible and yet give the board proper strength so as to avoid roughness of the ground surface. Notches ¼″ deep

[1] Seedling Fruit Stocks, H. B. Tukey, N. Y. (Geneva) *Exp. Sta. Bul. 569, April, 1929.*

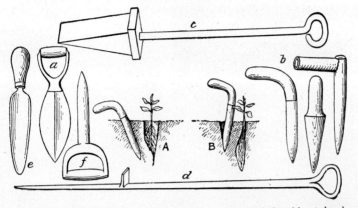

Fig. 188.—Dibbles, their use and abuse. a, flat bladed, wide style; b, home made "punch" style; c, pot plunger; d, root graft planter; e, trowel style; f, spade handle; A, right way to use—pressing soil from bottom of hole to top; B, wrong—pressing soil at top and leaving air space around roots.

and ³⁄₁₆″ wide have proved best, the notches being 1½″ apart and the board 3′ long.

An elastic drawn across the front has helped to hold the seedlings in place but has not been satisfactory because under field conditions it becomes too delicate an operation to fasten and release the band without snapping the seedlings. If the plants are the proper size and drawn down into the notches, they will catch on the seed leaves and be held in place fairly well without the band. Some additional hold like the band, however, is desirable.

A second type of board is patterned after the board just described, but it is better adapted to very small plants which it permits being placed low in the ground. Other improvements are being made which will facilitate the work, but the method is essentially the same regardless of the particular design of the board.

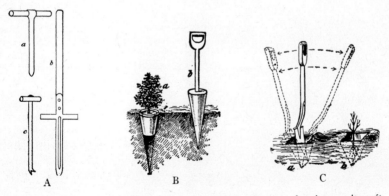

Fig. 189.—A, Transplanting, etc., nursery dibble; B, pot plunging, a, in soft soil, b, dibble itself; C, transplanting in loose soil with spade.

The plants (taken from flats or coldframes, tap roots cut, roots dipped in muddy water) are strung in the notches of the planting board, pulling them into the notches so the seed leaves will catch and help to hold them in place. Dipping the roots in mud not only prevents drying out but also gives weight to and helps hold the seedlings in place in the board. The frame of three boards is carried to a prepared trench, the seedling roots are placed straight against the straight side of the trench, and firmed in place. The board is removed, leaving the seedlings properly spaced and with straightened roots. Furthermore, American help does not object to this method.

The use of automatic transplanting machinery has not proved practical. Several hundred thousand plants have been used with three different types of transplanters. The difficulty lies in getting the plants to grow after the machine has placed them in the soil. First, in order to have the plants large enough for the fingers of the machines to grasp them they must be so large that they do not transplant well and suffer a severe shock. Second, the machines so far devised have not been able to put the plants straight in the soil. This results in a high proportion of "goose-neck" seedlings which break when dug and are otherwise worthless. Furthermore, machines have not yet been developed which will work in the heavy soils under which these tests have been conducted.

204. Balling plants is accomplished by digging

Fig. 190.—Dibble in use. A, hole made, dibble removed and plant ready for placing; B, dibble being thrust to push soil against plant; C, plant in place with soil firmed.

around them with a sharp spade or a shovel and keeping the earth intact with the roots. When all the way around, the plant is lifted by thrusting the spade underneath it to pry it up and laid on a square of burlap, shaped into ball form and the corners of the burlap tied around the trunk (Figs. 191 to 193). The soil should be neither too wet nor too dry for this operation. Large trees are usually balled.

205. Handling balled plants.—Always use both hands when handling balled plants, place one hand under the ball, the other to

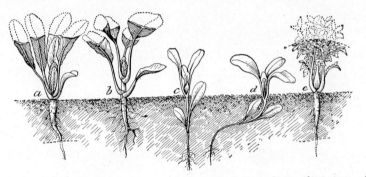

Fig. 190x.—Transplanting tricks. a, b, e, dotted lines show where tops of leaves have been removed; c, d, methods of handling leggy plants.

steady the stem. Place the ball in the amply large hole without removing the burlap. When filling the hole pack the soil thoroughly around the sides of the ball but do not break the ball or dislodge the fibrous roots by tramping *on top* as this may kill the plant. When the hole is partially filled, cut the cord at the top of the ball and turn down the burlap so it will be completely buried when the remainder of the hole is filled in. When the hole is three-fourths filled with soil, pour in water to the brim. When this has seeped away then draw loose soil around the body of the tree. Do not tramp it down. Never remove the burlap from the ball (except as indicated above). It will soon rot.

206. Warm Climate Transplanting.—In California and the Southern States, evergreen and deciduous trees and shrubs growing in the open ground may both be successfully transplanted during winter. In the Eastern and Northern States they are perhaps better planted in spring. Palms and bamboos, however, move best in late spring and early summer. When given proper care plants grown in pots or established in boxes may be planted at any time when conditions outdoors are favorable (Fig. 194).

Digging the holes for ornamentals. In preparing the holes for planting, be sure to make them larger than the root system of the plant to allow space for tramping around the outside. Always fill the holes about three-quarters full around the roots with friable top soil, tramp it hard, fill the hole with water. The following day level up the ground around the tree but do not tramp it.

207. Treatment of boxed plants.—When boxed plants are received, dig the hole large enough to receive the box, arranging to have the tree stand at least 4″ deeper than in the box. Dig the hole

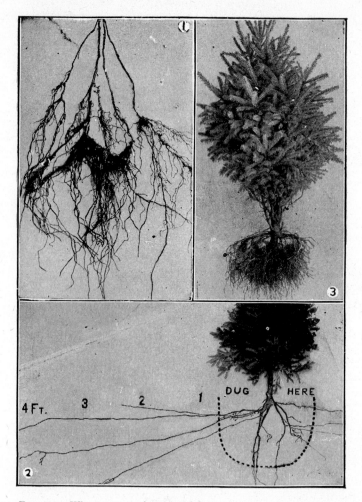

FIG. 191.—Why root-pruning is desirable. 1, roots of evergreen as ordinarily grown in nursery; 2, dotted line shows where plant would be dug with loss of roots; 3, evergreen root pruned as shown at 2 but after new roots have developed. Such plants are well worth their extra cost.

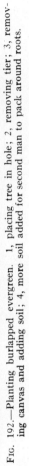

Fig. 192.—Planting burlapped evergreen. 1, placing tree in hole; 2, removing tier; 3, removing canvas and adding soil; 4, more soil added for second man to pack around roots.

sufficiently large to allow the box to tilt to one side so one-half the bottom may be removed, then reverse the operation and remove the other half. The sides should then be carefully removed, taking care not to disturb the plant. Next straighten the tree and fill around the ball with soil. Then make a good basin around the tree; and fill with water several times to insure soaking the earth even deeper than the bottom of the hole. It is a good plan to keep the tops well sprayed with water in the early morning and late evening for three to four weeks.

FIG. 193.—Burlapped for shipment. Trees so handled have usually been root pruned for two or more years to develop abundance of short, fibrous roots. They are almost sure to grow.

The tops of deciduous trees and shrubs should be pruned in proportion to the amount of roots lost in transplanting to establish a new balance between tops and roots. Nearly always it is advisable to give tree trunks protection to guard against sunburn by whitewashing from the ground to the first branches, then wrapping loosely with burlap. Sunburn induces borers to enter the tree.

208. Importance of staking.— Most deciduous trees should be firmly staked when planted to prevent heavy winds from loosening them and to insure straight growth. For small trees one stake may be enough; for large ones three set in a triangle are best. In fastening trees to stakes wrap burlap around the trunk before wiring so as to prevent chafing. Pieces of old garden hose or auto shoe are also good. The hose should either be split or the wire passed through it.

209. After care.—While of greatest importance, proper planting is only the beginning. Trees may live even though neglected, but will not render the satisfaction and pleasure possible unless well cared for. Never let them get dry during the first summer. When irrigation is done give the soil a thorough soaking. This is far better than a little water at a time. Keep the surface around the plants and trees loose. A good mulch is a great help. Stock properly planted and cared for will repay any little additional expenditure of time and money, by adding to the attractiveness of the garden and the home.

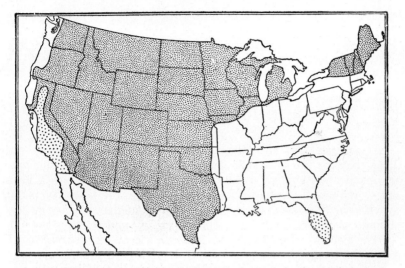

FIG. 194.—United States map showing seasons for transplanting in various regions. White areas are as favorable to fall as spring planting. Darkly stippled areas are unfavorable to fall planting without extra care. In lightly stippled areas evergreens may be transplanted whenever moisture conditions are favorable. Deciduous plants suited to the region may be transplanted as soon as dormant.

FIG. 195.—Top-worked apricot orchard with scions of uniform growth—a remarkably fine stand.

X

GREENHOUSE FUMIGATION

Though contact and stomach poisons are used effectively out-doors they are less desirable to use indoors; especially as fumigants are much more efficient because they are kept confined in a given space, more easily applied, do not soil or stain the plants or impair the color or the fragrance of flowers and often effect savings of 75% or more over the more cumbersome spraying and dusting methods.

The two principal fumigants are nicotine and hydrocyanic acid gas. The former is the active principle of several proprietary preparations which are either burned or evaporated to fill the air with fumes and which have long been popular in greenhouse work, mainly because of their relative safety to both plants and humans; the latter, however, is steadily gaining favor because of its greater effectiveness and convenience. When properly applied killings of 95% or more are usual. Moreover, it is not necessary to air the houses when low concentrations are used, so the risk of chilling the plants is avoided.

As proprietary preparations vary in their method of application with the materials and as there are many of them, the reader is referred to the manufacturers' directions in all cases. Only two of the three hydrocyanic acid methods need be discussed here because the third (liquid acid) has not yet passed the experimental stage.

210. How nurseries and greenhouses become infested.—Insect and other animal infestations of nurseries are perhaps most often due to plants or plant parts brought from outside sources, to the natural spread from surrounding properties and to plants delivered, exposed in infested localities but returned to the nursery. As a matter of precaution all suspected plants and plant parts to be grown or used outdoors should be fumigated, large pots in the fumigation house, small ones, cuttings, scions, etc., in the fumigation box (222).

Doubtless many greenhouses become infested with insects through the agency of plants commonly referred to as "boarders." The practice of turning over home-grown plants to a florist to care for during the absence of the owner on a vacation is prevalent over the entire country and often results in establishing pests not hitherto known to occur on the florist's premises. If the trade requires such a practice, plants of this character should be cleaned thoroughly of insect pests before being placed with the regular stock of the greenhouse.

211. **Essential precautions.**—1. When necessary to fumigate a greenhouse near a dwelling, the dwelling must be vacated during the fumigation and for at least half an hour after the ventilators have been opened.

2. Before doing any fumigation measure the cubic contents of the greenhouse to be fumigated and from these measurements compute the quantities of chemicals to be used. *Never guess at either.*

3. Make sure that the plants are dry before starting to fumigate.

4. Examine all steam pipes while steam is on to detect and plug all leaks and thus avoid having the air too moist. Should films of water form on the foliage they will absorb the gas and burn the leaves.

5. Always wait to fumigate until at least an hour after sunset.

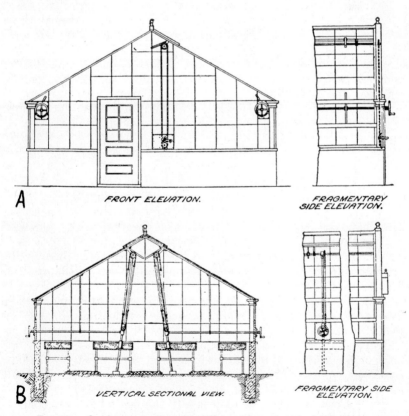

A   *FRONT ELEVATION.*   *FRAGMENTARY SIDE ELEVATION.*

B   *VERTICAL SECTIONAL VIEW.*   *FRAGMENTARY SIDE ELEVATION.*

FIG. 196.—Outdoor operation of ventilators—important in fumigation.

Never do the work during daylight because the plants would thus be killed.

6. Never fumigate any plants sprayed or dusted with Bordeaux mixture, eau celeste or any other material which contains copper in any other form or severe injury will follow.

7. Make sure that the temperature of the greenhouse is above 52° but below 70° F. The optimum temperature range is between 55° and 68°.

8. When a fumigating box is to be used keep the plants in the dark for at least an hour before starting and for several hours after the fumes have been allowed to escape.

9. Always keep the chemicals under lock and key, in air-tight containers and each one correctly and conspicuously labeled.

10. Before starting each fumigation always make sure that the skin of the operator is intact, without wound or even an unhealed scratch.

11. Never handle the cyanid any more than necessary, never without gloves, rubber preferred. It is well to have special gloves for this purpose and to keep them locked with the cyanid when not in use.

12. Before starting to fumigate always adjust the ventilators and test them to make sure they can be operated easily from the outside (Fig. 183).

13. Always post danger signs at all entrances to the greenhouse before starting to fumigate and see that the place is tightly closed, preferably locked.

14. Always have ample help when fumigating a large greenhouse. Never attempt to do the work alone.

15. If cyanid dust is on the clothing, go outdoors and shake thoroughly, being careful to avoid inhaling the dust.

16. Always wash thoroughly, the hands especially, each time after handling the cyanid. Throw away the first water and wash a second time and then rinse with fresh, clean water.

17. Avoid entering a fumigated house until several hours after the fumigation is over or at least an hour after the ventilators have been opened liberally.

18. *Always take every precaution.* To omit any one of those listed may lead to serious results, perhaps even death.

19. Read in some good encyclopedia about hydrocyanic acid gas and cyanids; note how these violent poisons act on animals and man; make a list of things to do in case either is taken accidentally and keep it posted where the poison is stored. Have antidotes and remedies always available.

212. Effects of gas on plants.—In fumigating a house containing a large variety of plants, using the correct dosage and under

proper conditions, the tender growth of some plants may be injured. This injury is not permanent, however, and such plants will show new vigorous growth in a short time. Moreover, the growth of many plants is stimulated by hydrocyanic-acid gas.

Satisfactory results are obtained only where it is possible to overcome the resisting power of the plant. Under favorable conditions greenhouses that do not contain roses, rose geraniums, asparagus fern, lemon verbenas, snapdragons, wandering jew, or sweet peas can be fumigated with safety with an initial dosage of one-half ounce of sodium cyanid (NaCN) per 1,000 cubic feet.

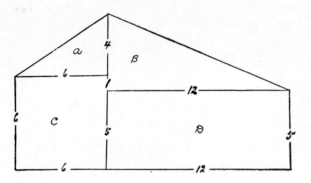

Fig. 197.—How to compute cubical contents of greenhouse.

In case there is any doubt as to the amount of gas a plant will stand without injury, it is preferable that the initial dosage be not over one-fourth ounce of sodium cyanid per 1,000 cubic feet and increased with subsequent fumigations until the fatal point for the pest to be controlled is reached, it being borne in mind that in some instances it is not possible to effect an absolute control of all stages of some insects with one fumigation without injury to foliage or growing parts of certain plants.

For example, the greenhouse white fly can be eradicated with three successive fumigations at intervals of seven to nine days, using one-half ounce of sodium cyanid (NaCN) per 1,000 cubic feet, in houses containing such susceptible plants as coleus, ageratum, heliotrope, fuchsia, etc., with no injury to the foliage. Moreover, such resistant pests as scale insects can be eliminated entirely by killing the immature stages with a small dosage repeated at frequent intervals.

213. To determine the cubic contents of a greenhouse [1] multiply the area of an end by the length. In the example given (Fig. 197) the end is first plotted into rectangles and triangles. Second, the areas of these are computed and added together. Third, the sum

---

[1] Slightly condensed from *Mich. Sta. Spec. Bul. 214.* A few explanatory phrases have also been added.

TABLE 19.—FUMIGATION WITH CALCIUM CYANIDE IN GREENHOUSES
AND FUMIGATION BOXES

[Plants designated by * were fumigated in a box]

Name of plant	Cyanide per 1,000 cubic feet of space	Length of exposure	Green-house tempera-ture	Green-house hu-midity	Effect of treatment on plants
	Ounces	Hours	° F.	Per cent	
Abelia grandiflora	¾	12	73	92	No burning.
Abutilon eclipse	¾	12	73	92	Do.
Acalypha godseffiana	1	10	69	90	Do.
Acalypha wilkesiana	1	10	69	90	Do.
Ageratum sp	¼	12	61	90	Do.
Do	½	14	74	61	Slight burning.
Ageratum dwarf	½	12	73	93	Do.
Allamanda hendersoni	¾	12	73	92	Do.
Alternanthera	2	1	68	83	No burning.
*Amaryllis (Hippeastrum sp.)	2½	16	86	56	Do.
Anthericum liliago variegatum	½	14	74	61	Do.
Aralia sieboldi (Fatsia japonica)	¾	12	73	92	Moderate injury.
*Artillery plant (Pilea muscosa)	1⁄16	16	69	59	Severe injury.
*Do	⅛	15	72	49	Severe burning.
Asparagus plumosus	¼	13	63	84	Trace burning on new tips.
*Asparagus sprengeri	⅛	15	72	49	No burning.
Aspidistra lurida	1	15	69	63	Do.
Aspidistra lurida variegata	1	15	69	63	Very slight.
China aster (Callistephus)	1	10	69	90	No burning.
*Azalea indica	½	6	63	71	Slight spotting of tips.
*Do	3	16	64	38	
Banana (Musa)	¾	12	73	92	No burning.
Begonia sp.	¾	12	73	92	Do.
Begonia sp.	2	15	71	00	Do.
Bleeding heart (Dicentra spectabilis)	1	10	69	90	Do.
Blue lace flower (Trachymene cærulea)	¼	1	61	89	Do.
Blue sage (Salvia azurea)	¾	12	73	92	No burning.
Brugmansia (Datura suaveolens)	2	1	68	83	Do.
Buddleia forresti	¾	12	73	92	Severe injury.
Buddleia variabilis	¾	12	73	92	Do.
Buxus sempervirens var. suffruticosa	¾	12	73	92	No burning.
Calla (Zantedeschia)	¼	14	59	83	Do.
Camphor (Cinnamomum camphora)	½	11	63	98+	Do.
Cape-jasmine (Gardenia florida)	½	11	63	98+	Do.
Carnation (Dianthus caryophyllus)	½	14	74	61	Do.
Caryopteris incana (blue spiræa)	½	12	70	91	Do.
Cereus (night-blooming)	½	11	63	98+	Do.
Chrysanthemum sp	¼	10	61	90	Slight injury.
Do	¼	13	54	76	No burning.
* Do	½	15	71	64	Severe injury.
Cissus discolor	½	12	73	93	No burning.
Coleus sp	½	11	63	98+	Severe injury.
Do	½	14	69	90	No burning.
* Do	1	6	69	51	Do.
Cosmos	¾	12	73	92	Do.
Cuphea ignea (cigar plant)	1	10	69	90	Do.
Cyclamen persicum (in flower)	½	13	61	89	Do.
Cyclamen latifolium	1	14	69	90	Do.
Cyperus alternifolius (umbrella sedge)	¾	12	73	92	Do.
Do	2	1	68	83	Do.
Delphinium (annual larkspur)	1	10	69	90	Do.
Dracæna (Cordyline indivisa)	2	15	71	68	Do.
Dusty miller (Centaurea cineraria)	1	10	69	90	Do.
Do	2	1	68	83	Slight injury.
Elephant's ear (Colocasia esculenta)	2	1	68	83	No burning.
Evonymus japonicus	¾	12	73	92	Do.
Evonymus radicans	¾	12	72	92	Do.
Evonymus sieboldiana	¾	12	72	92	Do.
Evonymus variegata (radicans)	¾	12	73	92	Do.
Ferns:					
* Adiantum sp. (maidenhair fern)	¾	16	69	67	Do.
Do	5	13	66	53	Slight injury (old growth).
Cyrtomium falcatum (holly fern)	¼	14	59	83	No burning.
Cyrtomium rochfordianum	¼	14	59	83	Do.

TABLE 19.—FUMIGATION WITH CALCIUM CYANIDE IN GREENHOUSES AND FUMIGATION BOXES—*Continued*

Name of plant	Cyanide per 1,000 cubic feet of space Ounces	Length of exposure Hours	Green-house temper-ature ° F.	Green-house hu-midity Per cent	Effect of treatment on plants
	Ounces	Hours	° F.	Per cent	
Dryopteris viridescens (g l o s s y wood fern).	1	14	69	90	No burning.
Nephrolepis sp	1	14	69	90	Do.
Nephrolepis exaltata bostoniensis (Boston fern).	¼	14	59	83	Do.
Do	1	14	57		Do.
* Nephrolepis furcans	¾	15	69	67	Do.
Pteris spp	¼	14	59	83	Do.
Ficus elastica	1	14	69	90	Do.
Ficus pandurata	1	14	69	90	Do.
Forget-me-not (Myosotis)	½	12	73	93	Do.
Freesia	¼	14	59	83	Do.
Fuchsia	1	10	69	90	Do.
Geraniums:					
Pelargonium sp	1½	14	69	90	Do.
Lady Washington (P. domesticum)	½	14	69	90	Do.
Rose (P. graveolens)	½	11	63	98+	Do.
Gladiolus	¼	1	61	89	Do.
Gloxinia	½	11	63	98+	Severe injury.
Grape, Concord, (Vitis)	¾	12	73	92	No burning.
Guava (Psidium)	½	11	63	98+	Slight injury.
Heliotrope (Heliotropium peruvianum)	½	14	69	90	No burning.
Hibiscus cooperi	½	12	70	91	Do.
Hydrangea otaksa	½	12	70	91	Do.
Ivy (Hedera helix)	¾	12	73	92	Do.
Jasminum:					
Grand Duke	½	14	74	61	Do.
* Grandiflorum	1⁄16	16	69	59	Tips burned slightly.
* Multiflorum	⅛	15	63	55	Do.
Nudiflorum	¾	12	73	92	Do.
Primulinum	¾	12	73	92	No burning.
Jerusalem cherry (Solanum pseudo-capsicum).	½	11	63	98+	Do.
Justicia rosea	¾	12	73	92	Do.
Kerria japonica	¾	12	73	92	Do.
Kudzu vine (Pueraria thunbergiana)	2	1	68	83	Do.
Lavender (Lavandula officinalis)	¾	12	73	92	Very slight tip burning.
Lantana camara	½	12	73	93	Very severe burn-ing.
Lantana camara	½	12	73	93	No burning.
Lantana sp.	½	13	61	89	Do.
Lemon verbena (Lippia citriodora)	½	13	61	89	Do.
Lilium giganteum (Giant lily)	½	14	74	61	Very slight tip burning.[1]
Marguerite daisy (Chrysanthemum frutescens)	¼	13	63	84	Slight injury.
Do.	¼	15	65	56	No burning.
Marigold (Calendula officinalis)	¼	13	61	84	Do.
Moonflower (Ipomœa grandiflora)	1½	1	72	75	Do.
Moonflower (Ipomœa tubiculata)	½	12	73	93	Very severe injury.
Night-blooming cestrum (Cestrum nocturnum)	2	1	68	83	Slight injury.
Oleander (Nerium oleander)	¾	12	73	92	No burning.
Orchid:					
Cattleya sp.	1	14	69	90	Do.
Cypripedium (2 varieties)	1	14	69	67	Do.
Lælia sp.	1	14	69	90	Do.
*Oncidium	½	15	68	42	Do.
Do.	4	14	61	49	Slight injury.
Do.	1	14			Severe injury.
Palms:					
Kentia sp. (Howea)	1	12	66	85	No burning.
Pandanus veitchi	1	14	69	90	Do.
Peristrophe	½	12	73	85	Do.
Periwinkle (Vinca)	½	14	69	90	Do.

TABLE 19.—FUMIGATION WITH CALCIUM CYANIDE IN GREENHOUSES
AND FUMIGATION BOXES—*Continued*

Name of plant	Cyanide per 1,000 cubic feet of space	Length of exposure	Green-house temper-ature	Green-house hu-midity	Effect of treatment on plants
	Ounces	*Hours*	*° F.*	*Per cent*	
Petunia	1	6	64	91	Slight injury.
Pittosporum	½	11	63	98+	No burning (older leaves).
Plumbago capensis	½	11	63	98+	Slight injury.
Plumbago capensis alba	½	11	63	98+	Do.
Poinsettia (Euphorbia pulcherrima)	¾	12	73	92	No burning.
Primula obconica	¼	14	59	83	Do.
Rose:					
America	⅛	14	63	84	Do.
American Legion	¼	13	63	84	Do.
Butterfly	¼	13	65	80	Do.
Cecile Brunner	¼	15	65	80	Do.
Claudius Pernet	¼	12	72	95	Do.
Columbia	¼	12	66	90	Do.
Do.	¼	14	57		Sepals burned.
Commonwealth	⅛	14	63	84	No burning.
Killarney (double white)	¼	13	63	79	Do.
Do.	1	10	69	90	Do.
Premier	¼	9	65	86	Do.
Rosa odorata	½	12	72	91	Slight injury.
Sanchezia nobilis	¾	12	73	92	No burning.
Sansevieria zeylanica	¾	12	73	92	Do.
Santalum (sandalwood)	½	12	70	91	Do.
Scarlet sage (Salvia splendens)	¼	15	65	80	No burning (1 bloom).
Schizanthus pinnatus	¼	1	61	89	No burning.
Sensitive plant (Mimosa pudica)	½	11	63	98+	Severe injury.
Serissa foetida	¾	12	73	92	No burning.
Silk oak (Grevillea robusta)	2	1	68	83	Do.
Snapdragon (Antirrhinum majus)	¼	13	61	84	Do.
Do	¼	14	59	83	Severe injury.[2]
Snapdragon (Antirrhinum sp.)	½	14	69	90	No burning.
Spanish iris (Iris xiphium)	½	11	63	98+	Do.
Spider lily (Hymenocallis)	½	11	63	98+	Do.
Spiræa billiardi	¾	12	73	92	Do.
Spiræa lindleyana	½	12	70	91	Slight injury.
Do.	¾	12	73	92	No burning.
Spiræa opulifolia	½	12	70	91	Do.
Spiræa vanhouttei	½	12	70	91	Do.
Sultan's balsam (Impatiens sultani)	½	12	73	93	Do.
Do.	½	12	73	85	Slight burning.
Sweet olive (Olea fragrans)	¾	12	73	92	No burning.
Sweet pea (Lathyrus odoratus)	¼	13	54	76	Do.
Do.	1	12	62	93	Slight injury.
Tapioca	¾	12	73	92	No burning.
Thistle (Onopordon)	¾	12	73	92	Do.
*Wandering Jew (Tradescantia)	⅛	15	72	49	Do.
Wax mallow (Malvaviscus arboreus)	½	12	70	91	Do.
Do.	¾	12	73	92	Do.
Weeping willow (Salix babylonica)	½	12	70	91	Do.

[1] In flower.   [2] Leaves spotted, flower sepals bleached.

is multiplied by the length of the greenhouse. To get the area of a rectangle or a square multiply the length by the breadth; to get that of a right-angled triangle multiply the breadth by half the height.

In the example: $c = 6' \times 6' = 36$ sq. ft.; $d = 5' \times 12' = 60$; $a = 6' \times 4' = 24' \div 2 = 12$; $b = 5' \times 12' = 60 \div 2' = 30$. Add these sums—$36 + 60 + 12 + 30 = 138$ square feet. Multiply this sum by 100 (length of house) = 13,800 cubic feet, the cubical contents of a 100' house of the dimensions given.

214. Calcium cyanid, dry method fumigation.—Of the various grades the dust, or G-grade, is recommended for greenhouse fumigation. It is applied by sprinkling the required amount on the dry walks of the greenhouse. Hence the grower's term "dry

Fig. 198.—Distributing calcium cyanide on greenhouse walk.

method," because it obviates using crocks, paper sacks, acid and water. The powder absorbs water from the air, slowly liberates hydrocyanic-acid gas and produces a low concentration over a long period of time. Such a low concentration is less dangerous to plants than the high concentrations obtained by the wet method.

The proper dosage is influenced by the tightness of the house, the nature of the insect to be controlled and the tolerance of the plants to the fumes. In a house where several different species of

FIG. 199.—Canvas curtain to screen limited part of greenhouse for fumigation.

plants are growing it is wise to begin with less than the quantity that the plant species most susceptible can stand (Table 19) and gradually increase the amount in subsequent fumigations until the desired kill of insects has been reached.

The first fumigation should be at the rate of one-eighth ounce per 1,000 cubic feet of air space (disregarding benches, pipes, flower pots and other things in the house). If necessary the next dose may be stepped up to one-fourth ounce, or in some cases (with extra resistant plants, leaky houses, etc.) to one ounce per 1,000 cubic feet.

Where weighing of the dust is inconvenient the powder may be measured. Two level tablespoonfuls weigh approximately one ounce. To apply the dust weigh or measure the proper amount (as calculated from Table 19 and the cubical contents of the house). Place this in a container which will enable it to be spread evenly on the walks. Avoid leaving the dust in lumps because these retard or prevent even distribution of gas. Start at one end and work backward toward the exit (Fig. 198). In a large house at least two persons should work in parallel walks at the same time when applying the dust. An evenly spread layer down the center will fumigate a house 40′ wide. In large ranges of houses where it is desired to fumigate certain blocks only, cloth curtains may be hung in such ways as to shut them off (Fig. 199).

Many growers simplify their fumigations by having a container (or containers) a bottle or a mason jar with a sifter top, (Fig. 198) for each house they wish to fumigate. The correct amount of the fumigant is put into the container so for each house it is established and will not have to be computed again.

215. Preparation of the house for fumigation.—The house should not be watered for at least 24 hours before the fumigation. The best conditions may be obtained by allowing the house to cool down during the day. At the start of the fumigation the temperature should be at least 55° F. and rising, rather than falling.

The walks need not be absolutely dry, but should have no pools of standing water. If steam pipes run under the walks thereby causing them to be unusually dry, it would be wise to sprinkle them lightly about two hours before starting the fumigation.

Plan to fumigate before an application of manure, rather than after, as ammonia tends to neutralize hydrocyanic acid gas and would, therefore, greatly reduce the concentration. Do not fumigate for at least a week after bringing manure into the house.

The Fumigation. You have the house properly prepared and the proper dosage of the material in the sprinkler-top containers, and ready for the fumigation, sprinkle the fumigant thinly and evenly on the walks of the house. Arrange the sprinkling so that it will not be necessary to walk over areas already covered with the material, on the way out of the house. Close and lock the door.

216. Avoid entering the house after the fumigation is over until after the fumes have dissipated. **ALWAYS REMEMBER: HYDROCYANIC ACID GAS IS ONE OF THE MOST DANGEROUS POISONS KNOWN.** Also remember that certain persons are susceptible to even minute quantities. *If the gas is accidentally breathed go at once to the open air and breathe deeply and fast. If the powder is accidentally swallowed promptly induce vomiting and take peroxide of hydrogen internally. Keep emetics and peroxide on hand in case of emergency.*

217. Cyanid fumigation is greatly influenced by the weather. It should not be done on a windy or a rainy night, nor when the relative air humidity and the temperature are high. A combination of 90% humidity with 70 or higher temperature is almost sure to result in burning. A rising temperature is preferable to a falling one because the latter causes moisture to deposit on the leaves and increases the danger of burning.

By morning in most cases the gas will have practically disappeared; therefore, it will not be necessary to open the ventilators to air the house.

The key to a successful and satisfactory fumigation is to have good evaporating conditions in the house during the fumigation.

The better they are the safer and more satisfactory will be the fumigation.

218. Special Procedure for Tender Plants and Mixed Houses.—Plants such as sweet peas, fern asparagus, jasminium, artillery plant, marguerite, wandering jew, snapdragon and lettuce are known to be rather tender. This tenderness may be overcome,

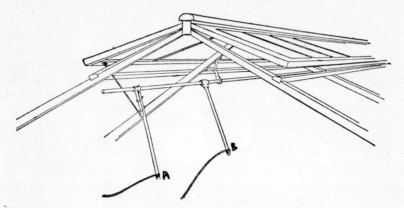

Fig. 200.—Cord method of opening ventilators from outside greenhouse.

by being particularly careful about the temperature while the fumigation is going on. It is recommended that the temperature be raised 5° or 10° F. during the fumigation and not be allowed to drop below any point to which it is raised. This is to insure good evaporating conditions, thereby preventing the possibility of moisture condensing on the plants.

Example of procedure: Mixed house infested with aphis and white fly. Time of fumigation—Tuesday night. House last watered—Monday morning. Temperature of house—about 55° F., dosage—¼ ounce of calcium cyanid dust per 1,000 cubic feet. Distribute as evenly as possible on the walks throughout the house. (A level tablespoonful of the material weighs about ½ ounces). Close house and arrange to raise temperature gradually to 60° or 65° by *morning. Be sure that the temperature is not lowered.* If starting temperature is above that in the example given, it should be raised in the same ratio as 60° to 65° or 65° to 70°.

219. Use of curtains.—In the open-range type of greenhouses where miscellaneous crops are grown, it is not always necessary or desirable to fumigate the whole series of houses at one time or with the same dosage. For example, when a particular insect is localized on one crop it may be unnecessary to fumigate the whole range, or it may be undesirable to do so when plants growing in the adjoining sections are likely to be injured by the dosage used. In such cases the house or portion to be fumigated may be separated from the others by canvas or muslin curtains cut in 50-foot lengths for convenient handling. The width should be such that the curtains when hung will make a partition from the roof to the ground.

The same object may be obtained by constructing a temporary partition of sash, resting on the ground and nailed to the eaves plate, or by using oiled or tarred paper fastened to upright wooden supports. When either of these devices is employed in mild weather the ventilators in the adjoining portions may be left open, or raised so far that any gas coming from the fumigated houses will soon escape. In extremely cold weather this cannot be done, because the plants might be chilled if the ventilators were left open (Fig. 200).

TABLE 20.—AMOUNT OF CYANIDE AND NUMBER OF FUMIGATIONS TO DESTROY GREENHOUSE PESTS

Insects	Ounces per 1,000 cubic feet.	Number of fumigations required.	Interval between fumigations.
			Days.
Aphids [1]	½	1	
Azalea lacewing	½	1	
Thrips	½	2	10.
Greenhouse white fly	½	3	7 to 9.
Long scale	¾	1	
Greenhouse Orthezia	¾	2	21 to 28.
Palm mealybug	2½	1	
Palm aphis	2½	1	
Long-tailed mealybug	2½	2	Do.
Florida red scale	2½	2	Do.
Thread scale	2½	2	Do.
Aspidistra scale	2½	2	Do.
Soft brown scale	2½	2	Do.
Hemispherical scale	2½	2	Do.
Tessellated scale	2½	2	Do.
Florida fern caterpillar	5	1	
Citrus mealybug [2]	5	2	Do.

[1] For the most part aphids can be controlled with ½ ounce of sodium cyanid per 1,000 cubic feet, although a few species are resistant to this gas and not so readily killed.

[2] The green house orthezia and mealy bugs around the roots of plants are difficult to kill so this dosage is recommended only for those occurring above the soil.

The data presented in the tables represent actual results of experimental tests under the conditions stated, and are not intended as definite recommendations. Differences in dosages and in length of exposure are intended to suggest the probable range of conditions under which a given fumigation might be expected to be safe or effective. For example, in the summer the duration of a fumigation may be restricted to from 3 to 10 hours, whereas in the winter months it might last from 10 to 15 hours.

Percentage mortality of various greenhouse insects obtained by the use of calcium granules at rates indicated.

220. How much cyanid to use.—To determine the dosage of cyanid [1] when various species of plants and insects are present, ascertain from Table 19 the plants most easily injured by the gas and

[1] If potassium cyanid is used in place of sodium cyanid, the formula should be as follows: For each ounce of 98 to 99% potassium cyanid containing 38.4% cyanogen use 1 ounce of sulphuric acid and 3 ounces of water. The yield from 1 ounce of high-grade sodium cyanid is equivalent to the yield from 1½ ounce of high-grade potassium cyanid.

note the amount of cyanid used per 1,000 cubic feet with little or no injury. Then multiply the cubic feet content of the greenhouse by the amount of cyanid to be used per 1,000 cubic feet. For example. if ½ ounce of cyanid is to be used per 1,000 cubic feet and the greenhouse contains 15,000 cubic feet, the total amount of cyanid necessary would be 7½ ounces.

Roses, rose geranium, asparagus, ferns, lemon verbena, snapdragon, wandering jew, or sweet pea can be fumigated with safety with an initial dosage of ½ ounce of sodium cyanid per 1,000 cubic feet.

TABLE 21.—PERCENTAGE OF MORTALITY OF VARIOUS GREENHOUSE INSECTS OBTAINED BY USE OF CALCIUM CYANIDE AT RATES INDICATED

Insect	Dosage per 1,000 cubic feet	Exposure	Temperature at beginning of exposure	Humidity at beginning of exposure	Number of specimens	Per cent of mortality
	Ounces	Hours	° F.	Per cent		
Greenhouse whitefly (adults), Trialeurodes vaporariorum Westw	¼	14	59	83	135	100
Thrips (adults)	1	10	69	90	65	85
Greenhouse leaf tyer (moths), Phlyctænia rubigalis Guen		4	65	65 .	32	100
Aphids :	½					
Brown chryanthemum aphid, Macrosiphoniella sanborni, Gill	¼	12	72	86	1,126	100
Green chrysanthemum aphid, Rhopalosiphum rufomaculata Wils .	¼	13	53	76	1,150	100
Peach aphid on carnation, Myzus persicae, Sulz	¼	13	63	84	880	63
Rose aphid :						
Macrosiphum sp.	¼	12	72	86	634	100
Myzaphis sp.	¼	12	66	90	3,000	100
Nasturtium or bean aphid, Aphis rumicis, Linn	¼	15	69	67	193	100
Sweet pea aphid, Illinoia pisi, Kalt	¼	13	53	76	238	98.7
Anuraphis helichrysi	¼	1	61	89	264	65.1
Mealybugs :						
Citrus mealybug, Pseudococcus citri, Risso	⅓	15	71	52	118	[1] 96.4
	5	13	72	55	199	93.9
Palm mealybug, Pseudococcus nipæ, Mask	½	15	68	42	413	97.3
	¾	15	70	59	158	96.2
Baker's mealybug, Pseudococcus maritimus, Ehrh	½	4	65	65	70	0
Greenhouse orthezia, Orthezia insignis, Dougl	½	12	73	85	25	100
Azalea bark scale, Eriococcus azaleæ, Comst	3	13	70	64	326	79.7
	3	16	64	38	70	100
Scale insects :						
Florida red scale, Chrysomphalus aonidum, Linn	½	15	68	42	90	97.8
	¾	15	70	59	355	100
Morgan's scale, Chrysomphalus dictyospermi, Morg	½	6	70	64	570	100
Orchid scale, Chrysomphalus biformis, Ckll	4	14	61	49	176	100
Boisduval's scale, Diaspis boisduvalii, Sign	1	12	66	85	650	100
Proteus scale, Parlatoria proteus, Curt	1	13	63	82	382 / 215	[1] 98.1 / [2] 23.2
Hemispherical scale, Saissetia hemisphaerica, Targ	½	15	68	42	21	94.4
	¾	16	69	67	75	100
Purple scale, Lepidosaphes beckii, Newm	2½	14	71	52	200	97.5

[1] Young. [2] Adult.

Table 20 gives the amount of sodium cyanid per 1,000 cubic feet needed to destroy insect pests most commonly found in greenhouses. Before fumigation is begun Table 19 must be consulted to determine the maximum dosage the plants actually in the greenhouse can stand without injury. If this dosage is less than that indicated in Table 20 complete control should not be attempted with one fumigation.

In case there is any doubt as to the amount of gas a plant will stand, it must be borne in mind that in some instances one fumigation will not be enough to effect absolute control of all stages of some insects without injury to foliage or growing parts of certain plants. Hence the necessity of smaller but repeated doses. For example, in houses containing such susceptible plants as coleus, ageratum, heliotrope, fuchsia, etc., greenhouse white fly can be eradicated with three successive fumigations at intervals of seven to nine days, using ½ ounce of sodium cyanid per 1,000 cubic feet with no injury to the foliage. Moreover,

Fig. 201.—Crocks and cyanide (in paper bags) placed ready for fumigation.

such resistant pests as scale insects can be eliminated entirely by killing the immature stages with small dosages repeated at frequent intervals.

221. The wet method still has many advocates though it is losing ground because it is more cumbersome and risky than the dry one. Among claims made for it are that it gives higher concentrations of gas in less time and thus proves more effective as a killer of animal life. On the other hand it is claimed with equal soundness that this very concentration is likely to damage the plants more than the weaker one. Doubtless the concentration of gas is greatest near the generators and weakest remote from them and therefore less uniform than from the evenly distributed powder on the walks as in the dry method. But both concentrations and effects are influenced by the operators.

The wet method (Fig. 201) is objected to chiefly because of its cumbersomeness, the extra work it entails and the greater risks run when handling the chemicals. Precautions necessary in using it are the same as for the dry method, except that additional care must be exercised when handling the sulphuric acid.

Glazed earthenware jars (½ and 1 gallon) serve as satisfactory generators, though it is preferable that the bottoms be rounded inside, so that the cyanid will be covered with even small doses of acid and water, thus insuring the maximum generation of gas.

Correct scales or balances, reading in tenths of an ounce, are convenient for accurate work. An 8-ounce graduate is desirable for measuring acid and water. To avoid splashing the acid should not be poured from the carboy or bottle into the graduate but into a porcelain pitcher, from which it may be poured with safety. It is well to have on hand a supply of small bags in which to place the cyanid.

The chemicals required in fumigating with hydrocyanic-acid gas are sodium or potassium cyanid, sulphuric acid, and water. Sodium cyanid should be practically free from chlorin and contain not less than 51% of cyanogen. It may be bought either in lumps or in 1-ounce "eggs." The latter are easily handled so weighing each charge is obviated, provided the dosage is in ounces. For example, if a greenhouse requires 10 ounces of cyanid, 10 "eggs" are used. In small dosages, however, where the cyanid is measured in grams, it is necessary to use small lumps.

Commercial sulphuric acid (about 1.84 sp. gr. or 66 Baumé) approximately 93% pure, commonly used, gives satisfactory results. It should be kept in a glass receptacle, properly labeled and tightly stoppered.

The chemicals should be mixed in the following proportions: For 1 ounce sodium cyanamid, 1½ ounce of sulphuric acid and 2 fluid ounces of water.

After the generators have been distributed throughout the greenhouse, and before the chemicals have been mixed, the cyanid should be weighed accurately and the proper amount for each generator placed in a paper bag near the generator. The chemicals should be mixed invariably in the following manner:

1. Measure and place in each generator the amount of water required; 2. measure and pour in the sulphuric acid required; 3. gently drop the cyanid into the diluted warm acid, immediately leave the greenhouse, and post a danger sign on the closed door.

The operator should begin at the generator farthest from the door and work toward the door. In case there are two rows of generators the cyanid should be dropped simultaneously by two operators. As little time as possible should elapse between the ad-

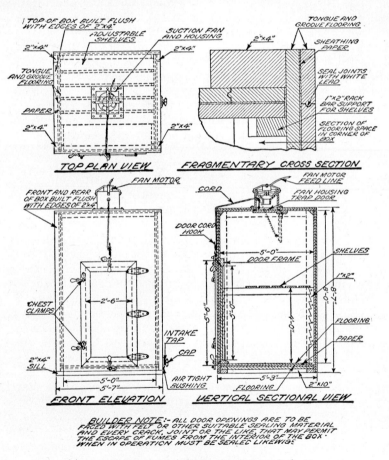

FIG. 202.—Box for fumigating small lots of plants.

dition of the acid and the addition of the cyanid, as the heat which is liberated by the mixing of the acid and the water assists in the generation of the gas.

The residue left in the generators after fumigation should be buried or poured into a sink and the generators washed before being stored for future operations.

The number of generators to be employed will depend largely upon the size of the greenhouse. They should be so arranged that the gas will be distributed uniformly throughout the inclosure. To secure this advantage several generators should be used rather than one large one. Generators should be spaced from 20′ to 25′ apart (Fig. 201), and in case of a light wind a few extra ones should be placed on the windward side of the greenhouse. An ounce to each jar is as small a dose as is practicable, unless the generators are well rounded inside at the base or well tilted.

Short exposure with a greater strength of gas is more satisfactory than a weaker strength of gas overnight. In fact, better results will be gained if the exposures do not exceed one to two hours. An exposure of one hour is satisfactory in most instances. Short exposures also have the additional advantage of permitting the greenhouse to become thoroughly aired previous to the rising of the sun.

222. **Fumigation box.**—Florists and nurserymen will find it advantageous to have a fumigation box for the following purposes: 1, In preliminary tests, to determine the quantity of gas that plants can stand without injury to the several stages of growth; 2, to rid individual or potted plants of insects when an isolated infestation is discovered, and thus to avoid the frequently used costly and laborious hand scrubbing of the plants; 3, when it is unnecessary to fumigate an entire greenhouse (Fig. 202).

Its use is almost indispensable for such plants as orchids, palms, aspidistra, and ferns, and has an advantage in that it may be used in the daytime; whereas house fumigation can be performed with safety only after dark. Moreover, in box fumigation such factors as leakage, light, moisture, and temperature, which influence the success of treatment, vary less than in greenhouses.

The capacity of the box will naturally depend on the size of the establishment and the amount of fumigating to be done. For the framework use 2″ by 4″ material, and for the double walls roof, and floor use 2″ tongue-and-groove pine sheathing, or matched lumber with heavy building paper or wall board between. The material of the inside walls should run horizontally and that of the outside walls vertically. The door should be built somewhat like that of a refrigerator and swing on three heavy hinges, the edges closing against a felt or rubber seat. Similar precautions should be taken to make the casings of the ventilator in the roof air-tight.

If the volume of business warrants it, the walls may be made of concrete, or glazed hollow tile laid in cement. A series of adjustable shelves, as shown in the plans, upon which the plants can be placed, permits a better diffusion of the gas around the material to be fumigated. The suction fan referred to in the plans is not absolutely necessary, except when the box is built within a commercial packing or shipping room in which many people may be working, or when time is a factor; in other cases the ordinary ventilator is a sufficient opening to permit the escape of the gas.

Fumigation boxes should not remain exposed to the weather, as they will soon warp and become unfit for use. For this reason it is advisable also to keep doors and ventilators closed when the box is not in operation.

XI

GRAFTING—GENERAL CONSIDERATIONS

223. Grafting which includes grafting proper, budding and inarching, is the natural or artificial process of making a part of one plant unite with and grow upon the roots of another. A graft, therefore, may be considered as a cutting which unites some of its tissues with those of another plant or plant part with or without forming either callus or roots, as always happens when cuttings are developed into independent plants. Graftage is not invariably used for propagation. In some of its forms (bridge and repair grafting) it is used to save broken limbs and even whole trees girdled by mice or other animals (Fig. 224).

Graftage is of ancient origin as a horticultural process. In his Natural History (Vol. 2), Pliny about 2,000 years ago, wrote about it as common practice, but its methods have been kept largely as trade secrets or mysteries until within the last half century or so. Pliny says the art was taught by nature. But he goes too far, for he declares that cherry has been found growing on willow, sycamore on laurel, laurel on cherry and so on. Such cases, except as noted (232), are not grafts at all but are merely trees of one kind growing on the soil held in crevices of another kind—cases by no means rare.

224. Stock, any plant part, usually root or stem, in which a bud or a scion is inserted to propagate a plant species, variety or strain.

225. Scion, any plant part, usually of a stem, inserted in a stock for propagation. It may consist of one bud with little or no wood, as in budding, or of one or more buds with one or more inter-nodes, as in grafting.

226. Objects of graftage.—Graftage may be used: 1, To alter plant character by modifying wood, foliage, or fruit produced. 2, To develop branches, flowers or fruit where they are lacking on trees or shrubs. 3, To enhance the vigor of defective or exhausted trees and shrubs. 4, To facilitate reproduction of diœcious plants by grafting in scions of the lacking sex. 5, To propagate and preserve varieties of countless woody and some herbaceous plants which cannot be conveniently reproduced by other means.

Necessity for graftage. Since seedage is usually quicker and

cheaper, graftage is seldom used to propagate species. Only such
species as produce seed sparingly under cultivation are so reproduced. For similar reasons cuttage and layerage are preferred for
most shrubs. Graftage finds its chief application, therefore, in the
propagation of varieties and strains of woody plants that do not
come true from seeds and that cannot be cheaply or conveniently
enough grown from cuttings, layers or by other asexual methods.
All our named varieties of tree fruits, nuts and many ornamentals
such as azaleas and roses (not all roses, by any means) are more

FIG. 203.—Living wood braces to prevent splitting of Y-crotches.

or less propagated by one or more methods of graftage. As in other
asexual methods, graftage will produce the same variety as the parent tree or shrub, bud sports excepted.

For these reasons graftage is a necessary business process, because planters demand stock true to a definite standard of quality,
size, trueness to type and ability to meet other requirements which
can be met, at least among woody and many herbaceous plants, only
by asexual means. Graftage has been proved by commercial nurseries to be economical. If this were not so, other methods would
be followed; for nurserymen are human enough to choose the ways
that give results most satisfactory to all concerned; otherwise they
could not long be in the business. Hence east of the Mississippi
Valley pome fruits are still largely root-grafted in winter; never in
the West. Even apples are now largely budded. Budding is popular
in the West. Pit fruits are budded in summer. Currants are grown

from spring-set cuttings and so on; each kind of plant is propagated by the method that most economically gives best results.

238. Unreliability of seeds. Graftage or some other asexual process is necessary also because seeds cannot be relied upon to produce, true-to-name, varieties of tree and bush fruits or of many shrubs, herbaceous perennials and other plants. The reason is that the type has not been fixed by seedage as in the case of many vegetables, annuals and perennial flowers.

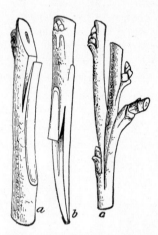

For instance, if seeds of Baldwin apple, Bartlett pear, or Salwey peach were sown, all we might be able to say of the young trees grown would be that they were respectively apple and peach trees; possibly not one would resemble the parent enough to deserve the varietal name in any of these cases.

The cause of this lies in the fact that from prehistoric time flowers of fruits have naturally cross pollinated, perhaps usually not been fertilized by their own pollen, by that from other flowers in the same cluster nor even the same tree, but from some different tree. Wind and insects are the chief carriers of the pollen which impress parental characters upon the ovules in the flowers of our Baldwin apple or Salwey peach so the seedlings may be better, but the overwhelming chances are they will not be even as good. This form of reproduction, continued for countless centuries, has mixed things up so that seeds cannot be relied upon in the classes mentioned. The exceptions are so conspicuous they prove the rule.

FIG. 204.—Grafting conifers. a, stock; b, scion in English cleft graft; C, English method for cypress, juniper, etc.

Among peaches the Honey group, grown to some extent in Florida, and the Heath Cling come fairly true to type from seed. Among apples it is said Oldenburg, Yellow Transparent and some other Russian varieties do likewise.

229. The cambium lies between the wood (xylem) of the stem or the root and the bark (phloëm). By bringing the cambium of the stock in close contact with that of the scion the union of the two parts is possible. The cambium is the growing or cell-multiplying part of the plant. It is limited to a layer comparable to tissue paper in thinness.

230. Importance of graftage.*—Though one of the most im-

---

* Paragraph 230 has been considerably condensed from Technical Bulletin No. 2, by F. A. Waugh, of the Massachusetts Agricultural College.

portant of horticultural processes, graftage is one of the most intricate. Because of its importance and the difficulties in solving its problems it has given rise to much study and many theories often based on imperfect observations in disregard of obvious and simple facts.

Graftage is said to be the union of a scion with a stock. So far as nurserymen and fruit grower are concerned this is the prime aim.

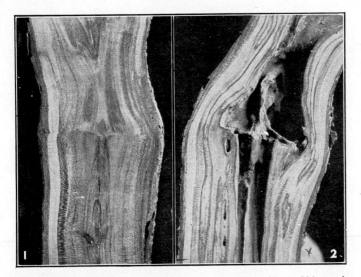

Fig. 205.—Plum grafts. 1, continuous layers of wood; 2, Old wood of stock and scion partly eaten out by ants. Work of ants in unprotected stock and scion.

Success or failure from their standpoint depends upon the nature of this union. The terms good and poor unions are among the commonest in horticultural parlance; yet their meaning is generally conjectured. The easy statement that stock and scion grow together does not satisfy the question, How do they unite? The popular idea is that the union is like the knitting of a broken bone, also that both stock and scion produce new tissues which commingle more or less as human skin does after the surgical operation of skin grafting. But both these suppositions are vague and far from the truth. Possibly in herbaceous grafting where soft growing tissues are used there may be unions of these characters, but even in such cases the blending seems to be purely local; for original stock and original scion maintain their individuality—each will produce fruit after its kind.

In graftage of mature wood such a blending is impossible; for with the exception of the cambium layer both stock and scion consist almost wholly of dead heartwood and dead bark which cannot unite with anything.

It is different to say the cambium layers of stock and scion unite. But even this statement does not explain the process, though it leads in the right direction, for the cambium and a few layers of cells on each side of it are the only part of an exogenous stem really alive. Upon the cambium depends the possibility of a graft union. (Fig. 206.)

Naked eye examinations of cross or transverse sections of successful grafts several years old will show 1, that scion and stock have not united and 2, that wood produced after the union is as continuous as in an ungrafted stem. At least in the layers that bury a graft junction whatever difference there may be is not apparent. The truth of the diagram (Fig. 207) is fully supported by photographic cross sections of both grafted and budded stems (Fig. 208). In every case the line of demarcation between stock and scion and also the continuous envelopes of new tissues may be clearly seen. Thus it is evident that: 1, Stock and scion do not unite; they remain distinct (Fig. 209). 2, Annual layers produced after grafting do not unite in the common meaning of that term; each is complete and continuous. 3, In hardwood graftage, "union" of stock and scion is different in its physical nature from the sense of common speech. (Figs. 210, 211.)

These simple obvious conclusions suggest questions and doubts

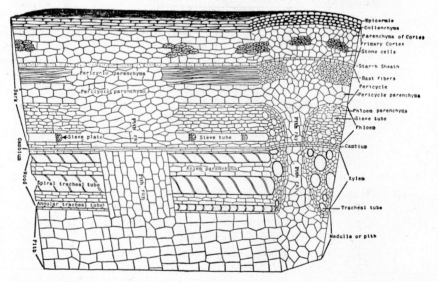

Fig. 206.—Diagram to show tissues derived from primary meristems (after Stevens). Note between bark and wood limited cambium layer essential to successful graftage.

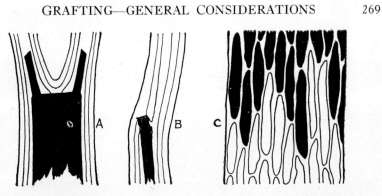

Fig. 207.—Diagrams of graft and bud unions. A, cleft graft three years old; B, bud graft at three years; C, separateness of stock and scion.

which do much to disguise the main facts. For instance, the horticulturist knows that when a pear scion is grafted on a quince stock, fruit buds above the union will produce pears and those below, quinces. But there is a division (and there must be) between the two kinds of wood (Figs. 212, 213). What is its nature? How definite is it? Is it physically strong or weak? Would answers to these questions be more than speculations? It must be remembered, however, that such answers are beyond the conclusions cited above and that the facts so far presented are not affected by the following discussion.

Sections of grafts (Figs. 214, 215) show that in spite of the longitudinal continuity of the annual layers there is sometimes a plainly visible line of demarcation between the wood of stock and scion at right angles to the longitudinal growth, yet the microscope

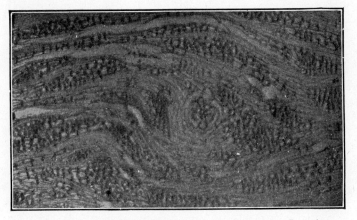

Fig. 208.—Highly magnified section through young graft. Round mass of scar tissue near center merely accidental.

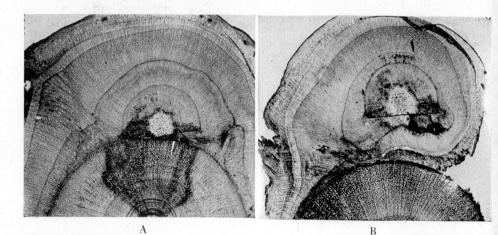

A

B

Fig. 209.—Inlay bark grafts. A, normal; die-back in wood exposed in grafting. Retarded union on right but normal in second year; B, defective, lack of pressure permitted callus from scion to penetrate between scion and stock. Original stock dead at this level. To accommodate stretching of scion more or less longitudinal re-orientation at union zone.

Fig. 210.—Bud union of apple on apple from first grade nursery stock. Union is well within bark flaps at points indicated by arrows. This is common condition.

does not reveal the secret of individual cells which compose the tissue. One can nearly always see less with the microscope than with the naked eye! In the section shown in Fig. 208 and magnified about 1,000 times, the little knot near the middle accidentally shows one point on the line of junction, but the vessels and the cells run from end to end without interruption. So it is harder than ever to see where stock ends and scion begins. Hence those gardeners who have been dreaming of producing new kinds of plants by grafting must needs wake up; for no matter how closely the two kinds of cells may be against each other their contents never mingle to produce a new cell. Every cell is the production by division of some other cell; never the product of fusion of two parent cells. The commingling of stock and scion cells is purely physical, not physiological.

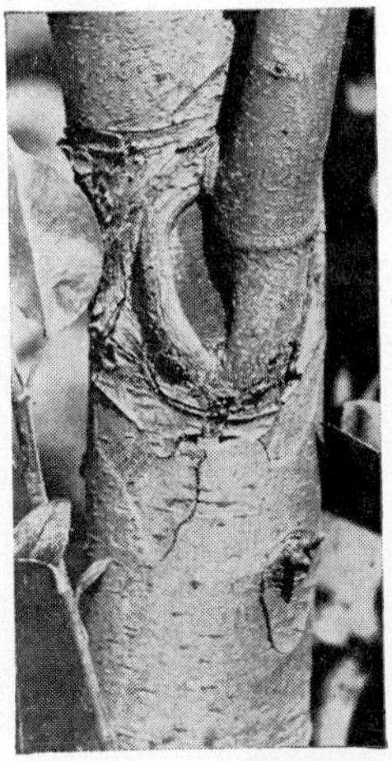

In budding (merely a form of graftage) the layers of new growth are continuous—just as in the graft. A successful bud graft cut shows precisely the same conditions as in grafting, except that the line of demarcation is less easy to see!

FIG. 211.—Growth from adventitious bud on callus lip has stimulated growth of lip on that side. This illustrates handicap of callus which must surmount rim (whether in wound or graft) with its source of supply below that rim.

The physical strength of unions is often discussed by horticulturists, many of whom claim that this is a point of weakness (231). Others claim that a successful graft union is the strongest point of the stem. Common observation shows that the region of graftage is

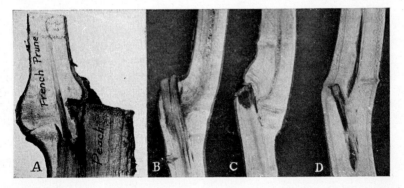

FIG. 212.—Sections of graft. A, French prune on peach—incompatability of stock and scion; B, C, D, bud grafts of plum one and three years old. Note old stock wood and continuous layers of young tissue.

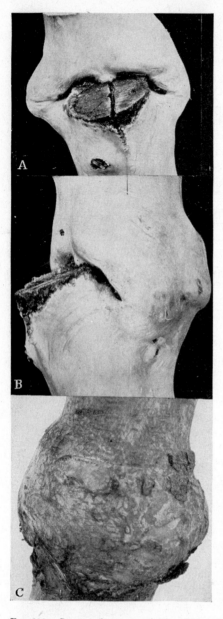

more or less swollen by the deposition of woody tissue and cross sections at such points show close-grained wood. Often when grafts are cut open and dried the tissues check and split less at the junction point than above or below, thus showing extra strength of fibers. Observation also shows that when winds break off branches in old orchards a majority of the fractures occur not where the grafts have been made but at other points.

Yet grafts do sometimes break even after years of apparently healthy growth. Why? Possibly because of physiological unlikeness or aversion (if such a term may be permitted). The wound heals slowly or poorly; loose primary or scar, instead of stronger tissue, fills the space and weakness follows. (Fig. 217.) Clairgeau pear on quince and domestica plum on peach are familiar examples. But setting aside such cases, if stock and scion are congenial to each other and if the scion (or bud) grows at all, the union should be good. Poor manipulation will cause many failures of grafts to grow, but will rarely affect strength of union in grafts which live. All degrees of physical strength may be seen in graft unions from those

FIG. 213.—Suspected uncongeniality—Rhode Island Greening on Oldenburg (Duchess). A, front view—bark removed; scion grew over stock without making union at rim; B, side view, scion turned away from rim of stock but in time grew part way over it from below rather than from above; C, rear view of specimen before bark was removed.

stronger than the contiguous parts of the same stems to those incapable of holding themselves in place.

231. Physical strength of graft unions. From the standpoint of plant anatomy and physiology grafts may be weak in several ways: 1, Physical weakness at point of union; 2, scion leaves may find it difficult to elaborate sap taken up by stock roots; 3, stock roots may find difficulty in assimilating plant food elaborated by leaves; 4, there may be an interruption in the upward flow of water and soluble minerals due to faulty connection of the xylem vessels at the point of union; 5, a similar one in the downward flow, due to faulty union of the phloëm;

Fig. 214.—Cherry scion on plum stock. Despite longitudinal continuity of annular layers line of demarkation is visible between stock and scion.

6, the quantity taken up by the root may be too much or too little for the proper supply of the scion.

Concerning these points N. O. Booth of the Oklahoma station conducted experiments from which the following points are taken.

Physical weakness is a difficult question because of the variation

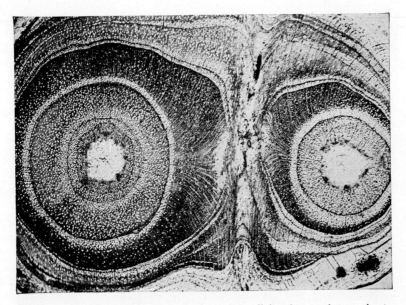

Fig. 215.—"Natural graft" of apple formed by living brace of two shoots twisted together from opposite limbs. Sections of this sort of union show decreased width in rings at zone of initial contact.

between different trees and different unions of stock and scion. To test it, the wood of 10-year-old trees was tested as to its physical strength by a machine used for such purposes. Except in the last case cited below, the tests were purposely made within three weeks of the trees felling, because it was believed green wood rather than seasoned represents more nearly conditions in growing trees.

TEST OF TRANSVERSE BREAKING STRENGTH

	At union point, lbs.	Above union point, lbs.
Plum, first block	2,540	4,750
Plum, second block	3,160	4,950

To eliminate possible discrepancy due to the breaking point of the union being closer to the ground, and hence possibly in softer wood, the next block was broken above and below as well as at the union.

TEST OF TRANSVERSE BREAKING STRENGTH

	At union point, lbs.	Above union point, lbs.	Below union point, lbs.
Apricot, first block	3,300	8,260	4,100
Apricot, second block ...	2,560	7,940	——

Tensile strength of one-half-inch strips of apricot: No. 1 broke at union with 1,330 pounds pull; above, 1,550; No. 2 broke slightly below union with 2,870 pounds pull, slightly above 1,770, but would not break at union.

TEST OF TRANSVERSE BREAKING STRENGTH

	At union point, lbs.	Above union point, lbs.
Apricot, seasoned four months	1,930	4,355

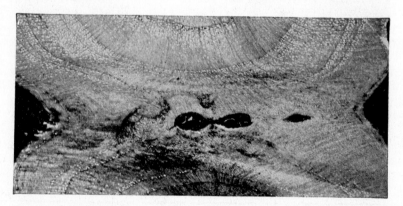

FIG. 216.—Complete union in natural graft. Bark inclusions at point of initial contact where pressures were directly opposite.

The results, Professor Booth points out, "are very positive and it does not seem at all likely that further tests will invalidate the statement that for many trees the point of union is a real and evident weakness. It is true, however, that all three trees tested were apparently strong, had made vigorous growth and had never broken in any way. They were about 8″ thick and about ten years old. For orchard purposes this weakness does not appear to be of importance. There is also no question but that the thickening of the trunk, which usually shows at the point of union, may lessen materially the weakness of the trunk at this point."

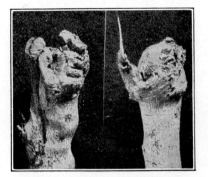

FIG. 217.—Defective pear bud graft on quince stock.

"On the other hand," comments W. L. Howard, "it is a matter of common experience in California to find incompatible graft unions where the trees seem to flourish for a time (two or three years) and then break off—prunes, almonds and some peaches on apricot and Bartlett or Kieffer pear on quince." (Fig. 269.)

232. Limits of graftage.—Theoretically, botanists and nurserymen have limited graftage to the exogens, plants which have a cambium layer in a definite region beneath a bark layer; for the process depends upon the intimate union of this layer between stock and scion. Of the 151 orders, 890 genera and 4,200 species listed in Gray's *Field Forest and Garden Botany,* 110 orders, 650 genera and 3,000 species come under this ruling and (theoretically) may be grafted, while the balance, the endogens which lack the cambium sheath (oat, bamboo, palm) cannot be grafted. With experimental exceptions this is so.

Among exogens botanical relationship seems in most cases to be fundamental to success in graftage which is usually easy between varieties of the same species (apple upon apple) and often between closely related species. But rarely, and then mostly experimentally, can distantly related species be grafted successfully; probably not at all from a business standpoint (313).

A few instances may emphasize these points. Though pear is commercially grafted upon quince to form dwarf trees, apple is seldom or never so treated, and quince does not succeed on either pear or apple; gooseberry may be grafted upon only one species of currant (*Ribes aureum*) but currants do not succeed on gooseberries: apples succeed commercially only upon apple stock; peaches and plums will each grow upon the other. For years Prunet tried to make chestnuts grow upon oak in the hope of preventing certain diseases. His conclusions are that the plan will not succeed commercially, though he was successful in many instances.

Fig. 218.—Natural braces. Limbs growing toward center of tree were twisted together. They will unite later.

While species of the same genus may be grafted successfully it may not be profitable so to do. From a physiological standpoint the best index of success is the general thriftiness of the plant so produced; from a business standpoint, the fact that nurserymen and other plant propagators stick by the methods that make them most money. To be successful, stock and scion must both unite firmly without seriously checking plant activity and continue growth until normal fruit is ripened.

233. **Common rules of graftage.**—Graftage in one from or another and with various species of plants may be done during almost any month provided the method be adapted to the time of year and to other conditions. Always it is essential that the parts fit snugly. Positively the cambium layer of the scion must be in intimate contact with that of the stock. This layer is most active during early spring when the buds are swelling and the leaves are expanding. A second period of activity occurs usually soon after midsummer, but

sometimes not until early fall, dependent largely upon the amount of moisture in the soil.

During these two periods wounds heal most rapidly and union between stock and scion is most certain. At other times, since the cambium becomes firmer and less distinct because of the develop-

Fig. 219.—Top working orchard trees. A, scion making, note convenient receptacle for scions, hook handled saw hanging from pocket and heater keeping wax pliable; B, waxing graft; C, gang of grafters, man on left saws branches, middle man makes clefts and inserts scions, man on right waxes. Note: Better results usually follow when grafting covers three or four years instead of only one or two when work is done on mature trees.

ment of other tissues from it, the union of stock and scion is less sure. At such seasons it is also more important to cover the wounds to prevent or check loss of moisture from the wounds. (Fig. 219.)

234. **Wax** or some sealing substance is usually used in outdoor work where the wood itself is cut, but where only the bark is wounded as in budding, it is necessary to bind only the bark firmly over the bud and the wound until the union is complete. Then the bindings must be cut to prevent strangulation. If rubber is used as a binding material, it need not be cut since it rots in due time, thus cutting down the overhead by eliminating one nursery operation (cutting of ligatures). It is an erroneous theory that cleft grafts will die if the adjacent bark of the stock is wounded seriously. The bark serves scarcely a greater purpose than that of protecting the tissues beneath. Scions often grow in the almost total absence of the bark of the stock, provided proper protection is given and the formation of new bark thus encouraged.

It is necessary that each scion have at least one sturdy bud. As a rule, only mature buds, or those approximately mature, are employed, though in herbaceous grafting younger ones may be used. Scions may be inserted in whole or piece roots, crowns, trunks, branches; in fact, any part that will meet the requirements of scion nutrition (as tubers of dahlia, potato). The way of setting may vary from merely placing a bud beneath the bark to inserting a woody scion in the wood of a stock, as in cleft grafting. Again the work may be done with dormant specimens at any time of year or upon active wood during the growing season. The methods and variations are countless; but in general only a few are simple and quick enough to be of wide or general use. The others are more for the specialist and for finikin subjects which the average nurseryman, gardener or florist will not "fuss with."

XII

METHODS OF GRAFTING

235. Classification of graftage.—Graftage methods naturally fall into three general classes: 1, Inarching, or grafting by approach; 2, scion grafting, or true grafting; and 3, bud grafting, or, to use its popular term, budding.

236. Inarching, or grafting by approach (Figs. 220 to 222), which is often placed in a class by itself, for convenience may be treated here. The only point that distinguishes it from other styles is that the scion is not separated from the parent plant until after union is complete. In other words, inarching makes one plant unite with another while still growing on its own roots.

In one method a small slice of stem of both stock and scion (Fig. 221), is cut with a sharp knife, the cut surfaces brought together and tied firmly until they have united. In outdoor practice waxing and staking are usually necessary to prevent drying and working loose. After union is complete the base of the scion and the top of

A   B   C   D

Fig. 220.—Inarching pears to cure black-end of fruit. A, one season's growth; poor practise to allow shoot (extreme left) to develop on seedling. Whole top of scion above union should be removed when inarch is made; B, long graft union with top of seedling removed, correct practice; C, ditto, after two season's growth; D, ditto five years old, inarch large enough to support tree.

the stock are cut away, thus leaving the scion growing on the stock.

While this is undoubtedly the original or natural method of grafting (since all grafts in the forest are formed in this way either between two trees or two limbs of the same tree), it has comparatively limited application in business horticulture, because other methods are less cumbersome and more economical of time and space. It is used, however, in Europe and elsewhere in the making of cordons, espaliers, etc.

In orchards where Y-crotches have been allowed to form it is also useful in establishing living braces between the arms of the Y. For ornamental purposes it has been used in the Boboli gardens at Florence, Italy, where an avenue 100 yards long has been arched over by European oaks whose tops have been united by modified inarching, the difference being that neither scion below the union nor stock above have been cut, but both allowed to grow.

In the tropics, inarching is used for propagating the mango. Seedlings are grown in 5″ or 6″ flower pots and placed on stands beneath trees to furnish scions and within easy reach of branches to be united, as already described. After union the potted trees are grown for a time in the nursery before being set in the orchard. Various citrus fruits and camelias were formerly inarched, but are now mostly veneer grafted.

Inarching on young seedlings, according to Oliver, has proved superior in simplicity, rapidity and results to inarching on plants in 5″ and 6″ pots. It has a wider range of adaptability than budding and requires less skill. The seedling may be

FIG. 221.—Inarching of potted plant. A, seedling stock; B, scion; C, stock and scion bound together; D, cuts on stock and scion to hasten union.

used either as stock or scion. Nurse plant propagation is a special form of seedling inarch in which the plants develop a strong aërial root from the base of the scion in about 18 months after the union of certain tropical fruits (mangosteen on related species of *Garcinia*) is considered complete and the stock top and seedling root have been severed. This root pierces the ground, after which both top and roots develop rapidly. The method has not been fully tested, but has been announced for other experimenters to test.

237. Inarching experiments.—Daniel concludes from many series of experiments with unrelated plants (kidney bean and cocklebur, kidney bean and castor bean, sunflower and melon, cabbage and tomato, chrysanthemum and tomato, Jerusalem artichoke and black nightshade, coleus and acaranthus, cineraria and tomato, aster and phlox, coleus and tomato, maple and lilac, zinnia and tomato) that "the old idea that only plants belonging to the same family can be grafted on each other does not apply to grafting by approach."

The most perfect grafts in these experiments were made between plants nearest alike in vigor and vegetation. The nature of the tissue of the different plants also played an important role. Tomato and cabbage and artichoke and nightshade gave good unions on account of their herbaceous nature and rapid growth, while aster and phlox, somewhat advanced in growth, and year-old maple and lilac united with difficulty except on very young shoots.

238. Inarching is extensively practiced on the Pacific Coast in commercial pear orchards which have been planted on Japanese root. Pear trees on this root produce fruit with hard or black calyx ends, and so are unmarketable. French pear rooted trees in the same sections produce normal fruits. Therefore, the attempt to change the Japanese to the French root system is made by inarching upon French pear seedling (Figs. 220 and 223).

Fig. 222.—Inarch of mango. A, stock; B, cutting scion in can of water; C, completed union with top of stock and bottom of scion cut off.

239. Grafting classified as to position.—So far as position is concerned, grafting may be classified as: 1, Root grafting, in which only a root is used as a stock; 2, crown grafting, in which scions are inserted in stocks at the collar; 3, trunk or stem grafting, in which they are set in the tree below the branches; and 4, top grafting in which the work is done among the limbs. Methods of inserting the scions may vary in all these classes.

Scion graftage is of three general kinds: Bridge or repair grafting, root grafting and top grafting.

240. Bridge or repair grafting sometimes erroneously called inarching, is not properly a propagation process, but it may well be discussed here, because it may be the means of saving valuable trees which have been injured by mice, rabbits, hogs, human carelessness or accident.

Unless the girdle or wound has cut through the sap wood it is an error to say that bridge grafting is necessary to re-establish connection between root and top; for the upward current of sap passes through the sap wood and not through the bark. It is correct, however, to say that the bridge establishes a connection between top and root, for the downward flow of elaborated sap is through the bark layers. As soon as the wound is discovered the operation should be performed. If the injury occurs in winter the wound should be protected to prevent drying. In spring when the buds begin to swell the grafting should be done. The operation is performed as follows (Fig. 224 and 225):

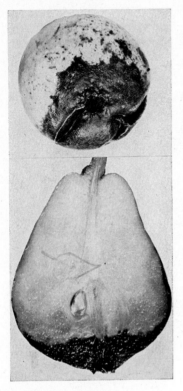

FIG. 223.—Black-end of Bartlett pear due to oriental pear stock.

The injured and perhaps dry bark, on both upper and lower edges of the wound is pared back to living tissue. Several scions are cut long enough to extend a little beyond these trimmed edges, and inserted beneath the bark both above and below, thus making little "bridges" across the gap. The ends of the scion are cut obliquely, to insure fitting of the cambium layers of scions and trunk. It is often a help to bow the scions outward slightly, because the spring thus formed aids in holding them in place. But these and other minor details may be left to individual preference. If placed 1″ or 2″ apart around the trunk, enough scions should succeed to save the tree. Both wound and scions should be completely covered with grafting wax, preferably made warm so as to fit into every chink and thus exclude air and water. In a few years the scions will grow together literally and in time lose their identity in a smooth trunk. (Fig. 226.)

Bridge grafting is a makeshift method not to be compared with proper protection of trunks by keeping animals out of the orchard, by avoiding accumulation of grass, straw, etc., in which mice might form nests, and by using trunk protectors—splints, tarred or building paper. but preferably ½″ galvanized hardware cloth—around the trunks at least until the trees have developed rough bark (Fig. 225). Such methods will prevent the necessity of bridge grafting except in cases of unusual accident.

When the girdles are narrow—say only 1" to 3"—no bridging may be necessary. In such cases, however, it is well to err on the safe side by covering the wound with grafting clay (half clay and fresh cow manure) and bandaging this in with cotton cloth, or by using grafting wax as described above. Often such wounds will heal over in a single season.

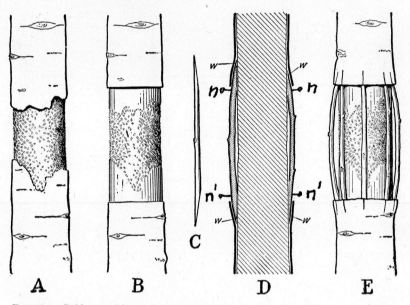

FIG. 224.—Bridge grafting. A, mouse gnawed; B, injured bark trimmed away; C, scion beveled at each end; D, scions slightly bowed in place across gap with beveled ends beneath bark. Brads driven to hold scions in place; E, ready for waxing.

241. Root grafting, perhaps the most generally practiced nursery method, is usually performed by means of the whip or tongue graft, a method employed only with small stocks generally one or two years old. It is oftenest done during winter in a cool, humid room. Should the air be too dry or too warm, the grafting wood may be injured by drying. Never should the work be done near a stove or a radiator for this reason. When necessary to use a warm room, stocks, scions and finished grafts should be kept covered with damp rags or burlap.

242. Grafting knives (Fig. 279) may be of any thin-bladed, sharp-edged style; at least for whip graft work. For herbaceous

FIG. 225.—Trees saved by bridge grafting. A, bridges several years old; B, young bridge. This latter was originally a water-sprout which started to grow below the injury. When a year old its top was bridged to the trunk.

and other delicate grafting a budding knife will answer. It is too light for most other methods. The knives popular in nursery practice have fixed wooden handles and cost about $2.50 a dozen.

243. Whole-root grafts.—(Figs. 227, 229, 230). When roots of seedling trees are used for grafting, just as they come from the soil, except for trimming and slight shortening, the resulting trees are said to be "whole-root grafts." To make such trees the graft is placed at the crown, so the term "root graft" is erroneously used, the proper term being "crown graft." The roots are by no means

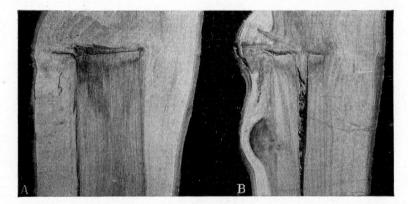

FIG. 226.—Sections of apple grafts. A, longitudinal; B, transverse.

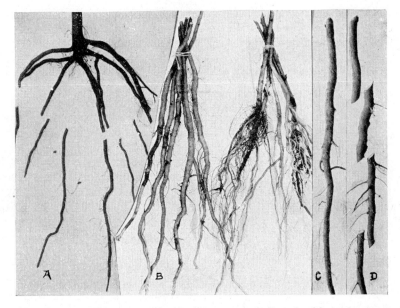

FIG. 227.—Seedling apple roots. A, one year, transplanted with tap root cut to make roots branch, popular for budding stocks; B, tap roots used for grafting; C, whole root; D, piece roots—exceptionally good specimen.

"whole"; first, because much has been unavoidably left in the ground when the seedling was dug, and second, because the roots must be shortened so the finished graft will not exceed 9″ and thus be too long for best handling in the nursery. The seedling roots are either single tap roots 4″ to 6″ long, or shorter where several branches occur near the crown. Usually the lateral roots are cut off close to the main root, otherwise the grafts are difficult to make and to handle both in bundling and in planting.

244. Piece-root grafts are made from scions 6″ or 7″ long and

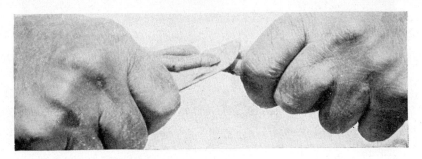

FIG. 228.—Cutting scion for whip graft.

bits of root only 3″ or 2″ long. (Figs. 227, 229, 230.) First grade, or number one, apple seedlings often make three and sometimes four pieces, though the average would probably be not more than 250

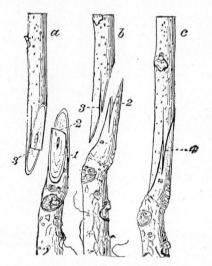

piece stocks to the 100 roots as bought. Number two seedlings will rarely reach 150 pieces to the 100 roots. When stock is costly or scarce nurserymen sometimes lengthen the scion and shorten the roots even to 1½″. One of the so-called advantages thus gained is that the scions develop roots after the grafts have been planted. The chief effect, then, of the root piece is to act as a nurse until the scion is able through its own roots to care for itself.

Short pieces have been specially popular in the Prairie States where, because of severe winters, roots as well as tops must be hardy. The practice there has been common to make scions 8″ to 12″ long, to use a very short piece and to plant as deep as the

FIG. 229.—Splice or whip graft. A, scion and stock, front view; b, side view; c, stock and scion fitted together.

top bud. By the time the tree is dug the nurse root may have fallen off or may be cut away. Thus trees are secured on their own roots and are considered superior to those in which the seedling roots are

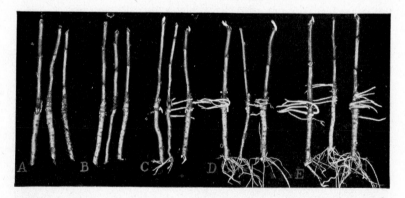

FIG. 229x.—Apple grafts (wealthy on French crab), stored in moist peat moss at various temperatures. Callusing proceeded nearly parallel with other growth activities. A, 5°C. for 48 days; B, 10°C. for 40 days; C, 10°C. for 48 days; D, 15°C. for 48 days; E, 15°C. for 48 days.

of unknown hardiness. Some varieties of apples readily take root from cuttings, but root grafting is favored.

245. Making root grafts.—The whip or tongue method is almost universally employed in the making of root grafts. A long oblique cut (Figs. 228 to 230) is made at the base of the scion. Then a sloping and very slightly curved cut is made half way between the lower and the upper ends of this first cut—about the center of the twig. Its direction is upward in the wood but not exactly with the grain. The knife blade is forced in not less than 1″ nor more than 1½″. Generally both cuts are made before the scion is cut from the scion stick. By this means the length of scions may be accurately gauged. Roots or stocks are cut in the same way, about 3″ long, except as noted. The top piece is cut at or perhaps ½″ above the crown or collar.

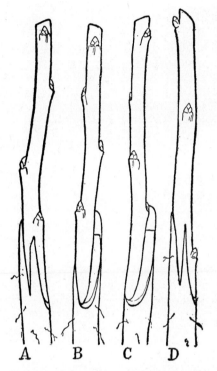

Fig. 230.—Importance of top bud position. A, in line with matched side of graft, best position; B, above lower lip of scion; C, above mismatched side of graft; D, above upper lip of stock.

Stocks and scions are then accurately and snugly fitted together so the tongues interlock and with the cambiums in contact. It is well that the diameters of stock and scion be approximately equal, though large stocks and small scions if properly fitted will give good results. Since it is usually impossible to have both sides of scion and stock come even, the cambiums on only one side need touch each other. When sloping and tongue cuts are made properly, stock and scion will fit together without overlapping ends of bark, which might not grow together and might thus present a point of infection for decay or disease. Crown gall (Fig. 318) or root knot, the chief enemy, seems unable to get a start except through a wound of some kind. Overlapping tongues mean imperfect unions and unhealed wounds for one or more years. (Fig. 235.)

After adjustment, stock and scion are bound together with knitting cotton, either waxed or not. Four or five turns around each end of the fitted parts are enough. To avoid tying, some operators pass

FIG. 231.—Growth of grafts according to position of top bud. A, *top,* top bud above lower lip of scion (Fig. 230B); B, above mismatched side (Fig. 230C); C, above matched side (Fig. 230A).

the first turn or two over the end of the string and draw the other end through the notch between stock and scion and snap off with a sudden jerk rather than a steady pull. Those who use waxed thread merely cross the last turn or two over the previous turns and break without tying or passing through the notch. The least possible quantity of thread of, say, No. 18 or 20 size, should be used— just enough to keep the parts in place until the grafts are planted. In order that the thread shall decay quickly, it should not be waxed. Indeed, some propagators contend that binding is a disadvantage because, they claim, that as the callus forms and the stem expands the cord cuts the soft tissues and thus favors the entrance of crown gall and hairy root (Fig. 318 and 319). Therefore they leave the grafts unwrapped, but use extra care in fitting the parts together.

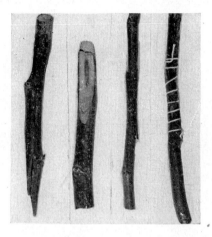

Fig. 232.—Whip graft winding. Starting at top, string is firmly wrapped across itself, then spirally downward, finally through lip of graft and cut off.

246. Callusing of Apple Cuttings and Grafts.—(Fig. 229 X). A particular impetus for the study of callus physiology, writes W. B. Shippy[1] has been given by the results of recent apple crown gall investigations which tend to show that the larger proportion of overgrowths on root-grafted trees are not bacterial tumors but callus tumors, formed chiefly as proliferations of the scion lip (Melhus, 1926). The fact that overgrowths may be non-parasitic in origin does not minimize their importance, but throws the emphasis of control on the regulation of growth processes of individual plants. This would obviate the consideration of their spread from one plant to another, the problem being rather one of inhibiting the excessive formation of callus cells at the graft union because of the frequent occurrence of overgrowths at this point.

Just as suitable conditions of heat, moisture, and oxygen are essential for the growth of all plants and animals, so are they essential for the growth of callus cells. Published information is limited as to the influence of temperature upon callus development, especially as to the callusing of apple stem and root cuttings. There has been an equal lack of information as to the effects of moisture, as well as of other environmental factors, on callus formation. It was thought that study with a view to gain more definite information on some of these points would yield data which, in addition to being of general scientific value, might be useful in apple root-grafting practices, applying not only to the formation of wound tissue but to the prevention of excessive callusing.

Shippy summarizes his extensive experiments, conducted at the Boyce Thompson Institute as follows:

[1] *Am. Jour. Bot.*, XVII, 290-327, April, 1930.

1. The complete range of temperatures permitting the formation of callus from apple cuttings (scion or root) and grafts was found to lie between 0° and 40° C. (32° and 104° F.). Only a small amount of callus developed at 3°-5° (37.4-41° F.) during a period of several months. Between 5° and 32° (41° and 57.6° F.) the rate of callus formation increased and the time elapsing before attainment of final volume decreased with rise in temperature. At temperatures above 32° injury usually resulted, and at 40° death of the tissues, accompanied by mold formation, always occurred within the first few days.

2. By the proper regulation of controlled temperatures the callusing processes may be so accelerated or retarded that, within reasonable limits, a desired degree of callus formation may be had within a given length of time. Hence, apple grafts may be callused within a few days, or, after being properly callused, they may be held in good condition for at least several months before planting.

3. For general callusing purposes, temperatures below 20° C. (68° F.) rather than higher have been found most satisfactory.

4. Variable temperatures do not change the general relations. Callusing is accelerated or retarded according to the degree and duration of the temperature.

5. Air moistures below saturation have generally been found to be inhibiting their effect on callus formation, since below this point dessication of the tissues occurs. As the moisture content of the air falls, the rate of dessication increases.

6. Liquid water, present as a film inclosing the cutting, appears to provide the most favorable moisture conditions for bringing about uniform callusing. Such conditions are supplied moderately by moist peat, sphagnum or sand.

7. Good callusing takes place in a peat moss medium containing 100% water by weight. Practically no increase is brought about by raising the water content of the medium and no perceptible injury or inhibitory effect occurs if the proportion of water to oven-dried peat moss is increased from three to four times. With a water content beyond this point, however, aëration probably becomes a limiting factor, and callusing is inhibited.

8. Dessication of callus tissue is accelerated by increase in temperature and decrease in humidity.

9. Proper aëration was found to be important for callusing. The evidence indicates that while some oxygen is required, an amount of oxygen below that of air (20%) is sufficient. Callusing took place in high concentrations of carbon dioxide, but was inhibited in 100% of oxygen. High concentrations of carbon dioxide, particularly with a limited supply of oxygen, prevented callusing.

10. Both scion and root cuttings of apple manifest a distinct polarity in callus formation. Dominance of the bottom end over the top end of cuttings held regardless of the position of the cuttings, whether upright, horizontal, or inverted.

11. Varieties differ both in the rate and the abundance with which they form callus. Yellow Transparent, Wolf River, Wealthy and Ben Davis are abundant callusing varieties; Jonathan, Delicious and Willow Twig are moderate callusing varieties.

12. The effects of polarity and varietal differences on callus formation of apple cuttings and grafts appear to be significantly related to the occurrence of overgrowths at the union of root-grafted trees.

247. Graft wrapping machines (Fig. 233) have come into use in some of the larger nurseries because they economize time and cost and do work superior to hand wrapping. In a circular describing one of these machines the following passage occurs (condensed):

An account carefully kept during several weeks of a grafting season shows the machine-wrapped grafts cost, on an average, five cents a thousand for twine, 11 cents for wrapping, a total of 16 cents a thousand; a saving of 34 cents a thousand over calico wrapping. But what is of more importance, the tension of the thread may be adjusted to wrap the graft so tightly that it may be taken by the

Fig. 233.—Wrapping whip grafts by machine.

root, thrown or shaken without risk of loosening. In many tests, either root or scion has broken, rather than loosen or break at the splice. Hence in planting, grafts may be handled almost like cuttings without fear of breakage, resulting in the saving of thousands of trees.

248. Root graft storage is the same as storage of cuttings; (234) the grafts being tied in bundles of 100, each bundle being correctly labeled with the name of the variety before being placed in damp, green sawdust, sphagnum or sand in a cold but frost-proof room or cellar until spring. Unless the temperature is below 40° and unless well ventilated, there is danger that the grafts may heat, rot or sprout and thus be ruined.

During the several weeks until planting time the wounds callus (Fig. 235) and the parts grow together so that when planted spongy tissue covers the points of contact.

Planting of root grafts in nurseries is done as soon as the ground can be worked in spring, the soil being fitted by deep plowing (preferably the fall before) and by several harrowings before being marked out. Three methods of setting are in vogue—dibbling, furrowing and planting with machines. In each case the grafts are set so the top bud of the scion is just above the surface.

Dibbling is done only in small nurseries or where only a few grafts are to be planted. Besides its slowness it is objectionable because of the risk of leaving air spaces around the lower ends of the grafts, thus effectively preventing growth. In its practice, holes about 8″ deep are made in the ground 8″ or 9″ apart with iron bars or pieces of rounded 2″ x 4″ scantling 6′ long, sharpened to long

Fig. 234.—Callusing bed for root grafts and cuttings.

points at their lower ends. In these holes the grafts are placed and earth pressed against them full length.

249. Variable growth of grafts.[1]—The usually small percentage of apple grafts that grow into salable nursery trees is due to variable development and poor stands traceable, in many cases, to a common cause—position of the top bud of the scion in relation to the point of callus union. (Figs. 230, 231). Another cause of heavy losses, in some varieties appears to be due in large part to the same source, callus gall.

To test the observations as to bud position, grafts were made with scions cut so the top buds were in the four following positions and a "check" in which the scions were prepared according to the commercial practice of cutting back the lower bud of the scion (Figs. 230, 231): Above the mismatched side of the tongues (A), above the lip of scion (B), above the matched side of the tongue (C), and above the lip of the stock (D). The numbers of trees observed in each lot (50 grafts) are far too small to use for definite conclusions, but the data clearly indicate that the reason galled trees in the nursery average smaller than ungalled ones is due to a higher percentage of galls on those grafts made out-of-line bud positions where the trees are also smaller. Roberts summarizes the tests as follows:

The stand and growth of grafts varied with the position of the top bud of the scion. Galling was affected by scion bud position. Galled trees grew as large as ungalled trees, considering the bud position. Small stocks were less affected by bud position than large ones. Large stocks produced larger trees than small stocks. Crown piece grafts grew better than piece root grafts. Doucin stocks produced slightly more uniform trees than seedling stocks. Scion differences appear to produce more variation in the nursery row than

---

[1] R. H. Roberts, *Factors Affecting the Variable Growth of Apple Grafts in the Nursery Row*, Wis. Exp. Sta., Research Bul. 77. 1927.

stock differences. Tree size depends upon period and rate of growth. Early starting is markedly related to large size.

250. Relation of scion variety to character of growth in apple trees.[1] Scion varieties determine root character when grafts are placed upon seedling roots. They do not much affect the root character when placed upon vegetatively propagated rootstocks. High budded trees do not have the uniform and characteristic root type of the scion variety. Double worked trees have the root character of the intermediate variety. It is believed at present that the influence of vegetative rootstocks is due to a stem effect.

FIG. 235.—Too much callus on whip grafts.

The investigations continued with variations over two more years when Roberts summarized *"Some Stock and Scion Observations on Apple Trees* in Research Bulletin 94 (Wisconsin) as follows:

The root type and anatomy of trees on seedling piece roots is determined by the scion variety. The root type and anatomy of trees on dwarf stocks is not much affected by the scion variety. Double worked trees commonly have roots which are typical of the intermediate variety. Budded trees have variable root types, apparently typical of the original seedlings. Obviously stock influence is due to the stem portion of the stock. Some stocks, especially the vigorous ones, appear to show no influence. The influence of a stock upon different varieties is variable, being best for one but poorest for another. The amount of growth made by the scion variety tends to be independent of the stock. The time at which a scion starts to grow is markedly independent of stock influence. The percentage stand, amount of growth and degree of "crown gall" varies with the method of preparing the graft.

Callus knot formations appear to be correlated to the soil moisture conditions and the development of caliper by the trees. Nursery trees tend to maintain the same relative differences in size that resulted from the first season's environment. Heavy cutting back as when budding trees markedly increases the uniformity of growth. It even appears probable that the commonly reported uniformity of nursery trees on clonal stocks is the result of the method of grafting rather than being due to the stock used. Scion source is an important factor in tree uniformity and growth.

Of 12 scion varieties, only Jonathan appears to have been invigorated by being budded upon other varieties. Seedlings from different sources have dif-

[1] Thomas Swarbrick and R. H. Roberts, *Wis. Exp. Sta., Research Bul.,* **78,** August 1927

ferent growth characters. To date, they appear to be little different as stocks. Seedling size has an inconsistent effect upon scion growth. Adhesive tape as a graft wrapping reduced callus knot formation. Some cases of "physiological incompatability" have been noted. Early blossom bud formation is obviously associated with quality of growth as diameter relations rather than lengths.

In the furrow method a furrow 8" deep is made with a turning plow, the grafts placed against the vertical side, and soil plowed back against them. The work is finished either by men tramping the earth against the grafts individually or by machine (Fig. 295) with two wheels set obliquely so as to press the soil downward and against the grafts when drawn by horses down the rows.

Fɪɢ. 236.—Scion wood kept cold and plump in storage gives best results.

Planting machines are similar to those used for transplanting cabbage, strawberry, sweet potato and other truck crops. During the growing season the nursery rows are cultivated by weekly shallow stirrings of the surface soil with cultivators and by hoeing out weeds among the growing grafts. At the end of the first season's growth fruit trees should be 3' to 5' or even taller in some cases. Trees of such heights are ready for orchard planting. Many trees, however, are allowed to grow till two or even more years old.

251. **"Incubator" boxes in grafting.**—Success has been greatly enhanced by an "incubator box" (Fig. 236) in which the grafts in bundles or in layers are packed with damp moss and kept at a temperature of 75° to 80° F. for about three weeks by which time callusing is good enough to permit removal. The grafts (made in the whip style) have their tap-roots shortened to 6" and are potted in 6" pots. When a few leaves have appeared, the plants are hardened off and placed in a frame for the first year. This method has given about 75% success.

252. **Root grafting vs. top grafting.**—In West Virginia, King apples top-worked on seedlings were in fairly good condition at 20 years old, whereas others root grafted and set in the same orchard were dead at 10 years. Ten Walldow root-grafted trees were all dead but one limb on one tree (most of the 10 died between 5 and 10 years), but the 10 top-worked were thrifty at 20 years. In an orchard of 100 root-grafted and 70 top-grafted trees 44% and 7.2%, respectively, died.

For propagating apple varieties with weak trunks, top grafting or double working is recommended, Tolman sweet being preferred as a stock because of its close, smooth bark, strong, yet not rapid growth and its great longevity. (These methods are thought to aid trees in resisting disease).

Own rooted, root grafted and budded McIntosh, Red Astrachan

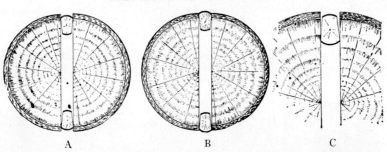

FIG. 236x.—Right and wrong graft making. A, cleft grafts properly placed—cambium of stock in contact with that of scion; B, improperly placed—cambiums not in contact. C, scion entered wrong way around and without cambium contact.

and Fameuse apple trees showed little difference in size after seven years of growth at the Indiana Experiment Station. Grimes trees on Virginia crab roots were larger than on any other of several stocks tested.

Northern Spy as a stock produced by asexual methods in England was reported by R. G. Hatton as having a dwarfing effect. This variety is valuable as a stock because of its resistance to woolly aphis—without regard to the scion grafted upon it.

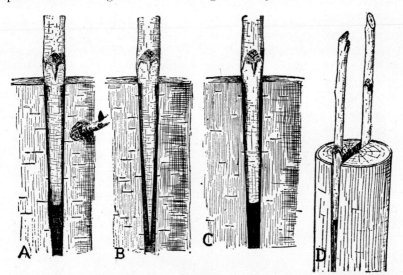

FIG. 237.—Right and wrong graft making. A, properly made scion correctly fitted; B, scion too long pointed—likely to have poor contact with stock and to rock or move; C, poor contact because scion is dished, usually due to poor edge on knife or "whittle" cut, proper cut is made by holding hand rigid and using arm muscles to make "draw" cut; D, scions ready for waxing. Note position of bud on near scion.

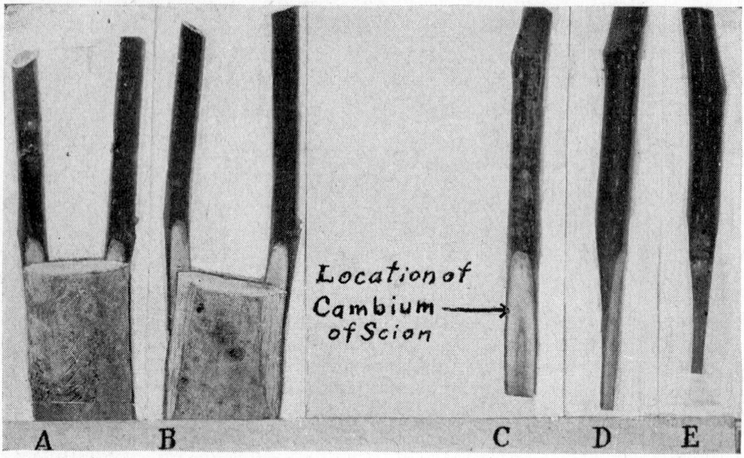

Location of
Cambium ——→
of Scion

FIG. 238.—Cleft graft. A, scions set in stock with bark intact, right one correctly placed, left too far out; B, bark removed from stock to show right and wrong ways as in A; C, side view of scion trimmed for cleft graft; D, inner edge—cut thinner than E, outer edge. (See Fig. 237D.)

253. Top grafting, while of widest application to established orchard trees, is of comparatively little importance in nursery practice. To the authors it seems this method might be more widely utilized by nurserymen as follows: (Figs. 195, 219, 270).

In top grafting, the stock, cut usually at or above the ground surface (Figs. 236x to 240) is either treated by the cleft or the notch method, one or more scions being inserted in the stub. Sometimes

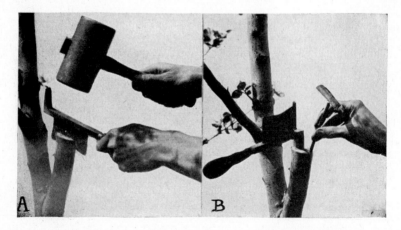

FIG. 239.—Cleft graft making. A, cutting slot; B, placing scion.

scions are forced between bark and wood. Usually the scions have only one to three buds and are rarely longer than 4".

In orchard (less in nursery) practice unsatisfactory trees are top-worked, also trees of strong growth are used as bodies for poor straggling growers and those that have trunk weakness (252). Thus any desired variety may be worked on trees by the individual orchardist. The method is of practically universal utility, because nearly every fruit grower is sure to have at least some trees that do not please him but which are too good to destroy—seed-

Fig. 240.—Sloping cut of stub to hasten wound healing.

lings, trees untrue to name, shy bearers, others in which graft or bud has failed but a sucker developed, and so on. Any desired number of varieties may be worked upon the same tree, the number being restricted only by the available branches or stocks.

254. Top grafting nursery trees.—C. P. Close of Maryland started summer apple trees on Northwestern Greening trees. Three to six of the best placed and strong limbs were pruned to stubs 2" to 3" long and whip grafted. All other limbs were cut off. The grafts were wound with waxed cord and painted with liquid grafting wax. The scion tips were also waxed. The roots were pruned back to 3" or 4" just before grafting and setting in the orchard. About 90% of the grafts made good unions. When one failed a shoot usually developed and was budded. This method is believed to be of special use where trees of desired varieties cannot be secured or are weak growers with tender trunks. Close also suggests that nurserymen might use it to re-graft their surplus strong, healthy trees instead of burning them or such trees could be sold at a moderate price for the fruit grower to re-graft.

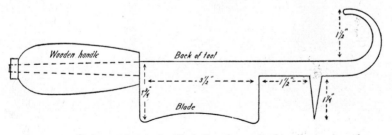

Fig. 241.—Cleft grafting tool. Hooked end permits hanging on branch.

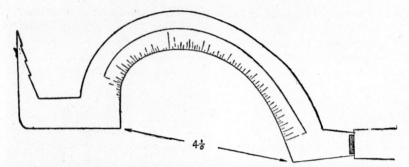

Fig. 242.—Cleft grafting tool adjustable to various sizes of stock.

255. Cleft Grafting, the method perhaps most widely employed outside of commercial establishments, finds its chief use in amateur practice to work over seedling and unsatisfactory trees to desired varieties. Everyone should know how to perform it, because there is no telling when it may become useful. Though it is, in a sense, not widely used commercially, it commands rather extended treatment in books on plant propagation (Figs. 236 to 244).

The stocks, ½″ to 2″ or perhaps even larger, sawed squarely across with a sharp, fine-toothed saw and made about 6″ long, are split 1½″ deep with a grafting iron and then wedged apart until the scions, usually containing three buds, and cut wedge shaped below are adjusted with a slight outward slant, one at each side of the slit. The wedge is then gently removed so as not to displace the scions,

Fig. 243.—California cleft grafting kit. 1, pruning saw with reversed teeth; 2, grafting knife; 3, grafting tool; 4, mallet; 5, shears.

and all the wounded surfaces thoroughly waxed over. The advantage of having two scions is that the healing will be quicker. Should both grow, the weaker or poorer placed should be cut off cleanly the following spring.

In making scions the lowest bud should be just above, almost between, the cuts that form the wedge. When placed in the stock this bud should be covered completely with wax—through which the sprout will push.

For outdoor grafting of this kind, scion wood, always of only one season's growth, should be cut while the trees are fully dormant and stored in an icehouse, the north side of a building or in some other cold place to keep the buds from swelling. The operation is best performed just when the trees are breaking into leaf. If the twigs are long and the lower buds poorly developed, these should be discarded. Because cleft grafting is a rigorous operation, preference, wherever possible, should be given to stocks of ½″ to 2″ in diameter, so the healing may be completed in one season, thus lessening the chances of decay. In such cases only one scion is needed. When

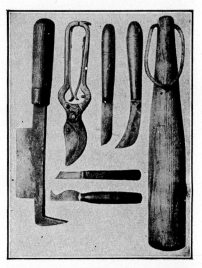

Fig. 244.—Eastern grafting and budding kit. Left to right—grafting iron, shears, budding knife, pruning knife, mallet with loop to hang over wrist; in center below—budding and string cutting knives.

large stocks are used it may be necessary to keep the cleft wedged apart so as not to squeeze the scion too much. Such wedges should be placed in the heart wood and cut off even with the face of the stub.

Cleft grafting is one method used in top working large trees, a line of work practiced by many men who charge a fixed rate, usually two or three cents a stub for the number of successes toward the close of summer. When the size, condition and shape of trees are favorable and when extensive preliminary pruning is not necessary, an expert grafter can make and wax an average of perhaps 600 stubs in a 10-hour day.

In top working an old tree, keen judgment is needed to re-shape the top. It is popular opinion that never should more than a third of the top be removed and grafted in any one year; a fourth or a fifth would be better. Always the general outline of old trees should be followed and branches smaller than 2″ used when possible, since the scions succeed and wounds heal best in such cases.

It is usually advisable to cut the principal stubs at relatively equal distances from the axis of the tree and then select minor side limbs. In handling trees with thick tops, care must be exercised to leave sufficient shade to protect the bark from sun scald. Better cut out all large branches that must be removed before the grafting is begun, because they are sure to develop excessively if left after the removal of the limbs for grafting. Thus bare pole-like limbs may be prevented. It is well to err on the safe side by having too many than too few stubs, because the excess may be cut out later. Young trees—say two or three years old planting—may be top-worked much more quickly, because a larger part, in fact even the whole top, may be removed at one feel swoop and grafted.

Never should a horizontal limb immediately beneath another one be grafted, because the tendency is for grafts to grow upward rather than outward. Similarly, when horizontal or nearly horizontal limbs are to be grafted, the cleft should never be vertical, always horizontal, so the growths from the scions will have the least chance of interfering. This upward tendency of scion growth explains the narrow and dense tops of top-grafted trees. Hence also the necessity for careful pruning and training to open up the tops again. Because of this necessity the folly of grafting old trees only on large interior limbs close to main trunks is apparent.

While top grafting is best performed when the buds are beginning to swell, it is usually necessary, on account of the rapid healing of wounds and the probably greater success at that time, to start two or four weeks earlier and continue as much later when many trees must be worked over by few hands. Under eastern conditions, late-set scions usually get so poor a start that they are weak and cannot withstand frost the following winter.

Time may be saved by having three men work as a gang, one to prepare stubs, a second to cut and set scions and the third to do waxing. The second, perhaps aided at first by the third man, makes a lot of scions while the first man is getting a start on the stubs. The scions as made are dipped in water and when placing begins, are carried in an outside breast pocket. The second man carries an 18″ mallet handily slung by a cord from his wrist. With it one downward blow on the knife makes the cleft, an upward one loosens the knife, a second down blow drives home the wedge. The mallet is then dropped, the scions placed, the wedge removed, and so on. The third man does the waxing and re-waxing a few days later.

From time to time during spring, summer and fall, the grafts should be examined and those which have loosened the wax and exposed the wood should be re-waxed to prevent entrance of decay. This should be repeated if necessary the following year or until the wound has completely healed. Probably wax is better than any other wound dressing.

256. Other uses of cleft grafting.—While cleft grafting is most used in working over trees in orchards, it has other uses. Established grape vines are often cleft grafted below ground, the completed work not being waxed. Often rooted grape cuttings are similarly treated. In these cases the stocks should have clefts cut rather than split because of the gnarly wood. Should the scion fit too loosely, it must be bandaged or tied to hold it in place.

In grafting fleshy plants, such as cactus, cleft grafting is popular, the scion being held in position by a spine or a pin before being wound with bast or raffia. No waxing is needed. Peony roots summer grafted, are similarly handled, but bound with wire because raffia or other vegetable tier quickly decays when buried in the ground up to the top bud. Dahlias are generally side grafted, but sometimes cleft grafted.

257. Grafting irons are of two general forms; one suggesting a sickle with its point reversed and thickened to form a 4″ or 5″ wedge, the other a straight shank with blade on one side and the wide wedge at the end on the other. (Figs. 241 to 244.) The former, usually home made, is more of a splitting tool, useful for straight-grained wood; the latter, sold by nursery and seed houses, rather a cutting tool suitable for gnarly stocks.

In waxing, time may be saved in cold weather if the wax is kept warm and soft in hot water. A cabinet-maker's glue pot is handy for liquid waxes to be brushed on wounds. In weather warm enough to keep wax fairly soft, application with the hands is to be preferred, since every crevice can thus be surely filled. To prevent wax from sticking to the skin grease the hands well.

Solid wax is best applied when worked out by the hands into ribbons of, say, ⅛″ thick. Starting at the top of the stock, the ribbon is pressed against and into the crack down the side of the stub, less being needed below than above. Next a ribbon is wound around the point where stock and scion join and pressed down well. The second scion is similarly treated. Finally the parts of the stub still exposed are covered with a spoon-shaped piece of wax, care being taken to use plenty to fill the top one-fourth or more of the cleft and to cover the edges all around. By this method much better covering, to say nothing of time saving, can be secured than by dabbing and patting the wax in place. Many grafters also put little bits of wax on the upper ends of scions if these have been cut off.

258. A special cleft tool[1] (Fig. 242) may be bought from orchard supply houses or made by a blacksmith. Its cutting edge is made concave to avoid tearing the bark before the wood is split as straight edge tools often do, especially if the wood has gnarly grain.

If this tool is purchased from an orchard supply house, the chances are that it will have a uniform curvature of the cutting edge and therefore be suited only to stubs of a certain size. A tool that has only a large radius of curvature and is fitted for only large stubs, will split the smaller stubs with little cutting of bark much as a straight edge tool acts. One with only a small radius of curvature will crush and tear the bark on large stubs before splitting begins. The most practicable tool for stubs of all sizes, therefore, is one which has a concave cutting edge of a steadily increasing radius. When using a tool of this sort holding the handle upward adjust the cutting edge to stubs. The cutting edge can be fitted to stubs of intermediate size by holding the handle somewhere near the level of the end of the stub.

The smaller the stub to be split, the greater the degree of convexity (the smaller the radius of curvature) should be. If a topworking job is to be done where considerable uniformity in size of stubs will be found, a tool can be made with the radius of curvature to fit the size of the stubs.

259. Veneer grafting, (Fig. 245) from the standpoint of union of stock and scion, is perhaps the ideal method of grafting, because the parts unite quickly and evenly and make perfect unions. As handled in America it resembles the English side graft, but has a longer stock tongue. Its chief application is to potted plants in greenhouses between November and March. Stocks which have been grown in the open air during summer are potted between late August and early October and placed in cool houses or pits prior to the operation, which is performed near the surface of the ground. It is not necessary to head back stocks until after union is complete. As good success follows the use of dormant as of active scions, but plants growing well must be plunged in moss in a frame and kept cool, moist but not wet, until the scions have united well.

Usually the resulting plants are kept in pots during the following summer, though some species may be transplanted to nursery rows or open borders in spring. Japanese maples, rhododendrons and certain coniferous plants are propagated in this way. This

FIG. 245.—Veneer graft for evergreens.

---

[1] M. B. Hoffman, *Topworking the Apple Tree, W. Va. Exp. Sta. Bul. 57, 1930.*

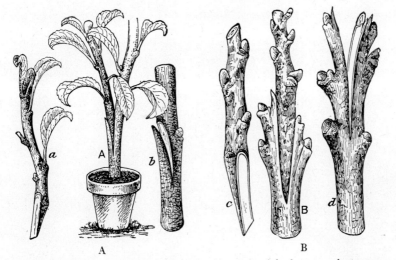

FIG. 246.—Side and terminal grafts. A, side graft of herbaceous plant, complete, *a*, scion, *b*, stock enlarged; B, terminal graft complete; *c*, scion, *d*, stock.

method has the advantage that failures do not injure the stocks, which may be re-grafted as often as necessary. Few methods are more easily learned or more simple.

In preparing the stock, a cut about 1″ long is made downward just through the end and the piece removed by a diagonal cut at the base, thus leaving a little notch. In this notch and against the cut edges of the stock the scion is made to fit by cutting in this form. Then scion and stock are fitted together, the small tongue of the bark on the stock serving to cap the base of the scion when in posi-

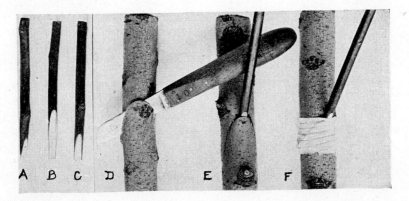

FIG. 247.—Side graft. A, B, C, views of scion; D, making cut to receive scion; E, scion in place on stock; F, wrapped with tape, ready for waxing.

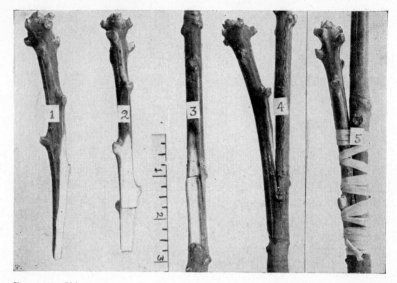

FIG. 248.—Side tongue graft of mango. 1, side view of scion; 2, face view; 3, face view of stock; 4, scion fitted in stock; 5, graft wrapped ready for paraffin—on all parts of union and scion.

tion. Tying with raffia completes the work. Since no incision is made in the wood, waxing is not necessary, except out of doors.

260. Side grafting (Fig. 246 to 249) has several modifications, but in all the scion is inserted without cutting off the stock. In one the stock is cut as for shield budding, but instead of a bud a wedge-shaped scion is placed beneath the bark, tied and waxed. This form may be used for rather difficult subjects, either with dormant scions in spring when the leaves have appeared, or with young twigs in late summer. By the former plan and by frequent heading in of the stock top above the scion, salable trees of such subjects as mulberries will be ready in autumn; by the latter plan plants of ornamental beech will be salable in 14 months.

In another form, used in grafting small grape stocks below

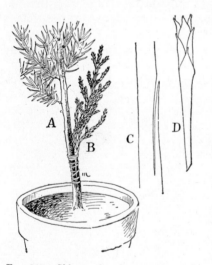

FIG. 249.—Side graft of evergreen. A, stock; B, scion; C, cut in stock; D, scion trimmed for insertion.

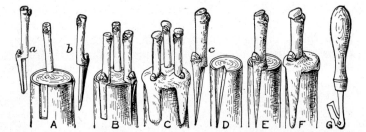

FIG. 250.—Two styles of crown grafting. A, slot of bark removed for scions, a, b; B, scions fitted in place; C, completed graft; D, slot of wood removed, c, scion cut to triangular wedge to fit slot in stock; E, stock and scion fitted; F, completed graft; G, slot-making or inlaying tool.

ground, a narrow thin-bladed chisel (preferably with a bent shank) or a knife blade is thrust about an inch deep obliquely in the stock and the scion cut to a thin wedge as in cleft grafting, is thrust into the incision until the cut surfaces are covered by the bark of the stock. Tying and waxing finish the work in the open air; tying alone, indoors. Heading back the stock aids union, since it throws more plant food into the scion. (Practicum XXIX and XXX.)

261. **Crown grafting or inlaying** (sometimes called notch grafting) is a form of grafting in which a small sliver of wood is cut out of the stock and a scion similarly cut is fitted in its place. (Figs. 250 to 254.) It has special value for grafting grapes and other "curly" grained woods. Since the necessary tying is slow, cleft grafting is better for straight-grained stocks. Another objection to inlaying is that the growing scion must be tied to prevent being broken off by wind. When this care is taken the method results in good unions and excellent growth.

In the most popular form the stock, being cut off square as in cleft grafting, has one or more V-shaped grooves, large above, tapering below, and made downward, either with a knife or an inlaying tool. In these grooves the scions cut to fit are placed and tied or nailed with No. 19 1″ flat

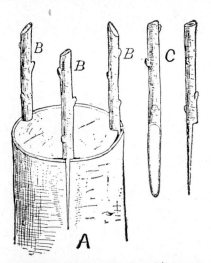

FIG. 251.—Crown or balk grafting trees whose thick bark makes fitting of cambiums difficult. A, stock of medium sized tree; B, scions; C, side and full view of graft to show method of cutting.

headed wire nails, and, if in the open air, are waxed. The tier should be weak and perishable, so it will decay and break before danger of strangling the scion might occur. Raffia, bast and No. 18 or No. 20 knitting cotton are all good. Winding should be tight.

262. Modified crown grafting.—Scions bearing two buds are cut beginning just below the lower bud on the opposite side. The stock is prepared as for splice grafting, the scion being inserted under the bark and at the tip of the stock. The union is said to form rapidly and without enlargement.

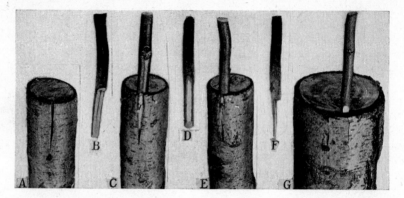

Fig. 252.—Common crown or bark graft. A, slit in bark of stock; B, side of scion to face cambium of stock, note shoulder to fit on top of stock; C, scion inserted, note position of nails through scion and bark of stock; D, side of scion which faces bark; E, ready for waxing; F, side view of scion; G, bark graft on large stock made without slitting, nailing or wrapping—waxing only.

263. Notch grafting is a modification of inlaying, in which the stock, though cut off as in cleft grafting, is not split and in which the wood may or may not be cut to receive the scion. It has proved of special value in grafting walnuts and is best used in spring when the bark separates readily from the wood. In one case a saw with wide-set teeth is used obliquely downward to make one or more slots in the stock. Scions cut on two sides to fit snugly are inserted and waxed. For best results the cut surfaces of the scion should not be parallel, but slightly wider apart outside than inside, so the scions may be pressed in place both from above and from the side toward the center of the stock. This form of notch grafting has the advantage of making the scions about as firm as in cleft grafting without wounding the stock so seriously.

Two other forms (Fig. 251, 255), are often called bark grafting, start the same way, but instead of notching the wood the scion, in one case cut to a thin wedge, is thrust between bark and wood, tied and waxed; in the other, narrow strips of bark about one inch

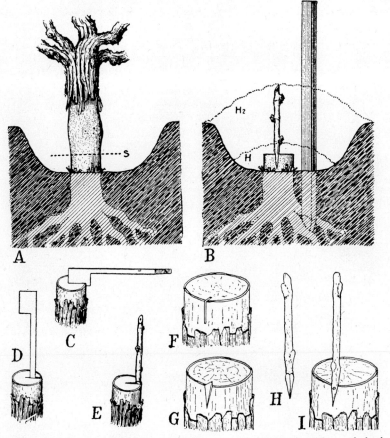

Fig. 253.—Notch, groove or inlay graft of grape. A, stock with rough bark removed to be sawed at S; B, finished work, lower dotted line first layer of earth, upper line second layer made when buds are growing; C, special grafting tool making slit; D, tool wedging slit open for receipt of scion; E, scion in place; F, (another method) slit made by saw; G, slit made for scion; H, triangular ended scion; I, scion fitted and nailed in place.

long are removed and the scions, cut with a shoulder opposite a well-developed bud, are set in the notches, tied and waxed. In tying it is well to use ½″ tape soaked in grafting wax and to bind tightly, to prevent injury by accident. Both stub and upper tips of scions should be covered with wax. Choose place to set scions as indicated in Figure 255.

264. Biederman's bark graft[1] is a distinct improvement over the common form, especially for grafting English walnut on black walnut. The stock is pre-

[1] A ½″ round chisel (or gouge) is the best tool for this operation. If the chisel is sharp the scion can be made concave and shaped with one or two strokes. It is use-

FIG. 254.—Making short cut of scion in bark or crown grafting.

pared as for the common bark graft but the scion is given a concave surface with a 1″ gauge. In the common bark graft the scion has a flat surface which, coming against the round surface of the stock, prevents contact of the cambium layers of stock and scion (Fig. 257C). In the Biederman form the concave surface of the scion comes in intimate contact with the convex surface of the stock and insures union of the cambium (D and C). The scion is pushed beneath the bark to within a ¼″ or ¾″ of the top of the scarf or cut surface and fastened with a 19-gauge flat headed nail through it. Another nail is also driven on each side of it to hold the bark against the stock. The little spaces on each side of the scion are filled with soft paper and all exposed surfaces covered with melted grafting wax. (Practicum XXV.)

264B. Mac Cooper bark graft for walnuts is the most satisfactory walnut graft coming to the authors' attention. It has been used by them with excellent results for years.

The stock is prepared for this graft, after it has been cut off at the desired points to receive the scions, by making a 2″ long slit and the bark lifting on the right side of the slit. (Fig. 258A.)

FIG. 255.—Good positions (flat and smooth) for scions in common bark grafting—arrows pointing.

Cut from the scion shoot, a two bud section, then opposite a bud and 1½″ below it make a cut with a hack saw half way through the scion (Fig. A). Remove wood from the scion by cutting with a

less to attempt the operation with a dull tool, so two or more chisels should be on hand, for thus work of preparing the scions may be speeded up. A curved knife is sometimes used. In this case the scion is first cut, then the wood is scooped out of the center of the cut so the scion may fit the stock snugly. Compare with the scion cut for the common bark graft and fitted on a small stock.

knife toward the operator (Fig. B). The scion is next finally shaped
(Fig. C). Make a cut on the back of the scion to sharpen it (Fig.
D). Next remove a section of bark and wood on the back of the
scion slightly to the right of the scion (Fig. E).

The scion is then ready for insertion. Lift the corner of the bark
of the stock on the right side of the slit already made. Insert the
scion and drive it between bark and wood being sure not to disturb
the bark on the left of the slit but hold the scion as near this edge as
possible while driving it in (Fig. G).

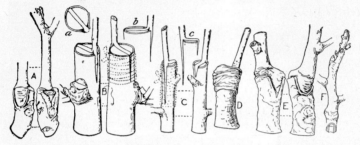

Fig. 256.—Smith's improved method of grafting. A, old, defective
"rind" grafting; B, large branches with graft in place, a, b, other views;
C, small branches grafted, ready for waxing; D, completed graft; E,
large graft one year old; F, small graft one year old.

Nail the scion in place with No. 19 or 20 ¾" wire nails by
driving the top nail (Fig. G) through bark of scion and stock. This
nail should be slanted toward the unlifted bark side to hold the
scion as close to that edge as possible. Similarly drive another nail
1" below the first and a third through the bark to the right of the
scion to prevent the bark from splitting from the wood of the stock
too great a distance, and a fourth nail 1" below the third.

Seal the job well with grafting wax or other material. Do not
neglect the top of the scion.

265. Smith's improved graft, an English method.—According
to a writer in the *Gardeners' Chronicle* (British), scions of one or
two-year wood of fruit trees are given a three-fold grip on the stocks
(½" to 1½" in diameter) which becomes covered the first year.
Figure 256 shows the defects of the old mode of "rind" grafting;
B and C show the preparation of the stocks—one small, the other
large. D is the finished growth. This plan offers more than ordinary resistance to wind.

266. Splice grafting, the easiest method of all, is done by making an oblique cut across both stock and scion, as if making the first
cut in whip grafting, but not forming a tongue in either part. The
two pieces, being of approximately equal diameter, are placed to-

gether so their cut surfaces match and are then tied and waxed. The method finds its most useful application to small tender shoots which cannot be safely split.

267. Grape grafting is usually a necessity only 1, for working over undesirable varieties or seedlings to desired kinds and 2, for growing European varieties in regions where the phylloxera (275)

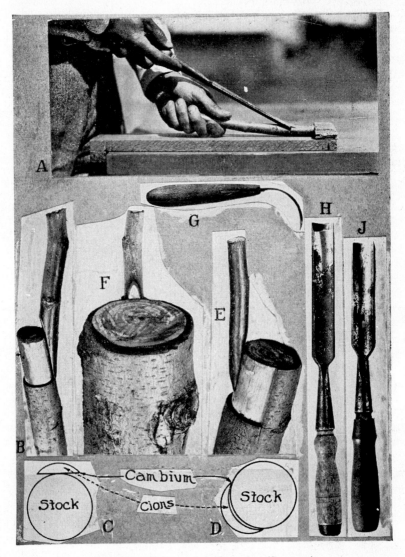

FIG. 257.—Biederman's bark graft. (See text.)

exists. The former, scarcely a nursery practice, is made by cleft grafts below the soil surface, without tying or waxing, but with earth mounded over the union and up to the upper bud. The latter is done in a variety of ways of which the notch style is perhaps most popular. (Fig. 253.) The reason for doing it is that American stocks, the ones always used, are less susceptible to phylloxera injury than are European varieties.

Care must be taken to prevent rooting of the scions, else no advantage will follow grafting. Attention is called to grape-grafting experiments in the paragraphs which follow (Fig. 258). Special tools for grape grafting are generally used (Fig. 253).

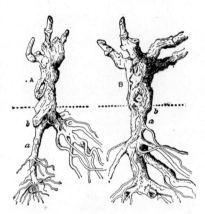

FIG. 258.—Grafted grapes. A, effect on resistant stock of allowing scion to take root, *a*, stock, *b*, point of union—small development below, *c*, scion roots—large; B, vine not allowed to root from scion. Note smooth union at *b* in each case.

Selection of Scion for Walnut Grafting is of utmost importance if the operation is to be successful. The scions should be taken from the past season's growth—preferably long watersprouts over ½″ in diameter. Only the base wood on these sprouts is used, one to three, two bud scions, being secured from each long shoot or sprout. The use of scions taken from tip wood with large buds and pith gives only indifferent results. Use the large base wood with the small buds and little pith.

Scion Wood may be collected any time in the dormant season and stored in a cool place in moist moss or sawdust until it is time to use it in spring. It should be dormant at time of insertion.

The time to bark graft walnuts is when the bark will slip in spring. Best results have been secured after the buds have broken and show small leaves on the stock. Walnuts can be bark grafted successfully for at least a month after the first show of leaves, provided the scions are dormant.

Degrully, a French scientist, has pointed out that variations in vines, due to grafting, should not cause apprehension. The thousands of acres reconstructed on American stocks still thrive and produce abundantly 20, 25 and 30 years after grafting. Variations due to grafting, he maintains, are as yet only of scientific interest.

268. Effects of vine grafting.—Because of agitation, the Society of Agriculture of France appointed a committee to investigate effects of grafting on yield and quality of grapes and wine. The committee concluded that where the factors of adaptation and affinity of stock and scion, as well as other necessary conditions for successful grape culture, have been realized, there appears to be nothing to warrant the claims that grafting has a deleterious effect on yield and quality of product.

269. Experiments in grape grafting.—In California, experiments in grape propagation warranted the following (slightly condensed) conclusions:[1] 1, A cutting graft of suitable variety makes as large and vigorous growth as a simple cutting, so by bench grafting no time is lost in establishing a resistant vineyard.

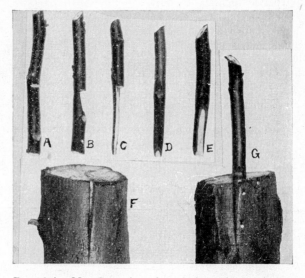

Fig. 258A.—Mac Cooper's bark graft for walnuts. A, two budded scion cut half way through, opposite and slightly below the lower bud of the scion; B, method of removing wood to shape the scion—shows first cut; C, scion shaped; D, scion sharpened to aid in insertion; E, cut made on back of scion or side which comes in contact with bark of stock when inserted—union takes place here; F, bark of stock loosened on right of slit and lifted; G, inserted scion with No. 19 flat-headed 1″ wire nails to secure it to stock.

2, Resistant varieties difficult to root but easy to graft when old should not be bench grafted. 3, Care in callusing, planting and treatment in nursery and especially in keeping the grafts moist from the time made till set in the callusing bed, (Fig. 234) will enable even an inexperienced grafter to obtain at least 60% of good, grafted plants. 4, Callusing in sand insures more perfect unions and a larger percentage of successful grafts than planting directly in the nursery period. 5, The moisture of the callusing bed should not be excessive and the temperature should be relatively warm. 6, The growing graft should be watched closely in order to see that the roots of the scions are removed before they become large and that the raffia is cut before it strangles the graft. 7, The English cleft graft (Fig. 260 to n) is preferable to the Champin (Fig. 261j to n), becauses it gives more perfect unions and can be made with more accuracy and rapidity. 8, Scions of two eyes are preferable to those of one eye, as they give

[1] *(Cal. Exp. Sta. Bul. 127)*

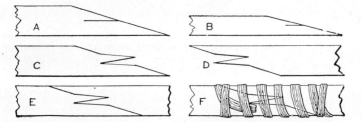

Fig. 260.—English "cleft" graft. A, improper angle for large cuts—should not be parallel, but slightly away from long side; B, ditto, for small stocks and scions; C, D, proper angle for tongues; E, F, uniting and tying.

more chances of success. 9, Rupestris St. George seems to be remarkably adapted to California conditions and soils (except the heaviest clays) and is to be preferred to any variety yet tested wherever deep penetration of roots is possible and desirable. 10, All the eyes of the Rupestris stock should be cut deeply and carefully. 11, A vigorous and large-growing *Vinifera* scion promotes an equally vigorous growth of Rupestris St. George used as stock.

270. Bench grafting of grapes experimentally reported by Hedrick of the New York state station presents the following main features: The grafted grapes were more productive than those on their own roots; they were a few days earlier; the 19 varieties employed were all congenial to the three stocks used. Two eye cuttings 6″ to 8″ long were taken in the fall and buried in sand till needed in late March, when the work was done. Roots were cut back to 1″ for convenience in handling by whip grafting (Fig. 262X). Grafts on the previous season's wood gave many suckers; those on the original much fewer. After the operation the grafts were stored for callusing until planting time. All three of the stocks used—Clevener, St. George and Gloire—are recommended for trial commercially, and three others suggested as promising; vis., Riparia Grand Glabre, and two hybrids between *Vitis riparia* and *V. rupestris* known as 3,306 and 3,309. During the growing season, shoots from the stock and roots from the scion (Fig. 262X) must be removed at least twice; the earlier the better.

271. Bench-grafting is unhesitatingly recommended by Biolitti of California for the following reasons: both stock and scion are young and of the

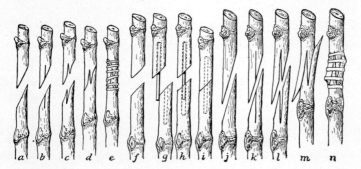

Fig. 261.—Three methods of bench grafting grapes. a to e, whip graft; f to i, grafting with galvanized wire; j to n, Champin graft.

same size; unions are therefore strong and permanent; grafting may be done under conditions favorable to rapid and effective work, in any weather, during three or four months, on rainy days when other work is not pressing or cannot be done; one man who thoroughly understands all details can oversee several

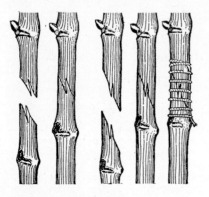

unskilled workmen, making it possible to employ cheap labor for much of the work; cultural conditions are more easily controlled; there is less danger of inferior results due to excessively wet or dry weather during the growing season; in the nursery the vines can be cultivated, irrigated and generally attended to much more perfectly than in the field; rigid selection of vines for planting can be made, rendering it possible to have nothing in the vineyard but strong plants and perfect unions; as perfect stands can be obtained in vineyards the first year in any soil or season as when planting ordinary non-resistant vines; unions of vines can be placed exactly where wanted; land where the vineyard is to be planted can be used for other crops one year longer than when field grafting is adopted; all cultural

FIG. 262.—Whip graft of grape. A, modified, requires no tying, popular in California; B, common style, requires tying.

operations during the first year are much less expensive than in vineyard grafting, as they are spread over a much smaller area; two acres of nursery will produce enough bench grafts to plant 100 acres of vineyard.

In short, starting a resistant vineyard by means of bench grafts is much better than by any other method used at present, because it is least costly and gives best results. This is true whether the bench grafts are produced at home or bought at present market rates. Growers are earnestly cautioned, however, against planting any but first choice bench grafts; second and third choice are little better than field grafts.

All that can be said in favor of nursery grafting and bench grafting roots, is that the vines so produced are fairly good when bench grafting is impractical. These methods permit root grafting with stocks which, owing to rooting difficulty, are very difficult to bench graft as cuttings. By their means resistant cuttings too small to bench graft may be utilized, and a larger percentage of well grown grafted vines obtained from the nursery.

On the other hand, as the stock is at least two years old when grafted, there is reason to fear that with some stocks many unions will fail as the vines become older. The vines are larger when taken from the nursery, thus increasing cost of removal. There is little if any gain from growth over bench grafts when vineyard planted.

Grafting resistant grape stocks. F. Gillet obtained best results with riparia stocks. One- and two-year rooted cuttings were used in preference to plain cuttings, because of a gain of one year and because a larger per cent will grow. In field practice he used rooted cuttings just grafted and rooted resistant stock in alternate rows. While he secured 85% to 90% of the former, only 60% of the latter grew and these produced few grapes the year set out; the former gave 8 to 11 pounds to the plant. Gillet considers bench grafting resistant vines the best, cheapest and quickest way to reconstruct a vineyard or start a new one.

272. Influence of grape stock on crop.—L. Ravaz, a French investigator, reports 28 years' consecutive yields of two varieties of European grapes grafted on various American stocks. Though much decadence is noted in the vines grafted on certain stocks, the decline in yield and vigor is attributed to such causes as variation in resistance to phylloxera (275), unseasonable weather, lack of adaptation to soil, etc., rather than to influence of grafting and old age. The general deduction is that under proper conditions grafted vines do not deteriorate with age more than do ungrafted ones.

273. Grafting green grape vines.—In Rumania the tongue graft has been successful with green wood not less than ¼″ in diameter at the point grafted, and the wood of both stock and scion hard enough to be with difficulty compressed between thumb and finger. The usual precautions of mature wood grafting must be observed. After union the grafts may be handled like cuttings, or roots may be started by layering on the stocks below the grafts. The advantages claimed are: 1, the method simplifies the operations by obviating stratification of both stocks and scions; 2, it is cheaper and a larger percentage of grafts succeed; 3, the chance element is reduced to a minimum; 4, it seems to promise greater success with varieties difficult to unite when mature.

274. Seedling vines as scions.—Trabut suggests that new varieties of grapes may be quickly brought into fruit by grafting the seedlings on green shoots of established vines. He has secured successful results by the following method: In early June the seedlings which had only their cotyledons, were cut as for ordinary cleft grafting and inserted in the tips of green shoots whose ends were wrapped with small paraffined bands secured with raffia. The completed grafts were then covered with paraffined paper bags to preserve humidity. In about two weeks the parts united and the scions grew vigorously. By October the unions were almost invisible and the canes often 10′ long.

274A. Grafts in moss and charcoal.—R. C. de Brialles has simplified grape bench grafting by the following plan: As the grafts are made they are placed in a box containing a 3″ layer of damp moss and charcoal (three to one) and covered with another layer about half as deep. So on till the box is nearly full, the remaining space being filled with packing. The box may thus be shipped or the grafts treated at once by being placed in a room warmed to 50° or 60° F. Within 24 hours the buds start to swell, and in a week may be ½″ long, when the moss is removed for inspection. If all is well, new packing is applied about half as thick.

If any grafts are rotting, the whole are exposed for 24 hours and then covered. If too dry, a thicker layer of packing is added and the box stood in water of the room temperature till the packing is moistened nearly up to the callus. The tops of the grafts must not be wetted, else rotting may follow. Watering thus once a week will be enough.

In two or three weeks the grafts will have callused and leaf growth will have started. The plants may then be hardened off and transplanted in the field.

Advantages of this method are that grafting is simplified, since no tying is needed, the grafts are placed in the box as made without unnecessary handling, a development of vegetation is secured in three weeks equal to that of two months by ordinary outdoor practise, a more perfect union and callus are secured and disbudding of the stock is unnecessary.

275. Phylloxera, a plant louse *(Phylloxera vastatrix)* which in its nymph stage feeds on roots of grapes and forms galls on the leaves, the latter being the most conspicuous sign of infestation. The insect does little appreciable damage to American species of grapes, hence these are used as stocks for European varieties, which are so seriously attacked that, except in California where the insect was unknown until recently, all attempts to grow European grapes in America during more than 200 years resulted in failure. When American vines were taken to Europe, the insect practically ruined the grape industry, as it has since threatened to do in California. American grape stocks seem to be the only salvation. (Fig. 258.)

276. **Bench Grafted Cuttings** of grapes require more care in planting than do cuttings. When removed from the callusing boxes they must be looked over one by one. All suckers from the stock

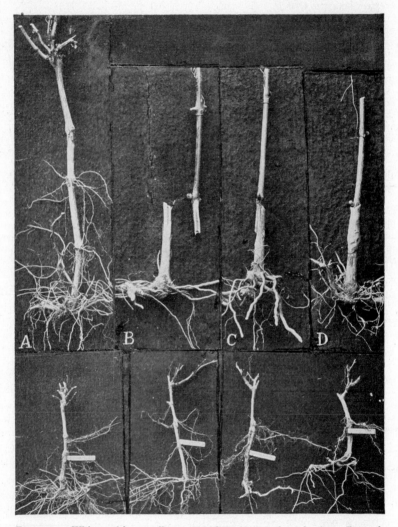

FIG. 262x.—Whip grafting small grape stocks. A, rooted stock vines; B, stock and scion; C, fitted; D, waxed; E, scions rooted above union, such roots must be destroyed.

and all roots from the scion must be cut close. If the scion shoots are several inches long and whitish, it is a good practice to cut them back to 1″. Trimmed thus the grafts, whether or not they have roots at their bases, are ready for planting in trenches as deep as the length of the grafts. In California nurseries a 4″ by 1″ planting board 16′ long and marked with a saw every 3″ or 4″ is an indispensable measuring and planting guide. It is held in place by an 18″ cross piece spiked on each end. Each graft is placed opposite a notch, with the union just above and in con-

FIG. 263.—Bottle grafting—used for difficult subjects. Akin to inarching.

tact with the guide, to insure even spacing and a straight line. Care and regularity in these respects are important for success. When a planting board has been filled, the grafts are "kept" in their position by dirt thrown into the trench, so the board can be removed to another portion of the trench. Water should be used to settle the ground firmly at the base of the grafts.

After the trench has been filled and a wide mound 2″ high above the scions formed with loose soil, nothing need be done to the grafts until July when the shoots will measure several inches. At this time, it is necessary to cut off scion roots and to suppress any suckers that have formed from the stock. The mound is opened, the operations performed and the soil replaced immediately thereafter. Irrigation should follow this work in a day or two. After mid-August the grafts should be gone over again in the same way, but this time the mound should be lowered to allow the unions to harden. If mildew is feared, the grafts should be sulphured. At this time also the nursery should be looked over by a man familiar with vine leaves to make sure the grafts are not mixed.

277. **Cutting-grafting**, as its name implies, is a union of a graft with a cutting, a special case of which is root grafting already described (241). Plants hard to propagate by cuttings are often grafted upon cuttings of other varieties or related species which root readily. When the work is done outdoors in spring the grafts are usually ready to have the stocks removed by fall, the cuttings having rooted; and when done in fall under glass they are ready by spring. The nurse plant may be removed little by little or all at once, according to the case in hand. A modification of the method is to let the scion extend downward into wet moss or a bottle of water (Fig. 263). This is used where stock and scion are more or

less uncongenial or are slow to unite. Various birches, magnolias and mulberries are handled in this way.

278. Grafting tubes (like laboratory test tubes), about 5½″ long and 1″ wide have been used with good results for propagating shrubs and trees at the Swedish Agricultural College. Each graft-cutting is covered with a tube, the lower end of which is pressed into damp moss. Any convenient method of grafting is used (whip, splice, etc.). Grafting wax was abandoned because as good results were secured without it. The plan gave good results in sand beds, flower pots and in open air. Among the subjects which did well outdoors were rose, maple, alder, birch, beech, fir, gooseberry, currant.

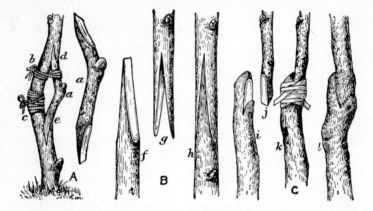

FIG. 264.—Unusual styles of grafting. A, bow graft of vine; *a*, scion, *b*, ligature to increase pressure of scion on stock, *c*, tightly wound ligature to check sap flow, *d*, *e*, slits for insertion of scion; B, saddle graft, *f*, stock, *g*, scion, *h*, parts fitted; C, veneer graft, *i*, stock, *j*, scion, *k*, parts fitted and tied, *l*, graft after union.

279. Herbaceous grafting, mainly by means of veneer, saddle and cleft methods, is easy. Any plant with semi-succulent stems, such as coleus, chrysanthemum, geranium, and the shrub-like begonias, can be grafted. Both stock and scion should have passed the watery stage and become as firm as for the making of cuttings. After adjusting the two parts the graft should be bound with raffia, placed in a propagating frame and kept in a humid atmosphere for perhaps a week. Wax is thus dispensed with; indeed, it is thought to be a detriment.

Some propagators bind moss around the wounds, but it is likely that roots will develop as in pot layering and the parts fail to knit together unless they are first bandaged. It is possible to graft shrubs and trees while the shoots are herbaceous, but this plan is not popular. Conifers (pines and spruces) and some deciduous trees (walnut) are occasionally saddle or cleft grafted in mid to late spring, bound with waxed cheesecloth and shaded with manila sacks.

Experiments at Cornell University have shown that the wood must be somewhat hardened to secure best results. Soft, flabby shoots are likely to be injured in the operation and the union does not occur readily. Cleft and veneer styles were most satisfactory. In most cases it is necessary only to bind the parts with raffia.

280. Grafted potatoes.—E. Laurent, a Belgian investigator, grafted light and colored flesh potatoes on each other by various methods, but after three years of experimenting found no color from a violet variety in the tubers of the light-fleshed stock.

281. Grafting beets has been experimentally done to increase the seed yield of desirable varieties. The "mother" beet root is sprouted. When the off-sets at the crown are about ¾" long they are removed with some of the flesh and inserted in new beets just below the crown, in cuts corresponding to the form of the scions. In one experiment 48 off-sets were secured from one "mother" and 31 of these grew into first-class plants, each of which yielded a normal amount of seed.

In European experiments with beets, nearly every graft was successful. The color boundary line between stock and scion was clearly marked, red varieties not blending with white ones.

Potatoes with smooth, green skin and deep eyes grafted on those with thick, rough, brown skin and shallow eyes often bore both kinds of tubers, sometimes parts of each kind on the same tuber.

282. Potato grafted on tomato experimentally produced no tubers and the tops, although they bloomed freely, bore no seed balls. Tomato on potato bore a fair crop of apparently normal tomatoes and a few tubers which, however, did not grow when planted.

FIG. 265.—One year trees from nursery row. *Left,* budded, with characteristic crook; *right,* grafted, with smooth union. White line shows point of union. These demonstrate that good results may follow each method.

283. Eggplant grafted.—Van Hermann asserts that the only practical way to grow eggplant during the rainy season in Cuba is to graft it on *Solanum tortum,* a wild species employed by the Cuba Experiment Station.

284. Cactus grafting, says an Iowa experimenter, hastens the flowering season of cacti, places trailing species on strong stocks at any desired height where their flowers may be seen to better advantage. It also prevents injuries from over-watering. Healthy stocks and scions readily unite in their actively growing season. The beginning of this period is best. Top working alone should be done, root grafting never, since the scion will itself strike root if in contact with soil. Cleft grafting is most popular, but whip grafting may be used with better results on slender species, and saddle grafting with thick ones. Ball species may be cut square across and the similarly cut scions fitted on top. Both should be about the same size. Strings over the scion and under the pot will hold the two in place. Another favorite way is to hollow the scion, sharpen the stock and fit the two, somewhat as in flute budding. Waxing is unnecessary. Watering should be sparingly done for a few days. Grafting greatly increases the number of flowers, hastens the flowering season and often augments plant vigor by checking the downward flow of food.

Mixed graftage, a French method, differs from the ordinary methods in that a few shoots are allowed to grow permanently upon the stock but kept pruned sufficiently to prevent their seriously checking the growth of the scion. By its means a successful union of sweet cherry *(Prunus avium)* and cherry laurel *(Prunus laurocerasus)* as a stock was readily made. This is considered a difficult one, because the former is deciduous, the latter evergreen.

Daniel concludes from his experiments: 1, Mixed graftage should be used with plants presenting marked differences, as between evergreen and deciduous subjects; 2, the stock does not influence the scion as much as in ordinary graftage; 3, such characteristics as may be attributed to environment (height, vigor, resistance to parasites, etc.) are affected less by the stock also; but, 4, characteristics peculiar to the variety of the stock (flavor, form of fruit, color of flowers, etc.) mix with those of the scion much more readily by this method than by the ordinary methods.

286. End-to-end grafting of grapes, a recent French method, gave a low percentage of successes but excellent unions in California. In operating it stocks and scions of equal size are cut at slight angles (about 70°) and each pair fitted together by a piece of stiff galvanized wire pushed into the pith of both parts. Bioletti considers this method "especially promising for machine grafting."

In experiments at the Good Hope Agricultural College, it was found that skillful grafters could make 300 end-to-end grafts an hour, while 100 an hour with the tongue graft was quick work. Students who had never grafted before could make 120 an hour, against 15 tongue grafts. In the field the two methods produced about equal percentages of vines when made by skillful men. Unskilled men secured almost as good results with end-to-end grafts as did the skilled men, while the tongue grafts proved almost total failures. Roots were less numerous on the scions of end-to-end grafts, thus facilitating removal. Results on the whole favored the end-to-end method.

287. Saddle grafting is especially useful for propagating small growing shoots. The scion, split by an upward cut, is placed upon the stock cut on each side to form a wedge. Tying and waxing finish the job. Its most popular application is to scions with terminal buds with wood too soft or weak to be easily whip grafted.

288. Adjuvant graft.—Couderc of France contends that the life of grape vines may be prolonged by using two stocks to one scion. His experiments show that companion stocks have a greater period of duration than either of the stocks used alone. By using a series of "adjuvant" stocks he has flowered and fruited vine cuttings the first year. This was accomplished by grafting a stock having one internode and a good root system under each eye of the cutting, which remains horizontal. The plan is suggested to overcome phylloxera attacks, which the author claims occur even with American species.

289. Fruit bud grafting.—C. Trehignand, a French investigator, has found that vigorous trees which fail to produce fruit may be grafted with fruit buds from other trees in August or September and fruit obtained the following season.

Fig. 266.—Blueberry budding. A, plant, cut to ground in early spring, sent up these shoots on each of which bud was inserted in mid July and protected from rain by wax paper cone, buds soon united but remained dormant until following spring; B, these stems developed from buds inserted previous summer. By using this new growth for re-budding selected variety may be rapidly propagated.

290. Grafted conifers, especially pines and firs, are never as successful as seedlings, because they rarely make a perfect leader and symmetry is sacrificed. Thuja, biota, juniper, cypress and retinospora may be usefully increased by grafting.   Stock for first and second is American arborvitæ *(Thuja occidentalis);* for the next two red cedar *(Juniperus virginiana);* for cypress family use funereal upright cypress *(Cupressus sempervirens).* (Fig. 204.)

In March on stocks established in pots use "leader" scions; cut the stocks about half through, make a tongue half way down the cut.   Prepare the scions similarly, leaving the growing point intact.   Fit stock and scion accurately, bind with raffia, cover with prepared clay, wrap and place under staging for a couple of days.   Then smear the union again with clay and plunge in a propagating case for a couple of weeks.   Avoid excess water, but sprinkle occasionally with a fine rose.   After hardening place in a nursery bed with soil heaped over the union.   To prevent annoyance from needles, cut with shears; don't pull out.

291. Pecan propagation tests conducted by S. J. Greer and W. T. Mallory in Mississippi proved bark grafting best for top working, especially when used on branches about 3″ in diameter.   Patch budding of latent buds on limbs up to 3″ in diameter gave promising results.   Whip grafts and patch buds were used in nursery propagation with results favoring the latter.[1]

292. Blueberry graftage.—According to Coville, though grafting is feasible, budding is almost indispensable in experimental work . . . but bushes so propagated are not suitable for permanent commercial plantations, because they are continually sending up new and undesirable shoots from the stock.   Budding, however, is the best known means of producing a large quantity of cutting wood from superior varieties and for testing the quality of new ones.   A budded blueberry when properly handled comes into bearing in two years from the time of budding (Fig. 266).

---

[1] *Miss. Sta. Bul.,* 275.

XIII

AFTER TREATMENT OF GRAFTED TREES, GRAFTING WAXES, WOUND DRESS-INGS, ETC.

294. Care of Topworked Fruit Trees.—Success with newly grafted fruit trees is often lacking because the necessary care is not given after the grafts begin to grow. When a tree has been cut back for top working it receives a severe shock as proved by the heavy watersprout growth that soon develops. It should throw its energy into the scions. Small spurs and leaves may be left for shade and photosynthetic purposes, but it is a mistake to allow long succulent shoots to use nourishment that should go into scion growth. Some operators, however, leave them in the belief that they help to elaborate plant food.

A newly set walnut graft often makes over 6′ of growth the first season so should receive care to avoid breakage (Fig. 267). It should be braced. One of the best and easiest ways is to nail a slat to the grafted branch parallel with the graft which should then be securely tied to it. This prevents waving in the wind and endangering the union, especially if it is weak.

The question often arises as to what should be done if all or several of the scions grow on the branch. The number left may vary under conditions but generally only one scion should remain permanently. If two or more are left a Y-crotch may result. If two scions grow on a small stub, it is generally advisable to cut off the weaker after appreciable growth has been made. If the stub is large at least two scions should be allowed to grow during the first season. During the second season the weaker or less favorably placed ones should be cut off near the stub but not exposing the stub itself. The advantage gained is quick covering of the stub. The small wounds made by cutting the superfluous grafts soon heal.

When it is desirable to leave two grafts, one should be cut severely back so as to check its growth and thus prevent forming a Y-crotch. The graft-union must be carefully watched after being made so any cracks that occur in the wax may be re-covered.

When scions fail to grow watersprouts may be allowed to develop for budding in summer or fall. Therefore when spring-made grafts fail, do not wait until the following spring to re-graft but bud as soon as possible. The common T-bud is used for most fruit trees; the modified H-bud or window-bud and the patch-bud for nut trees.

295. Necessity for wound coverings.—As time is required for the union of stock and scion, all cut surfaces must be thoroughly waxed to exclude air from the wounds to prevent drying. Wax also excludes fungi and bacteria.

Fig. 267.—Grafts badly and well cared for. A, young walnut graft neglected; B, lath cleat tied to stock and scion prevents breakage.

296. Grafting waxes used in the past were numerous and diverse, ranging from the mixture of chopped straw and blue clay to complicated kinds for special purposes. The majority of those popular today vary only in the proportions of the three ingredients, resin, beeswax and hard cake beef tallow or linseed oil, sometimes used instead of tallow. These variations are largely due to personal preference, though in some cases the consistency of the finished wax is thus purposely varied. For soft waxes the proportion of tallow should be increased; for tough ones, that of beeswax. Thus any formula can be varied to secure wax for any kind or character of use indoors or out.

As a rule, liquid waxes are less popular in America than in Europe, where also pitch waxes and grafting clay (fresh cow manure free from straw, three parts; clay or clay loam, seven parts and cow hair half a part) are more in use than here. In the table which follows the first formula is probably the most popular. The functions of grafting wax are to protect the injured tissues from decay and weathering and to prevent losses of plant juices by evaporation. Hence soft wax is better than hard, because it may be fitted more closely to the wood and into chinks. Large wounds should first be trimmed of ragged edges, then swabbed or sprayed with bordeaux mixture and finally covered with wax.

The resin and beeswax waxes are all started alike; the materials previously made into small lumps may all be placed in the pot together, but preferably the resin is previously melted over a very gentle fire and the other ingredients added. Boiling must be avoided. After stirring to make uniform, the melted mixture is poured into a tub of cold water and flattened out so it will cool evenly. When cool enough to handle, it is kneaded and pulled till the color resembles molasses taffy. To prevent its sticking to the skin, the hands are kept greasy. Should lumps occur because of improper handling, it may be re-melted and re-worked. Usually the wax is made into balls or sticks for convenient use. It will keep indefinitely. Linseed oil for making grafting waxes must be free from adulterations such as cottonseed oil.

Alcoholic waxes are considered too soft to stand the heat of American summers. They melt and run. For winter work, for covering wounds and for bridge grafting, their softness is an advantage. To make them the resin is melted slowly, tallow added and the kettle removed from the fire. When cooled somewhat, alcohol (and turpentine when in the recipe) is added. Stirring continues from the adding of tallow till the mixture is nearly cold.

The ideal grafting wax should have at least these qualifications: 1. It should exclude air, fungi and bacteria and retain the moisture of the wood; 2, contain no material that will injure live tissue in the strength at which it is used; 3, not crack in cold weather; 4, not run in hot weather; 5, be semi-permanent in possession of its various virtues; 6, be more or less elastic to accommodate itself to changes in temperature and dimension of stock and scion consequent upon growth.

No wax yet devised meets all these requirements perfectly but several meet them well enough for practical purposes under the conditions to which they are ordinarily exposed.

Various waxes. Most waxes soften with heat. Those which become pliable at the temperature of the hands are called hand, hard or cold waxes. Others, called brush waxes, have a higher melting point so are heated and applied with a brush while warm. Liquid waxes are made with some solvent, usually alcohol. They are applied cold. Evaporation leaves a solid residue.

Some proprietary waxes and wound coverings on the market have an asphaltum base and are applied cold—a distinct advantage over waxes that require heat.

297. Waxed string used in root grafting is made by placing balls of No. 18 or 20 knitting cotton in hot resin wax, turning them for a few minutes, removing and letting them drain and cool. Before immersing, the outside end of each ball should be definitely located where it can readily be found, else unwinding will be difficult. This string is used mainly for tying root grafts. It is strong enough to make a tight wind, yet weak enough to break without hurting the hands. It does not need to be tied, since it readily sticks.

298. Grafting pots and heaters.—Grafting wax should be warmed to a consistency that will spread with ease. Home made equipment may serve the purpose. Warm wax may be applied with a brush or a swab. It is well to heat the wax in a double boiler arrangement; setting the container with wax in the hot water of the boiler. Occasionally when the wax is applied too hot live bark may be injured, particularly on scions with thin and tender bark. The trouble is rarely encountered when a double boiler is used. Excellent heaters are on the market (Fig. 268).

299. Paraffin as a grafting wax.—Dr. Robert T. Morris, noted experimenter with hardy nuts, has introduced melted paraffin as a grafting wax. It is applied at a temperature as low as possible to insure a thin coating. If applied at too low a temperature it becomes flaky and soon cracks open. During extremely warm weather it is unsatisfactory as it is fairly certain to melt and run out of place. To remedy this and to prevent cracking, one-third part of commercial pine gum may be added. Encouraging results are reported.

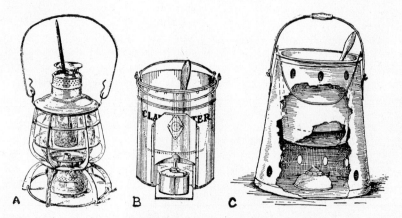

Fig. 268.—Alcohol heaters for grafting wax. A, Morris' railway lantern style; B, Clark melter; C, home made style.

300. Directions for making grafting waxes.

Formula I. A brush or hot wax. Resin, 4 pounds; beeswax 1 pound; raw linseed oil, 1 pint. 1, Weigh ingredients. 2, First place the resin in a one-gallon can. 3, Heat and melt it with a slow fire. 4, Add the beeswax and allow it to melt. 5, Then pour in the raw linseed oil and mix thoroughly. 6, Set it aside to cool. 7, Label with formula.

Formula II. A brush or hot wax. Resin, 4 pounds; beeswax, 1 pound; raw linseed oil, 1 pint; lampblack,[1] 1 ounce. 1, Weigh the ingredients and prepare in a one-gallon can as in Formula I. Add the lampblack after removing the can from the flame. 2, Label with formula.

Formula III. A brush or hot wax. Resin 4 pounds; beeswax, 1 pound; tallow, 1 pound. 1, Weigh ingredients and prepare in a one-gallon can as in Formula I. Add the tallow last. 2, Label with formula.

Formula IV. A hand or cold wax. Resin, 4 pounds; beeswax, 2 pounds; tallow, 1 pound. 1, Melt the resin as in Formula I using a mild heat. 2, Add beeswax and melt it. 3, When this is melted add the tallow. 4, As soon as the tallow has melted or disappeared, stir and pour the mixture into cold water. 5, Grease the hands with tallow or preferably oil. 6, When it has cooled sufficiently, work the mass with the hands until it becomes readily pliable and easily handled. It should become about the consistency of molasses candy and light amber in color. Form the wax into sticks and compress in oiled paper for future use. Work carefully at first to avoid burned thumbs for the mass sometimes cools on the outside while the inside is still hot.

Formula V. A hand or cold wax.[2] Resin, 3 pounds; beeswax, 1 pound; raw linseed oil, 1 pint. 1, Melt the resin as in Formula I or in a double boiler. 2, add the besswax and heat until it disappears. 3, Add the linseed oil and mix the contents of the can thoroughly. 4, After mixing completely, pour the mass into water to cool. 5, Grease the hands and pull until the mass looks like light molasses candy. 6, Form into sticks and wrap in waxed paper for storage.

Formula VI. A brush or hot wax. Paraffin, 3 pounds; pine gum, 1 pound. 1, Heat the paraffin with a slow fire until melted. 2, Add the pine gum and, when it has disappeared, stir to mix thoroughly. 3, Set the mixture aside to cool for future use.

Formula VII. A cold brush alcoholic wax. Resin, 16 parts; tallow, 1 part; wood alcohol, 8 parts. 1, Melt the tallow in a gallon can. 2, Pulverize and add the resin. 3, Stir and heat until melted. 4, Remove from the fire and stir until partially cooled. 5, Gradually add alcohol until the cooled mass has the consistency of paint. 6, Pour this into jars and seal to prevent evaporation. 7, The wax will remain liquid until ready for use. When used the alcohol evaporates, the wax covers the wound and becomes dry and hard. This wax should be kept away from a flame and applied cold.

Formula VIII. A brush or hot wax. Resin, 5 pounds; beeswax, ¾ pound; linseed oil, 1 pint; lampblack, 1 ounce; fish glue ⅒ pound. 1, Melt the resin as in Formula I. 2, Add and melt the beeswax. 3, Take from the flame, stir in the linseed oil and lampblack. 4, Allow the mixture to cool somewhat but have it still liquid when the fish glue is added. 5, Use only enough water necessary to dissolve the fish glue. If the dissolved glue is added while the wax is still warm the whole mass will boil over the container.

---

[1] Lampblack is merely to color the mixture. It has no other virtue in the wax.
[2] The use of handwax in the orchard is not pleasant, particularly in cold weather. Even when the hands are greased they are likely to become so sticky that the change from waxing to other operations is awkward. In cold weather the wax requires considerable working unless kept in warm water.

301. A wound dressing which possesses many desirable characteristics described by I. E. Melhus [1] is made by mixing one pound each of commercial cresol and concentrated furfural with 0.32 ounces of sodium bicarbonate in a reflux condenser and boiling until a resin forms. When it becomes slightly brittle on cooling in a thin film on a glass rod, discontinue boiling and pour the syrupy mass into a shallow pan to cool quickly. Dissolve this resin in equal parts of acetone and furfural. Dissolve four grams of mercuric cyanid in a small quantity of acetone and add it to the resin-acetone-furfural mixture.

This dilute resinous mixture, about the consistency of shellac, may be applied to a wound with an ordinary paint brush. It dries quickly and forms a smooth, dark brown, amorphous coating on both living and dead tissue. The rate of drying and penetration is determined largely by the proportion of acetone to furfural. The plastic and amorphous properties may be controlled by varying the degree of condensation of the resinous product. Dead tissues are penetrated from 1″ to 2″ by the furfural in the dressing, while living tissues are not penetrated nearly as extensively. The resin remains largely on the surface of the wound.

302. Waxed bandages may be prepared in the same way as waxed string. They are best made of old cotton sheets torn in strips of any desired width and wound in rolls like tape. For binding large wounds, as in bridge grafting, they are excellent.

303. Rubber strip in grafting.—R. B. Rogers, an English experimenter, has found pure rubber electric wire insulation strip useful in grafting. It is bought in rolls. The grafts are fitted as usual, the strip stretched well and wound tightly so as to cover the exposed part, exclude air and hold the scion firmly in place. A strip 4″ or 5″ long and ½″ wide is enough for ordinary grafts. Rubber solution should be used to make the ends stick. Strip need not be removed since it stretches and rots with graft growth. Old strip quickly spoils in the sun.

304. Wrapping grafts with cloth, rubber, waxed paper, plain thread with the unions waxed, were experimentally tried by the government to determine the effect on crown gall. From the large amount of data it is concluded that wrapping reduces injury, the best material being rubber, then cloth (which gave the largest percentage of smooth healthy trees). Cloth is also cheaper. The investigators strongly oppose wrapping with thread and then waxing.

305. Bass, the inner bark of basswood, was formerly used in greenhouses and nurseries to tie plants, buds and grafts.

306. Raffia, the lower epidermis of a Madagascar palm (*Raffia ruffia*), peeled in narrow strips and dried, is extensively used in America and Europe for tying vines, flowers, celery and in graftage. It is soft, strong enough for the purposes, and not quickly altered by moisture or temperature. Because of its cheapness it has displaced bass in nursery and greenhouse practice. Its chief fault is its tendency to roll when dry. Moistening overcomes this. As received from abroad, it is in plaits or skeins. Thin rubber strips ¼″ wide and 4″ long are now considered the best wrapping material for budding.

---

[1] *Phytopathology 16.*

308. Dressings for tree wounds.—Fruit growers have long used paints, tars, waxes and other substances as coverings for wounds on trees. The New York State Station (Geneva) reports results of experiments with white lead, zinc white, yellow ochre, coal tar, shellac and avenarius carbolineum. The summary of Bulletin 396, by Howe, is slightly condensed in this and the next two paragraphs. In all cases undressed pruning wounds have healed more rapidly than those whose surfaces have been protected.

The first season shellac seemed to exert a stimulating influence on wounds, but the second season this disappeared. Of all materials used shellac was least injurious, but it adheres to wounded surfaces poorest of all. Carbolineum and ochre caused so much injury that neither should be used. Coal tar not only caused injury, but quickly disappeared, either through evaporation or absorption. White lead and zinc caused some injury when applied, but the wounded tissues recovered rather quickly, and at the end of the first year the injury was not very marked; at the close of the second season it had nearly disappeared. These two are the best protective substances used, and of the two white lead is the better. Nothing is to be gained in treating wounds by waiting before applying the dressings.

The treatment of peach tree wounds with any of the substances caused so much injury that it may be said peach wounds should never be treated with any of them. This may be inferred for other stone fruit trees. There is nothing to show in the experiment that it is worth while to treat wounds large or small with any of the substances in common use. Had there been a longer period of observation, it might have been found that wood exposed in the larger wounds would have been somewhat saved from decay which often sets in on exposed wood of fruit trees. It may prove to be worth while, therefore, to cover large wounds, in which case white lead is undoubtedly the best dressing to use.

XIV

GENERAL POINTS CONCERNING FRUIT TREE STOCKS

309. Effects of stock on scion.—With few exceptions all cultivated fruit trees are combinations of two individuals, stock and scion. So far fruit growing has been carried on with little or no regard to their interactions. Yet no doubt each reacts upon the other and grafted fruits are influenced for better or worse by the stocks upon which they are worked.

Since we cannot always find clear-cut analyses of the effects of stock on scion, it is small wonder that fruit growers give little attention to stocks. After centuries of fruit culture, we actually do not know what the best stocks are for many fruits. Further to complicate the situation, trees are profoundly modified by soil and climate, the modifications frequently being confused with those caused by the stock. Our fragmentary knowledge of stocks being thus a thing of shreds and patches, few are willing to break away from time-worn dictums, so continue to plant trees without attention to possible reciprocal influences of stock and scion. Briefly, influences are as follows:

310. Fruit tree stocks may influence scions as follows: 1, Modify form and stature; 2, adapt a species or a variety to a soil; 3, fit a plant to endure an incompatible climate; 4, impart disease to the scion; 5, increase productivity; 6, hasten maturity of either wood or crop; 7, change the color of the fruit; 8, affect the flavor of the fruit; 9, shorten the life of trees of which they become a part (Fig. 269); 10, increase size of flower or fruit.

1. The dwarf effect obtained with pear on quince, and of apple on Paradise (though not always distinctly dwarf) is well known. Many varieties of apples worked on Northern Spy (a vigorous grower) are dwarfed. According to Gardner, Bradford and Hooker, common lilac on ash, though it does not make a lasting union, is said to be greatly increased in size over own-rooted lilac.

Form or habit of tree, some writers believe, may be changed by the stock. For instance, trumpet creeper, normally a climber, becomes round headed with pendant branches when on catalpa. Peach trees have changed tops when on plum or apricot stocks. (Same authorities.)

2. Adaptability of a species (through stock) to soil. If it be assumed that plum roots are more resistant than peach roots to wet soils, as many people believe, plum trees grafted on their own roots should be able to grow on wetter soils than if on peach roots.

3. Claims are made that certain varieties become hardier due to earlier maturity of the wood. This is probably true in some cases; but often examina-

tion reveals that the increase is due to substituting a hardy variety (by double working) in those parts of the tree particularly susceptible to winter injury.

4. Transmitting disease to scion is well shown by hard or black-end of European pear fruits due to Japanese pear stocks. When the same varieties of pears (affected by Japanese roots) are grown on French pear roots this disease seldom if ever occurs—clearly a case of disease-influence by the stock. Peach stocks infested with yellows transmit the disease to scions.

5. Increase in productivity of tree, some writers believe, is induced by grafting. Doubtless early bearing is favored by imperfect unions just as by ringing or any other obstruction of translocating tree foods. Vigorous seedlings and vigorous grafted trees are generally late to begin bearing. The greater fruitfulness of some dwarf apples and pears may be explained by curtailing scion vigor through graft union.

6. Changing time of maturity of both wood and crop is believed by some writers to be influenced by the stock but the evidence is somewhat conflicting. Rather good evidence has been given, however, that plums on Myrobalan stock ripen earlier than on late plums. Several varieties of peach ripen earlier when on Myrobalan stock. Wickson states that Riparia Gloire and Grand Glabre grape stocks induce fruit ripening one to two weeks earlier than does Rupestris St. George. Perhaps this ripening period of some fruits is due to degree of congeniality between stock and scion.

Early maturity of scion is reported by Hedrick who believes that Mahaleb stock makes hardier tops in cherries both in nursery and in orchard because of earlier wood ripening. *Prunus lusitanica* is said to ripen its wood earlier on *Prunus padus* stock than on its own roots. Because of this it is probably better

Fig. 269.—Incompatible grafts. A, Bartlett pear on apple—though this one year growth is good, union is not; B, Burton prune on almond—poor type seedling shows bad constriction.

able to withstand cold weather, but evidence of this is not fully convincing (Fig. 271).

7. The amount of red in the fruit may be increased by early maturity due to weak stock or imperfect union. If so, a vigorous stock with a good union should reduce the red.

8. Though many authorities agree that flavor is influenced, the extent of the influence finds diversity of opinion. Sour orange does not reduce the sweetness of sweet oranges on grafts set in its root stocks. Swingle reports that satsuma orange on sweet orange stock is coarse, dry, insipid and later in ripening but on trifoliate orange stock much improved in quality.

9. Shortening tree life is evidenced by apple on pear and vice versa; also by Bartlett on Kieffer. Jost reports that pistach normally lives 150 years but on lentisk *(Pistacia lentiscus)* it lives only about 40 years and on false terebinth *(P. terebinthus)* it lives 200 years.

10. Possibly a slow growing stock might limit the water and mineral nutrient supply to the top during certain months and produce smaller fruit. On the other hand, a stock with a scion restriction at the union might produce larger fruit than normal because the organic food supply would be increased. Anjou and Hardy pears on quince stocks often grow to enormous size.

Most of the influences of stock on scion, it appears, might result from varying ability of the stocks to supply water and mineral nutrients to the tops. This, of course, is influenced to some extent by the nature of graft union. It may account for the high quality of Angouleme pear on quince.

311. Influence of scion on stock is also decided. For example, the form of roots is much changed by the scion. Thus, in starting apples in a nursery varieties are budded or grafted on seedlings which presumably would have root systems much the same but at digging time the roots of the various varieties are as diverse as the varieties themselves; Red Astrachan, for instance, has an exceedingly fibrous root system with few tap roots, while Oldenburg and

FIG. 270.—Top worked trees. A, first year's early growths of water-sprouts removed (poor practice). B, second season's growths—water-sprouts removed while green (good practice second and later years).

Fameuse grown on either side of the Red Astrachan row, are almost destitute of root fibers, having instead deep tap roots with two or three prongs. Nurserymen declare the weaker the top growth and the sparser the foliage of a variety, the more deficient is the root growth.

Effect of rootstocks on blossoming of seedling apples was tested in England by H. M. Tydeman who reported that 50% of the seedling apples worked on

Fig. 271.—Double worked Clyman plum. A, below pencil, peach stock; B, from pencil to finger, Clyman plum; C, above finger, Grand Duke plum.

dwarf stocks bloomed in their sixth year, whereas only 9% of the same seedlings bloomed when worked on vigorous stocks, also that only one of the seedlings had bloomed on its own roots at the same time.

Many apple varieties grown by Swarbrick and Roberts of Wisconsin show almost invariable influence of scion on stock, especially with piece root grafts, as to size of root system, proportion of fibrous roots, general direction of root growth and point of origin of large laterals. No relation was noted between size of top and that of roots. Characteristic differences persisted in various soil types. Trees budded well above ground showed no apparent influence of scion

on root. Root types of double worked trees in which dwarfing stock was intermediate were generally typical of the intermediate variety and anatomica'
studies of such trees suggest that dominant varieties influence growth structure.
Because double working produced root characters typical of the intermediate
stock the authors (Swarbrick and Roberts) suggest that this method might
produce more practical results as to root uniformity than direct placing of grafts
upon roots.

312. **Plant chimeras or "graft-hybrids."**—To the general rule that stock
and scion retain their identity there is a seeming exception in the pseudo-hybrids
of experimenters. After grafting when scion buds fail to grow and an adventitious bud arises at the junction of stock and scion, including cells from both
parts, we have what for many years was known as a graft-hybrid, but is now
more accurately called a plant chimera. In a case of this kind the cells from
stock and scion reproduce themselves, sometimes the wood of one covering the
other like a glove, or it may be the wood of the consorting pair grows side by
side in parallel parts throughout the plant. These plant chimeras are more or
less familiar in apples half sweet, the other half sour; or in which a portion
of the apple is red or yellow and another russet. They are probably most often
found in citrus fruits.

313. Why nurserymen bud or graft trees.—Important though

the effects of stock are on scions, any and all are but incidental to
the true explanation for a two-part tree for practically all orchard
plants. At the proper season in the nursery world countless expert
workmen graft or bud so dexterously, precisely and rapidly that
their work is little short of marvelous. What are the reasons for all
this seemingly extra work of grafting and budding? Why do not nurserymen sell us plants on their own roots? The answer is that in no
other way can fruit trees true to name be propagated so rapidly. In
some cases there is no other possible method of multiplying a variety. Unfortunately, the stocks chiefly chosen by nurserymen are
those which can be worked most easily and soonest give a present-
able nursery tree. (As a rule the seedlings of a species make the
best stocks for that species.) Fruit growers if they give the matter
thought, choose stocks that do not sucker, or that best suit their soil
and in a few cases such as will give dwarf trees. All other effects of
stock on scion are ignored by both nurserymen and fruit grower.

It does not follow, however, that whatsoever stock one wants can
be used. Even when kinship is close some plants resist all appli-
ances of art to make a successful union, while some distinct species
of fruits seem foreordained to be joined. Thus, a pear will not grow
well on an apple nor an apple on a pear, closely related though they
be—both *Pyrus;* but the pear readily unites with quince and hawthorn—different genera, *Cydonia* and *Cratægus.* Sweet and sour
cherries grow well on mahaleb cherry, but mahaleb will not grow on
any of the cultivated cherries. Sour cherries upon sweet ones succeed less well than the latter on the former. The gooseberry will
not grow on red currant, but thrives on black currant.

Though botanical kinship is a fair guide. something more is

necessary. Horticultural varieties of exogenous plants may generally be inter-grafted freely; but not always; species less freely;
genera only occasionally and families rarely. Just what more is
necessary than botanical relationship no one knows beyond, of
course, the knowledge that there must be some conformity in habit
between stock and scion; that the two must start in growth at approximately the same time; and that the tissues must be sufficiently
alike to insure proper contact in the union. Yet these facts do not
sufficiently explain the affinities and antipathies which plants show.

Fig. 272.—Effect of leaves on root formation. Right hand tree of each pair
was intermittently defoliated throughout season.

Thus, the propagator has little to guide him in selecting stocks and can choose only after repeated trials, near relationship being the only guide, even though often an untrustworthy one.

314. Influence of stock propagation method.—Not only are grafted plants affected by kind of stock used, but also by manner of propagating stocks, whether from seed or from cuttings. There is no question, for example, that stocks propagated by cuttings do not produce the deep tap and prong roots that seedlings do. Again, seedlings lifted and root-pruned the season before budded or grafted have thicker root systems than if not so transplanted.

It seems necessary, therefore, to say that for the best interests of fruit-growing we cannot neglect the way in which stocks are grown. Undoubtedly for some conditions we shall find stocks from cuttings preferable; under others, and generally, seedlings will be better when we have a choice. So too, usually, when nursery practice permits, a stock is better for having been transplanted before budding or grafting.

315. Pedigreed trees.—We hear much about the individuality of orchard trees and the necessity of propagation from individuals having the best characters. Most present day horticulturists do not believe in "pedigreed trees," finding but little in either theory or fact to substantiate the claim of those who believe they can improve varieties by bud selection. The multitude of trees in any variety, all from one seed, it seems paradoxical to say, are morphologically one individual. A plant variety propagated by buds is essentially complete in its heredity. How, then, can the difference between individual plants in every orchard be explained?

Some authorities say that it is "nurture" without invoking a change in "nature." Soil, sunlight, moisture, insects, disease—and, more than any of these—the stock give every individual plant an environment of its own from which come characters that appear and disappear with the individual. Thus, it is believed, we can bend a variety by means of a stock, but not that we can permanently mold it into any new form given it by a stock. Let go the force, whatever it may be, which bends the variety and it snaps back into its same old self.

Bud sports, however, form exceptions to the above general rule. How they originate is still matter for speculation. Doubtless the most striking instance is the nectarine—the smooth skinned peach which may develop from a peach stone or from a bud that appears "by chance" on a peach tree. Among many other cases conspicuous ones are the "all red strains" of Jonathan, Stayman, York, Duchess and other apples, each developed from a single branch discovered on a tree which elsewhere bore "normal" fruit.

316. Necessity for stock breeding.—In the coming refinement of fruit growing we must breed stocks as we now do the varieties they support. The seed for our pome fruit stocks have come from cider presses and those of the stone fruits from canning factories and dry-yards. Under these methods it is mere chance as to whether one gets a tree on a good or a bad stock. Would it not be a safe stroke of business for a nurseryman to select his stocks and through his catalogue educate fruit growers as to the greater value of trees on good stocks?

Fig. 273.—Students planting root grafts made in winter practicums and stored until spring.

317. Incompatibility of stock and scion.[1]—Pomological litera-ture abounds with graft combinations which involve more or less incompatability of the parts destined to function as symbionts.[2] In some cases there is complete failure to unite or to grow. In others, growth starts with some promise, but gradually diminishes and finally death follows. In still other cases growth is reasonably vig-orous for an indefinite period and at least quasi-symbiotic relation-ship may continue until mechanical stress produces a fracture which reveals a faulty union. Botanical relationship is not an infallible basis for prediction. Experience seems to be the only guide as to the success of a proposed combination. Through repeated trial some curious incompatibilities between varieties have become recognized, particularly in the stone fruits and especially as reported by Hatton, Amos and Witt[3] and Heppner.[4]

[1] Defective graft unions in the Apple and the Pear. F. C. Bradford and B. G. Sit-ton, Mich. *Tech. Bul.* 99. pp. 3-106; 88 halftones. 1929.

[2] Symbionts-organisms that live in union, each being necessary to the welfare of the other, as bacteria on the roots of clovers and other legumes.

[3] *Plum Rootstocks: Their Varieties, Propagation, and Influence upon Cultivated Varieties Worked Thereon. Jour. Pomol. and Hort. Sci.,* VII pp. 63-91, 1928.

[4] *Grafting Affinities with Special Reference to Plums. Cal. Exp. Sta. Bul.* 438, 1927.

In the union of pear on quince, various degrees of congeniality and uncongeniality are commonly recognized in the practice of double working, which utilizes a congenial variety to make contact with the quince and to serve in turn as stock for the uncongenial variety whose fruit is desired. Double working of this sort is often practiced in growing dwarf Bartlett pears; many trees of this variety, however, are worked directly on quince. [Hardy pear unites well with quince, but Bartlett often does not; so Hardy is first worked on quince and then used as stock for Bartlett. Perhaps the varying degrees between compatability and the reverse may be due to differences in quince stocks as recorded by Hatton (322). Authors.]

Considering both the pear-apple and the pear-quince unions as types of uncongeniality in the pome fruits, it may be said that their most striking peculiarity is not their failure to unite but their failure to stay united. It seems significant that they exhibit abundant union of the type shown by wounds and by congenial grafts until the point of apparent cambial continuity is reached. In the first stages of association, while reserves of plant food in the tissues are presumably abundant, they grow side by side, with cambial edges suspended, forming parenchymatous tissue. Whether the vascular bridges [across the gaps between stock and scion—Au.] represent true cambium unions or whether they represent union of cambium derivatives cannot be stated. It seems, however, so far as the material examined permits any opinion, that true cambial continuity is rare; certainly it is of short duration.

318. Uncongeniality is clearly not the universal cause or attendant of dwarfing. It seems, plain, however, that uncongeniality which breaks continuity of bark must retard the growth of the stock and secondarily, as well as primarily, the growth of the scion. The dwarf Bartlett tree is apparently self-semi-girdled perpetually and the quince root, as well as the pear top, seems distinctly dwarfed, at least for some years.

319. Budding differs from grafting (Fig. 265) in that the primary union is between the surface of the cambium on the shield and the meristematic wood surface of the stock. Even in successful bud unions of apple and pear there is more or less parenchyma intervening between stock and scion. This type of primary union is not, however, essential since graft union may occur at the edges of the shield, as in chip budding. All bud unions involve more or less union by grafting.

320. Uncongenial grafts, as represented by pear on apple and pear on quince, differ from congenial grafts principally in failure to maintain cambium continuity. The break in the cambium comes apparently at the end of the growing season; re-grafting often occurs but becomes less common with advancing years. As stock and scion expand, the cambium failure leaves a zone of parenchymatous, sometimes suberized [corky], tissue between them. Both the transpiration channels and the phloëm become generally discontinuous.

The more uncongenial graft, pear on apple, produced no swelling at the union and had none of the external appearances generally associated with uncongeniality. Defective unions of apple on apple and [European] pear on Kieffer [Chinese hybrid] were found to be produced by faults in setting the grafts. In inlay grafts lack of pressure between stock and scion may jeopardize the ultimate healing of the union.

321. Contact between cambiums of stock and scion at the top of the stub is essential to proper healing of graft unions. Tilting of scions, preventing contact at the rim, gave rise to tissue changes which retarded covering of the stub, producing considerable swelling of the union, and produced the general appearance often considered to characterize uncongenial unions. Internally, however, there was no evidence of tissue break-down such as characterizes the uncongenial unions, so these unions are not considered as uncongenial.

In the various unions, the most uncongenial produced no swelling and the greatest swelling occurred in grafts which are not uncongenial. Within the latter group the swellings were greatest in the specimens which were most vigorous. This seems to indicate that the swelling is not *per se* an important obstruction to transpiration or translocation, that it is not *per se* a sign of uncongeniality and that much horticultural thought founded on the assumption of connection between uncongeniality and swelling at the union may be modified by re-examination without this dubious premise.

322. Types of quince stocks.—From the investigations of R. G. Hatton [1] it is evident that some strains or types of quince are more compatible than others and that, as has long been known, some varieties of pears show marked preference (or as decidedly the reverse) for quince—hence the practice of double-working. After seven years of experimenting, this investigator reported that of seven types only three proved of commercial value, the other four showing marked incompatibility with many pear varieties used in the study.

Certain European pear varieties [so far as the authors are aware not grown in America] manifested distinct preferences for particular quince stocks occasionally for the types proving generally unsatisfactory.

Unfortunately quince stocks are so badly mixed that variety names mean nothing. What is "Angers" in one locality may be called "Fontenay" or "Common Quince" or merely "Quince" in others and these names may also be applied to different types of quinces in different localities. Better than probably anything else that could be presented here, this evidence proves the necessity for more definite knowledge of compatible and incompatible stocks and the propagation of only the desirable ones for commercial purposes. It also emphasizes the high desirability of propagating varieties of tree fruits by stem cuttings

323. Root-grafted vs. budded trees.—For many years fruit growers and nursery men have discussed the relative advantages and disadvantages of whole root vs. piece root and budded vs. root-grafted trees, largely without experimental evidence. Arguments have mostly been generalized statements, only too often warped by individual prejudice or pocketbook. Before summarizing the experiments recently published, some leading opinions should be cited and methods outlined so the reader may choose what appeals to him. The following points must be borne in mind.

Nursery budding upon spring-set stocks is done during summer, but no growth occurs till the following season. The stocks before being planted in the nursery are trimmed for obvious reasons. In whole-root grafting the scions are crown set and roots similarly trimmed. In piece-root grafting several bits of root are used, the top piece with a crown. These latter are, of course, smaller. Thus piece-root grafting creates a problem of its own because of the varying sizes and vigor of the pieces. Piece-root grafting may therefore be said to be unfairly pitted against both budding and whole-root grafting, which under equal conditions are equally valuable methods of propagation.

Differences of growth characteristic of each method result from differences of stock trimming, not methods of propagation. Even casual observation will show differences in root development between budded and root-grafted trees, the latter being more horizontal, prolonged and shallower on one side of the tree than the former, when dug from the nursery row—all this apart from differences characteristic of variety. Such differences are due to differences in stock cutting.

Doubtless if stocks were cut alike for both budding and root grafting development would be closely similar; for when short pieces of root with few lateral branches are used they must grow differently from long roots with numerous

[1] *Jour. Pomol. and Hort. Sci.,* VII.

branches. In strong stocks where only the tips are cut off and budding performed root development is largely if not wholly lateral, whereas when small
pieces are used growth is mainly downward. Hence the theoretical conclusion
that at a given nursery age, whole-rooted trees have naturally and necessarily
longer and stronger roots than those grown from piece-roots.

When root pieces are very small the resulting trees will be small at the end
of the first growing season. Hence nurserymen often cut back the tops so as to
secure stout, straight bodies which show no trace of the growth ring between
seasons, and which do not branch too low or send up a crooked leader from a
lateral bud, due to the winter-killing of the terminal one. If the trees are sold
as two years old there can be no objection to this practise; but if the age is
reckoned from the cut, an injustice is almost surely done the fruit grower, because greater quantities of roots are removed at digging time than would be
the case with true one-year trees. The first season's growth should always be
high enough to form a good tree body of the right height, whether or not the
fruit grower is a believer in low or high headed trees.

Budded trees of the same age as root-grafted ones grown in the same field
usually average larger, the difference diminishing in proportion as the length of
the root stock piece increases. Similarly their root systems go deeper and show
more symmetry, but these characteristics also lessen as the root stocks lengthen.

It must not be concluded from the discussion so far presented that budded
trees are necessarily superior to root-grafted ones, though it is probably a fact
that large numbers of trees produced from small, short and weak stock pieces
are decidedly different in appearance and development. Opinion seems to be
general among fruit growers and nurserymen that budded trees root more deeply
than do root-grafted ones and make longer-lived trees when transplanted to the
orchard. It is therefore concluded that more depends upon the handling of
stocks at the time of performing the operations than upon the method *per se*.
In the northwestern states where trees on their own roots are preferred, piece-
root grafting is not only more economical of stocks, but has the merit that the
scions soon take root in the orchard, and the trees become "own-rooted." In
other sections budded stock is perhaps better than root-grafted trees of the
same age and grown under equal conditions, at least as dug in the nursery.
Nevertheless as good trees can be grown by the grafting method. As to results
in the orchard the following paragraphs are interesting.

324. Whole vs. piece root vs. buds in apple propagation.—
During the past decade or two work has been done at experiment
stations in Pennsylvania, Oregon, Kansas and Alabama, to determine the relative value of whole and piece roots and budding. Reports show that differences must be measured by decimal fractions
to be discovered at all. In Pennsylvania according to J. P. Stewart,
trees propagated on top-piece roots are slightly in the lead in all
respects, with those on whole roots second. In Alabama, trees on
bottom pieces of stock roots showed a slight superiority at the close
of the second season, with those on top pieces second, and whole
roots third. In Oregon, trees on whole roots were slightly ahead at
the close of the fourth season, in the single variety remaining at that
time, with those on top-pieces again second.

In Kansas 64 trees grafted on whole roots averaged 1/10″ larger
in trunk diameter, at the end of 10 years' orchard growth, than 30
trees budded in the usual manner on whole roots. They in turn

averaged 1/5" larger than 102 trees, involving some additional varieties propagated on piece roots.   No differences in growth or vigor were observable in the orchard.   In another Kansas experiment three varieties of 400 trees each, whole roots, were compared by Judge Wellhouse with 400 of the same varieties on 2" piece roots. In the latter case, the young trees had developed considerable numbers of roots directly from the scions, thus making the trees largely own rooted, while no scion roots were developed on whole-rooted trees.   After 19 years in the orchard, the only difference observed was in the greater number of sprouts from the whole-rooted trees.

From all these data it is obvious that none of the present forms of propagation has any material advantage over any other.   It may be of distinct advantage to get rid of the seedling root altogether, either by using the shortest roots practicable and then cutting them off during transplanting after roots have developed above, or possibly by a direct rooting of the scions.

Elimination of seedling roots would at least obviate the numerous ill effects of poor unions.   It would also reduce the opportunity for crown-gall infections, eliminate the possibility of harmful influence of variable seedling stocks upon scions, and make it possible to develop definite and standard root-systems, with which injuries from root aphis and kindred difficulties might well be greatly reduced or entirely eliminated.   This important array of advantages, all of them practical, is by no means impossible of attainment.

326. Selection of scions is of prime importance in grafting. None but thoroughly mature wood, cut while the buds are fully dormant, should ever be used.   Preferably it should be one-year old, though sometimes two-year and even three-year wood gives good results.   Pithy and soft wood is worthless for grafting.   Scions may be packed in damp moss or sand and stored in a cool cellar until buds on trees exposed to the weather begin to break.   If the moss is too wet the scions will become water-soaked and worthless.   The tips are often immature and should be discarded.

327. Shipping scions long distances.—The following method of shipping mango scions from Ceylon, India, to Washington, D. C., recommends itself to shippers of other scions.   The cut ends of the scions were covered with collodion, the bud sticks dipped in clay mud, packed with a small amount of moist coir (refuse cocoanut fiber) and forwarded in cylindrical tin tubes (Fig. 315).

325. Budding vs. grafting nursery trees.—As to the respective merits and advantages of budding and grafting fruit trees in nurseries, taking the country as a whole probably no general statement can be made because experience and opinion differ widely as may be seen from the compiled and condensed correspondence of large nurseries quoted below.   (Fig. 265.)

Barnes Brothers Nursery Company, Yalesville, Connecticut. General practise in our own and in other eastern nurseries is to propagate pome and drupe
fruits by shield budding as this method gives work for skilled men in summer
and has distinct advantages over grafting and since it uses buds when wood of
new varieties is scarce.

Chase Nursery Company, Chase, Alabama. In this section as many apple
trees are grown from buds as from grafts. Peaches, plums and pears are budded,
seldom grafted.

The Greening Nursery Company, Monroe, Michigan. We are budding our
fruit trees exclusively in preference to grafting. Much difficulty has been experienced in the past through crown gall. We find this is largely eliminated by
budding. When the graft union is not perfect crown gall frequently develops.

Harrisons' Nurseries, Berlin, Maryland. Nearly 50 years ago we propagated
only peach trees by budding, all others by grafts; about 30 years ago we began
budding apple, pear and plum on a large scale—about half of our total output;
about 15 years ago we discontinued grafting any fruit trees as budded trees
proved superior. Only a few of our older employees can do grafting!

Mount Arbor Nurseries, Shenandoah, Iowa. We grow about 75% of our
apple trees from grafts. Formerly the percentage was larger. In Wisconsin,
Minnesota, Iowa, Nebraska, Kansas, Missouri, Arkansas and Oklahoma grafts
are used from 75% to 90%.

J. H. Skinner and Company, Topeka, Kansas. In the middle West grafting
of apples is more extensively practised than budding. We graft apples altogether. We have heard of objection to budding because some of the seedlings
vary in hardiness and some kill out. What little budding is done in this section
is in attempts to eliminate root rot.

Stark Bro's Nursery and Orchard Company, Louisiana, Missouri. We graft
90% of our apple trees. Grafting is a convenience because it can be done in
winter when there is no other work. Then in summer complete attention can
be given to budding other fruits. As far as resultant trees are concerned we see
no difference, the grafted being perhaps the straighter tree.

It costs more to bud than to graft but budded fruit trees are superior to
grafted, grow more thriftily and generally live longer. Our buds are cut in
bearing orchards from vigorous, healthy trees of superior strains and extra heavy
bearing habit. Such trees come into bearing earlier than trees from buds cut
in nursery rows and bear better than grafted trees whether selected from orchard
or nursery row. The union of bud and seedling is as near nature as can be but
grafts are more artificial and the union is never 100% solid. When a budded
tree has grown two or three years it is almost impossible to tell whether it was
budded or whether the top of a seedling was cut off and an adventitious shoot
developed.

328. Commercial apple stocks were formerly produced almost
exclusively from wild French and Vermont crab seed collected at
cider mills, washed free of pomace and dried in the open air. Nor-
mandy and Southern Austria are the leading sources of European
seed. For some years Vermont seed has been falling into disfavor
because cultivated apple seed has been finding its way in increasing
quantities into commercial seed mainly due to the dying of seedling
trees and the increase of cultivated varieties, the culls of which are
used for cider.

There is great difference in the value of seed from different apple
varieties. Seed from Baldwin, Rhode Island Greening, Graven-

TABLE 22.—ROOTSTOCKS USED IN UNITED STATES NURSERIES

Tree and Stock	North-eastern States % [*]	South-eastern States %	North Plains States %	Pacific North-west %	California %
PEACHES on:					
Peach	100	98.1	100	74.7	97.6
Almond				1.0	
Apricot		0.05		10.1	1.1
Myrobalan		1.8		14.2	1.3
PLUMS on:					
Myrobalan	87.9	11.9	0.6	37.1	31.8
Peach	1.8	74.2	9.2	62.8	66.6
Apricot					1.6
Almond					
Americana (native)					
Mariana	0.2	8.2			
SWEET CHERRY on:					
Mazzard	9.3	10.7	15.4	81.7	58.7
Mahaleb	90.7	89.3	84.6	17.5	29.8
Morello				0.8	11.5
SOUR CHERRY on:					
Mazzard	4.9	0.6		35.3	52.4
Mahaleb	93.8	99.4	100	64.7	47.6
Morello	1.3				
PEARS on:					
Japanese	5.1	52.8	9.2	19.7	2.0
French	81.9	40.5	28.4	71.5	71.0
Quince	8.9			0.2	6.4
Calleryana				1.5	0.8
Old Home on French					19.1
Old Home on Ussuriensis ..			15.4		
Ussuriensis	4.1	6.7	47.0	7.1	
Old Home on Calleryana					0.7
PRUNE on:					
Myrobalan	included in plums			37.4	59.9
Peach				62.6	35.9
Almond					4.2
APRICOT on:					
Apricot					46.1
Myrobalan	not reported				15.9
Peach					
ALMOND on:					
Almond	not reported				62.9
Peach					37.1

Results of 1920-30 National Rootstock Survey. Unpublished data from Div. of Pomol., Univ. of Calif. Most recent decades figures available.

stein, and Tompkins King is markedly inferior in both germination
and vigor of seedling produced to seed from Whitney, Wealthy, Delicious, Rome Beauty, Winesap and Ben Davis which gives seedlings
of good vigor and uniformity. Accordingly seed from sections where
some of these varieties predominate such as the Pacific Northwest,
is preferred to seed from regions where the less desirable ones are
grown, such as New York and New England.

329. Securing apple seed.—In growing apple trees Hanson of
South Dakota has found that the seed should be separated from
cider pomace before planting since fermentation acts injuriously.
Clean seed washed from pomace within 24 hours of pressing should
be spread out to dry for a day or two, then mixed with moist sand
and buried in well-drained sites in small boxes with holes in the
bottoms for drainage, and left over winter. He has been most successful when the seeds were planted in beds 4′ wide, surrounded by
12″ boards and given lath screen shade as soon as the seedlings begin to appear.

After drying the seed is shipped to nurseries where it is handled
in one or other of the following ways:

1, In early winter the nurserymen mix the newly secured seed
with sifted river sand and store the boxes in sheltered places, such
as stables and outhouses, care being taken to prevent attacks of
mice. The sand, kept moist, is stirred occasionally. When the seeds
begin to swell (in about a month), they are either placed in cold
frames or sown in the field. In the former case the seedlings are
transplanted. Three or four weeks are needed for germination.
Lukewarm water, used by some growers, hastens germination, but is
considered inexpedient by many. Some growers soak the seed 48
hours before planting, but the plan is not widely popular. It is used
only when the season is precocious and hastened germination seems
necessary.

2, The seed is stratified over winter, or imported in late winter,
soaked for three days with changes of water twice daily and then
stored in canvas bags between ice cakes. They are sown as soon as
the ground can be handled. This is essential because they sprout
at low temperatures. To sow sprouted seeds means a poor stand
and crooked seedlings. Another method is to place the seed between
layers of muslin on moist moss and cover with muslin, then to place
it in cold storage (32° to 36° F.) for a four to six weeks period.

3, Best results have been obtained by placing the newly purchased seed in flats of sand and covered ¾″ to 1″. The flats are put
in cold storage for four to six weeks at 32° to 41° F., then placed in
coldframes or a lath house and allowed to grow. When the seedlings develop the second pair of true leaves their roots are trimmed
and they are transplanted to nursery rows.

Since the quarantine against the importation of foreign stocks, the American seedling industry has been greatly stimulated. Some seedling producers import French crab seed; others use domestic supplies from both wild trees and cultivated orchards, among them Vermont crab seed. Immense quantities of stock are grown in the Central Western States, notably Kansas, also in the region around Portland, Oregon and in the Yakima Valley of Washington.

330. Apple seedlings are of two main types, branch-root and straight-root. The branch-root seedlings are used in nursery sections where trees are raised by budding rather than grafting, since this type root becomes established easily and gives a good stand and growth the first season. Formerly secured from France, where the branch-root was obtained by transplanting the young seedlings in early spring of the first year from seed, the quarantine against their importation has necessitated the development of a system of production particularly adapted to American conditions.

For branch roots seed is planted in rows and the young seedlings are undercut carefully with a draw knife soon after they have appeared above ground, the area of land being flooded with water immediately to settle the plants and prevent loss from drying out. Accordingly this type of the industry is confined to the irrigated sections, particularly the Yakima Valley in Washington.

Rows are made 3' or 4' apart, the seeds dropped 1" asunder and covered 1" or less deep. In wet land, rotted, sandy compost or other loose material is often used. Cultivation is the same as for garden vegetables. When the leaves have dropped in the fall, the seedlings are dug with special implements which save 9" to 12" or even more of root. Part of the top is usually cut off, the seedlings tied in bundles of 100 and stored in green sawdust until needed.

Straight root seedlings are produced in deep, fertile soil, such as that in the Kaw River Valley of Kansas, where the rich, black earth produces long, straight, plump, tap roots. Hard, gravelly and shallow soils over hardpan contort the tap root and produce branches, thus spoiling the seedlings for grafting stock purposes. Long, plump, unbranched tap roots make two, three or even four stock pieces for piece root grafting. The ground is deeply plowed and loosened to 10" if possible, preferably in the fall, so it can be worked at the earliest possible moment in spring.

331. Hardy stocks for tender varieties.—At the Canadian Experimental Farms 90 varieties of apples were top-grafted on hardy stocks to see if they could thus be made hardy, but practically all were killed back to the stocks. One Wealthy stock grafted to Milwaukee and Martha carried the former through a very severe winter and matured a crop of fruit, while the latter was killed. Hence the conclusion: Trees tender on their own roots are also tender on hardy stocks.

332. Slow maturing stocks (Northern Spy) according to Gulley of Connecticut, do not delay the fruiting of quick-maturing varieties (Jonathan and Canada Red).

333. Quince effect on pear.—Two French investigators, G. Riviere and G. Bailhicke, tested the effects of stock upon scion of two pear trees of one variety upon quince and pear stocks respectively. The trees were 15 years old and had grown under apparently identical conditions. For three successive seasons the fruits were collected; samples were analyzed, etc. Each bore about 300 fruits annually. Those on the pear stock were green, those on the quince yellow with a rose blush on the sunny side. The average weight, density, acidity and sugar content were in favor of the quince stock. Observations on another variety tallied with these findings.

334. Hardness and softness of wood in apple grafting.—E. Leroux, a French investigator, has concluded from experiments with 200 varieties of cider apples that, 1, varieties with tender wood can be most successfully grafted on tender-wooded varieties and hard-wooded on hard-wooded; 2, success follows only rarely when a hard-wooded is grafted on a soft-wooded stock. These principles are believed to apply to other orchard fruits.

335. Effect of small growing stock on scion.—Booth reports an instance in which peaches on Mariana plum stocks grew fairly well for two years, though from the start the peaches grew much more rapidly than the plums, so the peach trunks at two years were twice as large at the union as below. During the second season the weather was very hot and dry, and the peach trees after wilting for several days but reviving at night, finally dried out and died, evidently because sufficient moisture was not furnished by the slow-growing Mariana roots to meet the demand from the peach leaves during a period of excessive transpiration. While such an instance is uncommon, there is but little question that the amount of growth will always be lessened, the life of the plant will be shortened and it will withstand adverse conditions less readily when the stock plant is noticeably slower in growth than the scion plant.

336. Pears on apple stocks.—A writer in *American Gardening* claims to have grown Flemish Beauty pears on Wagner apple stocks. The pears were larger and of finer flavor than those on the mother pear tree and were free from brown specks. The grafts bore every year for six years without a break, while the mother tree failed some years and the apple tree bore only biennially.

Camperdown, a weeping elm, when grafted on Scotch elm *(Ulmus glabra)* stocks "weeps" from the point of union, the top being more or less flat at first; but when grafted on American elm *(U. Americana)* it grows upright and tall, because the vigor of this stock overcomes the weeping habit to a large extent.

337. Paradise and Doucin stocks for dwarf apple trees are at present of small importance in America because dwarfs have not become as prominent as in Europe, but the demand for them is increasing, more especially in New England, New York, New Jersey and Pennsylvania. These stocks must be produced by asexual methods, usually by layerage, to transmit the dwarfing characteristics. Trench layers (Fig. 63, 64) of Doucin and Paradise apples are cut from the parent plants in the fall and either sold that season in spite of their small roots or transplanted and grown in nursery rows the following year to make vigorous plants.

338. Effects of standard and dwarf apple stocks were determined after ten years' growth by Rogers and Vyvyan of England after carefully digging up the trees. None of the trees had a tap root. The root systems of trees on vigorous stocks were two to three times as heavy as those on dwarf stocks and were more widely distributed, but did not penetrate the soil as deeply. The ratio of stem to root was practically the same on both stocks. The weight of fresh fruit produced during the lifetime of the trees was in all cases greater than the total green weight of stem and root.

339. Dwarf apples.—Hedrick of the New York State station reports a ten-year experiment with dwarf apples. That part of the summary which deals mainly with the results of propagation is slightly condensed thus:

The results show: 1. That the union between stock and scion is poorer with Doucin and French Paradise than with French crab, and that varieties unite less well on French Paradise than on Doucin stocks. 2. Doucin and French Paradise stocks are less hardy than French crab; and of the two dwarfs, French Paradise is much less hardy. 3. The greatest weakness of dwarfing stock for New York is surface-rooting in which character the two stocks cannot be distinguished. Evil results following surface rooting are winter-killing, uprooting of trees by wind, suckering and injury in cultivation. 4. Suckers from both dwarfing stocks prove much more troublesome than with standard trees. 5. Trees on the three stocks attained the size commonly ascribed to them; those on French crab, full size; on Doucin half dwarf; on French Paradise, true dwarf. In this test the dwarfing effect of dwarf stock is not as marked as is commonly reputed.

340. Dwarfing trees to be grown in the open requires that scions or buds be worked on slow-growing stocks and later headed in. Plants may also be dwarfed by growing them in confined quarters, such as boxes, tubs and pots too small for their normal development. Nurserymen can go no further than to supply the specimens; after-care depends upon the grower, who by neglect or ignorance may develop standards from those intended to be dwarfs.

When grafted or budded "dwarfs" are planted so deeply that roots are developed by the scion above the union with the stock, the tree will become "half dwarf" or even "standard." Such roots must be cut off from time to time as they develop. Dwarf cherries are grown on mahaleb stocks, but so are probably the majority of standard cherry trees. Morello root sprouts are used rather extensively in California to make dwarf cherry trees. Annual removal of roots from the scion and heading-in will keep the trees dwarf in habit.

341. Pear stocks used by American nurseries are mostly grown from seed secured from the French and Italian perry (pear cider) presses. It is several times more costly than apple seed because each seed must be picked by hand from the core. Though some seed, chiefly Kieffer, collected in Maryland, Delaware and New Jersey from canneries, is used in the United States it is considered less desirable than that from European sources. On the Pacific Coast some seed from locally grown pears, especially Bartlett and Winter Nelis, is used, though not all varieties make satisfactory roots or stands of plants. (Table 23.)

In the past Japanese stocks have been used to a limited extent by American nurserymen and the trees so propagated grown in orchards, with unsatisfactory results of faulty union of stock and scion. Recently they have been proved responsible for "black end," which renders the fruit unfit for sale, so their use has fallen into disfavor. The Manchurian pear *(Pyrus ussuriensis)* introduced from eastern Asia during the present century in the hope of securing a blight-

TABLE 23.—PEAR STOCKS USED IN AMERICAN NURSERIES

Variety	Number of Seedlings	Observations	Percentage Graded as No. 1 ($\frac{3}{16}$ to ¼ Inch)
Bartlett	359	Straight root	20.7
Beurre d'Anjou	149	Branched roots, strong plants	25.9
Beurre Clairgeau	41	Poor plants	21.8
Beurre Hardy	304	Straight roots	7.2
Burkett	380	Very straight roots, tall plants	23.1
Dept. No. 26591	55	Branched roots, strong plants	49.0
Doyenne Boussock	—	Poor stand	
French pear	2,265	Mostly straight roots	27.6
Garber	160	Strong plants	31.2
German pear	1,732	Few branched roots	11.9
Kieffer	270	Straight roots	20.3
Old Home	10	Very straight roots	30.0
Seckel	95		15.7
Sudduth	445	Straight roots	7.8
Tyson	7	Poor stand	0.0
Winter Nelis	9	Branched roots	44.0
Worden Seckel	36	Poor stand	16.6

[1] H. B. Tukey, *Seedling Fruit Stocks, N. Y. (Geneva) Exp. Sta. Bul. 569.*

resistant stock has proved disappointing for this same reason and for others noted further on. Points that attracted attention to these oriental pears and their hybrids are their larger size as seedlings, comparative freedom from leaf spot and exceptionally straight roots.

Of the many pear stocks tested in Oregon the French pear has proved most satisfactory. Selection within this species has revealed great variability with respect to vigor, type of root growth and resistance to disease. Superior strains have been isolated and propagated. Old Home and Variolosa are deemed highly promising pears to serve as blight resistant trunk and framework stocks for improved varieties. The Japanese sand pear *(Pyrus ussuriensis)* has proved unsatisfactory on shallow and heavy adobe soils. The Callery pear *(P. callery-ana)* and the birchleaf pear *(P. betulæfolia)* are considered highly promising stocks, the latter being more resistant to alkali than is the French pear. Both are resistant to root blight and pear woolly aphis.[1]

342. Double working is sometimes used (Fig. 271) to make a straight tree instead of a straggling one (Winter Nelis, Beurre Hardy pears), to give vigor to one that grows weakly or poorly (King and Grimes apples—subject to collar rot), or to provide blight resistant trunks or frame limbs for pears (Fig. 274). The strong or healthy grower is first grafted or budded upon a seedling stock and when old enough grafted or budded with the desired variety, thus performing two graftage operations and having three different kinds of wood—that of the seedling and that of the second bud or scion upon the first. Generally the first scion is allowed to grow a year before the second is grafted on it; but sometimes when the "sandwich" of intermediate wood is to be short, as with pears, both are set together; that is, a scion of the desired variety is grafted in the scion which is

[1] *Ore. Bien. Rpt.,* 1929-30,

to produce the intermediate wood, and this one then inserted in the seedling stock. Considerable skill in grafting is needed to offset the extra risk of failure by this plan.

The trees most often double worked are probably pears, some of which do not form good direct unions with quince stocks, and which must therefore, have a go-between stock which does make a good union, both with them and with quince. Among varieties usually treated this way, the following are perhaps best known: Bosc, Winter Nelis, Sheldon, Washington, Marie Louise, Gansel's Bergamot, Josephine de Malines, Dix, Dunmore and Paradise. These are worked on one of the varieties that do make better unions on quince than on pear; for instance, Angouleme, Louise Bonne, Vicar, Glout Morceau, Easter, Diel, Amalis and Autumn Long Green. Always in double working dwarf pears both operations must be as near the ground as possible, so only 1″ or 2″ of the first pear wood shall be left when the double work is complete.

Popular apple "go-betweens" for such weakling but choice varietties as Tompkins King and Grimes Golden (Fig. 274) are Northern Spy, Tolman, Ben Davis and Delicious. Among plums Lombard is perhaps most in favor.

343. Double working to prevent pear blight is also gaining in favor. In addition to the strains of French pear under test as go-between stocks in Oregon, Old Home and Surprise pears are highly regarded on the Pacific coast, especially for Bartlett on French roots. French seedlings are budded to one or other of these varieties which in turn are budded to Bartlett (or other desired variety). If blight attacks the Bartlett top, it will kill no further than the frame limbs which again may be budded or grafted and a new Bartlett top soon grown. Another method of using Old Home is to graft or bud it on the French rootstock, grow it in the nursery for one season, bud it high to Bartlett and thus have a blight-resistant trunk

Fig. 274.—Double worked Grimes Golden apple on rot-resistant trunk which has seedling grafted root.

(Fig. 274). The degree of resistance is not as high as in the other method, but the cost is less.

344. Dwarfing stock for pear is quince.—Seed gives stocks inferior to those produced by stools (or mound layers) and from cuttings. Though formerly production was confined largely to Angers, France, the quarantine against nursery stock importation has resulted in establishing the industry in this country, especially in the Pacific Northwest and Texas. In the former area stools are used; in the latter cuttings. Nurserymen who have tried other stocks give the so-called Angers quince the preference. Dwarf pears are more often budded than grafted.

Kieffer pear is so strong a grower that attempts to dwarf it result either in the scion taking root, thus making the trees standards, or in the top outgrowing the stock so much that the union, being poor, breaks off. The Kieffer, struck from cuttings so that the trees are on their own roots, makes exceptional orchard plants.

Dwarf pears have much to commend them. They are smaller than standards (may be planted 12' or 15' apart). They come into bearing young and since there are more of them in a given area than of standards the first few crops may be more profitable. The trees, having uniform stocks, should bear more uniformly than standards on seedling stocks. In proportion to their top growth compared with standards they seem to fruit more heavily and the fruit is usually more highly colored.

Fig. 275.—Orange trees staked and tied in nursery.

LeClerc du Sablon attributes the larger fruits and bigger yields usually characteristic of dwarfs to the greater accumulation of reserve food (carbohydrates) during fall in the trunk and limbs above the pear-quince union. This food in spring helps form fruits in larger quantity and of greater size. No reason is assigned for such larger starch accumulation, but it is now believed to be due to the effect of the union in limiting the downward movement of carbohydrates manufactured in the leaves.

345. Preliminary budding for double working.—Pear shoots into which F. C. Bradford of Michigan inserted buds of desired varieties in August were utilized as scions in whip grafting and later made satisfactory growth. This method is deemed of potential value in double working and in the propagation of poor rooting plants.[1]

346. Spring-budding pears.—In Maryland, Japanese seedling pear stocks were placed in a hotbed in early April in 6″ of sand. The manure and sun heat made the sap start so that in eight days the stocks were ready to bud by the ordinary method. They were taken to a warm room, budded with Mikado pear buds and placed back in the sand to "take." In about eight more days, all having taken nicely, they were transferred to damp sawdust to prevent further growth till they could be set in the nursery a few days later. During summer, under good culture, they grew about 2″, and by fall were large enough to transplant in orchards. The method is practicable on a large scale.

347. Pear propagation.—Standard pears are generally propagated by whip grafting on whole stocks at the crown in the eastern United States. Only a small part of the lower end of the tap root is cut off. The scion is shorter than in most apple grafting—about 4″. Waxing is necessary. When this is done indoors, and when the wood is fairly warm, injury from the warm wax is avoided by dropping the grafts as waxed into cold water, after which they are made into bundles and stored like appleroot grafts. Greater care is needed in planting because of their length. Larger percentages of these grafts will grow than would in the case of ordinary root grafts in which the loss is counted at about 50%. As with apple, American nurserymen prefer branch-rooted to straight or tap rooted seedlings. So the young seedlings are undercut in early spring and the

Fig. 276.—Seedling orange lopped above bud that has "taken."

[1] *Mich. Sta. Quart. Bul., 12.*

beds flooded immediately. Hence such seedlings are mostly grown in irrigated sections.

348. Peach stocks.—The peach is the most important root-stock for peach. It makes an excellent union with commercial varieties. California nurserymen use seedlings grown from Lovell, Salwey, Elberta, Muir and occasionally clingstone pits. Seed considered best comes from seedling trees in the mountainous parts of the Carolinas and adjacent states, Oklahoma and Arkansas. Pits from the canneries are not favored by some nurserymen, but are extensively used by others. They are often planted in the fall in nursery rows (Fig. 276A); otherwise they are stratified as soon as received in autumn or early winter, the object being to provide them with proper temperature and moisture conditions for after-ripening, since they must complete certain internal changes before they will germinate.

On a small scale stratifying may be in shallow boxes of sand or soil, but, on a large scale, basin-like pits large enough to hold several bushels are made in soil. Earth is thrown over the seeds and kept moist or frozen all winter. If planted in spring without being strati-

FIG. 276A.—Peach pit planter. 1, natural wild peach pit; 2, canning factory pit, not good for planting; 3, hopper of machine. Most nurserymen contend for the "natural pit" as against pits of cultivated varieties secured from canneries and drying yards.

fied only a small percentage of seeds will sprout the first season, the balance continuing the following year or two.

According to a survey by M. J. Heppner the peach was used almost 99%, apricot 0.8% and almond 0.3% by California nurseries. Though popularity usually indicates which rootstock is best, the individual merits of the rootstock for conditions in the orchard should also be considered. The rootstock should make a good union with the peach, be adapted to the soil conditions, resistant to diseases and insects, and be uniformly true to type.

The peach rootstock succeeds best on deep, light, well-drained soils; poorest on heavy wet soils. It is also susceptible to alkali injury and particularly to attacks of the peach root-borer, crown gall, soil nematode and oak-root fungus. When free from pests and under favorable soil conditions it is long lived.

As a stock for peach, apricot root will grow on a wide range of soils, but does best on moderately heavy, well-drained, fertile land. It is more subject to gopher attack than either peach or almond. Crown gall, oak-root fungus and the peach root-borer also attack it. Its possible value as a peach rootstock is resistance to attacks of soil nematode. Attempts made to propagate peaches on apricot, however, have not been satisfactory. The union is sometimes uncongenial though there is no tendency to break. When peach is budded 6″ or more high on apricot it is claimed to do better than when budded near the ground.

349. **Seedlings of Prunus davidiana** are considered promising as rootstocks for peaches for planting in alkali spots where the original trees on other stock have died. Peaches on it appear vigorous with green foliage, under conditions where trees on other rootstocks have yellow foliage, stunted growth and are gradually dying. According to F. W. Anderson of the Kirkman Nursery Co., however, nurserymen are not using this rootstock because of its susceptibility to crown gall.

349. **Almond roots deeply** so has been used as a rootstock for peach in the drier soils. This supposed advantage over the peach is probably overemphasized. At present almost no almonds are used thus by nurserymen. The union is good but the almond root is susceptible to crown gall and attacks of peach root-borer and oak-root fungus.

350. **Seedling peaches are usually budded in mid-summer.** In times of scarcity, the "June bud" is also used but the resulting nursery trees are generally small. Buyers object to this small size so June budding is less favored than mid-summer or later. Sometimes "dormant buds" are planted in orchards the winter or spring after budding, before the buds start. This practice, however, is expensive and the stand is seldom as good as with June buds or one-year-old trees.

351. **June budded vs. August** budded peach trees were tested by J. C. C. Price[1] who reports that the former were superior in production, survival, prun-

---

[1] *Miss. Sta. Bul. 277.*

ing and training. The trees were kept dormant over winter and planted in spring.

352. Uncongeniality of stocks.[1]—The death of peach trees worked on Mariana plum roots is considered proof of the low value of this plum as a peach stock. Mariana plums and peach trees planted in the holes from which the dying trees were removed made vigorous growth, thus indicating the absence of pathological organisms.

353. Plum stocks.—Nurserymen differ widely in their preferences of plum stocks, depending mainly on cost, ease of working and adaptability of scion to stock. Myrobalan is the leading general purpose stock, though Japanese and peach are often preferred for sandy soils, *Prunus americana* for American varieties and St. Julien, though costly, for domestica and institia varieties. Mariana is still used in the Central Southwest, but in most other sections is unpopular because it makes poor unions.

It appeals more to nurserymen than to fruit growers, because it readily strikes root from cuttings, and nursery growth is ideal. Growers favor it less than formerly, and it is declining in popularity because it has a dwarfing effect and is prone to sucker.

St. Julien has been claimed to produce longer-lived, thriftier, hardier deeper-feeding trees which sprout less than those on other stocks; but its cost, hardness to bud, poor growth and liability to fungi in the nursery are against it. Horse plum is now "wholly superseded."

Peach is largely used for many varieties of plum to grow on warm, sandy or gravelly soils. It conduces to quick growth and early bearing and the roots produce no sprouts. Budding is easy, the trees make vigorous nursery growth, probably at less cost than on any other stock. Japanese varieties do specially well on peach. For domestica and institia varieties it is not so valuable because of poor unions and tender roots. Varieties said not to unite well with the peach are: Lombard, Damson, Yellow Egg and Washington. Peach borers are often troublesome on peach stocks.

Americana seedlings are the only ones that will withstand the rigorous northwest winters. They are used only for native varieties. It is not known how successfully other plums can be grown on them, though W. & T. Smith of Geneva, N. Y., report their use as satisfactory. As yet they are expensive, so they are not likely soon to compete with myrobalan and peach stocks. Their chief fault is their suckering habit.

Munsonia is reputed to be "pre-eminently adapted for low, wet lands." Kerr believes *P. hortulana* excellent because it never suckers. *P. angustifolia,* var. *watsoni* promises to be a dwarfing species. *P. bessyi,* according to Hansen, also dwarfs varieties worked on it,

---

[1] *Amer. Soc. Hort. Sci. Proc.,* 22.

TABLE 24.—BEHAVIOR OF PLUMS AND PRUNES TOP-WORKED ON OTHER VARIETIES *

Stock \ Scion	Apex	Beauty	Burbank	Burton	California Blue	Climax	Clyman	Diamond	Duarte	Formosa	French	Gaviota	Giant	Grand Duke	Hungarian	Imperial	Kelsey	President	Quackenboss	Robe de Sergeant	Santa Rosa	Satsuma	Standard	Sugar	Tragedy	Wickson
Apex	X	S	U		U	S	U	U	S	S	U	D	U	U	U	U	D	U	U	U	S	S	U	U	U	D
Beauty	S	X	D		U	S	U	U	S	S	U	D	U	U	U	U	D	U	U	U	S	S	U	U	U	D
Burbank	S	S	X	U	U	U	U	U	S	D	U	U	U	U	U	U	U	U	U	U	U	U	U	U	U	U
California Blue	U	U	U	U	X	U	U	U	U	U	U	U	U	U	U	U	U	U	U	U	S	U	U	U	U	S
Climax	S	S	S	S	X	X	X	X	S	S	U	S	U	U	U	U	U	S	U	U	S	U	U	U	U	U
Clyman	S	S	S	S	D	S	X	U	S	S	U	S	U	U	U	U	S	S	U	U	S	S	U	S	S	S
Diamond	U	S	S	D	S	S	S	X	S	S	U	S	U	U	U	U	D	U	U	U	S	S	U	U	S	S
Duarte	S	S	S	S	S	S	S	X	X	S	S	U	U	U	D	U	U	U	U	U	D	U	U	U	D	U
Formosa	S	S	S	S	S	S	S	X	X	S	S	U	U	U	D	U	U	U	U	U	D	U	U	U	D	U
French	S	S	S	S	S	S	U	U	X	X	S	S	U	U	U	U	U	U	U	U	S	U	U	U	U	U
Gaviota	S	S	S	S	S	S	S	S	S	X	X	S	U	U	U	U	U	S	U	U	S	S	U	S	S	S
Giant	S	S	S	S	S	S	S	S	S	S	X	U	U	D	U	U	U	U	U	U	S	S	U	U	U	U
Grand Duke	S	S	S	S	S	S	S	S	S	X	U	U	D	U	U	U	U	U	U	U	S	S	U	U	U	U
Hungarian	S	S	S	S	S	S	U	U	U	U	U	X	U	U	U	D	U	U	U	U	S	S	U	U	U	U
Imperial	S	S	S	S	S	S	U	U	U	U	U	U	X	U	U	U	U	U	U	U	S	S	U	U	U	U
Kelsey	D	D	U	S	S	S	S	U	U	U	D	U	U	U	U	X	U	U	U	D	U	U	U	U	U	D
President	S	S	S	S	S	S	U	U	D	U	U	D	X	U	U	U	U	U	U	U	S	U	U	U	U	U
Quackenboss	S	S	S	S	S	S	U	U	U	U	U	X	U	U	U	U	U	U	U	U	S	S	U	U	U	U
Robe de Sergeant	S	S	S	S	S	S	U	U	U	U	U	U	U	U	U	U	X	U	U	U	S	S	U	U	U	U
Santa Rosa	S	S	S	S	S	S	S	S	S	S	S	S	S	S	S	S	S	X	S	S	S	S	S	S	S	S
Satsuma	S	S	S	S	S	S	S	S	S	S	S	S	S	S	S	S	S	S	X	S	S	S	S	S	S	S
Standard	U	U	U	U	U	U	U	U	U	U	U	U	U	U	U	U	U	U	U	X	U	U	U	U	U	U
Sugar	U	U	U	U	U	U	U	U	U	U	U	U	U	U	U	U	U	U	U	U	X	U	U	U	U	U
Tragedy	U	U	U	U	U	U	U	U	U	U	U	U	U	U	U	U	U	U	U	U	U	X	U	U	U	U
Wickson	D	D	U	D	U	S	S	S	U	D	S	S	S	S	S	S	S	S	S	S	X					X

Explanation of Chart:
    S—Satisfactory combination.
    U—Unsatisfactory combination.
    D—Doubtful combination.
    X—Scion on own stock.

* Blank spaces indicate sufficient data not available.

but is hardy and produces precocious and prolific trees. For top-working domestica varieties Lombard is probably best. The sooner done the better because slow and crooked growth is common with late working. Early spring grafting and late summer budding are best.

355. Myrobalan or cherry plum furnishes the most desirable plum stock. Though not a vigorous grower it is hardy, long-lived, and deep rooted, notably adapted to deep and heavy soils, especially where rainfall is heavy or the orchard is given liberal irrigation. It also gives satisfactory results on deep, comparatively dry soils. Hence its extensive and until recently, almost continent-wide use as a stock for plums. Its seed is now largely produced by local nurserymen and an effort is being made to eliminate as many variations as possible between the various types. The brown roots usually distinguish myrobalan seedlings from other stocks used for plums.

In Europe, Myrobalan is considered a dwarfing stock which produces short lived trees; in America it is widely preferred because it produces larger and finer two-year trees than do other stocks. In the South, however, it suckers badly, and in the Prairie States it winter-kills. Its cheapness, ease of budding and general perfection of unions are strong points. Because of its variability there are many "true" and "false" Myrobalans among nurserymen. Formerly stocks in France were grown from cuttings; now apparently from seed.

Peach, though not so well adapted to heavy or wet soil, has been gaining in popularity during the past few years as the most desirable stock for plums in the earlier shipping sections of California where the soil is comparatively shallow, light or sandy. Peach roots are usually regarded as shallower and wider spreading than those of plum. They are, therefore, inclined to start growth earlier and to be better adapted to the earlier varieties growing under such conditions. Some growers believe peach stock may increase size and earliness of fruit. Experimental data, however, are not available on these possible influences.

Practically all Japanese plums seem to make satisfactory unions with peach but not so some European varieties. A recent survey of California nurseries shows that of the various shipping varieties more than half are now propagated on peach stocks. Trees on peach stock can usually be told by the light yellow young peach roots and the dark red of older ones.

Size of stocks for plum trees.[1] Plum trees propagated on various sized stocks in Nova Scotia showed but little difference after thirteen years between

---

[1] *Can. Exp. Farms Kentville, N. S. Sta. Rpt. Supt.* 1926. [This indicates that if a stock is too small it should not be budded—Authors.]

the resulting trees in respect to growth or yield, except in the case of the smallest sized stocks, which gave smaller trees and lesser yields.

Japanese apricot as a root stock.[1] As *Prunus mume* was found to be highly resistant to crown gall, C. O. Smith of California budded five commercial varieties each of almond, Japanese plum, prune, apricot and peach on its seedlings with the aggregate result that it is deemed of little promise as a rootstock for any of the stone fruits except apricot.

356. Apricots in the United States are most largely grown in California, usually on apricot stock, some on peach and myrobalan plum and a small percentage on almond. The last makes a weak union so should not be used. Apricot seedlings are grown in much the same manner as almond seedlings. The seeds, regardless of variety, are collected from California dry yards and canneries.

357. Tests of stocks in California[2] have shown affinities between species and varieties. Peaches and almonds generally fail to grow well when grafted on plums. No European plum is successful on Japanese types, yet many Japanese types succeed on most European varieties tested. California Blue nearly always fails as either stock or scion in top working. Clyman, Diamond, French, Giant, Sugar and Tragedy make excellent stocks for all other varieties, except California Blue, worked on them. Peach makes good stock for practically all Japanese plums tested but not for all European types. Certain plums can be grafted successfully on some almond trees, others cannot. Only a few varieties of plums appear to do well when grafted on apricot trees. These and similar facts indicate that many common variations in size and vigor so frequently shown in the same variety of tree, both in nursery and orchard are due to differences in congeniality of scions and seeding stocks (Table 24).

358. Cherry Stocks.*—Despite the antiquity and the importance of the cherry, the question of stocks is unsettled. Fruit growers favor mazzard; nuserymen, mahaleb, which they consider fit, at least, for sweet, and best for sour kinds. Further, they say it is impossible to grow cherries on mazzard at prices fruit growers are willing to pay. No systematic attempts have been made to settle the controversy.

The mazzard or wild sweet cherry (*Prunus avium*), used for centuries as a stock, grows 30′ to 40′ tall with trunks often 18″ in diameter. In America it is tender to cold, but grows vigorously. Its seedlings are badly attacked in nurseries by fungi, but it produces uniform trees and fruit.

Mahaleb (*Prunus mahaleb*) is a thick, slender-branched, low tree with inedible fruits, differing markedly from both sweet and sour cherries. The wood structure "one would expect to differ very materially" from that of sweet and sour cherries so that even if the union proved normal there would be difficulty in the passage of

[1] *Amer. Soc. Hort. Sci. Proc., 25.*
[2] *Univ. Calif. Exp. Sta. Bul. 438.*
* Synopsized from *The Cherries of New York* by Hedrick. Brought up to date by H. B. Tukey of the N. Y. (Geneva) Exp. Sta.

solutions between stock and scion. This cherry is propagated almost wholly from seed, though it may easily be grown from layers, cuttings and suckers as is also the case with Morello. The American supply formerly came from France but since the quarantine against the importation of foreign stocks it is produced in the West. Mahaleb seems to have been used in the United States since about 1850, first as a dwarfing stock but now for all purposes. Probably 95% of our cherries are budded on it. Why?

Doubtless it is easier to make better-looking nursery trees on mahaleb than on mazzard and it is cheaper. Mazzard has the faults of its species—capriciousness as to soils, climates, cultivation, pruning, diseases and insects; mahaleb is adapted to wider range of soils, is hardier to heat and cold, less particular as to tillage, will stand more pruning, is less susceptible to insects and is not badly affected by shot-hole fungus. It is more easily worked, both as to actual budding and to length of season. It also ripens its trees better and may thus be dug earlier than trees on mazzard.

Fruit growers in their turn find trees on mahaleb stocks hardier, though not as hardy as might be wished; more dwarf; more precocious as to bearing; as good as to size of fruit borne; poorer in union than mazzard; better adapted to diverse soils, especially light ones; also to shallow culture; shorter lived; less productive and profitable under equal conditions of soil and climate than trees on mazzard, this last being the concensus of opinion among cherry growers in the great cherry regions of California, Oregon, Washington, Michigan and New York.

359. Other cherry stocks.—Few fruits have such a wealth of stocks to choose among, yet have been tried so little. Russian cherries, come fairly true from seed and make good orchard plants on their own roots. Only sour kinds should be used—Bessarabian, Brusseler, Braune, Double Natte, George Glass, Lutovka, Early Morello, Ostheim and Vladimir. These, it is believed, would have some dwarfing effect. Ostheim and Morello have been used successfully in the north Mississippi Valley.

Bird, pin or pigeon cherry (*Prunus pennsylvanica*) is often used as a hardy stock for cold regions and as a makeshift, since it dwarfs the trees and suckers badly. In the Northwest the sand cherry (*P. pumila*) is used in cold, dry regions for sour cherries. It is as easy to work as mahaleb and its seedlings are large enough to set in nursery rows the following spring for August budding. Winter-rooted cuttings set in the nursery with 2″ to 4″ growth can also be budded in August. This species has made good unions with hardy cherries by budding and does not dwarf more the first five years than does mahaleb.

In Japan the Dai-Sakura, supposed to be a variety of *P. pseu-*

docerasus, grown for stock by nurserymen from mound layers and cuttings, has a somewhat dwarfing influence on European cherries. It should be tried in America. Among the many other stocks available some have already been introduced by the Department of Agriculture. Probably several of these or the others mentioned, will prove better than mazzard and mahaleb.

Cherries are usually budded; they may be more or less easily root grafted, though perhaps not as profitably. Whole roots are generally used, the union being made at the crown. In the cold Northwest the work is done with the intention of making the trees own-rooted.

Cherry buds are generally taken from nursery stock. Apparently varieties do not wear out, since old kinds have lost no characters accredited to them, even centuries ago; nor does taking buds from vigorous, mature trees or even decrepit trees seem to make a difference—all alike produce the variety. Hence, the hypotheses that fruit trees degenerate and that they may be improved by bud selection finds no support in the cherry.

Mazzard stocks[1] indicate by yields and growth of sweet, sour and duke cherries that they are better than mahaleb stocks in New York. At the end of fourteen years nearly all the mazzard rooted trees were living whereas more than half the mahaleb rooted ones had died and most of the others were lacking in vigor. Stocks had an effect upon the time of blossoming in the case of sweet and duke varieties on mahaleb roots, but the time of ripening and the size of the fruits were not significantly affected. Mazzard rooted trees, because of their greater size, were naturally much more productive than the others. Sour and duke varieties thrived better on mahaleb than sweet varieties did. The fact that mahaleb stocks are easier to bud and less exacting as to soil requirements has unfortunately led to their extensive use by nurserymen in recent years.

Morello[2] as a stock is gaining in favor for cherries in California. It has a desirable dwarfing habit. Cherry trees on mazzard and mahaleb grow too tall for convenient harvesting. However, the tendency of Morello to sucker is objectionable. Stocks are propagated from suckers dug annually. Nearly all varieties make strong and lasting unions with it. It grows well in many types of soil, will tolerate wetter soil and endure more cold than either mazzard or mahaleb. Though its seedlings are usually vigorous the individuals vary greatly in size and color of fruit, size of pits, time required for germination, rate of growth and form of seedling trees. Seedlings, therefore, should never be used for budding or grafting if the type of variety is to be kept pure.

359x. To identify mahaleb and mazzard stocks B. R. Nebel suggests immersing small pieces of root in aqueous solution of 4% to 10% iron alum. Mazzard will begin to darken the liquid in a few minutes and reach a maximum in one to 48 hours, according to the size of the pieces and the amount of solution used. Under the same treatment mahaleb roots will not produce discoloration.

360. Seed for cherry stocks.[3]—Wellington reports that at the New York (Geneva) Experiment Station early maturing varieties of cherries produced

[1] *G. H. Howe, N. Y. (Geneva) Exp. Sta. Bul. 544.*
[2] *Amer. Nat. 65.*
[3] *Amer. Nurseryman. 45.*

seed of low vitality, mid season kinds of moderate vitality and late season varieties, such as Downer and Oswego, seed of high vitality. He observes that this information should be of value to nurserymen who produce cherry stocks.

Mahaleb stocks [1] have been proved better than mazzard stocks for Montmorency cherry in Nova Scotia. The trees were more productive in the early fruiting period and maintained this supremacy. No difference was noted between the size of the fruits or the hardiness of the trees on the two stocks, thus supporting popular contention among fruit growers.

361. Cherry grafting.—At the Canadian Experimental Farms root grafts of Morello on commercial stocks gave poor results; crown grafts good ones. For budding, the bird cherry (*P. pennsylvanica*) gave so much sap that buds did not unite well.

362. Cherry grafting and budding.—Cherry scions, according to a writer in the *Gardeners' Chronicle* (British), should be cut at least two months before grafting and buried in a sheltered frost-proof place. Established stocks are budded in July, not at the base, but at the exact height of the head. Stocks that fail to take are grafted the following spring, when the stocks are headed back as close to the ground as convenient and whip grafted, scions being about 5″ long, bound with raffia and covered with prepared clay (clay and fresh horse manure). A point is made above and below the bandage to shed water. In less than a month the buds should start. The shoots are brittle and need staking.

363. Florida citrus stocks.[2]—Probably no horticultural crop has as complicated a rootstock problem as that of the Florida citrus fruits. The great variability of soils and the suitability of certain rootstocks to certain of these largely account for this, though the influence of stocks on some varieties is also a factor. (Figs. 275, 276).

Historically speaking, the early groves were of seedling sweet orange. When budding began sour orange was generally used as a stock because of its adaptability to soils then popular for citrus planting and because many of the old seedling groves suffered badly from rot. Sweet orange stocks, it was supposed, would merely repeat the trouble.

The trial of and interest in other root-stocks, notably rough lemon and grapefruit, has been in the attempt to make citrus trees grow in the light soils on which the sour orange does not make satisfactory growth. Of these the rough lemon has been outstandingly successful.

Grapefruit as a stock, at one time attracted considerable attention doubtless because it makes an excellent seedling tree that bears well. People judged it would be good on that account. Many tried it in a small way. At present probably no Florida nursery could supply trees on its roots. The only groves on it in Florida are old ones. For more than a decade groves on it have been pulled out and replaced by trees on other stocks.

---

[1] *Can. Exp. Farms. Kentville, N. S., Sta. Rpt. Supt., 1926.*
[2] Condensed from *Fla. Exp. Sta. Bul. 227, April, 1931,* and correspondence with A. F. Camp, the author.

At present the two stocks used widely in Florida are sour orange and rough lemon. Several others—sweet orange, grapefruit and trifoliate orange—are now used much less. Recently the Cleopatra mandarin has been developed as a rootstock and is now being tried extensively. Various hybrids—citranges, tangelos, and citrange-quats—are also being used experimentally.

The sour orange is well adapted to the moist hammock and moist flatwoods soils where the water-table does not come too close to the surface. It is extremely resistant to root and crown diseases, particularly foot rot, hence its great success on moist soils where other species of citrus are severely attacked by this disease. The fruit produced on this stock is of excellent quality and, in the opinion of many growers, is better than that produced by any other stock. The stock, however, is considered unsatisfactory for satsumas, kum quats, limequats and limes.

The chief difficulty with this stock is its inability to make a tree at a satisfactory rate on the more sandy and rocky soils. Hence its practical elimination on such soils, since the young trees may require several years to become sufficiently established to produce satisfactory crops. On this account many groves on soils adapted to sour orange have been planted with trees on rough lemon stock with the result of crop production sooner than would have been the case had sour orange stock been used. Sour orange is also less satisfactory than rough lemon in the nursery because it does not make a tree as quickly or grow as vigorously.

The rough lemon is a vigorous grower, produces a nursery tree and brings grove trees to size and bearing quickly. It grows well on light and extremely sandy soils where sour orange fails to produce a tree in a reasonable time, but is less resistant to foot rot and similar diseases, though more resistant than most other rootstocks. On sandy soils there is less danger from foot rot and similar diseases than on the heavier ones, so little difficulty is experienced with this trouble in rough lemon roots in such soils.

The general opinion is that it produces a quality of fruit somewhat inferior to that produced by the sour orange, the rind being rougher and the texture coarser. Doubtless this attitude is accentuated by the fact that it has been used extensively on sandy soils, which naturally tend to produce coarser, drier fruit. Several groves on rough lemon stock in heavier soils have a reputation for the high quality of fruit produced. As all the groves are of considerable age, observations would indicate that the quality of fruit produced by trees budded on this stock improves as the trees become older. The coarseness of fruit on young trees is probably in part due to the vigorous growth of the trees when budded on this stock.

The effect of rough lemon stock is less apparent in grapefruit but most apparent in tangerines, Temple and early oranges. Rough lemon seedlings are less resistant to cold than sour orange seedlings and trees budded on them seem to flush a little quicker with the advent of warm weather than do trees on sour orange.

Trifoliate orange (*Poincirus trifoliata,* formerly *Citrus trifoliata*) is used chiefly as a rootstock for satsuma oranges and kumquats. The trifoliate orange is deciduous, thorny, highly resistant to cold and a relatively slow grower. The addition of the evergreen top by budding appears to increase the vigor of the root system. In spite of this, however, there is usually some stunting of the top. Outside of northern Florida where it is used extensively for satsumas on account of the cold hazard it is little used except as a stock for kumquats, though some of the old groves have other varieties budded upon it. Fruit from trees budded on this stock is usually of excellent quality and particularly smooth. Such trees usually bear while younger than similar trees on other stocks.

Various other rootstocks have been tried to some extent but have not come into general use. Cleopatra mandarin, widely recommended and tried, is a good grower, makes a good nursery tree, as to both union and growth and seems to be well adapted to the lighter soils. Within a few years it will be possible to determine its desirability. It is hoped that it may prove better adapted than rough lemon to the production of tangerines on light soils.

Commercial lemon is frequently found as the rootstock of occasional trees in groves presumably planted on rough lemon. The seed in these cases probably were mixed accidentally with the rough lemon seed, as it is not considered a desirable rootstock because of its poor resistance to disease and the short life of the trees budded on it.

At present various hybrids such as citranges and tangelos are being tried as rootstocks, primarily in the hope of finding a substitute for the trifoliate orange. Several of these hybrids exceed the trifoliate orange in vigor and make satisfactory unions, but it will take time to determine their suitability in other respects.

364. Stocks for commercial growing are produced from seed, though stem and root cuttings are used experimentally to some extent. The seed are planted in beds from which the seedlings are lined out about a year later 1' apart in nursery rows and allowed a year's growth before being budded—usually in the fall and by the shield bud method. When the buds start to grow the seedling tops are cut off just above the buds. Lopping the tops may be resorted to when extra large stock is budded—as in rebudding stocks in which the first bud failed to take. (Fig. 276.) In commercial practice on regularly sized nursery stock lopping the tops is never done.

The trifoliate orange, in tests conducted by W. W. Bonns of California, did not live up to its reputation as a dwarfing stock with all citrus varieties or on various types of soil. Results vary on light and heavy soils. This stock, however, dwarfs the lemon to an undesirable degree.

364A. Citrus Rootstocks for California.—Although there are seven possible rootstocks for citrus trees in California only three are used commercially. These are sour or bitter orange seedlings, sweet orange seedlings and pomelo (grapefruit).

Sour orange stocks should be used for oranges and pomelos (grapefruit) on low, heavy or wet soils and for lemons at all times because of their resistance to brown-rot gumming and foot-rot. Orange trees make a quicker start into growth and bear fruit earlier on sweet stock, but after six or eight years there is practically no difference in size or fruitfulness of the trees. *Sweet orange as stock* for the orange has gained in popularity in California, so approximately one-half the nursery stock now grown in that state is on it. It is used on the lighter soils as it is suited for the heavier wet soils. *Pomelo (grapefruit) as a rootstock* is increasing in use. It gives pronounced success for lemons on the open gravelly soils of the interior California valleys. Trouble is experienced with it in the seed bed by gumming and because the seedlings bloom and set fruit when only 2″ or 3″ high.

The rough lemon is said to be hardy and to a certain extent drought-resistant; but since it is susceptible to brown-rot gumming it is not likely to become popular. *Trifoliate stock* though largely used in Florida, Louisiana and Texas almost exclusively for growing the satsuma orange is but little used in California. It shows no advantage there over sour or sweet orange stocks and is objectionable for lemon trees. Failure of this stock for lemon is common in California. *Chinese lemon,* has been found to force trees into extremely rapid growth resulting in the production of coarse fruit. The stock is susceptible to various root decays and is short lived. *Ordinary lemon* in California produces inferior stocks subject to root-rot. It does not appear to reduce the quality of the oranges produced or transmit its characteristics to the orange.

Oranges are seldom grown from cuttings because they root with difficulty. Hardiness of cold-resistant stock such as the trifoliate does not seem to be transmitted to the scion.

364B. Propagation of citrus root stock seedlings.—In California the seedlings are grown both under lath and, in favored localities, in the open. The trees seem to grow faster under lath shelter. One inch lath with 1″ open space is used (Fig. 296).

When irrigated by running water in furrows, the seedling rows are laid off 12″ wide with shallow furrows 8″ to 10″ wide. The seed is planted broadcast on the wide rows, every sixth row being left vacant for a walk. When irrigated by overhead sprinklers the seed is broadcast over the entire surface of the ground except for 12″ paths every 10′.

The seed is planted approximately 1″ deep and 1″ apart each way, and pressed into the soil with a board. A satisfactory stand is 30 plants to the square foot. Good practice is to cover it ½″ to 1″ deep with coarse river sand to prevent baking of the surface and drying of soil below. This also lessens the danger from damping-off fungus.

When seed is dry before planting it should be soaked in water for 24 hours. Sweet orange seed should never be allowed to dry out.

The usual time of planting citrus seeds is April. The seedlings should be large enough for setting in the nursery one year later. They are dug and planted with a dibble or a spade, keeping the roots straight 18″ asunder in the nursery rows 3′ to 4′ apart. Tops of seedlings are trimmed off and about 50% previous to transplanting. Irrigation should follow transplanting.

Budding, the usual method of propagation used in America, is best done during October and November. The buds remain dormant until spring. Where these buds fail, rebudding may be done in April or May.

Shield or "T" budding is the usual method, the buds being completely covered with strips of waxed cloth. The inverted "T" bud is probably best for fall budding because the buds tend to remain quiescent until spring. Winter injury is likely to result from earlier growth. The "T" bud with the cross cut above the bud tends to produce strong lateral growth so is best for spring budding. Budding should be fairly high to take full advantage of the resistance of sour orange stock to gum disease which comes from the soil.

The buds should be unwrapped and examined after about 10 days. If they have taken, which is shown by a grayish line of callous tissue around the edges, the wrappings should then be loosened and removed entirely in and about 30 days for fall buds and 20 days for spring buds or, whenever the bud is well healed, removed entirely.

The tops of fall budded stocks are cut back in spring to within 6″ of the buds to force uniform growth. After 8″ or 10″ of growth has been made the stub is sawed off smoothly and the edges trimmed with a knife. The cut surface is then waxed.

The tops of spring budded stocks are often partially cut back at first or "lopped" half through and bent down in the middle gradually to change the flow of sap. After a month or six weeks the tops are removed entirely (Fig. 284).

365. Persimmon Rootstock.[1]—Three species of persimmons have produced our cultivated varieties: kaki or Japanese persimmon (*Diospyros kaki*), dateplum (*D. lotus*), a Chinese species, and common or American persimmon (*D. virginiana*). All three have been used as root-stocks. In California the older plantings are almost entirely on the kaki root since the trees were imported from Japan where it has been almost exclusively used. In the Southern States virginiana stock is favored. The date plum came into prominence some years ago and large importations of seed were made both by the United States Department of Agriculture and by private agencies. Importations of nursery trees ceased because of Quarantine Order No. 37.

Kaki produces a long tap root with few fibrous laterals. These are difficult to pack and in general have caused much dissatisfaction among nurserymen and growers. However, it makes a satisfactory union with all varieties at present grown and produces fine orchard trees.

In order to limit the length of the tap root and to stimulate the development of fibrous laterals it is suggested that the tap root be cut with a long-bladed spade while the trees are in the nursery rows. This practice gives satisfactory results with walnuts and pecans so it is believed that if used on kaki seedlings much better results could be obtained than in the past. The kaki roots are not as resistant to excessive soil moisture as are those of either lotus or virginiana, nor

[1] Condensed from *Univ. of Cal. Bul. 416.*

as susceptible to crown gall as lotus so they are again becoming popular, especially in a wild form said to be hardy, introduced by the United States Department of Agriculture.

Wild native American persimmon early demonstrated its superiority over the kaki root for the Southern States where it is adapted to a much wider range of soil conditions. Trees on it show superior growth. It produces many fibrous roots which make it easier to transplant than the kaki, but it has the disadvanage of suckering, particularly if the roots are injured. Trees on this root will stand unfavorable soil conditions, particularly excessive moisture, much better than on either of the other two stocks. In parts of California where tested the blooming period was delayed about 30 days thus insuring freedom from frost injury. In poorly drained areas where water may stand for considerable time during the rainy season, the root has also been found to produce better trees than has the kaki rootstock.

The date plum is the newest stock used to propagate oriental persimmon yet it has superseded the others. It has produced thrifty, rapidly growing, uniform stands of nursery trees and maintained this rapidity in young orchards. The root system is fibrous, does not sucker and is easily handled in the nursery. The greatest drawback is its susceptibility to infection by crown gall. Nurserymen are, therefore, looking for a strain that possesses its good qualities but is resistant to this disease. Its stock is more resistant than either of the others to drouth but will not withstand poorly drained soils. It can be recommended generally for planting except where crown gall is known to exist.

366. **Black Walnut** (*Juglans nigra*), is the only American species which has produced recognized horticultural varieties. No other species has been used for stocks in its propagation except by experimenters who have not as yet made recommendations. It is satisfactory as a stock when properly handled, with no apparent need for a substitute. Carefully chosen seed planted and grown in rich loamy soils and well cared for grow rapidly and quickly develop into vigorous seedlings. Despite popular opinion to the contrary, budded and grafted trees of the present varieties begin to bear about as soon as apple trees.

Hinds Walnut (*Juglans hindsi*) and California black walnut (*J. californica*) are used for practically all California orchards. The Persian or English walnut (*J. regia*) has been abandoned as a stock.

The Paradox walnut, a cross between the English and one of the black walnuts, is supposed to possess unusual vigor of growth, and the Royal hybrid, a cross between black with the California black, is also supposed to grow rapidly. Some trees do but only a small percentage of either hybrids can be depended upon to outgrow ordinary stocks. No practicable way of determining which ones these are is applicable in the nursery. Only a few commercial orchards are planted on either of these hybrid stocks.

367. Filbert Rootstocks.—In the Pacific Northwest the tree hazel (*Corylus colurna*) is being used as a filbert stock to develop trees that will not throw out suckers from the base. Efforts have been made by various planters to obtain seed of the Chinese hazelnut (*C. chinensis*) for the same purpose, but apparently without success. The propagation of the filbert is therefore largely confined to layerage.

368. Hickory rootstocks.[1]—Propagation of hickory varieties in general is of comparatively recent origin. Shagbark and shellbark hickories (*Hicoria ovata* and *H. laciniosa*) are the best of this group so far as value of the nuts is concerned, but they are slow growers and not easy to propagate. Therefore, more rapid-growing species have been sought, with the result that northern pecan (*H. pecan—* authors) and bitternut (*H. cordiformis*) are in present favor. As the northern limit of the indigenous range of the pecan is reached by the river-bottom sections of southern Indiana, central Illinois (and Iowa—authors) it may be reasonable to question the hardiness of the species as a stock at materially higher latitudes. However, as it is an established fact that the pecan tree is hardy beyond the range of nut production, this doubt may not be well founded. Perhaps the bitternut hickory would be safer for more northern use, but further experiments will be necessary before this point can be determined.

On private experimental grounds in Nassau County on Long Island, W. G. Bixby has found that during two seasons of tests the shagbark hickory has been satisfactory as a stock for most varieties, insofar as immediate success in grafting is concerned. Likewise, the pignut (*H. glabra*) and the bitternut were found satisfactory to much the same extent.

369. Rootstocks for the Pecan.[2]—The pecan is propagated almost entirely upon stocks of its own species. Experienced nurserymen are convinced that marked differences occur in the influence of stocks of certain varieties upon the subsequent growth of the grafted trees. For instance, in the Southeast, seedlings of Moore and Waukennah, two local varieties from Waukennah, Fla., are said by nurserymen to grow rapidly and to impart that characteristic to the new tops when used as stocks. Teche and Moneymaker are used to some extent with much the same results. In southern Louisiana the water-hickory or bitter pecan (*Hicoria aquatica*) is largely used. By some it is preferred to pecan.

[1] From *U. S. Dept. of Agr. Far. Bul. 1501.*
[2] *U. S. Dept. of Agr. Far. Bul. 1501.*

Several other species of closely related hickories have been used. The mockernut (*H. alba*) has been most often top-worked but with distinctly variable results, more often unfavorable than otherwise. The species is therefore not in favor with most of those who have had longest experience with it.

370. **Chestnut propagation** in this country at present is largely confined to hybrids, American chestnut or chinquapin with either European or Japanese species. In general, stocks of one species are unsatisfactory for varieties of another, though Morris has found chinquapin as a dwarf stock to take almost all other chestnuts kindly. Seedlings of these hybrid varieties are usually most desirable and so far as known are the only stocks being used commercially. The Italian chestnut has been successfully used on the Pacific Coast and is recommended as it makes thrifty trees.

371. **Pistache Nut.**[1]—The pistache of commerce (*Pistacia vera*), grown in this country to only a limited extent, is grafted upon stocks of the Chinese pistache (*P. chinensis*).

372. **Rootstocks for the almond.**—Most almond trees are budded on bitter almond roots; but sweet ones are satisfactory for rootstocks. Soils less than 6' deep or with gravelly or hardpan layers at lesser depths are often unsatisfactory. Under these conditions peach root is better. It is next in importance to almond root. Peach root is not as satisfactory because it does not root as deeply; but where the soil moisture varies much in different parts of the orchard or from time to time during the growing season, it is sometimes the more satisfactory. It is a little better where irrigation is practiced during summer, especially where there is danger of an excess of water remaining too long in the soil. Although peach does not thrive in standing water around its roots, it will withstand fluctuating or temporary extremes in water supply better than almond. Myrobalan plum makes a good union with almond but the plum root grows much more slowly than the almond top giving a pinched-in effect below the union. The trees on myrobalan are not as large nor do they bear such satisfactory crops in many sections as do those on almond or peach roots.

373. **Rootstocks for the Avocado.**—In the early years of the industry any kind of seed procurable was used to raise seedlings— West Indian, Guatemalan or Mexican; large, small, mature and immature. As a result many nursery trees failed to make satisfactory growth and many orchard trees failed after planting. In recent years seed of the Guatemalan varieties have been widely used because they produce vigorous and thrifty trees; but they are more susceptible to frost than the Mexican. Feurte because of its re-

---

[1] *U. S. Dept. of Agri. Far. Bul. 1501.*

markable vigor and fairly uniform seedlings has been propagated in recent years. The seed must be fully mature, well developed and from well-shaped fruit, rather than from undersized and immature fruit. It is obtained from the cooperative marketing agency.

374. Rose stocks are sometimes grown from seeds sown as soon as ripe or stored in the hips till spring; hardy species outdoors, tender ones under glass. Layers and root cuttings are often used, but semi-mature stem cuttings from forced plants in midwinter under glass are most popular. Budding in America is done close to the ground, but in Europe the popular "tree" roses are made by inserting buds at 3' or 4'. Multiflora is a producer of quick results. Its spring-made cuttings are ready for budding in six months. Home-grown seedlings usually require two years to reach budding size. Winter grafting with dormant wood makes good pot plants of hybrid perpetual varieties. *Rosa rubiginosa* (sweet briar), *R. watsoniana,* and several other species are used to some extent. Usually the shield method of budding, but sometimes veneer grafting, is employed.

Hybrid stocks for roses.—A writer in *American Gardening* considers manetti stocks unsuited to American climatic conditions. Where perfect hardiness is required he has found *Rosa setigera, R. wichuraiana* and *R. rubiginosa* superior; for, he says, "all make good, deep roots, and are not at all disposed to sucker." The best of all stocks he considers to be a cross between Clotilde Soupert and Crimson Rambler, both varieties of *R. multiflora.* These stocks are exceptionally vigorous, do not sprout, are easily budded and in hardiness little inferior to the native species. The roots are easily splice-grafted, but the stems are not so satisfactory for grafting. For tree rose effect he prefers to bud high on strong sweet briar shoots and trim off all other shoots as soon as the bud has formed a fair top.

375. Grafted roses for forcing.—A. B. Scott has grown half a dozen varieties of forcing roses on their own roots and on manetti stocks. Since all but American Beauty and Perle des Jardins did much better as grafts, he concludes that grafted roses make strong, vigorous plants much quicker than roses on their own roots, produce as many, if not more flowers, of which a larger proportion are extra fine, and the plants are said to have more vitality. Manetti is considered best for stocks.

376. Rosa odorata vs. R. manetti [1] (a variety of *R. chinensis*) as grafting stocks for indoor roses were tested by F. F. Weinard and H. B. Dorner, who used Columbia rose as scions. No significant differences resulted over a three year period, the total yields were approximately equal and no differences of any practical importance were noted in respect to stem length. The result of a single year's test with other commercial roses agreed with those obtained with Columbia. On odorata stocks, Souvenir de Claudius Pernet grew better and flowered more freely than on manetti.

---

[1] *Ill. Sta. Bul. 290.*

XV

METHODS OF BUDDING

377. Bud grafting is so special a form of graftage that it is generally called budding. It is a form in which a single bud with little or no wood is applied to the cambium of the stock (always growing in normal position), usually beneath the bark. Many species of plants are propagated by either budding or grafting; others do better by one and not the other method, but there is no general rule by which decision can be made, though thin-barked plants with copious sap generally succeed best when grafted or when buds are used at the time of smallest sap flow.

Budding is widely popular for propagating fruit trees of all kinds, especially the stone fruits. In nurseries it is more extensively employed than is grafting. Roses, lilacs and many ornamental trees are similarly treated.

378. Condition of nursery for successful work. The nursery ground must have been well worked and kept free from weeds. Moisture must be available to the trees at all times so the stocks will make strong, rapid growth. It is essential that the cambium layer be active at the time of budding so as to have the bark lift easily for the budding operation. In arid regions, an irrigation a week before budding may be required to loosen the bark if the previous moisture supply has not been sufficient to do so.

379. Budding knives are of many styles, and operators have their pronounced preferences, but probably the one most used in the big commercial nurseries for field work is in Figure 279. It costs about $1.75 by the dozen. The budding knife should be made of the finest steel, have a thin blade about 2″ long; the cutting edge, kept razor sharp, should extend from front to back in a quarter circle. The blade should be set in a light, convenient handle, which may be stationary or slotted to receive it. The straight part of the blade is used for general purposes, such as bud cutting, and the curved end for making incisions in stocks. Many budding knife handles extend into a thin bone, ivory or celluloid, spatula-shaped blade used to lift the bark of the stocks. Probably the great majority of expert budders have no use for such a device; they raise the bark with the knife blade.

380. Seasons for budding.—Budding may be successful whenever the cells of the cambium layer are actively dividing. This is indicated by the ready separation of the bark from the wood. When budding is done late in the season the buds do not expand until the following spring. Thus the shoots which grow from the inserted buds have a full season to grow and mature. Trees budded in May or June, especially in the South, grow to marketable size the same season.

The usual season for budding peach and plum in the North is from midsummer to early fall; in the South a month or six weeks earlier. Thus southern nurserymen have an advantage over northern ones, because they save practically a year's time and the trees, if well grown, are as good as northern grown trees. June budded trees may be fall planted in the South the same season as budded; later ones not till the following fall, because the buds remain dormant till spring.

381. When stocks are budded.—Apple and pear seedlings

Fig. 277.—Budding peaches. This is usual tiring attitude; some men kneel.

grow one year where the seeds are sown. The following spring they are transplanted to other nursery rows after the unavoidable shortening of roots. All that grow large enough between June and September are budded that season. The age of the stock is then forgotten. The age of the nursery tree dates from the time when the buds or scions start. Thus peach budded this year in the North during August will start to grow next spring and by the following November become a "one-year" tree, though 15 months have

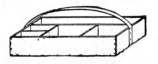

Fig. 278.—Handy tray for carrying budders' supplies.

elapsed since the budding; but a tree budded in the South in June of this year will become a "one-year" tree when only five months old in November this year. In each case the trees may be sold for fall or for spring planting as "one-year" and "June-budded" trees respectively, though the southern stock is usually not ready soon enough for fall planting in the North.

382. Stock "dressing" or trimming is done to apple, pear and other transplanted stocks prior to setting in the nursery; that is, both root and top are shortened a quarter to a third. This prevents

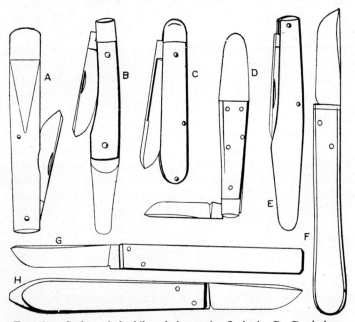

Fig. 279.—Styles of budding knives. A, florists'; B, D, knives with closing blades and bone bark-lifters; C, E, closing blades without bark-lifters; F, G, H, styles of stationary bladed nursery budding knives.

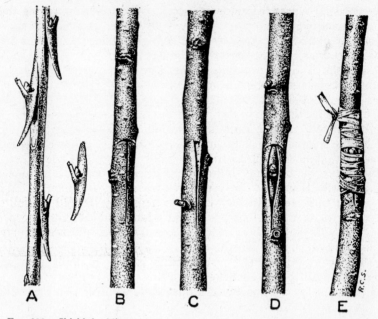

FIG. 280.—Shield budding. A, bud stick; B, T-shaped cut through bark of stock; C, bark raised to admit bud; D, bud in place; E, bud wrapped with raffia.

the re-formation of tap roots and makes the roots branch. It also favors the development of a sturdy top. The effect of the former development is to make a more easily dug and transplanted tree; that of the latter, one more readily handled.

383. Preparing the stocks. To be budded without difficulty stocks should be ½″ in diameter or larger, though in nusery practice those ⅜″ are also budded. A day or two before the budding, boys or girls rub or cut the leaves and twigs off the lower 4″ to 8″ of the stems, so they will not impede the budders (Fig. 284). If longer ahead of budding than three days, the bark will "set" and thus hinder speed in budding. Buds are set as near the ground as the operator can work—1″ or 2″. This brings the union so low that the unavoidable crook in the stem is inconspicuous. It also permits setting the tree in the orchard slightly lower than in the nursery. Best results in the northern hemisphere are claimed to follow setting the buds on the north side of the stocks so the sun will not shine directly on them. Doubtless in the southern hemisphere, the southern side will give best results.

384. Budwood for June or summer use (Fig. 282) always of the current season's growth consists of plump shoots of the desired varieties with well developed axillary buds. As the buds near the base may be dormant and those near the tip too immature both groups are discarded.

385. Cutting the ligatures.—When raffia, tape or other inelastic material is used for tying it is necessary to cut the tier within three weeks of the budding to prevent strangling. The usual way is to draw a budding knife upward through the windings on the side of the stock opposite the bud and let the cut pieces fall off. Since

FIG. 281.—Shield budding, step by step. A, making cut across vertical slit in stock and rolling corners so bud may be easily inserted; B, lifting bark with flattened end of knife handle (skillful budders use knife-blade); C, starting bud into slit while still holding on blade; D, pushing bud in place with thumb.

raffia and tape are inelastic they will not "give" with the growth of the stem and the setting bud, so, unless they are cut they will either kill the bud or force it to "break" i.e., grow. For success in cold climates, however, the bud, to winter over, must be wholly dormant until spring, otherwise it will probably winter-kill. Stocks in which

Fig. 281x.—Operator using budding tape. Notice convenient way rolls are carried.

the buds, at tier-cutting time, are shriveled and brown instead of green and plump, may be re-budded. If warm and wet weather in the fall starts the buds there is little remedy, though some sprouts may be saved by heading them back; others may survive the winter if covered by snow.

386. Budding tape is considered superior to raffia by many nurserymen because of its convenience, saving of time and protection to buds. As it comes in rolls like medical adhesive tape it may be carried suspended from the budder's neck (Fig. 281) thus being both accessible when needed but out of the way at other times. This avoids the necessity of carrying or pushing trays of material along

the row and permits the budder to move without impediment from one side of the row to the other and from place to place. Should budding be delayed, rolls obviate the necessity of caring for previously prepared material to prevent possible injury or destruction by sun or rain; for the unused tape is always in the roll. When the buds have "set" or "taken" and the tape is cut to avoid strangling the buds it does not drop off like cut raffia but still adheres to the trees thus protecting the buds better than raffia though "giving" as the trunks expand.

Fig. 282.—Budding with rubber strip. A, ideal budding wood, leaf stems saved for "handles"; B, stocks and buds, *a*, cross cut; *b*, longitudinal and cross cuts; *c*, bud inserted; *d*, buds removed from bud stick; *e*, starting wrap, showing strip tucked under at completion of wrap.

387. Budding rubber is considered by many operators the best budding material. It has the advantages of not requiring to be tied, not strangling the stock and avoiding the extra operation of removing the ligature. Also it binds the bud more uniformly than does raffia to the stock. It rots and breaks free in due time. The rubber ($\frac{1}{4}''$ wide) is cut in lengths approximately 4″ long. One end is placed across the bottom or the top of the vertical cut and held firmly in place. A turn around the stock is made, the rubber being stretched and brought across the end (Fig. 282). Four or five other rounds are made, care being taken to avoid covering the bud itself. Finally the loose end is tucked under the last round and drawn snug.

388. Shield or "T" budding, the style most generally used in

America, is so called because the bud is shield-shaped—an elongated oval—and the cuts on the stock are T-shaped or more properly cruciform. In many respects the small details differ in the hands of various budders; for instance, height and length of vertical cut, position of cross cut, cutting of bud and method of tying.

Making the incisions for shield budding two cuts are necessary. Neither must penetrate deeper than through the bark. The second is usually placed near the upper end of the first, with which it makes a cross. The first generally made extends about 1½″ lengthwise of the stock, the rounded end of the knife being used. (Fig. 280.) Some budders prefer to place the cross cut below. So far as results are concerned, one is probably as good as the other. Placing the bud in position may be easier for one man to "bud up" and for another to "bud down." (Figs. 277, 280, 281).

After the corners of bark in the angles of the cross are lifted slightly from the wood the bud may be inserted and gently pressed into place by the fingers, which grasp the leaf petiole handle (Fig. 281). If any part of the bud sliver protrudes from the slot, it must be cut off, for unless the entire piece is closely applied to the stock wood so the cambium layer of each is in intimate contact with the other and is covered by the bark, it may make a poor union, or not unite at all, with the stock. When the bark lifts readily no such trouble will be experienced, for the bud will slip readily into place.

Tying follows. Until recently raffia has been the most widely used tier. It is cut in lengths of about a foot prior to the work. The hank of raffia held near its middle between both hands, is placed against the lower end of the vertical cut. The hands are then moved to the rear of the stock where they exchange the ends, which are made to cross each other. The crossing is repeated in front over the cut but higher up than the first round. So on till the whole cut is covered, only the bud being left visible. Three or four double rounds complete the ligature, which is tied at the top. In another method of tying, the raffia is wrapped around the stock twice or thrice at the bottom of the bud and twice at the top, where it is tied in a single knot. Some operators can make better speed by passing one end of the raffia under the other at the last round. The bud itself must not be covered, else it might "strangle." (Fig. 282b, 282f).

389. Correlation studies of apple and cherry tree growth[1] in nurseries from seedling to two year budded tree with 18,000 closely graded No. 1 imported mazzard and French crab seedlings have led the investigators to make the following statements (somewhat condensed):

The data show practically there is only small likelihood of large seedlings

---

[1] H. B. Tukey and Karl D. Brase, N. Y. (Geneva) *Exp. Sta. Tech Bul. 185.* October, 1931.

Fig. 283.—Steps in production of apple tree. A, seedling under-stock grown from seed in first year, to be lined out in nursery row following spring for budding in summer; B, seedling under-stock budded near ground (second year); C, yearling whip (third year of stock); D, two-year tree (fourth year of stock (root), second of scion, top).

when planted remaining large at the end of the season, but as good a chance for a small seedling to produce a large yearling whip as for a large seedling to do likewise; as good a chance for a small seedling to produce a large yearling tree as for a large seedling to do so; a strong likelihood for the largest understocks at the end of the budding season to produce the largest one year whips or the largest two year trees; and a very strong likelihood for the largest one year whips to become the largest two year trees.

The correlations are higher with cherries than are similar correlations for similar factors with apples. The stand of cherry trees is less than that of apple trees, but the percentage of good trees is greater. The suggestion is made that since apple stocks bud more easily than do cherry stocks, varying degrees of successful apple bud unions survive, thus introducing the factor of partially successful bud-unions; whereas in the case of the cherry the less successful unions fail to develop.

The importance of the bud union in the production of a large nursery tree is shown to be of lesser magnitude than the development in size of the understock during its first season in the nursery row.

The authors hazard the opinion that in this test—typical of western New York nursery conditions—the most important factors in tree growth have been local environmental ones rather than genetic—not that genetic differences between seedling understocks are of no importance, but that in this case they have been masked by environmental factors such as trimming, planting, culture, soil drainage and general climatic conditions.

Since the growth of the seedlings the year they are lined out in the nursery row is shown to be of such importance in determining the size of the yearling whips, it follows that the lining-out stock should not be overlooked as regards cultural practices, such as cultivation, control of foliage troubles by spraying and the like Too often more attention is given to the two-year trees than to the lining-out stock. And since the size of the two-year tree is so closely correlated with the size of the one-year whip, it would seem that special attention should also be given to the yearling trees. The growth of two-year trees, then, becomes more dependent upon the previous season's performances.

The importance of local environmental conditions is also emphasized. With due respect to the importance of size and quality of lining-out stock, the more important considerations seem to be handling, planting and subsequent care—factors which everyone recognizes but which are many times disregarded or overlooked because of their simplicity.

The stand of cherry trees in the tests was less than that of apple trees, but the percentage of good trees greater, due to the fact that cherries do not take a bud as well as do apples, so that unless a good union is made a cherry tree does not develop, whereas some sort of apple tree does, even though possibly inferior. Accordingly, more careful budding of cherry trees should result in a higher percentage stand, whereas in the case of apple trees it should result in a reduction in number of low-grade trees.

Perhaps most important of all is the impression that seedling variability is less a factor than is often supposed and that general climatic conditions and local environmental factors are the more important.

390. Dormant or early spring budding is done to a limited extent in a few Southern States. With fully dormant buds saved as for grafting scions budding may be done as soon as the bark loosens in spring. It is essential to speed and success that the bark lift readily from the wood. Clear, dry weather also favors the work. Activity is indicated by the swelling of the buds. If the nurseryman

failed to bud his trees the previous year he may do so in spring
without much loss in growth by the end of the season. At this time
the trees whose buds did not "stick" or "take" the summer before
may again be worked. The work is usually done in March or April,
but the trees may even be out in leaf if the buds are dormant.

Fig. 284.—Treatment of budding stocks. A, seedling tree before trimming; B,
tree trimmed ready for budding; C, June or spring budded tree with two-
thirds of top broken over to stimulate bud growth.

Wood used for spring budding usually has dormant buds. The
bud sticks are gathered during the dormant season and stored in
moist moss or sawdust until trees start growth. It is possible to use
active "pushing buds" if they are not too far along. Such bud sticks
may be gathered immediately preceding the budding. The inserted
buds start growth soon after they have united with the stocks. It is
necessary to reduce the top of the stock to force growth. This is
usually done by breaking two thirds of the top of the tree over but
not severing it completely (Fig. 284). After the bud has made some
growth the entire top of the stock may be removed at a point just
above the bud. Practically a full growing season may be realized
and a tree of orchard planting size secured by fall or winter.

391. **Early summer or June budding** produces a smaller tree
in the one growing season than is produced either from mid-summer,
fall, or spring budded trees. This method may be practiced in sections with a long growing season such as the South and to some ex-

tent in California. The work may be done at any time during the month.

In "June budding," stocks ¼″ to 1/3″ in diameter are favored. Instead of stripping the lower part of the stocks completely of leaves, as in northern budding, a few leaves are left below the point of budding to serve as feeders. Because of the heat of the soil surface, in hot, dry climates, it is customary to place the buds an inch or two higher than in northern practice. To avoid the sudden and violent check to the stock which would follow removal of the whole top early in the season, several cuts of the top are made. Sometimes the stock tops are bent over, or broken, twisted or partially stripped of leaves and twigs or otherwise treated so the bud shoot will graually accustom itself to its work. In due time, of course, the stock is cut off. The ligatures must be cut sooner than in the North, say in a week to ten days, depending on how vigorously the stock is growing.

Summer or June budding of tree fruits is often done but the stocks have grown in the nursery row a year or two. Sometimes the buds used are dormant, having been cut and stored, like scions for cleft grafting, sometimes current season's growth. This plan is annually becoming more popular, partly because the nurserymen think they thus get better trees than by grafting and partly because they are thus enabled to keep the men busy to better advantage by extending the work over a longer period. For top working trees, either those that failed to "take" the previous season or those established in orchards, this method also has its obvious advantages. The buds grow as do scions in cleft grafting, so a full season's time is gained.

June budding is not widely practiced but may be desirable when trees are scarce and must be grown for orchard planting in one year from seed.

Budwood for June budding usually is of the current season's growth. Buds may be forced to mature early by cutting off the ends of the growing shoots and pinching or cutting off the leaf blades leaving only the stems in the area of desired buds. Active buds are inserted in the stock. The top of the stock is reduced as with spring budding and the buds start growth immediately following their union with the stock. The growing season, before the dormant period arrives, is short (June to fall) hence the small tree. Trees which are to be June budded must have a habit of strong rapid growth such as peach, almond and apricot or grow more than one season.

392. Late summer to fall budding.—Budding nursery trees in July, August and September is a general practice with the bulk of the work falling in August. Current season's well matured wood growth made between spring and mid-summer is used for bud sticks.

Well formed wood the size of a lead pencil from the branches of
the tree are preferred; but there is no reason why well ripened and
mature water-sprouts may not be used. Buds
inserted during this period usually remain
perfectly dormant until spring. If they
should grow in fall the sprouts would be injured, if not killed, during winter. The buds,
however, should remain green and fresh. If
they shrivel and become brown even though
they adhere to the stocks, they are worthless.
When cutting the strings any stocks that
have failed should be noted and rebudded.

393. **Cutting back the stock.**—The
spring following the budding, stock must be
cut off just above the bud as soon as the
stocks begin to show activity. (Figs. 284,
285, 287, 288.) This will throw the entire
force of the plant into the bud. If the root
is strong and the soil good, the bud will
grow 2′ to 6′ the first year, depending on

Fig. 285.—Stock top cut
off (always sloping) just
above bud. Usually this is
done just before growth
starts in spring.

the species, soil, climate and care. Peaches, almonds, apricots and
some other fruit trees are sold after having made one season's
growth from the bud, but pears and apples except on the Pacific
Coast may not be sold until the second year, though one year trees

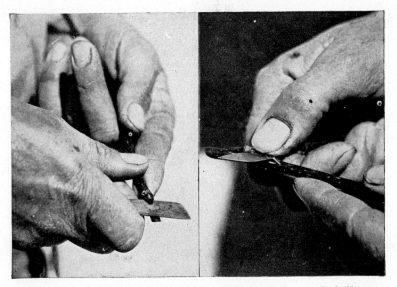

Fig. 286.—Removing bud from bud-stick. A, start of the cut; B, knife passing beneath bud parallel with bud-stick.

FIG. 287.—Bud sprout tied to stock. When union is firm stump will be cut. This method is less common than that in Figure 285.

of even these species are growing in favor. Under ideal conditions it is possible after budding to produce good trees of these latter in one season.

394. Budding wood for summer work always consists of well-hardened wood of the present season's development and of the desired variety. The twigs, which should be about $\frac{1}{4}''$ in diameter at their bases, are severed from the parent trees and the leaf blades cut off. The leaf stems may be shortened to about $\frac{1}{4}''$ so as to serve as handles when the buds are being placed in the stocks. After trimming, the twigs are called "bud sticks." They may bear half a dozen to two dozen buds developed enough for use, but the average is probably ten. The leaf buds near the tips of the twigs are generally not mature enough to be safe to use, so they and the flower buds are thrown away. Flower buds are plumper and more rounded than leaf buds, so are easily recognized.

The buds are cut from the bud sticks with a thin-bladed, razor-edged knife usually as follows: With the bud stick held in one hand (Fig. 286), the knife is started about $\frac{3}{4}''$ above or below the bud, according to the preference of the operator, and a cut through the bark into the wood is made toward the operator's body until a bud with about 1″ of bark and wood is almost severed from the twig. The knife is then withdrawn and the other buds treated in the same way until all that are fit for budding have been cut but are still left attached to the twigs. The bud sticks are then usually dipped in water, wrapped in wet cloth and taken to the nursery row for budding.

Many operators prefer to cut the buds fresh as needed, because there is less risk of drying. The chief advantages of the plan outlined are that it saves time, and less high priced labor than that of the actual budders can do the work. The buds as needed are cut from the bud stick with a single motion.

For years budders have disagreed as to the advisability of removing the little chip of wood beneath the bark of the bud as cut from the bud stick. No experiments seem to have been tried to prove its use or harm. Many budders pry it out with the tip of the knife blade or by twisting

FIG. 288.—Budded cherry trees after one season's growth. A, cut properly; B, improperly.

the stick as the bud is being cut. No difference is apparent in the
resulting trees whether or not this wood is removed. It would seem
that the wood might help to hold moisture until the bud has united
with the stock, but that if removed the cambium layers would grow
together more quickly. This sliver of wood certainly gives rigidity
which aids in inserting the bud in the stock. If the bud is cut thick
the older parts of the wood doubtless do not unite, though the
younger parts probably do; so it may be well to cut at least this
dense part. An exception to the above rule is the walnut. Experience has proved that the wood sliver should be removed.

F<small>IG</small>. 289.—Uncommon budding methods. *a*, annular or ring; *b*, terminal; *c*, plate; *d*, H; *e*, flute; *f*, prong; *g*, chip.

396. Plate or patch budding (Fig. 290).—Instead of making
one longitudinal cut in the stock, two of equal length are made parallel. The upper ends are then joined by a cut and the bark lifted,
thus forming a rectangular flap still attached below to the stock and
1″ to 1½″ long. A bud on a piece of bark, but with no wood, is cut
to fit the space, inserted, covered by the flap which is made to cover
it, and tied. From then forward treatment is the same as for shield
budding. Two slight modifications of this method may be noted:
The flap may be split so a part may be fitted on each side of the bud,
or it may be shortened so the bud itself will not be covered, but only
that part of the scion bark below the bud end.

397. Prong, spur or twig budding (Fig. 289) is shield budding modified by the use of a short spur or twig instead of a bud and
removal of the upper part of the stock. The bark of both stock and
scion are cut in the same way. English walnuts while dormant are
often budded thus in California. This form resembles grafting in
the removal of stock above the bud at the time of budding and in
the use of grafting wax over wounds to prevent drying and the entrance of decay. In budding thick-barked subjects, such as walnut,
wood beneath the bud bark must be almost all removed, so the cam-

bium layers will come in better contact than if left.   The little piece
of wood that extends up into the prong should not be cut out.

398. H-budding (Fig. 289) is a variety of plate budding in
which one cross-cut is made about midway between the ends of the
longitudinal cuts, thus forming two flaps between which the bud is
placed.   Because the bud may thus be covered both above and below
a good fit of bud to stock can be secured.   The modified H-bud is
much simpler to make (Fig. 292).

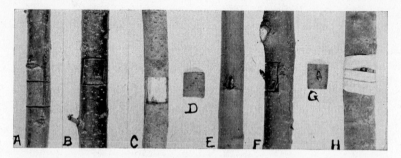

Fig. 290.—Patch budding. A, first two cuts in stock; B, next two cuts; C,
stem ready for patch bud; D, patch removed; F, bud stick with bud to be
removed; F, bud cut ready for removal; G, bud removed; H, bud inserted in
stock, wrapped with industrial tape, only bud protruding.

399. Patch Budding and its Modifications.—The "T" or
Shield bud is not usually applied successfully on thick barked or old
limbs.   In such cases the patch bud or one of its modifications may
be used.   Patch budding is extensively practiced with the pecan in
the South and to a considerable extent with other nut trees in the
North, and somewhat on the Western Coast.   It can be employed
only when the sap is flowing at moderate rate.   Too free a flow of
sap causes the bud to "drown" and too little will result in its drying
up without "taking." (Fig. 290.)

The common patch bud is made by removing a rectangle of bark,
approximately 1″ square, from the stock to be budded.   Then a
patch the same size as that from the stock and having a bud is removed from the bud stick and inserted in the opening of the stock.
The "patch" is then well wrapped and covered except for the bud
which may be seen between the wraps.   In making the patch bud it
will take practice to cut a piece of bark from the bud stick that will
exactly fit the stock patch section.   Therefore, it is best to cut it a
little large at first and trim it down.   In a short time the size can be
closely estimated.   One need not be alarmed if it does not fit exactly
at the outside edges for it will often take without a fit at these points
if it fits at the top and bottom.   This may be assured by using a

special budding tool. (Fig. 291.) Rubber has been found to be the best wrapping material.

Stocks for Patch Budding may be $\frac{3}{4}''$ to $3''$ in diameter. Larger and smaller sizes have been used successfully. By paring away the thick, scaly bark, buds may be inserted in fairly old trunks or

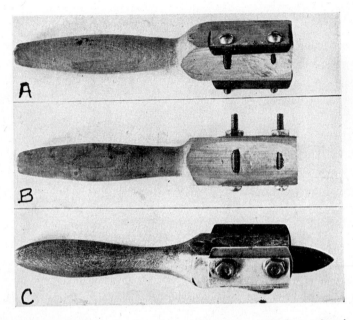

Fig. 291.—Tool for patch budding. A, B, wooden tool; C, metal tool with knife blade extending to make cuts for "window" budding.

branches. The most readily worked trees are the vigorous growers usually found in the rows of well-cared-for nurseries during the summer of the second year after the seed has been planted. Pecan and walnut trees budded when the stocks are of this size should become suitable for transplanting at the end of the following year, thus making the stock three years old by the time the tree is ready for the orchard. Patch budding need not be confined to nursery trees. With walnuts it has been successfully applied to trees three to five years old.

400. Modified H or window budding gets its name because it it a modification of the regular "H" bud (Fig. 292) the "H" bud being on its side and the flaps swinging out like casement windows. Of the two the modified H is the easier for beginners to make. It is a satisfactory method and is preferred to the patch by many operators.

Patch and modified "H" buds may be placed at any time the bark slips readily. If practiced from March first to June first wood should be used which was gathered before the buds broke (January and February). This wood must be kept in cold storage or buried rather deeply in a cool place (the north side of a building) in moist soil or sand if it is to be kept long. Recent work has indicated that best results are secured with spring budding and freshly cut buds.

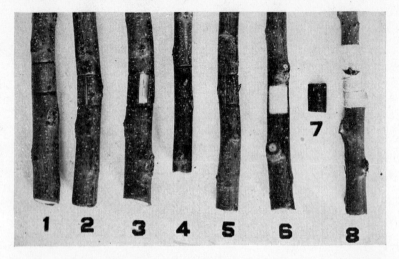

Fig. 292.—Modified H-budding. 1, first cuts on stock made with budding tool; 2, second cut connecting first two; 3, flaps or "window" open to receive bud; 4, first two cuts on bud stick; 5, second two cuts; 6, slot opened; 7, patch with bud; 8, bud inserted and wrapped.

When such wood is used in walnut budding it is not always possible to slip the bud off without leaving the core behind, this having hardened over winter. In late summer or early fall the patch slips off readily, taking the core with it. In spring it will be necessary to use a budding or a grafting knife to cut the core free as the patch is lifted off. Removing this core intact with the bud is essential— otherwise the bud will dry up and fall off. When spring budding is done the new bud will start growth that season. Immediately after the bud has taken the stock is cut back 6″ to 8″ above the bud, so as to throw the growth into the bud. Later when the bud has started growth the stub should be cut back to the bud.

401. Top Working Large Black Walnut Trees.—The modified "H" and window patch bud are good to work over black walnuts to an English variety. A good procedure is as follows: In spring when the leaves begin to appear cut the tree back to the framework branches. Then put in three Biederman or Mac Cooper grafts on each limb (257, 258A). If all these take it may be advisable to cut off one or two after the stub of the stock has been partially grown or healed over.

Those limbs which did not take with the grafting should be allowed to develop water-sprouts. In August these sprouts should be budded, using the modified "H" or patch bud. If any buds fail to take, the same limbs should be budded by the same method the following spring. If there are still some limbs that did not take they may be budded during the summer of that year. Men working over old black walnut trees usually estimate that it takes two years completely to change the top to an English variety as all grafts and buds do not take well on walnuts.

402. Chip budding (Fig. 289) consists in cutting a mortise in a small stock and inserting a one-bud chip of bark with a little wood cut to fit snugly. This is held in position by tying and is usually waxed. It is used while the stock is dormant in spring before the bark will slip.

403. Flute budding (Fig. 289) is a development beyond plate budding, because in it a rectangular piece of bark in the stock is removed entirely and replaced by a bud-bearing piece of bark cut to fit the space. As a rule this work is done in late spring on plants with thick bark. Tying is needed as in shield budding.

404. Veneer budding, a synonym for flute budding.

405. Annular or ring budding (Fig. 289), the same as flute budding except that a ring of bark is removed from the stock, which must be rather small, by making two parallel cuts $\frac{1}{2}''$ to $1''$ apart around a stock, joining these by a cut at right angles, removing the ring, fitting in a bud-bearing ring of bark with a bud and tying as in shield budding. This method is popular for budding pecan and walnut. The work is best done in summer when the bark peels readily. The buds must be taken from twigs rather younger than the stocks.

406. Budding old peach trees.—For old peach trees that require new wood an Australian experimenter sharpened a piece of bone like a lead pencil, fitted it to a handle, made incisions in the bark of 10-year-old trees and fitted buds in the holes. The buds were kept in position by small pieces of leather, held in place by upholsterers' enameled gimp pins, which did not rust and which became loose as the buds swelled. An advantage claimed is that the method does not interfere with bearing while the buds are being matured. Neither clay nor wax was needed.

407. Stock sucker's influence.—H. M. Stringfellow of Texas found that when a peach tree was budded high (18″) and developed a sucker below the bud, the branch from the bud gradually failed and died. He also noted that where scions on budded-stocks were planted deep enough to send out their own roots, dwarfing and even killing of the stock roots followed. He therefore recommends high budding (12″ to 15″ from the ground), in order to secure long-lived budded trees, because this, he contends, will allow reasonably deep planting without burying any part of the scion.

408. Winter budding of peaches in Texas, according to R. H. Price, was experimentally done by the following method: Cuttings were taken when the sap was dormant. A slice of bark was cut down the stock, but left attached at the lower end. Part of the top of the loose strip was then cut off, the bud of a desired variety fitted over the cut place and bound on firmly with raffia. The stocks were then kept in sphagnum moss till spring, when they were planted. All but one of the 50 made strong shoots during the growing season.

409. Top working peach.—When peach trees begin to fruit and are found worthless, the question is, Will it pay to top work them? Eastern orchardists generally contend that usually time and money will be saved by pulling them out if over four or five years old rather than "dehorning" them, waiting till water sprouts or other limbs in desirable positions are large enough to bud, and then running the risk of failure of the buds to "take" and of possible loss through accident or disease. New trees require only three or four years to come into bearing; but at least as much time is required with top-worked trees plus the likelihood of having poorer trees in the end.

On the other hand, though the usual commercial life of an eastern peach orchard is ten years, the senior author knews of one at Towson, Maryland, which when he last heard of it was bearing well though 29 years old. Both authors know of orchards 15 to 20 years old.

410. Mango budding, according to G. W. Oliver, an American experimenter, is best done when the new leaves are not far enough developed to show bright green, because the bark is then easiest removed. The thick part of the stem, a few inches above ground, is the best place, a rectangular piece of two-year-old wood containing a central bud of the desired kind replacing it. After fitting the bud, a light coat of liquid grafting wax, rich in resin is brushed on and the bud tied in place with raffia. The stem just above the bud is then wound with an 8″ strip of wrapping paper tied in place as a protection. As stocks, moderate sized two to three-year-old seedlings are best. Stems 1″ or slightly more give best unions.

Higgins of Hawaii finds that patch budding (Oliver's method) is superior to inarching, but can be done only when both bud wood and stock are in active growth, a condition rarely found in both at the same time. Shield budding with inverted **T** gives better results and is quicker than patch budding. It may be used when the bud wood is not in active growth.

411. Yema grape budding is best done during August but possibly can be performed until about September 10. In the ordinary yema or "bud" graft, the bud carries some wood, unlike ordinary buds. The stock is cut (Practicum XLIII) with a special budding knife, so as to make a groove to receive the scion. The bud is removed from the scion canes in the same way, except that cut No. 3 is made so as to get a plane surface below the bud. It is then inserted on the stock and tied. (Fig. 293.)

411A. Summer budded vs. winter grafted roses.[1]—Winter grafting has long been the standard practice in the propagation of greenhouse roses, January being the usual time. The young plants are sold in late winter or early spring and usually benched before July. The proposed embargo on imported rose stocks has stimulated domestic stock growing, especially on the Pacific Coast,

---

[1] *Ill. Exp. Sta. Bul. 358,* 1930.

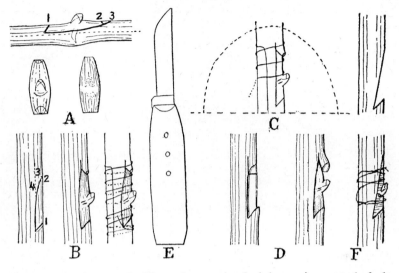

Fig. 293.—Yema grape budding. A, removing bud from scion cane, 1, 2, 3 sequence of making cuts of scion; B, stock cut, bud inserted and tied; C, how graft should be mounded up with earth; D, modified yema budding; E, Australian knife used in yema budding; F, new modified yema bud.

so field budding during August and September has gained ground. The plants rest with buds dormant. They are lifted, cut back, stored and later shipped to florists in January or February. The question that arose as to how such plants compare with grafted plants led to a two year experiment with manetti and odorata rose stocks in Illinois with the following conclusions;

It has been shown with Matchless, Mme. Butterfly, and Templar that flower production of well-grown summer-budded plants under glass may be as good as or better than that from grafted plants. This is true with respect to quality as well as to number of flowers. With Pernet the yields from summer-budded plants were slightly lower than from greenhouse budded plants. The latter in this case had the advantage of a somewhat earlier start.

Possible losses in starting dormant stock and perhaps a shorter planting season are factors to be considered in connection with the use of summer-budded plants. Methods of handling dormant-bud plants to best advantage by the grower are being made the subject of further tests.

411B. Shield budding of blueberry is best done from mid July to mid August. In selecting bud wood, attention should be paid to the following points: A bud forms at the base of each leaf; at first the scales covering the bud are green; when they are older they become straw colored and later brown. When the buds have reached this brown stage they are of proper age for use. All three stages may occur at the same time on a single branch. In such a case the upper part of the branch should be discarded. . . . Care should be taken to discard the large fat flowering buds that occur toward the ends of the branches. In most blueberry plants, however, these flowering buds do not develop until after the budding season.

The best wood on which to bud is the lower portion of vigorous basal shoots of the season, especially those from plants cut to the stump in the preceding winter or spring (Fig. 266). On such shoots the bark can be lifted with ease much later in the season than on older stems. In taking the bud from the stick of budwood the cut is made just deep enough to leave a thin layer of wood attached to the middle of the bud slice. The raffia should be tied rather tightly, so the juice almost begins to be squeezed from the soft bark. Special care should be taken that the raffia wrapping does not become wet immediately after budding and fermentation ensue between the raw surfaces of bud and stock. Plants budded in a greenhouse should therefore be watered on the ground, not on the foliage. Buds on outdoor plants liable to be wet by rain are sometimes protected by pieces of strong paraffined paper about 6″ square made into little cones around the stems just above the bud wrappings and securely tied with raffia, the lower part of the cone hanging around the stem like a little skirt.

In the greenhouse experiments a growth of more than 8′ has been obtained in the first season from an inserted bud on a vigorous plant and when the shoot has been made to branch repeatedly by removing the growing tips as many as 70 cuttings have been produced the first year from a single valuable bud.

XVI

STOCK AND SCION HANDLING—ROOTSTOCKS

Seeds are used in horticulture usually only where it is not essential to reproduce the exact parental forms. This is true with most rootstocks under present practices. Most rootstocks are grown from seed and later budded or grafted to desired varieties. Variations and lack of uniformity in these rootstock seedlings are not desirable but seedage is a cheap method of producing rootstocks, hence popular with nurserymen. Rootstock variations are bound to produce variations in the grafted or budded plants.

412. Named varieties of fruit trees are made up of two unlike individuals; a root of one kind, usually a seedling and the desired variety budded or grafted on it. The root part is called a stock; the graft or bud, a scion.

413. Clon[1] **stocks** are stocks propagated by vegetative methods. They give a uniform lot of trees essentially like the parent plant. Much scientific interest has centered upon the production of superior clonal stocks with the idea of securing greater uniformity in orchards. Abundant data proves their superiority; but the nursery trade still depends upon seedling rootstocks mainly because of their lower cost and the public demand for low priced trees for orchard planting.

414. "Own-rooted" is a term for trees produced either from seed, cuttings, or otherwise than by grafting or budding, so they have roots of the same wood as their trunks. Grafted and budded trees are said to *become* "own-rooted" when they develop roots from the scion above the union and the stock ceases to function. Grafted grapes, roses and other plants often become own-rooted in the same way. In certain cases it may be an advantage for grafted trees to become own-rooted, as in the northwestern states, where the winters are severe and only roots from hardy tops can withstand the rigorous weather. In other cases it is a disadvantage; for instance, dwarfs which would thus become standards. Again, if own roots are allowed to grow on grafted or budded roses the plants would "go wild" and the desired tops be killed. When scions of European grape

---

[1] A clon is a group of cultivated plants composed of individuals propagated vegetatively from a single original seedling or stock.

grafted on phylloxera-resistant American stocks, take root the vines would be as open to attacks of this insect as if not grafted.

414x. "Standard" is an arbitrary term applied to trees of a size commonly accepted as normal for the species and variety.

415. "Dwarf" applies to trees made smaller than the normal for the variety or species by some method that prevents full development; for instance, grafting or budding pear on quince stock or any apple on Paradise or Doucin stock. The Japanese practice other methods but these are more properly of a stunting nature rather than propagating methods.

The production of seedlings is a branch of the nursery business for the most part in the hands of specialists who sell their product to other nurserymen for budding and grafting. The former usually are not concerned with the work of the latter and vice versa. However many growers of nursery trees raise their own seedlings.

416. Production of nursery trees for orchard planting is a highly specialized business. Under average conditions it is better for planters to purchase planting stock from nurserymen rather than try to grow their own trees.

Production of high-grade nursery trees suitable for orchard planting involves a continued process requiring knowledge and skill at each of a long series of steps. Selection and care of the seed before planting, location of the seed bed and preparation of the soil, choice of season, manner and depth of planting, determination of the distance between the seeds in the row and of space between the rows, care and cultivation of the young seedlings, combating diseases and other troubles, proper selection of time and technic of budding or grafting, training of the young trees while in the nursery and finally digging and preparation for shipment or transplanting all require special knowledge without which costly errors are practically inevitable.

417. Conditions for Planting a Nursery.—The nursery should be located where the soil is well drained and not too heavy; yet a heavy soil is to be preferred to one too sandy. The land should be plowed in the fall 8″ to 10″ deep as soon as possible after the first or second good rain. (Practicum XXXVI.)

In many parts of the country it is useless to try to grow a nursery unless irrigation water is available or sufficient rainfall during the growing season is assured. Whether or not irrigation is to be practiced the land should be leveled for irrigation at the time it is plowed since drainage of the plot will then be good. It should be left in such shape that only shallow cultivation will be necessary to put it in condition for early planting. In the south and in southern California myrobalan seed may begin to sprout and require planting by the middle of January or even earlier, hence the importance of early preparation of the land is realized.

418. Methods of Laying Out the Rows.—After the nursery soil has been put in excellent condition, is free from clods and in fine shape the rows should be marked 36″ to 48″ apart by stretching a wire the full length of the plot, drawing it taut between the stakes and tramping on it. When removed it will leave a line on the ground. Use a wheel cultivator with a shovel attachment on this line to mark the row. Open a furrow for planting by running the wheelhoe (Fig. 294) rather deeply two or three times. The furrow will then be 2″ or 3″ deep.

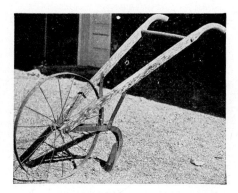

Fig. 294.—Wheelhoe with shovel attachment to open furrows for seed sowing.

After the furrows have been opened, planting may be started. Seeds must be covered with varying amounts of soil depending on their type and size. The soil must then be firmed over them.

Starting at the front in the left corner, labels must be placed where each variety starts in the rows. Reading is always from front to rear and from left to right. Each label must carry the following data: Variety name of seed, species or variety, date planted, and planter's name.

419. Nursery care.—Cultivation must be frequent and thorough. A one horse cultivator is the most satisfactory implement to use. The land must be worked after each rain or irrigation so as to prevent crust formation. If a crust is formed in early spring before the seeds have broken through the ground, it must usually be broken with a shallow-set spike-tooth harrow or weeder, a hand cultivator with similar narrow teeth or a garden rake, depending on the size of the nursery. The injury from this practice is not great enough to be important and the benefit is marked in the stand obtained.

420. Types of Roots.—Though we may have many types of root growth as well as variation in top growth we can arbitrarily divide the roots of seedlings into two classes, *straight* and *branched*. Today branched roots are usually the more popular because they are the type lined out and budded, whereas straight roots are used primarily for bench grafting. Branched roots develop a spreading growth and are believed to be better feeders than straight ones.

421. Seedlings are produced by four methods: 1. Growing in one year (without transplanting) and budding or grafting them that same year (stone fruits, almonds, etc.). It is commonly employed with various modifications in domestic seedling sections because it tends to produce a high proportion of straight roots. The seeds are sown in the field or in beds as early in spring as possible. In tests, no difference in growth of seedlings was noted where the seed was planted in rows or broadcast in beds, but solid beds broadcast give trouble in cultivation, care and sometimes in irrigation.

2. Growing in two years without transplanting; budding or grafting at the end of the second year (sometimes with pear, plum and apple). This plan differs from the first only in the length of time the seedlings require to grow.

3. Growing in the nursery for one year; digging, replanting, growing a second season in the nursery, then budding or grafting (pears, apples and slow growing stocks). The work may be handled as in the one year method but the plants prevented from growing too large the first year by sowing thickly either in the row or broadcast in a bed. The plants may be left in the nursery until the following spring when they should be dug, graded and planted. Before lining out the second season, the roots should be trimmed by cutting them in bunches with pruning shears. This will cut the tap roots and induce branching. The seedlings may then be lined out in the nursery 6" asunder in rows 4' apart, the distance between rows being determined by ease of horse cultivation. As far as growth is concerned the distance might well be 18". A substitute for digging and replanting is sometimes used by running a tree digger under the trees and cutting the roots at 12" to 16".

4. Growing the seedlings in flats or beds and transplanting to the nursery when the second pair of true leaves develops. This is desirable for pears and apples. The seedlings may be budded either at the end of the first or the second growing season in the nursery, depending on their growth. By this method the most desirable type seedlings are produced, for budding apple and pear. The seed should be after-ripened or the rest period broken by stratifying in moist sand or moss in an ice-house or some other cool place. It must not be sown too thickly. Sowing may be done in coldframes either direct or preferably in flats, before the outdoor season opens. Flats are easier to handle though the coldframe method is perhaps cheaper. Seed in the coldframe may be sown in late March or early April in a normal season under eastern conditions; on the Pacific Coast three weeks earlier. Seedlings must have plenty of air to prevent damping off. They will be ready to transplant in four to eight weeks.

Almonds require only three or four weeks stratification before they sprout. Therefore, they should not be stratified longer than that before planting. The seeds must be carefully watched. They must be planted when the seed coats begin to open, 3″ to 5″ apart in the furrow, covered 2″ to 3″ and the soil slightly packed over them. Sprouts must not be allowed to develop more than ¼″ before planting. The moisture supply must be adequate at all times. Method one should be followed since the trees will be ready to bud by midsummer if seeds are sown in March or April. A good root system is developed by this method.

295. Planting machinery. A, row trencher and marker; B, graft, cutting and small plant firmer—center wheels carry most of weight and pack earth beside plants. Weight may be increased by loading side boxes.

422. Pear Seedling Culture.—With pears as with apples, a high proportion of straight roots is produced in one year from seed by using method number one. When leaf blight is not severe pear seedlings have a tendency to size up better than apple seedlings. This disease is a serious menace to both stocks in some sections. Vigorous growing seedlings are attacked little or not at all, hence efforts must be made to keep the seedlings growing well.

When grown by the second method in two years from seed, the seedlings are even larger than those of apple. Almost every seedling will develop to a No. 1 size or greater. However, the stocks are worthless for practical field planting because the roots are straight and coarse and the tops heavy and branched. At the depth of 3′ many roots will be ⅛″ in diameter with no strong lateral roots.

The third method produces branched roots. In some instances branching is too low on the stock, so lateral roots may be removed in trimming, previous to lining out for budding. As with the apple, therefore, it is important to trim the roots of young seedlings to within 3″ of the crown prior to planting the second season. It is a good plan to grow the seedlings close together the first season to keep them small.

Though this method insures growing branch root pears cheaply it is not so well adapted to this tree as to the apple because the seedlings are subject to leaf-blight through two seasons. Furthermore, since pear seedlings are likely to make sufficient size in one season it should be better to follow a method which will give the desired type in one season.

423. Nut trees are usually easy to grow from seed by method number one, (35). The popular practice has been to plant the sprouted nuts or those which have been stratified in sand over winter and with the seed coats cracked. The seeds are sown 4″ to 6″ apart in furrows about 4″ deep and covered with 3″ of well prepared nursery soil. They will usually make trees suitable for budding the same year as planted. Sometimes, however, two seasons will be needed. So far as the authors are aware, no tests such as outlined (421) have been undertaken. It seems reasonable to suppose that results would be similar to those obtained with peach pits.

424. Olive Stocks.—Olive seeds should first be clipped and germinated. Redding seeds are considered best. Successful germination depends on both the condition of the seed when planted and the environmental conditions afterwards. The higher the temperature up to 80° F. the better the germination. This temperature in the greenhouse often gives 90% germination. Too much moisture has a deleterious effect on germination. An ordinary daily sprinkling will give good results. The seed should be planted ½″ deep in a medium light sandy soil.

XVII

NURSERY MANAGEMENT

According to the United States Census, the nursery industry had been increasing normally until the World War. In 1899 the area reported was 59,492 acres; by 1909 it had increased to 80,618 acres; during the following decade hundreds of nurseries and other plant propagating concerns either failed or greatly reduced their business, for the figures reported in 1919 were only 51,453 acres. From then until 1929 the industry was estimated to have increased three-fold though the (acknowledged incomplete) Census figures reported 141,133 acres. Following that date the second slump of the century occurred and again hundreds of concerns failed or curtailed their output. At this writing figures are not available to indicate the reduction since 1929.

As further figures to indicate the fluctuation, the Census reported that 4,991 nurseries filed reports in 1899; in 1909 there were 5,582; the War reduced these to 4,049 in 1919 and inflation increased them to 7,207 in 1929. Gross receipts for 1899 were $10,123,873; for 1909 they were $21,050,822; in spite of the lessened number of establishments this fell only to $20,434,389 in 1919; but had increased to $58,182,562 in 1929. Omitting odd cents, the average gross receipts were $170. an acre in 1899; $261. in 1909; $397. in 1919 and $412. in 1929. A large proportion of this increase (estimated by the American Association of Nurserymen at 75%) was due to the demand for ornamental plants, especially evergreens. Since 1929, however, this demand has fallen off greatly.

In 1899 "Greenhouses, flowers and vegetables under glass and flowers in the open" were not reported by the Census. In 1909 when they are listed for the first time 10,614 establishments were reported; in 1919 there were 17,199 and in 1929 only 14,982. Gross receipts increased from $34,872,329 in 1909 to $77,380,230 in 1919 and $109,894,904 in 1929. These figures coupled with those of the nursery industry indicate the importance of only two branches of plant propagation. To them should be added the acreage, value, etc. of plants grown for transplanting and sold both wholesale and retail; but since these are propagated mostly from seed they cannot properly be included in either nurserymen's, florists' or seedsmen's classes. Figures are available to cover seed, not as plants but as seed.

It must be emphasized that though annual gross acreage receipts may seem large, expenses are heavy, partly because nursery lands usually command high rent and partly because of the necessary equipment and the skilled labor needed in the business. This may be judged by the general discussion and the illustrations in this volume; so there is not as much money in nursery stock as may at first appear.

425. Laying out a nursery.—Since horse or tractor cultivation is necessary, nurseries should be laid out with ample turning ground at opposite ends of the rows, and cross alleys at convenient distances both for the removal of stock and for labeling. In most nurseries the rows vary from 100′ to 300′ long, but in large ones they are sometimes a quarter of a mile long.

426. Shelters are advisable where the prevailing winds are strong. They help protect young bud and graft shoots from being broken or blown off and aid the trees to grow straight. Where natural shelter—a hill or a wood to windward—is not available, mixed shelter belts of deep rooting deciduous and evergreen trees, placed beyond their root reach of the nursery rows, will serve well. Low grounds, though sheltered, are not desirable because usually

Fig. 296.—Citrus nursery seed beds under shingle lath shade.

frosty. Everything that will cause snow drifts among the stock should be avoided.

427. Digging stock may be done at any time the ground can be worked after the leaves fall in autumn and before the buds swell in spring, except when the temperature is below freezing. In a small way nursery spades may be used to lift individual trees. On a larger scale a furrow may be thrown away from the trees on each side of the rows and then spades used. In big commercial nurseries the tree digger (Fig. 297) is drawn by horses (Fig. 298) or by

FIG. 297.—Methods of digging nursery stock. 1, extreme case of "the good old way" with nursery spades; 2, modern style with tree digger and cables.

tractors (Fig. 299). Nursery spades of steel and wood, costing several dollars each and made strong enough to stand heavy strains, are generally worked in pairs or threes around and a foot or more from the bases of the trees. The blades, at least 15″ long, are thrust full depth in the soil under the trees, which are lifted by leverage, care being taken to cut or break the roots as little as possible. On some styles the handles are reinforced by steel both front and back almost full length and riveted at 6″ intervals. Thus they also serve as measures of height for small shrubs and evergreens. Citrus nursery trees and evergreens may be dug with roots in a ball of earth. (Figs. 300, 317).

FIG. 298.—How tree digger works. As levers are lowered wheels rise and curved blade sinks about 18″ below surface, cutting tree roots in semicircle and raising tree slightly in loosened soil. Trees are lifted by hand.

428. Nursery soils and their care.—Best nursery stock is usually produced on heavy soils. If level, so much the better. Thorough drainage, natural or artificial, is essential because nursery trees "don't like wet feet." At least one season prior to planting the land should be devoted to some, preferably inter-tilled, farm crop—corn, potatoes, cabbage, turnips—so it will have had deep and thorough cultivation.

Since the nursery crop usually requires two years or more, the land must be in prime condition when trees are started in it. Otherwise the crop will be mediocre, if not poor. Since sales of fruit trees at least, depend upon age, size, caliper, etc., growth must be sturdy and quick; with ornamental trees and shrubs price is fixed scarcely at all by age, but more by the size of the subject. Hence land too poor to produce good fruit trees may yet be suitable for producing ornamental stock.

It is generally conceded that soil which has just produced a crop of nursery stock should not be devoted to nursery stock again without a "rest"; this, too, in spite of the fact that instances of success under repeated cropping may be cited. Cherries and apples often produce a second crop of good trees without a rest between, and plums have been known to do well for five, ten or even more crops when the ground has been well manured. Pears rarely do well twice in succession. Nurserymen, therefore, change their land and in many cases rent what they need for terms of several years.

Fig. 299.—Modern tree digger at work. *Top*, machine in operation hauled by tractor. Note that trees remain standing after having roots cut; *middle*, men guide machine; *bottom*, digger on sled to be hauled back for next row.

The New York state station (Geneva), after analyzing large numbers of nursery trees, presents the following statement based on the table condensed below:

It will be seen that since, upon an average, it requires from three to four years to grow a crop of nursery stock, cereals make a far greater demand upon the soil than does nursery stock, and it is a matter of common observation that removal of a tree crop leaves the soil in excellent condition for cereals.

TABLE 25.—PHOSPHORIC ACID AND POTASH REMOVED FROM SOIL BY VARIOUS CROPS

	Phosphoric Acid	Potash
Nursery stock, 11 tons	21.4	27.1
Wheat, grain, one ton	18.4	12.5
Barley, " " "	18.2	11.5
Rye, " " "	16.4	10.6
Oats, " " "	14.1	10.3
Maize, " " "	12.7	7.7
Wheat straw " "	5.7	12.4
Rye, " " "	5.5	16.1
Barley, " " "	4.7	22.5
Oats, " " "	4.3	21.3
Maize, " " "	9.1	38.9

429. Effects of nursery crops on soil.—Roberts of Cornell University has published analyses of nursery stock to show what plant food is removed by the four leading kinds of fruit trees. The quantities are as follows:

TABLE 26.—POUNDS OF FERTILIZING COMPOUNDS NEEDED BY NURSERY STOCK

	Apples	Pears	Peaches	Plums
Nitrogen	29.07	24.83	22.42	19.75
Phosphoric Acid	10.13	7.83	5.42	4.42
Potash	19.73	13.33	11.75	11.50

The significance of these figures can best be appreciated by a comparison with those of other crops; for instance, silage corn. This crop grown in drills yields 12 to 20 tons an acre and will repeat the performance on manured land, fully as well, at least once. Yet, to quote Roberts' statement, "the amount of green corn necessary to remove an equal amount of fertilizing ingredients per acre, taking the average of the . . . nitrogen, phosphoric acid, and potash . . . removed by an acre of trees (three years' growth) would be 4,779 pounds." Nursery trees are, therefore, seen to take only small amounts of plant food from the soil. Nursery lands, it is reasoned, should supply three to ten times the plant food needed by the trees. Experience also supports this deduction from the analyses and shows that good crops of potatoes, beans, wheat, etc., are secured after land has been "treed." Why not nursery stock?

The reason is not a chemical but a physical one. The very methods of thorough and deep tillage necessary to produce good trees injure the soil texture by "burning up" the vegetable matter, a result most noticeable in heavy soils, the very ones which produce

A

B

Fig. 299A.—Nursery machinery. A, trencher making three rows at once; B, attachment for tractor digging 22′ poplar saplings. The blade penetrates the ground 16″ deep.

best nursery stock. As a rule no system of cover cropping and none of manuring between the rows is practised, so there is neither protection of the soil during winter nor renewal of vegetable matter while the trees are growing—one to three or more years. Then, too, when the trees are dug their roots go too, and since the work

FIG. 300.—Pruning and digging nursery citrus trees. A, reducing branches to mere stubs; B, cutting roots and removing leaves and twigs; C, final stage—tree lifted; D, lifting tree. Worker thrusts spade beside tree and, as he pulls trunk with his left hand uses spade handle as lever.

is usually done in the fall, often when the ground should not be worked at all, the soil must pay the penalty; namely, puddling more or less serious the following spring and summer and refusal to "work up" again for nursery stock until after a rest in grain, hay or pasture.

430. Cover crops for nursery lands.—Since nursery lands are usually heavy, it would seem that sweet clover should have special value in bringing them back quickly into good heart, because this plant burrows deeply and opens up the soil well, besides adding considerable humus, both by its decaying roots and its tops, when these are turned under. Perhaps it would reduce the resting period to two or three years, as against three to five or even more under common practise.

If cover crops such as crimson clover, buckwheat and rye (the latter preferably with winter vetch), were grown between the rows and plowed or disced under in early spring, the evil effects on land would also be lessened. Coarse manure certainly has helped where applied between the rows in autumn or spring, but among nursery stock it is not always convenient to apply. It should therefore be liberally added after a nursery crop has been harvested. A second crop might thus be planted within two years with good prospects of success.

Commercial fertilizers are popularly believed to be useful in growing nursery stock so are often applied because of the following beliefs: 1, "Usually nitrogen is needed in liberal supply to insure strong growth." 2, "When the trees are showing yellowish leaves on poor spindling growth, a top-dressing of soda nitrate or ammonium sulphate, about 300 pounds an acre, during late spring or early summer, will help." 3, "Nitrogenous fertilizers must be used with great caution, otherwise they may force too succulent a growth. This might not ripen especially if produced near the close of the season. The trees would thus be subject to winter injury, they would transplant with greater difficulty and be unsatisfactory to the planter."

In view of such rules-of-thumb the following slightly condensed quotations will prove suggestive if not illuminating:

Production of nursery stock [1] is limited largely by the natural conditions which favor vegetative growth and at the same time permit proper maturity. In those regions which experience has shown to be adapted to nursery stock the questions arise as to how to secure better growth of stock and better ripened wood. Accordingly nurserymen have tried various fertilizers from time immemorial, ranging from iron filings and "land plaster" to barnyard manure and the newer synthetic commercial fertilizers. Potash is applied by some growers "because it ripens up the wood," while nitrogen is supplied "because it produces

[1] *The Response of Apples, Cherries and Roses to Fertilizer Applications in the Nursery,* H. B. Tukey and Carl D. Brase, *N. Y. (Geneva) Exp. Sta. Bul. 599,* 1931.

top growth." Accurate information is meager, however, so that nurserymen have little reliable data either to support or to condemn their practices.

"Does potash ripen the wood? Will nitrogen give greater top growth? Is barnyard manure more beneficial than urea or nitrate of soda? Is a complete fertilizer best? Experiments were designed to answer these questions with apple and cherry trees and with rose bushes. The plants under test were McIntosh apple trees on French crab seedling roots, Montmorency cherries on mazzard seedling roots during three seasons each and to three varieties of hybrid tea roses during their two years in the nursery. The soil is an Ontario clay loam of good fertility located in the nursery region of western New York at Geneva. The experimenters' practical application of the data secured as follows:

So far as results with apple and cherry trees in the nursery are concerned, they show clearly that the fertilizers used in this experiment, namely nitrate of soda, urea, barnyard manure, superphosphate and muriate of potash, have been thrown away. They do not mean that on poor land or that under different climatic conditions there may not be a definite response. They indicate solely that under western New York conditions, on well drained nursery soils of high fertility and good humus content from legume growth, and under a system of clean cultivation, the growth of apple and cherry trees is not affected by fertilizer applications.

They indicate that the addition of nitrogen will not stimulate growth and will not affect maturity or ripening of wood; that potash and phosphorus have no effect upon the growth and will not hasten maturity or "ripening-up" of the wood; that the growth of plants under such conditions is at its maximum for its environment; and that rainfall and temperature and the general combination of factors which we call "local environment" are the limiting ones—not fertilizers.

Just what the results might be on soil low in fertility, or soil in poor physical condition, and on soil in different regions are questions that may well be asked but which often upon second thought need no answer, for the reason that it is an economic error to attempt to grow nursery stock in a large commercial way upon poor land or in unfavored conditions. Experience has shown that marginal land may produce stock at a profit in periods when cost of production is not the important factor, but that it is a liability in periods of keen competition and over a period of years. Barring the small, local grower, therefore, the question of marginal land is seldom a factor, and it is a question whether even in his case the practise is economically sound in the long run.

More important than fertilizers are the factors of more or less common knowledge, such as adequate drainage, good physical conditions of the soil, and other local aspects. The removal of any excess moisture from the soil during the active growth period of early spring looms especially large. Apples and roses will make satisfactory growth and apparently will be uninjured by a water table that will adversely affect cherries growing beside them.

As for the practical application from results with roses, little can be said other than that while one may conclude with finality that apple and cherry trees do not respond to fertilizers, he can say the same for roses. He can say, however, that roses have made satisfactory growth *without* fertilizer applications, and he can say also that where growth has been greatest and most prolonged there has been most winter injury. It would seem that, although roses may show a response to fertilizer applications, here again the greatest emphasis may well be placed upon drainage, location, soil type, and physical condition of the soil. These factors are of prime importance, and fertilizer applications will not correct them.

And finally, a close study of the data, comparing the growth season by season, shows in a general way that plats which may make the least growth one year may make the greatest growth next, and ultimately by this zigzag method of progression, may reach the same height and size. Since climatic factors are the same over these adjacent plats, the proposition is immediately suggested that the general "lay of the land," height of water table, and physical nature may vary just enough so that climatic factors may favor the conditions in one parcel of land one year, another the next, and vice versa. Throughout the entire experiment, although designed as a fertilizer experiment, the facts have consistently turned away from fertilizer applications towards the many already enumerated, practical considerations, which underlie the choice of any site for the growing of nursery stock.

Fig. 301.—View in nursery cellar. Stock dug and stored in fall.

431. Winter protection of nurseries.—From more than 100 replies to inquiries concerning behavior of nursery stock in a severe winter in the Northwestern States and adjacent Canada it is deduced that the results of injuries suggest: 1, The value of snow as a covering for nursery stock, 2, the advisability of planting nurseries so far as practicable on north slopes, 3, interspersing nursery blocks with evergreen wind-breaks extending east and west. Next to snow as a cover is litter for which oats, buckwheat, peas, vetches, or mammoth clover are advised as catch crops, the clover only for wet seasons.

432. Storing nursery stock in frost-proof winter quarters (Figs. 301, 302) is popular with a majority of the large nurseries 1, because the stock may be dug when in prime condition and going into dormancy rather than into activity as is always the case when dug in spring; 2, because it avoids risk of loss or damage by winter injury, rabbits, mice or other animals; 3, because it is believed that stock stored at an even temperature approximating the freezing point will be in better condition in spring than when allowed to stand in the nursery and be subjected to wide fluctuations in temperature; 4, because, regardless of weather conditions, it enables nurserymen to fill their orders promptly in spring; 5, because it prevents damage to the soil due to early spring digging when the ground is wet; 6, because packing may be done under most favorable conditions (Fig. 303).

Whether or not the trees are actually better when they reach the grower is an undecided point. It may be said, however, that though a freshly dug tree or shrub is unquestionably more vital than one which has been stored for three to six months—stacked like cordwood—nevertheless millions of trees and shrubs are so handled annually. If the results were not satisfactory to the public the nurseries would not practice the method!

Winter storage should be at a uniform temperature of 28° to 30°. At this temperature little ventilation is necessary, loss of vitality from drying is slight, the tendency to mold is minimized and packing the roots with damp material or spraying with water, less.

FIG. 303.—Shelf supports in nursery cellar—triangular blocks fastened to uprights with cleats for shelves to rest upon.

Storage studies at New York (Geneva) Experiment station showed the importance of allowing stock to ripen properly in the field, such material being more resistant than immature stock to cold and disease in the nursery cellar.

433. Nursery tree trimming.—Stockiness is one of the main points nurserymen aim to secure in their trees. To obtain this they give the trees plenty of space, usually not less than 9″ in rows 3′ apart for small trees and 12″ and 3½′ to 4′ for large kinds which are to remain in the rows not over two years. Greater space is usually needed for longer periods. The first year the leaves should not be rubbed from the tree stems (except the removal of those necessary to allow for budding) or the trees will grow too slender and too tall. Should branching start too low, or should there be Y-crotches, trimming will be needed. By fall of the first year stock budded in the North the previous summer and that started from root grafts in the spring, should be 4′ or more tall. That budded in the South in June should be as tall or taller.

In the spring the height is usually reduced to 3′ or 4′ to form the head. Some nurserymen head as low as 2' or even 18"; to meet the increasing demand for low-headed trees. Shortly after heading back the earth is hoed away from the trunk bases and all sprouts from crowns and roots cut off. The leaves that appear on trunks and branches should not be removed, because they are needed to ripen and develop the adjacent wood and to help supply the roots with plant food. The practice of rubbing them off early in the season

Fig. 304.—Unpacking and heeling-in nursery stock should be done immediately upon arrival. If stock is in prime condition it may be planted at once; if dry or shriveled it should be buried for week or plunged—root and branch—in water and soaked for two or three days.

cannot be too strongly condemned. Trees deprived of these leaves are forced to develop other leaves higher up, thus tending to make top-heavy, weak, spindling trunks.

Cutting off undesirable shoots on the trunk shortly after mid-summer is a very different thing. By that time they will have fulfilled at least a part of their function and can thus be spared with less disadvantage to the appearance and the well-being of the trees. Moreover, their removal at that time will not force extra top growth, because the trees will be busy ripening the wood they formed quickly in the first half of the season when moisture was more abundant in the soil and conditions better favored quick development of wood.

In removing the undesirable twigs mentioned, if the cuts are made with a sharp knife close to the trunk, they will heal over by October. When the cutting is over the fewest number of leaves on trunk and branches should be sacrificed.

434. Cost of nursery stock.—Prices of nursery stock vary almost as greatly as do the catalogs. Cultivation, fertilization, spraying, trimming, training, root pruning, method of digging and packing, age and size of tree, and a dozen other factors influence price. The cost of specimens should always be reckoned on the basis of quality. Often a high-priced tree is cheap at its price, and often a low-priced tree is expensive even as a gift. The initial cost is in most cases a mere trifle when compared with the after value of the specimen as a producer of fruit or beauty. Far better esteem the nurseryman and his business methods than compare or contrast his prices with those of his competitors. Such factors as trueness to name, plumpness and quantity of roots, and thoroughness of packing are beyond price.

435. Buying and handling nursery stock.[1]—In ordering one should emphasize especially the necessity of trees being true to name, thoroughly healthy, properly mature and vigorous. By the last is meant they should be old enough but not too old, with a perfect union of stock and scion, be dormant but in strong, living condition when received by the grower, not shriveled or discolored, nor show other evidence of premature or improper handling. Straight stock is specially desirable. The union of graft or bud should be good. The roots should be free from all evidence of woolly aphis, San Jose scale, crown-gall or hairy root disease. So far as orchard growth is concerned each particular form of propagation—whole or piece-root (243, 244)—is immaterial. The region in which the tree is produced appears to make no difference so long as the tree is sound and of the right variety for the locality involved.

One-year-old trees of good size 4′ to 6′ tall, neither stunted nor overgrown, are usually best. Never should they be older than two years from bud or graft. The advantages are that one-year trees usually cost less to buy, to ship and to plant, are more readily shipped and transplanted, those fit for sale are sure to be strong growers and their heads can be formed as desired. If older trees are preferred, however, their limbs should be properly separated, well distributed around the trunk and located approximately at desired heights.

It is best to deal direct with responsible nurseries and to order early, submitting requirements to several firms for bids. The trees may be held at the nursery, subject to order at planting time. Where winters are not too severe, fall planting is advisable, otherwise planting is best done in spring as soon as the ground is fit, though it may be done later if the trees are kept satisfactorily dormant. When received the trees should be examined and heeled-in at once (Fig. 304). Roots should be shortened as little as possible, just enough to fit into a fair sized hole. It has been found by investigators that the less the roots are pruned the better the resulting growth of the tree. Those broken or bruised should be removed with a smooth cut above the place of injury. This pruning is preferably done before heeling-in so the wounds may callus before planting.

The heeling-in may be done on a large scale by plowing two or more deep furrows, preferably east and west, so the trees can be leaned south or southwest, at an angle of 30° to 40°, thus to escape sun scald. They should be completely unpacked, all straw and other material likely to attract mice removed, and then be laid along the furrow in a single row or layer. The roots and a third or more of the tops should be covered immediately with earth which must be packed thoroughly around them. This covering may be done at least partly

---

[1] Founded on an article by the late John P. Stewart of the Penn. Exp. Sta.

with the plow. Successive layers may be laid when needed. The place should be well drained. Where there is likely to be damage from mice, the whole area should be surrounded with furrows or ridges of earth.

In the past it has been the practice of some orchardists when planting nursery trees to cut off all side limbs, leaving a straight whip. This is not a wise practice. Those side limbs properly situated for framework branches should be retained, and cut back when planted to 2″ or 3″ stubs. Young, rather than old trees, as a rule, will give better results in customers' hands and thus establish good feeling toward the nurserymen. Slender trees are usually undesirable.

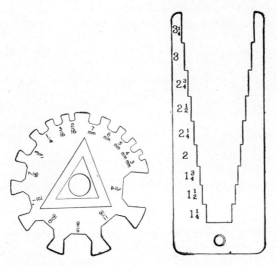

Fig. 305.—Tree calipers. A, small sizes; B, large trees.

436. Tree grades.—It is greatly to be regretted that the public considers mere straightness, girth and good appearance the indices of nursery tree quality, because this has largely helped to eliminate many of the best varieties of fruit from the nurserymen's lists, their places being taken by varieties that normally grow straight. Of course, the difficulty of cultivating and handling sprawling and crooked trees has also helped. No economical amount of care will make such varieties as Rhode Island Greening and Canada Red apples or Winter Nelis pears assume the straight and narrow form that Baldwin, Northern Spy and many other varieties develop with minimum attention (Figs. 305, 306).

Again, the demand has been for large trees, because of the belief that bearing will come earlier than with small ones. Unless trees have been transplanted or root pruned in the nursery, this is usually an error, mainly because of unavoidable root losses in digging. It is only human nature, then, for the nurserymen to grow and sell what the public demands—size and looks first rather than vigor, health and form characteristic of the variety, as well as trueness to name.

Needless to say, a first-class tree should be true to name, well grown, mature, old enough but not too old for planting, have a perfectly healed union of stock and scion or bud and have smooth, clean bark free from blemishes and disease, have a strong, stout trunk and good roots characteristic of the variety and also free from disease and insect injury.

Mere height is not alone a recommendation; far better a rather short stocky tree with numerous branches well placed low down on the trunk. Those not needed can be easily cut out, but if not present

Fig. 306.—Nursery tree counter for use in field. Careful man can accurately count trees of various sizes standing in rows.

new ones may be hard to get where wanted. Nursery trees are universally measured by height and diameter (caliper), about two inches above the bud or crown. Both dimensions vary with amount and character of trimming.

437. Official tree grades.—The American Association of Nurserymen has published a pamphlet called "Horticultural Standards" which were established at various conventions to meet the needs of nurserymen and the public for standard rules and practice. Changes and additions will doubtless be made as experience shows the wisdom of making them. So it is advisable for readers who wish to keep posted to write the secretary-treasurer of the Association, Charles Sizemore of Louisiana, Mo., for the most recent issue of this pamphlet. It includes decisions as to the numbers of plants of various species and sizes to be tied in bundles, tables of fruit and ornamental tree and shrub grades, conifers, lining-out stock, and various other data of importance. This information is too voluminous for inclusion here.

438. In packing for shipment, care must be taken to prevent drying out, heating, freezing and breakage during transit. (Fig.

310.) For economy's sake, packages should be light and strong and the packing material light, cheap and respectively retentive of moisture or capable of resisting wet for plants which demand one or the other condition. For mail shipments, the most popular materials include sphagnum or chaff, oiled or paraffined paper, express paper, stout twine, pot and tree labels, shipping tags, cardboard, corrugated paper and light wooden boxes. In California tules (bullrushes or club rushes) are used for wrapping around the trees. For express and freight, all the above list may be included, also burlap, baskets, crates, heavy wrapping paper, excelsior, straw, cord, rope and packing cases, the largest preferably iron bound or battened.

FIG. 307.—Nursery packing room with bales and cases ready for shipment.

Fig. 308.—Bunching machines. Especially useful for handling vicious shrubs such as roses, blackberries and barberries.

To save postage, as little moist packing as possible must be used. This must not be wet, or the package will be refused by the post office. Legal weights of mail packages must not be exceeded. The roots must be washed free of earth, straightened, laid close together, tops all pointing one way to form bundles of 3″ or 4″ in diameter. They must be covered with ½″ of damp moss and wrapped first in oiled or paraffined paper, with the tops loose but the roots snugly wrapped. By rolling the bundle diagonally and turning in the corner of the paper, tying may be avoided. To finish, the bundle should be

Fig. 309.—Packing room of hardy perennial nursery.

wrapped completely in manila paper; tied securely around the center once or twice and across the ends, the address written on the package and also on a shipping tag, fastened preferably where the strings cross.

For basket and crate packing in warm weather, the plants are left with their tops visible in the bundles made as above and stood

Fig. 310.—Packing and packages. 1, for mail; 2, for express.

upright on excelsior, which is also packed around the sides. Burlap or cotton cloth is used to protect the bundles in baskets; (Fig. 310) battens serve the same purpose in crates. In cold weather the packing is increased and the tops covered completely. Bales are used for small orders of trees, shrubs and vines (Fig. 311).

Heavy shipments are packed in large boxes, the larger trees in 2″ or 3″ of damp cut straw or similar material and fastened in place with battens nailed through the sides. (Fig. 304.) Small trees, shrubs and berry plants beginning with the largest, are placed in their order of size till the box is full, packing and battens being used as necessary to fill the box solid full, so there will be no shifting in transit. After the cover is nailed on it should be marked "TOP" in large letters and the address painted or inked on with a brush. Trees and plants so handled may be shipped thousands of miles

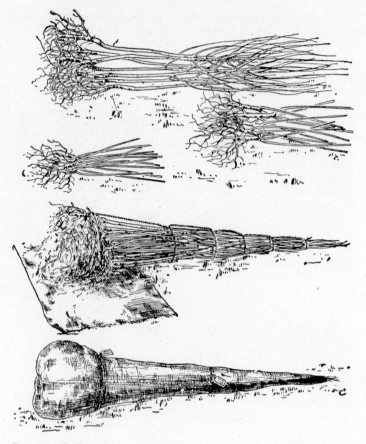

FIG. 311.—Baling nursery stock. *Top,* trees; *next,* two sizes of shrubs; *next,* trees combined with shrubs and corded; *bottom,* finished bale with damp packing around roots.

with confidence that they will arrive in good condition and give satisfaction to buyers.

For shipping long distances, say to or from Australia and the United States special care must be taken as described and illustrated by the U. S. Department of Agriculture (Figs. 314, 315).

439. Reducing Nursery Stock Losses during and after **Storage.**[1]—One of the important nursery problems is to get some kinds of trees to grow after planting. The difficulties are due to various factors which affect the vitality of plants. Possibly the most important are drying and the attacks of saprophytes (organisms that

[1] J. A. Neilson, Mich. State Coll. in address before Am. Assn. Nurserymen, reported in *Flor. Exch.,* 78.

feed on dead organic matter). Both occur in storage, in transit and after planting. Other contributing factors are frost injury in the nursery, cold dry or hot dry weather after planting, exposure of roots to sun and wind and the inability of some kinds of trees to strike root quickly after planting.

Recent developments show that such losses may be reduced by coating the stock with various waxes and other materials. The idea of using paraffin wax for this purpose was suggested by the good results secured in protecting scions and buds in topworking sweet cherry. The experiments, including several hundred trees, showed definitely that paraffin wax when applied over the entire scion and on buds prevented drying and thus helped to secure a better set. The plan, first proposed and employed by

Fig. 312.—Case of trees and shrubs showing heavy paper lining to keep out cold and heat and hold in moisture.

Dr. Robert T. Morris, has since been called the Morris method.

Experiments in widely separated places and on many kinds of stock resulted in the treatment of more than a million trees and shrubs. In addition, wax has been used on nearly two million cuttings and several hundred thousand buds and scions with good results.

From these experiments it is now known that wax prevents 1, drying and conserves vitality, thereby favoring a more prompt growth after planting and helping to secure a better stand; 2, helps to revive transplanted trees dormant for some time after growth should have started; 3, prevents mold on roses and some other shrubs in storage, probably due to the exclusion of air from the surface of the plant and possibly to the temperature of the hot wax when applied; 4, repels borers; 5, reduces summer sunscald and 6, does not appear to hinder respiration. In any case, experience shows that roses dipped in a suitable wax at the proper temperature retain their freshness and plumpness right through to the planting season and when planted usually make a good response in growth and bloom.

Summer sunscald is due to rapid drying out on the south side of

Fig. 313.—Avocado plants. A, grown in soil, weight 7¾ pounds; B, in sphagnum moss, weight, 4¼ pounds. Note superior roots of latter.

newly planted trees. It is always more prevalent in hot, dry seasons or in areas where hot weather and strong winds occur. In the South, it occurs frequently on pecans and in the North it affects smooth barked trees such as beech and maple. Borer infestation is usually associated with a weakened condition of the bark, due to injury or excessive drying out. Since attacks and summer sunscald are associated with drying out the prevention of drying would lessen the damage.

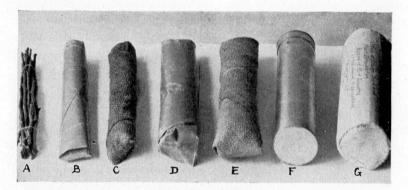

Fig. 314.—Packing materials used in wet burlap method. A, bundle of scions; B, scions wrapped in waxed paper; C, wet burlap added; D, waxed paper again; E, dry burlap tied on; F, tin tube; G, canvas cover, ready for shipment to Australia or other distant country.

Insofar as can be determined from observation on a large number of plants, in storage or after planting, there are apparently no injurious effects from the wax checking respiration. It is believed enough minute openings occur in the wax to permit the escape of respiration products that might be injurious.

Various kinds of waxes have been used in these experiments, but one of the best is a mixture of paraffin wax, four parts and pick-up gum,[1] one part. This makes a moderately tough wax with good ad-

Fig. 315.—Shipment of plants from Yokohama to United States Department of Agriculture. Some sprouting en route but plants grew when planted.

hesive properties. Several commercial products compare favorably with it. Experience suggests that a wax already prepared for heating would be preferable to one that must be made up, because of convenience in handling, the assumption being that the price is not too high. In sections where high temperatures occur, it would be desirable to use waxes with a high melting point, or to add one part beeswax to two of the paraffin-gum mixture.

Recent observations show that most hardwood plants will stand temperatures of 180° to 190° F. without injury, provided the plant is dipped in and out quickly. When the wax is at 180° it forms a thin film over the plant and remains on for a considerable time; if below 170° the coating is thick and is likely to crack and flake off, thus partly destroying its effectiveness. On the other hand, it is possible to have the wax too hot and thereby injure or kill the plants. All who try waxing trees or shrubs are therefore urged not to let the wax reach or at any rate exceed 190° F.

---

[1] Trade name for a resin-oil combination which mixes well with paraffin.

Containers for wax should be large enough to accommodate the largest trees or shrubs capable of being dipped and be constructed of heavy galvanized iron or other strong fireproof material. As trees and shrubs vary greatly in size, it is advisable to have two containers, a small one for shrubs and a larger one for trees. A heavy galvanized garbage can of about 16″ diameter and 36″ deep makes a good vat for roses and other small shrubs. One of the best outfits for roses is made like a double boiler. A galvanized can 16″ by 36″ is set inside another container large enough to allow 3″ clearance around the smaller vessel. The space between the cans is then filled with hot water and covered to keep in the heat.

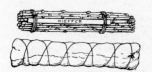

FIG. 316.—Scions for shipment. A, labeled bundle; B, wrapped and tied.

A good vat is made of a farm feed cooker with a tank 68″ by 22″. Inside is placed another tank small enough to allow 3″ clearance at sides and ends and 5″ at the bottom. This space is filled with hot water. An inexpensive vat may be made from an empty oil barrel by removing the top and burning out the oil residue.

Various types of heaters have been used, including electric hot plate, bottled gas burner, gasoline stove, kerosene burner, farm feed cooker, wood, coke, coal, salamander heaters and steam heaters or boilers. From the evidence at hand, it is advisable to have one or more heaters of a high efficiency type such as a gas, gasoline or steam heater. For a small double boiler outfit, one single heater will probably be sufficient, but for longer vats two or three are necessary. It is also desirable to have the heaters easily movable so that when the wax gets too hot they may be withdrawn; this may necessitate having the vat on a stand.

Another excellent outfit is a hot water heater from which pipes are laid to carry hot water to the vat. This type is more expensive than the others but has the desirable feature of safety. It should not be forgotten for one moment that the paraffin wax is highly inflammable, so it is necessary to keep the wax away from immediate contact with flames.

As waxes require time to melt in quantities sufficient to treat large numbers of plants, it is desirable to dip the greatest number possible at one session. The plants should be prepared in advance to avoid delay, roses and other shrubs or small trees given the pruning customary before shipment and all evidences of mold and other injuries removed. When the wax is at the right temperature the trunk and branches of the shrub or tree (or the bundle) must be quickly immersed.

The wax must not come in contact with the roots. In dipping

roses best results are obtained by taking a single plant (or a bundle) by the roots, turning it upside down and plunging the top quickly into the wax down to the roots withdrawing it immediately and giving it a quick snap to shake off excess wax. In this way it is possible to dip a large number of plants in a short time. Fruit or other trees of medium length should be dipped in a slanting position in long shallow vats.

Fig. 317.—Modern apparatus for moving large trees.

Frequent immersions of cold plant material tend to lower the wax temperature. Being highly important, this must be closely watched. When the thermometer falls below 170° the heat must be increased; if it goes above 190° reduced by turning down the flame or withdrawing the heater for a few minutes.

In view of the susceptibility of roses and some shrubs to molds and other injurious organisms in storage, it would probably be desirable to treat the plants before storing them. Other kinds of trees or shrubs, not susceptible to molds, but difficult to transplant, could be treated before shipment.

When only a few shrubs or trees are to be treated the wax may be melted in any suitable container and applied with a paint brush, using quick, long strokes.

The cost of dipping roses varies from ¼ to 1 cent a plant. The first figure is reasonable, the last too high. In the case of 500 nut trees 4' high the cost was about 1½ cents a tree for labor and material when the wax was applied with a brush; if the trees had been dipped, the labor cost would have been much lower. From figures furnished by one large pecan grower, it is estimated that the cost was 0.3 cents a tree to dip 75,000 trees. These figures include cost of equipment so it is probable that the cost for subsequent treatments could be considerably lower.

A new method of reducing the cost of wax consists in partly filling the wax container with hot water and then adding the hot wax which, being lighter, remains on top and is thus readily accessible to the plants. A more recent development consists in making a wax emulsion and spraying it on trees and shrubs but this scheme is only in the experimental stages.

XVIII

PEST CONTROL

In plant propagation, neglect to control pests and diseases probably results in more losses than all other causes combined. Yet, so far as the individual plant is concerned, preventives are effective, easily applied and of trifling cost. Remedies are less desirable because often the perhaps invisible insect bite or puncture may have inoculated the injured plant with an incurable disease. Hence the necessity to maintain healthful environment, keep plants healthy and insect-free from the start rather than to attempt to make them so after they have become disease- or insect-infested, perhaps mostly destroyed. For though the losses may be limited to the propagating establishments they often extend much more widely. Hence the necessity for quarantines.

Though the careful propagator may prevent damage to his plants it is advisable that he be able to decide what kind of pest may have entered his domain. So far as practical purposes of control are concerned he should determine this by noting the effects somewhat as follows:

440. How to identify plant enemies.—When the plants seem stunted or the leaves have poor color but nothing else apparently wrong the trouble may neither be pest nor disease but unfavorable soil conditions—lack of fertility, alkaline instead of acid (as for azaleas and related plants) or acid instead of alkaline (as for most other plants). Such cases suggest their own remedies. Sometimes, however, similar effects may be noted when the soil is favorable. These may be due to parasites such as nematodes, aphis (Fig. 318), or other creatures in the soil interfering directly or indirectly with plant welfare. Careful examination will determine such causes and suggest remedies so far as afflicted plants are concerned and also indicate preventives of the same results to other plants.

When several leaves wilt in spite of plentiful water and mineral nutrient supply in the soil, when they show sickly or yellowish areas or turn brown the trouble may be (respectively) "wilt," yellows, fire blight or mosaic, the first three due to bacteria, the last to a "virus" of undetermined origin. In such cases the only remedy is immediate destruction of all affected plants by fire. To prevent the spread of these and similar pests the propagating medium should be replaced

or thoroughly sterilized and all other possible sources of re-infesta-
tion destroyed or, in the case of tools, benches, etc., disinfected.

When the leaves show downy or powdery deposits, black or other
colored spots the pest is probably of fungus origin. With the appearance of the first preventives are indicated. These cannot remedy the parts already infested but they can prevent the spread of
such pests to other parts or plants.

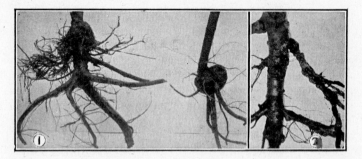

FIGS. 318-319.—Nursery tree pests. 1, hairy root and crown gall due to
bacteria (*Bacterium tumefaciens*) is primarily a nursery disease, not
usually serious in North, but often devastating in South. Destroy
infested stock and treat other trees it has contacted with formaldehyde or corrosive sublimate solutions; 2, woolly aphis attacks both
roots and tops, sucking juices and checking development in proportion
to its abundance. Nicotine sulphate is best remedy for attacks above
ground; liberal tobacco dust applications to soil for those beneath.

When notches or holes are bitten in leaves the cause is probably
a chewing insect (beetle, caterpillar). As these creatures chew and
swallow plant tissue they may be destroyed by poisons which they
take into their bodies with their food. Hence the importance of
applying poisons preferably in advance of expected attacks or as
soon as possible after such attacks are noticed.

When leaves are contorted or rolled more or less irregularly toward their lower sides the cause is probably aphis, as may be determined upon examination. These and many other insects, especially
leaf hoppers, mealy and scale insects which appear most numerous
upon the branches and twigs, suck the juices of the plants which
they kill. Because of their method of feeding, internal poisons are
useless—wasted when applied. The insects must be struck individually with a caustic, suffocated by a dust or an oil or poisoned by a
gas. These remedies will also destroy chewing insects that happen
to be present.

In addition to the above groups of plant parasites are borers
which burrow in the stems of many species of plants, miners which
tunnel beneath the upper and lower surfaces of leaves and various

insects that attack seeds in storage. The first may be cut out individually or poisoned by gases, etc., the second must be prevented from laying eggs on or in leaves and the last by fumigating seed suspected of being infested.

Fungi and bacteria are minute plants of low order which live on higher plants (or animals). The former are reproduced by spores (or seed bodies) distributed mostly by wind and water. Hence their dissemination and prevalence during humid and windy weather.

Fig. 320.—Box method of steam sterilizing greenhouse soil. Straw mat in foreground covers heated soil to hold heat as long as possible.

The spores of at least some species may continue alive for months or even years. Among characteristic diseases caused by them are damping off (Fig. 73) root rots, root and stem cankers, crown gall and hairy root (Fig. 319), "shot holes," leaf spots, mildews and rusts. Bacteria more rarely have a spore stage so are less often carried by wind but more frequently by water, insects and other creatures that feed on infested plants and later on healthy ones. Hence the importance of preventing the attacks of such creatures, more especially by killing the insects that carry infection.

441. Soil disinfection.—Formaldehyde (40% strength—one pint to 25 gallons of water) and about one gallon of the mixture to the cubic foot of freshly dug and fined soil is often used to destroy animal and plant life in greenhouses, the surface being covered with sailcloth or other densely woven material for two or three days to prevent undue loss of fumes. Before replanting, such soil must be thoroughly aired for a week or longer. It is less dangerous but also less effective than mercuric chloride (corrosive sublimate)—one ounce to seven gallons of water—or any one of several more recently discovered compounds of mercury or arsenic marketed under various trade names and applied according to manufacturers' directions.

Calcium carbide may be used out doors to destroy insects and other animal life in the soil, paradichlorobenzine and carbon disulphide better, especially to kill peach

Fig. 321.—Bordeaux mixing for small nursery. One of upper barrels contains copper sulphate stock solution; other, lime solution. Tubs are used to dilute these solutions. Lower barrel mixed two solutions which then pass as one through seive to spray tank. Larger size hose would be decided improvement.

borers, because their fumes being heavier than air, penetrate the soil deeply. To apply the former of these two earth is hoed an inch or two deep from the bases of the trees or other stock, the material spread not closer than two inches from the plants and covered with three or more inches of earth.

Live steam when properly applied and for sufficient time in greenhouses is not only highly effective in destroying bacteria and fungi but nematodes, worms, and insects in all stages of develop-

Fig. 322.—Nursery spraying outfit which reaches every part of every tree from collar to tip of 4 rows at one passage.

ment—eggs, larvæ, pupæ and adults. It may be applied beneath inverted "pans" (Fig. 320) upon the surface of newly forked soil but this does not usually heat the earth deeply enough for best results (210° F. at the bottom of the bed for 30 minutes or longer) and as each spot should be steamed for three hours considerable time and labor is required.

The more effective way is by means of perforated pipes placed 15″ or 18″ apart on the bottoms of raised bench beds or 8″ or more

FIG. 324.—Trees ready for fumigation in special house. Enough hydrocyanic acid gas is generated in crock from little bag of potassium cyanide to kill everything in closed quarters.

below the surface of solid beds before the soil is put in. As a temperature of 180° or more is necessary it may require three to six hours to attain, depending upon the steam pressure—high pressure (40 to 70 pounds) requiring the shorter time—but as an entire bench or even an entire house may be sterilized at one time its advantages are obvious. Its high cost is more than offset by its effectiveness. Another advantage that steaming has over fumigating is that as soon as the temperature falls sufficiently the soil may be sown or planted to a succeeding crop.

442. **Fungicides and insecticides,** by which fungi and insects, respectively, are killed, are classified as sprays (Fig. 321, 322), dusts and gases (Fig. 324) depending upon the form in which they are applied or in which they take effect, the last being used only to kill animal life. Both of the two former are used as dusts and sprays, though in propagating establishments sprays are more popular than dusts for the control of fungous diseases, probably because apparatus was bought before the effectiveness of dusting was recognized.

In nurseries the two leading fungicides are lime-sulphur and bordeaux mixture, the former used mainly as a dormant spray upon woody stock, the latter as a spring and summer spray for foliage. Of the two the latter is the one spray mixture better to be made on the premises than to be purchased. It is more often used than any other fungicide because of its wider scope, its effectiveness, persistence and relatively low cost. Its components and most popular formula are copper sulphate, 5 pounds; hydrated lime, 5 pounds; and water, 50 gallons, (or as weak as 100 gallons). Often such formulas are abbreviated to 5—5—50, etc.

Because of their rapidity of solution and convenience of handling the smaller sizes and the pulverized sulphate are to be preferred to the coarser grades. For similar reasons hydrated lime, an almost impalpable powder, is preferred to lump (stone or quick) lime, even though the latter is about a third stronger and therefore is used in a 4—4—50 formula.

The more nearly limestone approaches 100% calcium carbonate the better quality its lime for making bordeaux mixture and lime-sulphur solution. Magnesian limestones, such as dolomite, of which there are large deposits in Missouri, Wisconsin and Iowa, are inferior for both these fungicides, so should be avoided or the proportion of lime increased. It is advisable to have an analysis of the lime before purchasing.

Bordeaux mixture may be prepared in several ways, the most convenient of which are the stock solution and the pulverized copper sulphate, or "instant" method. The former is of special value where large quantities are to be used within a short time; the latter for any quantity needed. Excellent results have been obtained with the two-package commercial bordeaux.

In making stock solutions two 50-gallon wooden barrels, preferably with wooden hoops are nearly filled with water. In one 50 or 100 pounds of copper sulphate are suspended near the surface in a clean burlap bag of loose weave the night (or several hours) before the solution will be needed. When the material has dissolved, enough more water must be added to fill the barrel and be stirred with a paddle to make the solution uniform. When 50 pounds are used the solution will contain one pound of sulphate to the gallon; when 100, two pounds. It is advisable to stick to one or the other proportion so there may be no mistake in measuring. The latter strength will save storage space and also time when making Bordeaux because only half the number of gallons need be measured into the spray tank. It is generally preferred where extensive spraying must be done, though with larger tubes and hose (2″ or 3″) this advantage may be offset.

In the second barrel 50 or 100 pounds of lime are washed with a hose through a fine strainer to remove any possible lumps of grit. Hydrated lime is more convenient to use than lump or quick lime because it is generally free from grit, is usually sold in 50 pound paper sacks and needs only to be washed into the barrel and stirred to get it ready for use. For this reason only enough stock solution for a day's work need be made at one time. Lump lime is objectionable because it requires a shallow slaking trough, patience and labor in slaking, careful straining before being placed in the stock barrel and there is always the doubt as to whether the final solution is of correct strength.

When stock solutions of either copper sulphate or lime are to be kept for more than a day or two it is well to use tight covers on the barrels or to add a tablespoon of any lubricating oil to prevent evaporation.

To use stock solutions follow this order of procedure: 1, Nearly fill the spray tank with water. 2, Start the agitator and keep it going. 3, Add the required number of gallons of copper sulphate stock solution, according to the formula used and the capacity of the tank. 4, Either pour in the required number of gallons of lime stock solution or wash in the number of pounds of hydrated lime through the sprayer strainer. This may be done with water from a hose or by a stream from the spray nozzle. 5, Add any more water necessary to bring the total up to that of the formula. 6, When lead arsenate is to be used add it with the last water. 7, When nicotine sulphate is to be used add it last. Keep the agitator going from start to finish— until the tankful has been sprayed.

The pulverized copper sulphate or "instant" method has been

gaining in popularity during recent years mainly because no stock solution is needed. The usual sequence is as follows: 1, Fill the spray tank about one-third full of water. 2, Start the agitator. 3, Wash in the powdered copper sulphate through the tank strainer. 4, Nearly fill the tank with water. 5, Keep the agitator active for three to five minutes to insure solution of the sulphate before adding the lime. 6, Add the lime stock solution or wash in the hydrated lime. 7, Add lead arsenate or nicotine sulphate, if either is to be used. 8, Add enough water to fill the tank. 9, Keep the agitator going till the solution is used up.

Lime-sulphur is prepared by boiling lime and sulphur in water until both are dissolved and the solution registers 32° or 33° on a Baumé hydrometer scale and becomes a rich wine red. As its manufacture demands care and special equipment and as it keeps well it is safer to purchase one of the standard brands than to make a home product with unskilled labor.

Lime-sulphur has both insecticidal and fungicidal properties and is especially useful in late winter to destroy scale insects and the over-wintering stages of fungous diseases. When applied just before the buds swell it will also penetrate the softening shells of insect eggs and kill the insects inside. For use as a dormant spray 10½ gallons of the standard solution are diluted with 90 gallons of water. When to be used on foliage the dilution must be much greater (1½ gallons to 98½ of water); otherwise it will burn the leaves, especially during humid and hot weather. Either lead arsenate or nicotine sulphate may be added to the latter solution, the former to kill chewing, the latter sucking insects.

Dry lime-sulphur, a yellow powder which must be kept in airtight drums has fungicidal effects about equivalent to those of the original liquid. It consists of liquid lime-sulphur to which a stabilizer such as cane sugar is generally added and from which the water is driven off by heat. To use it multiply the number of gallons stated in a formula by four to arrive at the number of pounds to use with the same quantity of water.

The chief dusts used in nurseries for fungicidal and insecticidal purposes consist usually of sulphur and copper sulphate, the former sometimes coated with a sticker, the latter dehydrated and both reduced to impalpable powders (to pass through a 300-mesh-to-the-inch screen). Lead or calcium arsenate, usually 5% to 15%, equally reduced may be applied with 95% or 85% sulphur or with hydrated lime as carriers. With calcium arsenate 70% hydrated lime is used.

So-called nicotine dust [nicotine sulphate combined with hydrated lime or gypsum] is an effective destroyer of aphis during warm, dry, clear, windless days which favor liberation of the fumes without danger of their being blown away before taking effect. Its efficiency is reduced in proportion to the unfavorableness of conditions. As the lime with which it is mixed dilutes and thus reduces the effectiveness of the other dusts mentioned it should always be applied separately.

Nicotine, one of the most important contact poisons, is applied either as a simple decoction or "tea" made by steeping tobacco stems in water or as nicotine sulphate prepared by distilling nicotine into sulphuric acid to an actual nicotine content of 40% or 50%. The former is most useful in greenhouses, the latter out doors.

As nicotine sulphate is not highly insecticidal it must be broken down to release the nicotine. This is done by applying it in an alkaline solution such as fish oil soap or casein spreader (three or four pounds of the former or one of the latter to 100 gallons). These materials increase the effectiveness of the spray by reducing the surface tension and thus increasing the spreading power of the liquid. Hydrated lime (5 to 20 pounds to 100 gallons) will serve the same purpose, the larger quantity preferred because of its greater effectiveness though its residue sometimes causes trouble. As bordeaux mixture and lime-sulphur act in the same way as soap, nicotine sulphate may be added to either without losing its effectiveness. These combinations by being applied together permit the control of both sucking insects and plant diseases, thus saving the time needed to make separate applications.

Mineral oils applied either in miscible forms or as emulsions are highly effective contact insecticides. Manufacturers make them miscible or emulsify them in various ways so as to render them applicable as sprays in water. They may be prepared on the premises by methods described below.

One of the simplest ways of rendering an oil miscible has been published by the Washington State College [1] according to the following formula and procedure:

Material	Per cent by weight	Per cent by volume
Lubricating oil	90	91
Cresoap	10	9

Cresoap, the name given here to the cresylated fish-oil soap emulsifier, is made by dissolving 5 parts by volume of potash-fish-oil soap in 4 parts of cresylic acid, or technical cresol. By weight the proportions are 5½ to 4½. The soap should contain no free alkali and should have 30% of moisture. When the soap is mixed with the cresol the emulsifier becomes fluid and will dissolve at once in oil. Soda or weak potash soap should not be substituted for the potash-fish-oil soap specified here.

This is the most concentrated miscible oil, since it contains no inert ingredients. It requires care in being diluted [as do other miscible oils—Authors] and the first water must be worked in. Four and one-quarter gallons of stock are needed to make one hundred gallons of 4% spray. Where water is very hard,

---

[1] Melander, Spuler and Green, *Wash. Exp. Sta. Buls. 184, 186.* 1924 and 1925.

this miscible oil is not advised; a non-soap spray should then be selected. [This remark applies also to other miscible oils.—Authors.]

As a rule, miscible oils are fairly stable blends which may be stored indefinitely and easily used in most waters. As the majority of them will not blend with lime-sulphur the spraying apparatus should be thoroughly cleaned before either succeeds the other in it. To be on the safe side in their storage and use the manufacturer's instructions for each brand should be followed implicitly. Some brands are injured by freezing.

To make emulsions some emulsifying agent such as soap is dissolved in water, oil is then added and churned until the three continue intimately mixed without having the oil separate and float. When thus properly made they will keep indefinitely and may be mixed with water for application. But should a film of oil appear on the surface the material should be re-emulsified. Home made emulsions cost less than proprietary miscible oils but are less convenient to store and use. They also demand greater care to prevent the separation of the oil.

Popular emulsions, which fall into two groups—boiled and cold mixed (or cold pumped)—vary widely in their characteristics and effectiveness. When the former are properly made they may be stored for several months without change; the latter should be used at once or re-emulsified if stored for even a day. This is simpler than it sounds as all that is necessary is to pump the mixture forcibly back into itself through a nozzle. At their freezing temperature (15° F.) common soap emulsions may separate and have to be re-emulsified.

One good bordeaux emulsion may be conveniently made according to the formula in Table 27 and in the order of procedure that follows.

TABLE 27

	Ounces	Formula Pints	Pints
*Copper sulphate stock solution	*2	1	½
*Lime stock solution	*3	1½	¾
Red engine oil	1 gal	8	8
Water	2 qts	—	—

* Instead of stock solutions pulverized sulphate and hydrated lime may be used in these proportions.

1. Nearly fill the spray tank with water. 2. Start the agitator. 3. Add the copper sulphate solution. 4. Add the lime stock solution. 5. Add the oil. 6. Direct the spray nozzle in to the tank and pump forcibly until emulsion is complete; i.e., with no visible free oil.

By considering the above formula as a unit any desired percentage of oil in the spray may be calculated. For instance, to make a 1% oil solution only one quantity of each material need be added to 100 gallons of water; to make a 4% spray four times these quantities must be used; namely, four gallons of oil, eight ounces of copper sulphate, and 12 of lime. When dry sulphate and lime are used one additional quart of water must be added for each two ounces of the former and three of the latter to make the proportions exact.

When casein spreader is used instead of bordeaux mixture to emulsify the oil the formula is: Oil, one gallon; spreader, two ounces; water, two quarts. The same mixing procedure and calculation of per cents as above must be followed.

As the above formulas and those of various commercial emulsions consist of about two-thirds oil the calculation of quantities to add to the water is the same. When the percentages are greater, proportionately less emulsion and more water must be used; when lower, the reverse—more emulsion and less water.

When water is hard certain soap emulsions tend to break down. This may be prevented by "softening" it with lye or caustic soda (one pound of either to 100 gallons) before adding the materials to be emulsified.

The internal or stomach poisons most used in nurseries to kill chewing insects are lead arsenate and calcium arsenate. Each may be employed during the growing season as a dust or a spray, alone or in combination with Bordeaux mixture, lime-sulphur solution, or nicotine sulphate. In fact, combination dusts or sprays are often made containing three of these components—a fungicide, a contact and a stomach poison. When used as a dust the proportion of arsenate may vary from 5 to 15 pounds to the hydrated lime, sulphur or copper sulphate filler. As a spray it may be applied with water or either of the fungicides mentioned, 4 to 10 pounds to 100 gallons of either.

Glue in solution has proved an excellent contact spray for red spider (one of the mites) both in greenhouses and outdoors. As it dries it flakes off and carries the mites with it. One and a half to two pounds of flake glue are dissolved in cold water over night and applied when the air is dry. Several applications may be needed to obtain complete control.

Pyrethrum, prepared from the flowers and seeds of various species of plants (*Pyrethrum*) and sold under many trade names is more or less useful as a contact insecticide but its relatively high cost and its variability often make it less satisfactory than nicotine sulphate and some other insecticides of the contact class. Pyrethrum solutions have recently come on the market, but the authors do not know of their being used in nurseries.

Fumigation is necessary to kill insects that hibernate on dormant nursery stock, either before being stored or before shipment. It should be done in a permanent structure of wood, concrete or brick, lined with gas-tight material and located some distance from dwelling houses and live stock quarters. This building should be used for no other purpose and its gas-holding capacity should be tested at least once every six months. Preferably it should have doors on opposite sides, so wagons or trucks may be driven in (Fig. 324) fumigated without unloading, and driven out after the fumigation, thus effecting a saving of work and time. It is advisable also that one of the doors should face the prevailing wind, so the breeze will remove the gas quickly. The doors on the lee side should be opened first, to reduce the rush of gas that would occur in the reverse case. As a further precaution the means of opening should be well to one side of the door opening, so men will not have to expose themselves to the escaping gas.

Calcium cyanide is scattered on the dampened floor at the rate of two ounces to each 1,000 cubic feet of the fumigating room. This capacity is obtained by multiplying the length, breadth and height together, but disregarding the displacement of the truck, wagon or other container as well as the stock itself. See Chapter X on Fumigation.

XIX

FEDERAL PLANT QUARANTINE ACT AND REGULATIONS *

443. Quarantine legislation.—The United States was the last of the principal countries of the world to enact plant quarantine legislation. The plant Quarantine Act of August 20, 1912, was the culmination of several years of effort to have some type of legislation passed by Congress that would serve to protect the agriculture and horticulture of the United States from plant pests from foreign countries and that would also enable the control and prevent the distribution within the United States of any such pests that might have gained limited foothold. Prior to 1912 not only could plants be imported without regard to their freedom from pests, but America actually became a dumping ground for plant refuse from other countries. This unrestricted entry has resulted in the establishment in the United States of an enormous number of foreign plant pests which are, and will remain, a tremendous burden on the garden, field, and forest products of this country.

As an indication of the effectiveness of this act in its primary purpose of excluding foreign plant pests, it may be pointed out that during the few years immediately preceding its enactment there came into this country such major pests as the European corn borer, the Japanese beetle, the oriental fruit worm, the gipsy moth in New Jersey, the citrus canker, the chestnut blight, the white-pine blister rust, the potato wart, and others of similar destructive nature. In contrast with this formidable list of important pests, during the years of the enforcement of the act only three major agricultural and horticultural pests have gained entry and establishment, namely, the pink bollworm of cotton and the Mexican fruit fly, both from Mexico, and the Mediterranean fruit fly in Florida and neither fly is now known to occur in the United States. This very creditable showing has been achieved by means of a series of embargoes and restrictive quarantines regulating the entry of foreign plants and plant products. A port inspection service has been built up to inspect and pass or reject commercial shipments of restricted plants

---

* For this section the authors are indebted to Mr. Lee A. Strong, chief of the Plant Quarantine and Control Administration of the U. S. Dept. of Agri.

and plant products.   In some instances it is necessary to disinfect the plant material.

This service also intercepts and prevents the bringing in of casual lots of restricted plant material, which are often more dangerous than commercial importations.   Plant quarantine inspectors are stationed at all the principal ports of entry, as well as along the Mexican border and at strategic points along the Canadian border. At the maritime ports the inspection is extended to passenger's baggage, crews' quarters, and ships' stores for contraband plants and plant products.

The entry of certain plants, fruits, and vegetables is prohibited. The entry of all others is controlled under a permit system.   (See list of Federal quarantines.)   Experience has shown that of all plant material, nursery stock has been the most prolific means of entry of foreign plant pests.   Obviously, a reduction in the volume of importations of plants proportionately reduces the risk of pest introduction.   Therefore, with the exception of certain bulbs and seeds, cuttings, scions and buds of fruits or nuts, and rose stocks, with a minimum of risk, it has been found necessary, in order to carry out the purpose of the act, to limit the importation of plants to those which are necessary to meet the propagating needs for the horticultural development of this country.   The rules that have been laid down under which plants may be imported are set forth in Circular P. Q. C. A. 249, a copy of which may be obtained on application to the United States Plant Quarantine and Control Administration.

444. Results Obtained from Domestic Quarantine.   The Mexican fruit fly, which came across the Mexican border and heavily infested the citrus orchards of the Lower Rio Grande Valley of Texas, has apparently been completely exterminated from that important citrus-producing area.

The Mediterranean fruit fly, perhaps the most destructive tropical and subtropical fruit insect, was discovered in Florida in April, 1929.   The source of the infestation has not been determined.   Surveys showed 1,000 properties, scattered through 20 counties in the heart of the Florida citrus belt, to be infested in greater or less degree.   So successful has been the intensive eradication campaign which was immediately instituted that only three slight infestations were found since August 27, 1929, none since July 25, 1930 and on November 15, 1930, the quarantine was lifted.

The gipsy moth in New Jersey, which in 1920 was found to occur in an area of more than 400 square miles, has apparently been completely exterminated.

The Federal quarantines on account of the gipsy and brown-tail moths in New England, the European corn borer, and the Japanese beetle have been very helpful in preventing long-distance jumps of these pests by the inspection and certification of the articles covered by these quarantines for shipment to points outside the regulated areas.

445. State Nursery Stock Regulations and Quarantines.— *Inspection.* All the states have legal requirements to prevent the distribution of dangerous insect pests or plant diseases through the selling or shipping of nursery stock. Most states inspect nurseries annually or oftener to determine whether there may be any infestation, and if so, to prevent its being carried to other sections. Certificates of nursery inspection are issued in case the stock is found free from infestation. Moreover, in the case of incoming shipments, nearly all the states require certification of nursery stock by the state of origin. California, Montana, Washington, and certain other western states do not require the certificate on incoming stock, preferring to rely upon the inspection which is made when the shipment arrives in the state. Stock harboring injurious plant pests is not permitted to be delivered in these states.

The inspection of nursery stock for general classes of plant pests is purely a state activity. Federal restrictions consist of quarantines, each relating to a specific pest and a designated area. The Plant Quarantine and Control Administration, therefore, does not inspect nurseries (outside the District of Columbia) except for pests on account of which federal quarantines have been established.

The interstate shipper needs to take into consideration the fact that the regulations of the various states differ as to the kinds of plant material which must be accompanied by the state nursery inspection certificate, or which is inspected at destination as the case may be. All the states require it for nursery-grown woody plants, many for greenhouse-grown plants, and strawberry plants, while others include in the list herbaceous and bulbous plants, as well as annuals, cut flowers, and seeds. The following table gives the classes for each state.

Other Requirements which differ in the various states will also need to be taken into consideration in doing interstate business. Some of the more important ones are, furnishing a bond; securing a license or special permit tags; filing certain affidavits and agreements; furnishing invoices for all stock shipped; fumigating and defoliating; and insuring that the nursery stock shipped is true to variety, age, and grade represented.

446. State Quarantines on interstate shipping generally relate only to infestations other than those which are the subject of federal quarantines. The following state quarantines are mentioned as the more important in extent of territory covered or in variety of classes of nursery stock involved.

1. The oriental fruit moth quarantines of seven states of the

TABLE 28.—PLANTS AND PLANT PRODUCTS OF WHICH STATE NURSERY INSPECTION IS REQUIRED FOR ENTRY

Kinds of Plants and Plant Products	States of Destination of Shipments																
	Ala.	Ariz.	Ark.	Calif.	Colo.	Conn.	Del.	D.C.	Fla.	Ga.	Idaho[1]	Ill.	Ind.	Iowa	Kans.	Ky.	La.
Field-grown woody plants and parts thereof capable of propagation:																	
Cultivated or nursery grown	X	X	X	X	X	X	X	X	X	X	X	X	X	X	X	X	X
Wild	X	X	X	X	X	X	X	X	X	X	X	X	X	X	X	X	X
Greenhouse or house-grown plants:																	
Herbaceous, such as geraniums		X		X	X	X	X	X[1]			X						X
Woody, such as roses	X	X	X	X	X		X	X	X	X	X	X[2]	X		X	X	X
Herbaceous biennials and perennials:																	
Cultivated flowering, such as phlox and peonies		X		X	X		X	X[1]			X		X		X		X
Native or wild		X		X	X		X	X[1]			X		X		X		X
Vegetable perennial, such as rhubarb		X		X	X		X	X[1]			X				X		
Aquatic perennial				X	X		X	X[1]			X						
Strawberry	X	X	X	X	X		X	X	X	X	X	X	X	X	X		X[5]
Bulbous plants:																	
Rhizomes, such as iris		X		X	X		X	X[1]			X		X		X		X
Corms, such as gladiolus		X		X	X		X	X[1]			X						X
Tubers, such as dahlias		X		X	X		X	X[1]			X						X
Bulbs, such as tulip and narcissus		X		X	X		X	X[3]			X		X		X	X	X
Annual plants:																	
Flowering, such as asters	X	X		X	X						X		X				X
Vegetable, such as sweetpotato and cabbage		X[4]	X[4]	X			X				X				X	X	X
Decorative plant material:																	
Cut flowers		X		X			X										
Others cuttings incapable of propagation																	
Seeds:																	
Fruit pits		X	X	X			X			X							
Other seeds of fruit and ornamental trees or shrubs		X	X	X			X			X							

X—A nursery inspection certificate of the State of origin is required.
(1) See footnotes on page 141.

TABLE 28.—PLANTS AND PLANT PRODUCTS OF WHICH STATE NURSERY INSPECTION IS REQUIRED FOR ENTRY—Continued.

Kinds of Plants and Plant Products	States of Destination of Shipments															
	Maine	Md.	Mass.	Mich.	Minn.	Miss.	Mo.	Mont.[1]	Nebr.	Nev.	N. H.	N. J.	N. Mex.	N. Y.	N. C.	N. Dak.
Field-grown woody plants and parts thereof capable of propagation:																
Cultivated or nursery grown	X	X	X	X	X	X	X	X	X	X	X	X	X	X	X	X
Wild	X	X	X	X	X	X	X	X	X	X	X	X	X	X		X
Greenhouse or house-grown plants:																
Herbaceous, such as geraniums	X	X				X				X						
Woody, such as roses	X	X	X	[2]X		X	X	X	X	X	X		X	X		X
Herbaceous biennials and perennials:																
Cultivated flowering, such as phlox and peonies	X	X		X	X	X	X		X	X				X	X	
Native or wild	X	X		X	X	X	X		X	X				X	X	
Vegetable perennial, such as rhubarb		X		X	X	X	X		X	X				X		
Aquatic perennial	X	X			X	X	X	X	X	X	X		X			
Strawberry	X	X	X		X	X	X		X	X				X	X	
Bulbous plants:																
Rhizomes, such as iris	X	X				X	X		X	X					X	X
Corms, such a. gladiolus	X	X		X		X	X		X	X						X
Tubers, such as dahlias	X	X				X	X		X	X					X	X
Bulbs, such as tulip and narcissus					X	X	X		X	X				X	X	X
Annual plants:																
Flowering, such as asters	X	X				X			X	X						
Vegetable, such as sweetpotato and cabbage		X				X				X						
Decorative plant material:																
Cut flowers	X			[7]X		[6]X							X		X	
Other cuttings incapable of propagation	X															
Seeds:																
Fruit pits									X				X			
Other seeds of fruit and ornamental trees or shrubs									X				X			

	Wyo.	Wis.	W. Va.	Wash.[1]	Va.	Vt.	Utah	Tex.	Tenn.	S. Dak.	S. C.	R. I.	Pa.	Oreg.[1]	Okla.	Ohio
Field-grown woody plants and parts thereof capable of propagation:																
Cultivated or nursery grown	X	X	X	X	X	X	X	X	X	X	X	X	X	X	X	X
Wild	X	X			X	X	X	X	X	X	X		X	X	X	
Greenhouse or house-grown plants:																
Herbaceous, such as geraniums	X			X			X	X			X			X		
Woody, such as roses	X	X	X	X	X[2]	X	X	X	X		X		X	X	X	
Herbaceous biennials and perennials:																
Cultivated flowering, such as phlox and peonies	X	X		X			X	X		X	X	X		X		
Native or wild	X	X		X			X	X			X	X		X		
Vegetable perennial, such as rhubarb	X	X		X			X	X	X	X[8]	X	X		X		
Aquatic perennial		X		X			X							X		
Strawberry	X	X	X	X	X		X	X		X	X	X		X		X
Bulbous plants:																
Rhizomes, such as iris	X	X		X		X	X	X	X		X	X		X		
Corms, such as gladiolus	X			X		X	X	X	X		X	X		X		
Tubers, such as dahlias	X			X		X	X	X	X		X	X		X		
Bulbs, such as tulip and narcissus	X	X	X	X		X	X	X	X		X	X		X		
Annual plants:																
Flowering, such as asters	X	X		X			X	X						X	X	
Vegetable, such as sweetpotato and cabbage							X	X						X	X	
Decorative plant material:																
Cut flowers							X	X[9]			X			X	X	
Other cuttings incapable of propagation							X		X		X			X		
Seeds:																
Fruit pits		X	X				X						X	X	X	X
Other seeds of fruit and ornamental trees or shrubs		X					X						X	X	X	X

(1) Inspection is made at destination and the nursery certificate of the State of origin is not required, or less emphasis is placed upon it.
[2] Roses are required to be inspected only when sold for outdoor planting.
[3] Inspection at origin is required only as to narcissus under Federal quarantine No. 62. Other incoming bulbs are inspected when entering the District of Columbia.
[4] A special permit is required for shipping these and other cruciferous plants into Arkansas.
[5] This includes *Citrus trifoliata*.
[6] This applies only to citrus.
[7] Christmas trees and evergreen boughs are required to be certified.
[8] Asparagus should be certified but rhubarb need not be.
[9] This applies to Cape-jasmine.

Pacific Coast and Rocky Mountain region prohibit the entry of al-mond, apple, apricot, cherry, chokecherry, nectarine, peach, pear, plum, and quince trees and parts from many of the states in the eastern half of the United States. Six of these western states include Texas also in the quarantined area.

2, The alfalfa weevil quarantines of nine western and southern states require special fumigation of nursery stock entering from the weevil-infested territory. Two other states prohibit the entry of nursery stock from such territory.

3, The citrus white-flies quarantine of California prohibits the entry of citrus plants and some 16 species of ornamentals, as well as persimmons from 10 southern states. Citrus plants are also restricted by eight other states, on account of citrus canker and various other pests.

4, A Califronia quarantine on certain pecan-infesting insects restricts the entry of walnut, hickory, and pecan plants from all parts of the United States east of and including Montana, Wyoming, Colorado, and New Mexico; and similar quarantines of Arizona and Utah prohibit the entry of Japanese walnut, hickory, and pecan plants from all states other than California.

5, The filbert blight quarantines of California, Oregon, and Washington prohibit the entry of filbert plants from that part of the United States east of and including Montanta, Wyoming, Colorado, and New Mexico.

6, Regulations relating to certain virus and other diseases of the raspberry have been issued by Michigan, Minnesota, New York, and Wisconsin, requiring two inspections of these plants during the season, and special certification to this effect. These regulations apply to plants offered for sale within the state, as well as those shipped in from other States.

447. How to Obtain Information.—Requests for information on state regulations may be addressed to the Departments of Agriculture of the states from which, and to which, the shipments are to be made. Digests of the general requirements of the various states have been published by a few of the states, however, so any one interested may inquire of the state nursery inspection officer of his own state whether such a digest is available.

A summary of state quarantines has been published by the United States Department of Agriculture, and may be obtained upon request. It is entitled, "Summary of State and Territorial Plant Quarantines Affecting Interstate Shipments," Miscellaneous Publication No. 80.

XX

PLANTING ORCHARD TREES

448. Care of trees previous to planting.—Upon arrival from the nursery, trees should be carefully inspected for diseases and pests (440). If they are to be planted immediately they may be put in a cool cellar or basement or in a shed, covered with straw and thoroughly soaked with water. If they are not to be planted for a week or more they should immediately be heeled-in.

449. Preparation of ground for orchard planting.—Where grading is necessary to prepare the land for irrigation it must be done first so distribution of water will be equal. The land must also be put in good tilth. Whenever possible this should be started at least a year prior to planting by growing some hoed crop such as corn, potatoes, beets, or turnips on it. When planting is to be done in spring it is generally advisable, especially with heavy soils, to plow the area deeply in the fall previous and leave the furrows rough over winter. This aërates and enlivens the soil. A hoed or cultivated crop during the summer will keep the ground in good shape and may also help pay expenses. If no cover crop is grown, the land should be cultivated by plowing the weeds under as long as the surface soil is moist enough to start them. Keeping the weeds down in this manner conserves moisture.

If it is not possible to follow the above plan and it is thought desirable to plant the land immediately upon breaking up, plow 10″ or 12″ deep and harrow thoroughly. Where feasible, it is a good plan, to follow the furrows with a subsoiler, going down to 14″, as early in the fall as possible to do deep work. Before planting, the ground may be disked or harrowed again.

450. Planting the trees.—Precautions should be taken to protect the roots during the planting operation by a wet blanket or a canvas while distributing them. If put out in the field more than 15 minutes ahead of the planters the roots should be covered with soil.

If the field has been properly prepared the tree holes should be dug just deep and wide enough to accommodate the roots. There is no advantage in digging them larger. The top soil should be placed in one pile and the bottom soil in another. When the tree is set the top soil should be put in first so the best earth will be in contact with

FIG. 325.—Tree planting step by step. A, tools needed; B, planting board in place, with tree stake in center and temporary ones at ends; C, digging tree hole; D, planting board re-set; E, pruning tree roots; F, tree in place ready for earth; G, hole filled with tramped earth; H, cutting top.

the roots. The holes may be dug well in advance of the planting if desired; but when the trees are planted the sides of each hole should be shaved down and the dried earth thrown aside. This method is not as good as digging the holes just previous to planting.

451. A tree setting board (Fig. 325, 326) is used to keep trees in line and their trunks in the same place as the stakes. It is made of 1″ board, 4″ wide and 4′ or 5′ long. A notch is cut on one side in the center and one at each end. Two pointed stakes are made 1′ long and of a diameter to fit the end notches—but not snugly. When being used the center notch is placed against the tree stake. Then the two stakes are driven in the end notches. Then the planting board is lifted away and the hole dug. After digging, the board is placed over the end stakes in its former position and the trunk of the tree stood upright in the center notch. It will then be in exactly the right place.

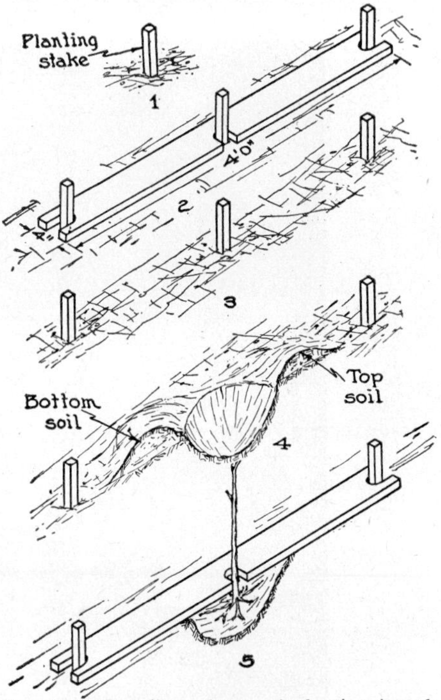

After some top soil has been thrown in the bottom of the hole the roots are

Fig. 326.—Details and use of planting board. 1, stake placed in position for tree; 2, board set over this stake and marking stakes placed at ends; 3, board removed so hole may be dug; 4, hole dug, with top soil in one pile, subsoil in another; 5, board replaced over marking stakes and tree set in center notch— original place of tree stake.

spread out in their natural position, care being taken when the soil is loose to have the tree set an inch or even two deeper than it grew in the nursery, to allow for settling. Some soil is thrown about the roots and settled by lifting the tree slightly and shaking it. Usually planting is done by two men. One holds the tree in place and tamps the soil, getting it close around the roots and trunk with his toes. The secret of successful planting is to firm the soil thoroughly about the roots. Fill the hole and tramp nearly to the level of the ground. Then throw in several shovelfuls of soil around the tree but leave loose.

452. Whitewashing the tree to prevent sun-scald should follow the pruning after planting (Fig. 327).

453. Laying out an orchard on the square system [1] (Fig. 328, 329).—Before going to the field prepare an annealed wire No.

Fig. 327.—Whitewashing is a safeguard against sun-scald in many parts of United States.

14 gauge by fastening rings $1\frac{1}{2}''$ in diameter at each end making the over-all length 208', 9''.[2] Beginning at the other side of ring, measure 16', $10\frac{1}{2}''$ [3] on the wire and attach a piece of solder the size of a pea to indicate the necessary width of turning ground or "head-

---

[1] These directions are for a one acre plot but they will serve as a guide for laying out larger areas and for other distances between trees.

[2] An acre, approximately 208 feet, 9 inches square, makes a good sized piece of ground for a practice exercise, but a wire as long as 300 feet may be used in actually laying out an orchard.

[3] Twenty-five feet is a good planting distance for many California fruit trees and those that do not grow too large. In the East, apples are set at 40 feet so the distance between solder points on the wire should be that between trees.

land" at the ends of rows. Apply other bits of solder at 25' intervals to represent the distance between trees.

454. To make a square field proceed as follows: (1) Use one boundary as a base line (Line I), 208¾' long. (2) Make a right

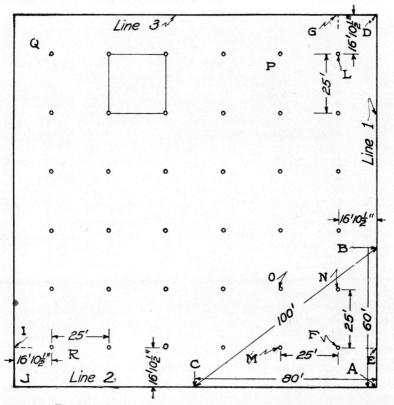

Fig. 328.—Laying out one-acre orchard on square system.

angle at A thus: (Fig. 329). Measure 60' on Line I and drive a temporary stake at B. (3) Again begin at A and stretch the wire about 100' from A at as nearly a right angle as can be judged by the eye. Call this line, Line II. (4) On it measure 80' from A and place a temporary stake. (5) From the 60' stake at B stretch the tape diagonally across the corner toward the 80' stake at C. If the distance from B to C is exactly 100' the lines AB and AC will form a right angle at A; but if this diagonal distance is more or less than 100' move the stake C until the distance *is* exactly 100' from B and 80' from A. (Figs. 328 to 330).

The other corners and sides are determined as follows: (1) Begin at A and measure 208¾′ along Line I to make the second side of the field. (2) Place a stake at the end of the wire, D. Do the same on Line II. (3) Square the two adjacent corners to A (at the ends of Lines I and II) in the same way as at A. (4) Extend the 80′ lines until they meet at the corner diagonally opposite to A. If test-ing (as at the angle, A) proves this angle, Q, to be a right angle the field is square. If not, an error has been made and must be corrected or the tree rows will not be straight. (5) Mark all cor-ners with stakes.

Next place a stake at the headland solder points on the wire—eight stakes in all. These stakes will also indi-cate where the tree rows would extend across the bor-ders of the field.

The 25′ distances be-tween trees does not divide 208¾′ evenly—eight times and 8¾′ over. Tractors and teams require 16′ to 18′. So the first row of trees must be set in from the boundary enough to provide for this. To determine the amount needed in the orchard under consideration add 25′ to the 8¾′ mentioned and divide the sum by two (33¾ ÷ 2 = 16′ 10½″). This is the width of the headland or turning ground.

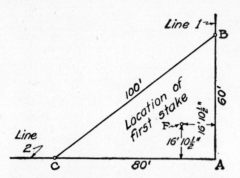

Fig. 329.—How to make accurate right angle. 1, from A at end of straight boundary line 1, measure 60′ and place stake B; 2, from A measure 80′ in general direction of line 2, and set stake tentatively at C; 3, from B measure 100′ in general direction of C. When the dis-tance AC is exactly 80′ and BC 100′ angle CAB will be right (or square) angle.

To determine the position of the first tree place the ring over a stake on Line II the width of the headland from A. 1, Stretch the marking wire tightly from it parallel to line No. 1 through point G. This line can be made parallel by making the distance from D to G 16′ 10½″ the same distance E-E, placing a stake at G. 2, Stretch the wire so it extends to and touches the stake G. 3, Place stakes at each of the soldered points along the planting wire. This will place the last tree 16′, 10½″ inside of boundary line at the point G. There will be 8 stakes for trees from F to L. 4, Beginning at point F, measure with the planting wire, a line parallel to line A-J as was done for line F-G. 5, Place stakes along this line, F-I, using the planting wire as before. 6, Having two outside lines of stakes the proper distance apart and at right angles to each other (a) stretch the planting wire from the next stake, M, on line F-I parallel to lines A-D and F-G and make parallel by measuring 25′ from line F-G at stake L.[1]   (b) Place stakes, (beginning at stake M) as in the first row.   Continue with other rows until the field has been all staked.

447. **Staking the orchard by sighting.**—With the base line to start from square the corners as directed above and enclose the orchard site on its four sides with a row of stakes set at intervals of 25', beginning at 16' 10½" from each corner.   The stakes indicate the tree rows in each direction.   Run a tree line of stakes through the center of the field in each direction.   In extra large fields several such lines may be needed.   By sighting from two adjoining sides of

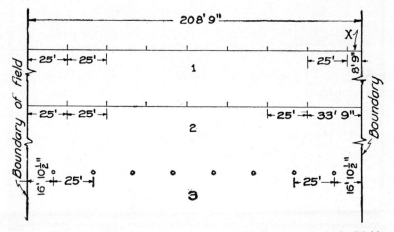

Fig. 330.—Laying off orchard headlands. Measure distance across field. Divide this distance by distance between trees. To any remainder add distance between trees and divide by two. Answer is width of headland. Applied in above example: 1, distance across field 208' 9". Divided by 25 (distance between trees) leaves remainder of 8' 9"; 2, to this add distance between trees (25'), equals 33' 9"; 3, divide by 2. Answer 16' 10½"—width of headland at each end of row in direction measured.

the field through to the stakes already placed, the rest of the stakes may be placed by a third party who sets them where the two lines of sight intersect.

455. **Another system for staking.**—A base line is laid out through the center of the field from A to B (Fig. 331) and stakes set at the desired distance; for instance, 40' apart. A second line from C to D is now measured at right angles to the first and stakes set as in the first. The method of erecting the line C-D at a right angle to A-B is shown below. If B and C represent stakes 40' apart in the base line, one may stretch a tape 30' long from the point B and one 50' long from point C. The line from B to O is at right

---

[1] The marking or planting wire may be stretched at right angles to line A-D at point G and a line of stakes put out. This will save measuring the 25 feet distance each time a new row is laid out.

angles to the original base line, O being the only point at which the two tapes can be joined. In order to set the stake for a tree at S the required distance may be measured with two boards of the right length or by stretching tapes simultaneously from the nearest stakes

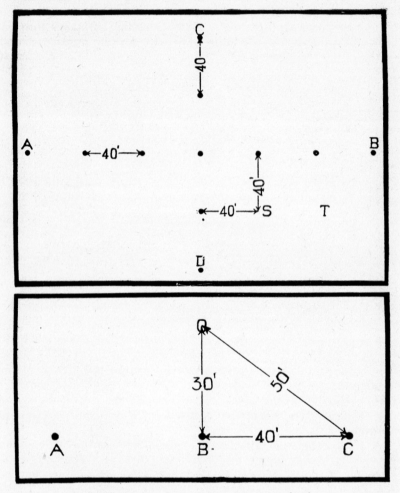

Fɪɢ. 331.—Board system of laying out orchard.

in the lines CD and AB. Similarly the stake for the tree at the point T is found by measuring from the tree S and the next stake in the line AB. Continuing in this method the whole orchard may be set. This system is simple but is usually accurate enough to ordinary conditions

456. Hexagonal or equilateral triangle system.[1]—With this system instead of having 25′ between rows, each tree will be 25′ from its neighbor but the rows only 21.65′ apart. (Figs. 332, 333).

A measuring wire should be made previous to planting as follows: 1. Place two stakes in the ground 25′ apart to their outer edges. 2. Place a 1½″ ring over each stake. 3. Connect the rings with an annealed galvanized wire (No. 14 gauge) stretched taut. 4. Remove one ring from its stake and place another loose ring over that stake. 5. Connect this ring with another wire stretched taut to

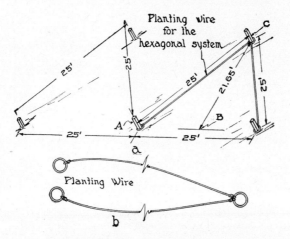

Fig. 332.—Planting wires and their use in hexagonal system.

the other stakes and attach to the ring already there (Fig. 332). This ring will thus have attached to it two wires each with a ring on its distant end. When each of these terminal rings is placed over each of two stakes in a measured row an equilateral triangle will be formed by placing a third stake in the other ring when the wires are stretched taut.

To Locate the first tree: 1. Compute the distance between rows one way. It will be seen (Fig. 333) that the trees form 25′ equilateral triangles but the distance between rows is 21.65′. This distance between rows is the altitude of the right angle triangle A-B-C and is found by the methematical formula: Hypotenuse squared,

---

[1] By this method the trees will be equally distant from each other and the ground divided as evenly as possible. The system is called hexagonal because a hexagon is formed by drawing a line through six trees which encompass a seventh. It is sometimes known as septuple planting because seven trees enter into it. This method of planting gives 15% more trees to the acre than the square system when the distance between trees is the same, but it brings the rows closer together as may be seen from the diagram. See Figs. 334, 335 for other systems of planting and thinning trees.

minus base squared, equals the altitude of the triangle squared. The square root of this square is the altitude of the right angle triangle which in this case is 21.65'.

To get the number of rows divide 208' 9" (or 208.75) by 21.65 = 9 rows but 13.9' over. Divide 13.9' by two equals 6.95. As this is not enough turning space 21.65' must be added to it (the distance between rows) 13.9' plus 21.65' equals 35.55'. This divided by two gives 17.78' at each end of the row for headland. Therefore, the

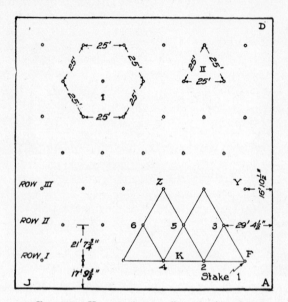

F<small>IG</small>. 333.—Hexagonal or equilateral triangular
orchard plan.

first row of trees must be located 17.78' from the boundary line A-J. To fix the exact point, determine the distance at the end of row 1, by dividing 208' 9" (the length of the square acre field) by 25', the distance between trees in this row, *the same as for the square system.* It goes eight times and 8' 9" over. This remainder divided at each end of the field is not enough to turn with a tractor as headland. Therefore, add 25' (the distance between two trees) and get 33' 9". This divided for each end of the field equals 16' 10½" or the distance from the boundary to the first tree in the first row. Thus the headland on this side of the field differs somewhat from that on the other which was 17' 9⅜". Therefore, the first tree will be located 16' 10½" from line A-D and 17' 9⅜" from line A-J. Where these two lines intersect place a stake for the first tree in the first row at point F, then proceed to determine the positions of the other trees by the following routine:

To Lay out the rows: (1) Use the measuring wire as in the square system.   Starting at point F, measure off and place stakes 25′ apart along the row.   (2) When this is done place the two loose rings of the planting wire over Stakes 1 and 2.   (3) Hold the third ring and pull it until both wires are taut.   (4) Drive Stake 3 through the ring into the ground. This marks the first tree in the second row.   It will be 29′ 4½″ from the boundary line A-D and 25′ from trees 1 and 2.   (5) Next repeat the operation with the two loose rings over stakes 2 and 4 to establish a new stake at 5. Continue on Row II and lay out the rest of the trees in the same

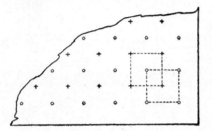

Fig. 334.—Quincunx orchard setting— five trees to each square (one in center).

manner.   Repeat the process with other rows until the field has been staked.   (6) A few of the end stakes are not easily reached by the wire method.   By sighting from two rows these may be placed by sighting from K on row I and Z on Row III.

457. The Quincunx system of laying out an orchard and several other methods of planting and thinning are shown in Figures 334 and 335.

TABLE 28.—NUMBER OF TREES REQUIRED PER ACRE

Planting distances, in feet	Number of trees per acre square or alternate planting*
18 x 18	134
20 x 20	108
22 x 22	90
25 x 25	70
27 x 27	59
30 x 30	48
35 x 35	35
40 x 40	27
50 x 50	17
60 x 60	12

* Figures are exact only for a multiple of acres.   For hexagonal planting add 15 per cent to above figures; for quincunx planting add 100 per cent.

Thinning trees in closely or interplanted orchards, or orchards with fillers, often becomes necessary.   Plans for fillers in an orchard are shown in Fig. 335, and results of such thinning in Table 29.

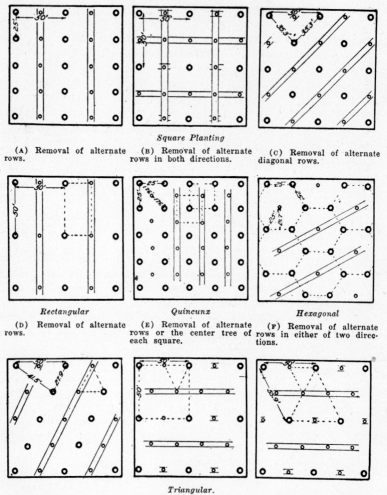

Square Planting

(A) Removal of alternate rows.

(B) Removal of alternate rows in both directions.

(C) Removal of alternate diagonal rows.

Rectangular

Quincunx

Hexagonal

(D) Removal of alternate rows.

(E) Removal of alternate rows or the center tree of each square.

(F) Removal of alternate rows in either of two directions.

Triangular.

(G) Removal of alternate diagonal rows.

(H) Removal of alternate rows and each even tree in the remaining rows.

(I) Removal of alternate rows and each odd tree in the remaining rows.

FIG. 335.—Various orchard lay-out plans including fillers and methods of thinning.

TABLE 29.—DIAGONAL DISTANCES BETWEEN TREES

Distances of planting (1)	Distances on the diagonal			
	Square planting (2)	Alternate planting (3)	Quincunx planting (4)	Hexagonal planting (5)
18 x 18	25.5	20.1		
20 x 20	28.3	22.4		
22 x 22	31.1	24.6		
25 x 25	35.3	27.9		
27 x 27	38.2	30.2	One-half the distances given in column 2.	All trees equidistant. Same as column 1.
30 x 30	42.5	33.5		
35 x 35	49.5	39.1		
40 x 40	56.6	44.8		
50 x 50	70.7	55.9		
60 x 60	84.9	67.1		

TABLE 30.—RESULTS OF ORCHARD THINNING [1]

Orchard	Fruit	Planted		Thinned		Results
		When	How	When	How	
E. A. Gammon, Hood	Pears	1890	16 x 16	1915	22.5 x 32	Better trees and fruit and larger Yields
Wm. McKenzie, Monticello	Prunes	1890	20 x 20	1917	28 x 28	Larger and better fruit and greater Yields
Henry Wheatley, Napa	Prunes	1900	18 x 18	1915	18 x 36	Much larger trees. Yields, thinned and unthinned trees, 1925, same, but more fruit of good size on thinned trees.
H. G. Boyce, Winters	Apricots	1893	24 x 24	1913	34 x 48	Trees using all 34-foot space. Large crops.
H. G. Boyce	Almonds	1883	24 x 24	1913	34 x 48	Large crops.
W. D. Wilkins, Mountain View .	Apricots	1898	22 x 22	1910	22 x 44	Large tree heavy yields.
Limoneira Ranch, Santa Paula	Walnuts	1891	40 x 40	1916	40 x 80	No increase in yields for several years previous to thinning. Yields now doubled.

TABLE 31.—SYSTEMS OF THINNING [1]

System of planting	Method of thinning	Reduction in number of trees	Form of planting after thinning	Remarks
Square.....	Alternate rows.................	50%	Rectang.... Square.....	Relieves crowding in only one direction.
	Alternate rows both directions.	75%		Usually too severe. Too few trees left.
	Alternate diag. rows or alternate trees in each row.	50%	Quincunx...	Most common method. Remaining trees well spaced.
Rectang....	Alternate rows.................	50%	Square.....	Trees quickly crowd in one direction.
Quincunx...	Alternate rows or removal of tree in center of square.	50%	Square.....	Best method with double planting to secure even distribution.
Hexag......	Alternate trees in alternate rows or tree in center of hexagon.	25%	Hexag......	Thinning too light to be of great value.
Hexag......	Alternate tree in each row or alternate diagonal rows.	50%	Irreg. diag..	Relieves crowding in only one direction.
	Alternate rows either on the square or diagonal and alternate tree in remaining row.	75%	Square or triang....	Satisfactory with large, thrifty, long-lived trees which will satisfactorily utilize space. With smaller, weaker trees, thinning too severe.

FIFTY PRACTICUMS

TEACHERS' NOTES FOR PRACTICUMS

To carry out these practicums it is desirable (though not essential) to have available a plot of ground of not less than one-half acre, preferably one acre, on which to grow materials. Substitute methods of handling the work may be used. It should have a water supply.

Although much of the material and equipment may be purchased, it will be advisable to have some growing close at hand. For example, plants suitable for layerage where they can be reached easily from the class room, so students can execute the practicum and see the results.

A plan of the plot for growing the necessary plants is given in the form below. It may take several years to establish all the materials required. This, however, should not prevent carrying on most of the class work since many practicums concern the propagation and culture of plants desired for permanent planting; for example establishing ornamentals from which to secure seeds and cutting material. In such cases material could likely be secured from locally grown shrubs, made into cuttings and planted under the instructions given in Practicums XVI to XX, then rooted the cuttings and seedlings would be potted as in Practicums XXVII and XXVIII. In this manner many permanent plants can be established for class use.

If a plot is not available the next alternate probably would be to visit places where the materials are being grown. If it is not advisable to have the class participate in the propagation or culture work, the teacher or owner should demonstrate the methods.

A greenhouse in which to carry on much of the work is also highly desirable but not essential. Hotbeds and coldframes will do nicely.

A lathhouse is so readily and economically constructed that one should be the property of every school intending to conduct practicums. It need not be an elaborate structure. Directions for building one and frames for hotbeds are given in Practicums XXV and XXVI.

A suggestion for a source of materials for some of the practicums is to have students carrying on projects at home along the lines of the practicums; for instance, having a nursery of fruit trees, bushes and vines or ornamentals. The class may be taken there to carry on work such as planting, transplanting, budding or grafting, digging nursery stock and balling plants. A profit should be realized on such projects.

It will be well for the teacher to go over the list of materials and equipment listed on the following pages before the year's work is started and to buy necessities in advance. Many may be obtained locally.

In Smith-Hughes Agriculture most of the work may be given to the first year class. The authors recommend that the exercises not applicable to such a class be offered to the more advanced classes in horticulture. This arrangement will permit the student during the course to follow through and complete certain practicums started in the first year class. For instance, the practicums on raising seedling fruit tree rootstocks is followed later by one on budding. The student may plant seeds and raise seedlings the first year and bud the trees the second or third year.

Though it is preferable to allow only a short time to elapse between a laboratory study and its application in the field, the practicum may be so arranged that the indoor laboratory practicums may be given one year and the field practicums the next. For example, the first year practice in budding or grafting may be given on branches brought into the laboratory, but application of this study in the field delayed until the second or third years.

Students should work in pairs wherever possible in these practicums.

PLANTING PLAN OF PRACTICUM PLOT

Enough planting material is indicated to supply a class of ten students. Rows are 50′ long (but may be made longer) and 3′ to 5′ apart.

Sedum (Division—offsets) 1 row
Cannas (Division—rootstocks) 1 row
Trailing blackberries (Tip layerage) 1 row
Upright blackberries (Root-sprouts) 1 row
Loganberries (Tip layerage) 1 row
Dewberries (Tip layerage) 1 row
Blackcap raspberries (Tip layerage) 1 row
Red raspberries (Roots, sprouts) 1 row
Gooseberries (Mound layerage, cuttage) 1 row
Currants (Mound layerage, cuttage) 1 row
Strawberries (Runners) 1 row
Doucin or Paradise dwarf apple rootstocks (Mound, continuous layerage) 1 row
Filberts (Continuous, simple layerage) 1 row
Pear seedlings (Transplanting, bench grafting, budding, digging) 3 rows
Apple seedling planting (Transplanting, bench grafting, budding, digging) 3 rows
Myrobalan plum seed planting (Seedage, budding, digging) 3 rows
Almond seed planting (Seedage, budding, digging) 3 rows
Peach seed planting (Seedage, budding, digging) 3 rows
Black walnut seed planting (Seedage, patch modified "H" budding, digging) 3 rows
Bulbs (Separation) 2 rows
Ornamentals (Balling, cuttage, budding, grafting, transplanting) 5 rows
Roses (Cuttage) 1 row
Grape cuttings (Cuttage, layerage, budding, grafting) 3 rows
Dahlias (Division—root tubers) 1 row
Iris (Division—rootstocks) 1 row
Vegetables 10 rows

INDEX OF STANDARD MATERIALS AND EQUIPMENT FOR EXECUTING PRACTICUMS *

The amounts indicated are for a class of 10 students

No.
1 Seeds, beans (¼ pound)
2 " peas (¼ pound)
3 " corn (¼ pound)
4 " squash (¼ pound)
5 " castor bean (¼ pound)
6 " rice—unhulled (¼ pound)
7 Gummed labels 1¾″ × 4″ (2 boxes)
8 Seeds, canna (50)
9 " honey locust (100)
10 " radish (150)
11 " asparagus (150)
12 " sour or bitter clover (250)
13 " apricot (1 bushel)
14 " peach (1 bushel)
15 " hawthorn (2 oz.)
16 " Myrobalan plum (1 bushel)
17 " black walnut (2 bushels)
18 " apple (¼ pound)
19 " pear (¼ pound)

No.
20 Seeds, almond (1 bushel)
21 " pyracantha (⅛ pound)
22 " cotoneaster (⅛ pound)
23 Fern spores (1 ounce)
24 Glass vials containing crop seeds for study
25 " " " weed " " "
26 Mounted specimens of weed and crop plants
27 Seeds white clover (¼ pound)
28 " alfalfa (¼ pound)
29 " rye grass (¼ pound)
30 " vetch (¼ pound)
31 " rye (¼ pound)
32 " radish and melon (¼ pound)
33 " oats (½ pound)
34 Small labels with string attached
35 Seeds, wheat (½ pound)
36 " celery (1 ounce)
37 " onions (2 ounces)
38 " cucumber (2 ounces)

---

* Only such of these items need be provided as are to be used in the practicums decided upon.

No.
39 Seeds, beets (2 ounces)
40　" 　rye grass (2 ounces)
41　" 　lettuce (1 ounce)
42　" 　tomato (1 ounce)
43　" 　pepper (1 ounce)
44　" 　greenhouse tomatoes
　　Any of the following varieties: English:
　　(a) Carter's, (b) Sunrise. American: (a)
　　Glove, (b) Bonny Best, (3) Stone
45 Seeds, greenhouse cucumber; any of the fol-
　　lowing: English forcing type: Telegraph,
　　Duke or Edinburgh. American field type
　　forcing strains: Abundance, Davis Per-
　　fect, Long Green, Telegraph, White
　　Spine
46 Seeds, greenhouse varieties of lettuce: Head
　　lettuce: May King, Boston Market,
　　Hothouse. Loose leaf lettuce: Grand
　　Rapids
47 Garden Seeds to be furnished by student
　　for home garden
48 Gooseberry (10)
49 Currant (10)
50 Blackcap raspberry (10)
51 Blueberry (10)
52 Dewberry (10)
53 Strawberry (20)
54 Trailing blackberry (10)
55 Upright blackberry (10)
56 Loganberry (10)
57 Red raspberry (10)
58 Abelia grandiflora (10)
59 Oleander (10)
60 Grape vines (10) for cutting material
61 Snowball (10)
62 Dogwood (10)
63 Filbert (10)
64 Azalea (10)
65 Euonymus japonica microphylla (10)
66 Quince (10)
67 Dracena (10)
68 Croton (10)
69 Rhododendron (10)
70 Rubber plant (10)
71 Pandanus (10)
72 Forked sticks or heavy wire (25)
73 Houseleek (10)
74 Artichoke (10)
75 Hydrangea (10)
76 Indian cedar (1)
77 Italian cypress (1)
78 Juniper (1)
79 Yew (1)
80 Arborvitæ (2)
81 Tallow (5 pound)
82 Rose (10)
83 Plumbago (3)
84 Jasmine (3)
85 Coprosma (3)
86 Diervilla (3)
87 Cuphea (10)
88 Veronica (10)
89 Lantana (10)
90 Boxwood (10)
91 Viburnum (10)
92 Broom (15)
93 Fuchsia (10)
94 Lilac (10)
95 Oxalis (10)
96 Passion Flower **(1)**
97 Salvia (10)
98 Hoya (10)
99 Gloxinia (10)
100 Coleus (20)
101 Geranium (10)
102 Impatiens (20)
103 Pomegranate (3)
104 Oregon grape **(6)**
105 Privet, (10)
106 Plane tree (1)
107 Hibiscus (5)

No.
108 Spirea (10)
109 Flowering quince (10)
110 Deutzia (10)
111 Currant (10)
112 Wisteria (10)
113 Willow (1)
114 Peat moss
115 Apple (1)
116 Pear (1)
117 Plum (1)
118 Hawthorn (3)
119 Pyracantha (5)
120 Cotoneaster (10)
121 Myrtus (10)
122 Tamarix (10)
123 Virginia creeper (10)
124 Barberry (10)
125 Buddleia (10)
126 Euonymus (10)
127 Choisya (10)
128 Pittosporum (10)
129 Gummed labels 1¼″ × 1½″ (2 boxes)
130 Fig (1)
131 Myrobalan plum (1)
132 Japanese plum (1)
133 Crape-myrtle (10)
134 Horseradish (10)
135 Lilium leichtlini, L. umbellatum, L. ele-
　　gans, L. testaceum, or L. candidum
136 Plants from seeds or cuttings with roots
　　½″ long
137 Rooted　seedling　plants　(ornamentals)
　　showing second true leaf (100 or more
　　growing in flats)
138 Rooted nursery plants for balling (100)
139 Carnation (100)
140 Poinsettia (10)
141 Begonia, shrubby (30)
142 Begonia rex (10)
143 Two flats or more pear and apple seed-
　　lings
144 Cutting material of greenhouse plants
145 Ornamental　plant　materials　growing　in
　　community (branches)
146 Philadelphus (10)
147 Bougainvillea (2)
148 Azalea (10)
149 Ivy (10)
150 Flowering currant (10)
151 Veronica (10)
152 Boston Ivy (10)
153 Climbing fig (10)
154 Hyacinth bulbs (20)
155 Easter lily bulbs (20)
156 Gladiolus corms (20)
157 Crocus corms (20)
158 Irish potato (1 or more bushels)
159 Dahlia clumps with root tubers (10)
160 Asparagus crowns (20)
161 Clumps of iris (10)
162 Clump of canna (10)
163 Stout knives (3)
164 Carborundum stones (5)
165 Scissors (2 pairs)
166 Grafting knives (10) and budding knives
　　(10)
167 Pruning shears (10)
168 Pruning saws (5)
169 Grafting chisels or tools (5) (Figs. 241 to
　　244)
170 Mallets (5)
171 Grafting wax heaters (2)
172 Pine gum (5 pounds)
173 Grafting waxes and waxed string (No. 18
　　knitting cotton, 5 balls)
174 Metal slot grader for grape grafting (2)
175 Resin (10 pounds)
175A Linseed oil (2 gals.)
176 Beeswax (10 pounds and tallow)
177 Lampblack (2 ounces)
178 Wood alcohol (1 gallon)

No.
179 Paraffin (2 pounds)
180 Raffia (1 skein)
181 No. 16 wire annealed or galvanized (200')
182 No. 14 gauge annealed or galvanized wire (2 pieces—150' and 220' long)
183 Stakes 1" × 3" × 16" (100)
184 Chalk line (150')
185 Stout string (3 balls)
186 1" No. 19 flat headed wire nails
187 Growing lily plants: Lilium leichtlini, L. umbellatum, L. elegans, L. dauricum, L. testaceum, L. candidum, or L. longiflorum
188 Soft strong twine (1 ball)
189 Budding rubber (1 pound)
189A Budding tape ½" wide (1 pound)
190 Canton flannel (5 yards)
191 Paper toweling; Scott tissue (3 doz.)
192 Paper bags No. 2 (200)
193 Muslin—unbleached (5 yards)
194 Paper plates (100)
195 Pieces burlap 16" square (old sacks will do) (100)
196 Botanists' driers (300)
197 Newspapers (500 sheets)
198 Note books, small (10)
199 Gummed paper strip (2 rolls)
200 Blotters, white (enough to cut out 200 circles 6" in diameter)
201 ½ or ¾" hose two lengths—75 feet long (2 pieces)
202 Gallon fruit cans (200)
203 Sprinkling cans with fine rose nozzles (2)
204 Paper 8½ × 11 (250 sheets)
205 Pencils—drawing (10)
206 Erasers (10)
207 Labels ¾" × 1"—gummed (3 boxes)
208 Muslin
209 Compasses for making circles (5)
210 ⅛" mesh screen on a 14" × 36" frame (2)
211 ½" mesh screen on a 2' × 4' frame (3)
212 ¼" mesh screen on a 14" × 36" frame (3)
213 Outside bevel gouge for making Biederman's bark graft (1)
214 Tack hammers (5)
215 Wheelhoe cultivator with shovel and weed cutter attachments
216 Dibbles (10)
217 Pear fruits: Bartlett, Beurre d'Anjou, Beurre Hardy, or Winter Nelis
218 Apple fruits: Fameuse, Winesap, Delicious, McIntosh, Northern Spy, Ben Davis, Gano, Jonathan, or Tolman
219 Plum fruits: Myrobalan best; others will do
220 Cherry fruits: Mahaleb or Mazzard
221 Asparagus fruits: (1 pint)
222 Myrtus communis fruits (1 pint)
223 Oregon hollygrape fruits (1 pint)
224 Pyracantha fruits: (1 pint)
225 Cotoneaster fruits: (1 pint)
226 Other small seeded fleshy fruits (1 pint)
227 Sulphuric acid 5% commercial strength by volume (½ pint)
228 Sulphuric acid 10% commercial strength by volume (½ pint)
229 Sulphuric acid 50% commercial strength by volume (½ pint)
230 Sulphuric acid commercial strength (½ pint)
231 Fumigation materials: 1 package powder form cyanide fumigant specially prepared for this purpose.
232 Coarse gravel (1 gallon)
233 Old bricks powdered (6)
234 Composted soil (quantity)
235 Medium-texture, sharp, clean sand (5 yards)
236 Peat blocks (1)
237 Clay or heavy loam (1 gallon)
238 Good garden loam (5 yards)
239 Sphagnum or peat moss (2 bales)

No.
240 250-cc beakers (24)
241 8" × 8" pieces of window glass (100)
242 Window glass size 10" × 20" (3)
243 Glass vials medium size (250)
244 Window glass cut in pieces 15" × 17" (20)
245 Pot labels, ⅝" wide × 5" long, painted white on side (1000)
246 Garden labels—1" × 12", painted white one side (1000)
247 Tree labels—½" × 3½", painted white one side (1000)
248 Garden trowels (10), rakes (5)
249 Garden dibbles (10) (Figs. 195 to 197)
250 Garden hoes and rakes (10)
251 Nursery spades (10)
252 Manure forks (3)
253 Good garden loam (5 yards)
254 2" Flower pots (1000)
255 2½"   "   "   (1000)
256 4"   "   "   (1000)
257 6"   "   "   (1000)
258 8"   "   "   (500)
259 Flower pot saucers—6" or petri dishes (200)
260 Broken pieces of pottery (quantity)
261 Garden flats 14" × 16"—3½" or 4" deep—inside measurements (250)
262 Blocks ½" thick—6" square faced with fine sand paper (2)
263 Quart fruit cans (12)
264 Blocks 2" × 4"—13½" (10)
265 Boards 1" × 4"—13½" (10)
266 Sheet metal—galvanized, medium weight—4" × 13½" (10)
267 Horse manure, fresh, (25 yards)
268 Wood: any species (such as apple, willow, etc.) of last season's growth from ¼ to ⅝" in diameter for scions and stocks in practice grafting and budding
269 Thick bark wood: black walnut, willow, cottonwood, etc.) which slips, and is from 1½ to 5 inches in diameter, for indoor grafting
270 Scions and bud-sticks of desired variety for orchard or bench grafting and budding (past season's growth—dormant)
271 Mature fruit or nut trees for top-grafting
272 Nursery trees for whip grafting and budding and digging
273 One or two year old seedlings of apple or pear for root grafting
274 Scions of apple or pear for root grafting
275 Grape canes for bench grafting
276 Pear or apple seedlings
277 Old grape vines for grafting
278 Shoots of past season's growth (pear, apple, or other trees)
279 Bud sticks of fruit trees of past season's growth for budding
280 Dormant bud sticks of fruit trees
281 Bud sticks for June budding (Fig. 282)
282 Black walnut limbs—½" to 1¼" in diameter
283 Black walnut limbs—½" to 1¼" in diameter (past season's growth)
284 Budded nursery trees ready for orchard planting
285 Propagating frame (2)
286 Greenhouse (1)
287 Crank case oil (1 pint)
288 Flat files 8" long (2)
289 Wire cutting pliers (2 pairs)
290 Vasculum (plant collecting can)
291 Plant collecting tools
292 50-pound stone for pressing plants or 5-gallon can filled with gravel
293 Herbarium paper (300 to 500 sheets)
294 Herbarium paste (2 jars)
295 Hand lenses, 8 or 9 X (5)
296 Collection of crop seeds in vials
297 Balances weighing to second decimal place in grams (2)
298 Compass (5)

No.
299 Teaspoon (5)
300 Tablespoon (5)
301 Sulphur (½ pound)
302 Glass—14½″ × 16½″ for covering flats of cuttings (25)
303 Frame for bundling grape cuttings (Figs. 120, 122)
304 Rulers
305 Grape planting board
306 Marker

No.
307 One-inch flat-headed brads (½ pound)
308 Patch or modified "H" budding tool
309 Tree setting boards (Figs 325, 326) (6)
310 Commercial fertilizer (300 pounds)
311 Poinsettias
312 Chlorine water (2 drops of saturated chlorine water in 60 cc of tap water)
313 Lug boxes (24)
314 Olive seeds (300)

PRACTICUMS

I. STUDY OF SEEDS, GERMINATING SEEDS AND SEEDLINGS

Materials and Equipment: * 1 to 5, 205, 206.

----

* Numbers refer to Index of Standard materials, page 459.

Directions:

1. Make sketches of whole seeds of bean, corn, and castor bean.
2. Label all parts.
3. Make sketch of soaked bean seed split open.
4. Refer to Figure 10 and label all parts.
5. Make sketch of soaked corn kernel and castor bean cut in longitudinal sections to show embryos.
6. Refer to Figures 5 and 14 and label all parts.
7. Make sketches of bean and squash plantlets just losing their seed coats, showing how coats are detached. Label parts (Fig. 15).
8. Make sketches of bean, pea, castor bean and corn plantlets which have made a growth of 6″ or more above ground. (Figs. 5 and 15).
9. Label sketches after referring to these figures.

Questions and Assignments:

1. How many cotyledons has pea? Bean? How are these plants classified according to number of cotyledons?
2. How many cotyledons has corn plantlet? How classified?
3. Describe how squash, pea and bean lose their seed coats.
4. Where are cotyledons of squash, corn, pea and bean located in relation to surface of soil?
5. What is function of (1) cotyledon? (2) Seed coat?
6. Of what is greater part of corn seed made? What use is made of this material by growing plantlet?

II. SEPARATION OF SEEDS FROM THEIR FLESHY COVERINGS

Materials and Equipment: 192 to 194, 201, 202, 210, 212, 217 to 226, 245.

A. DECAYED FRUITS WITH SEEDS OF MEDIUM SIZE—PEARS AND APPLES

Directions: (See Table 22 for rootstocks for various fruit trees).

1. Place decayed fruit of one variety on screen ($\frac{1}{8}$″ mesh-screen door) cver pit (Fig. 16).
2. Rub fruit on screen with hands until pulp has been thoroughly reduced and seeds show on screen.
3. Continue rubbing and at same time apply stream of water to wash plup through screen.
4. Remove seed and debris that remain on screen.
5. Place mass in gallon fruit cans of water.
6. Stir briskly. Pulp and stems, being lighter than seeds, remain suspended. If water is poured off rapidly this refuse will be carried off. Repeat washings until finally seeds are clean.
7. Remove seeds and spread to dry on labeled paper plates.

8. When dry place seeds in paper bags, and label each by inserting pot label in each bag.

9. Continue with work until all seed has been separated from coverings.

B. Large Seeded Fruits—Plums and Cherries

1. Place dead-ripe plum fruits on quarter-inch screen.
2. Work off pulp as directed above.
3. Separate skins and refuse as above.
4. Place seeds in labeled flats or trays to dry.
5. When dry keep in labeled bags until to be used in stratification and planting exercises.

C. Small Seeded, Fresh Fruits of Ornamentals and Other Plants—Asparagus, Hawthorn, Pyracantha, Cotoneaster, Mahonia, Myrtus, etc.

1. Place fruits of pyracantha in piece of cheese cloth or muslin 12" square.
2. Mash fruits to pulp by rubbing with heel of hand or mallet on flat surface, such as table top.
3. Place mass in bucket of water and proceed as with previous fruits. Do not be alarmed by seeds which float off. They are not viable.

Questions and Assignments:

1. How are dry seeds harvested and separated? Seeds from fleshy fruits?
2. At what stage of maturity should dry seeded vegetable plants be cut for seed production?
3. How are seeds of barley, wheat and alfalfa harvested?
4. Does drying injure or improve germination qualities or seed? Keeping qualities?
5. How are seeds packed for foreign shipment?
6. What are ideal storage conditions for seeds? Are they usually attained?

III. PROPAGATING FERNS FROM SPORES

Materials and Equipment: 192, 232 to 236, 239, 241, 257, 258, 260, 285, 286.

A. Spores on Soil and Brick Dust in Flower Pots

Directions:

1. In 6" flower pot place piece of broken pot over hole in bottom.
2. Place 1½" layer coarse gravel in bottom of pot.
3. Fill pot with composted soil to within ¾" of top and firm it.
4. Sprinkle fine layer of brick dust $\frac{1}{16}$" deep over composted soil and make surface firm and uniform.
5. Place pot in oven (Fig. 41) and sterilize thoroughly to destroy spores that might cause troublesome growths. (If oven is not available this operation may be dispensed with).
6. Place dry fern fronds in bag. Remove spores by shaking bag vigorously (Fig 17). (Drying should be done previous to this exercise).
7. Sumberge pot up to rim in container of water to moisten soil.
8. Sprinkle spores over powdered moist brick dust on surface of soil.
9. Place several inches damp moss on bottom of 8", 10" or 12" pot. Then set sterilized pot inside large one.
10. Fill space between two pots with moist moss.
11. Cover small pot with glass plate.
12. Place both pots in propagating frame or greenhouse where there is heat. (Figs. 44 and 45).
13. Keep moss always moist.

Note: Another method is to set pots in saucers of water and cover each with glass; or better, place in heated propagation frame.

Treat resulting sporelings as directed under B.

B. Spores on Blocks of Peat or Sandstone

1. Place block or small cube of firm peat or sandstone in saucer of water.
2. Sow spores on surface of either of these.
3. Place material in greenhouse or hotbed and cover with bell jar; or better, place in propagating frame with heat. Temperature should be maintained at 65° to 90° F.

Note: In either case germination will take place in three to six weeks.

4. Prick off sporelings while still small and plant in pots of composted soil.
5. Give these transplanted sporelings same conditions as they previously enjoyed in the greenhouse or hotbed.

Questions and Assignments:

1. Describe how spores are produced by ferns.
2. Do spores of ferns correspond to seeds of flowering plants?
3. Are spores a sexual or an asexual product of plants?
4. Give life history of fern plant.
5. See if you can locate sporelings growing under natural conditions. What is this stage of fern's life history called?

IV. STUDY OF FACTORS NECESSARY FOR GERMINATION

Materials and Equipment: 1, 6, 129, 235, 237, 240, 241, 259, 287.

A. Oxygen Excluded by Puddled Soil (Fig. 19).

Directions:

1. Place layer of puddled clay or heavy loam in two flower pot saucers previously soaked in water and label "1" and "2."
2. Put ten bean seeds on soil in each saucer.
3. Cover seed in Saucer "1" with moist sand and those in saucer "2" with puddled clay or loam.
4. Press wet clay or loam in saucer "2" closely around beans to puddle it.
5. Cover both saucers with glass.
6. Place saucers in warm room for two or more days.
7. Observe results and answer question 1 below.

B. Oxygen Excluded by Placing Oil Over Boiled Water

1. Label two 250cc beakers "1" and "2," respectively.
2. Fill two-thirds full and boil water to expel oxygen.
3. When cool drop ten unhulled rice seeds in each beaker.
4. Cover boiled water in beaker "1" with oil to prevent re-absorption of air or oxygen. Do not cover water in beaker "2" with oil, but leave free to take up oxygen from air. Occasionally stir vigorously.
5. Observe results and answer question 2 below.

Deep Planting:

1. Plant bean seeds at 3 different depths in loam next to the glass sides of a mason jar (Fig. 20).
2. Observe growth and record the dates when the seedlings first appear at surface for various depths.

C. Light Excluded (Fig. 22).

1. Plant ten beans in each of two flower pot saucers containing moist sand.
2. Cover with moist sand and label saucers "1" and "2."
3. Cover saucer "1" with glass, place under box in complete darkness and observe results from day to day, watering when necessary.
4. Place number "2" in light of window after covering with glass.
5. In four or five days compare results and answer question 4 below.

D. TEMPERATURE (Fig. 18).

1. Plant ten beans in each of two flower pot saucers, labeled "1" and "2," containing sand.
2. Place Saucer "1" in ice box and cover with glass.
3. Place Saucer "2" in warm room and cover with glass.
4. Compare results in four or five days and answer question 5 below.

E. MOISTURE EFFECTS

1. Place ten beans on air dry sand in flower pot saucer labeled "1." Cover air dry sand and do not water.
2. Place ten beans on slightly moistened sand in flower pot saucer labeled "2" and cover with slightly moistened sand. Do not moisten any more. Cover with glass.
3. Place ten beans on thoroughly moistened sand in flower pot saucer labeled "3" and cover with thoroughly moist sand. Cover with glass. Keep sand moist while waiting for germination, but allow no free water in this saucer.
4. Place ten beans on wet sand in a flower pot saucer labeled "4," cover with sand. Pour on more water until sand is saturated and there is free water in saucer. Keep sand saturated and covered with glass at all times.
5. Place all saucers in warm place for beans to germinate.
6. Record results and answer question 6 below.

Questions and Assignments:

1. Explain differences observed in germination of seeds in sand and in puddled soil.
2. What were your results in section B; namely, Excluding oxygen by using oil? How do you account for them?
3. Why does planting seeds deeply give results you noted?
4. Is light always essential for germination?
5. Explain differences in germinating ability of beans in sand varying in temperature.
6. What is meant by optimum moisture content of medium for germination? What would you say it is for beans?
7. From results of this exercise, what would you say are factors necessary for germination?
8. Explain why deep planting may not sometimes give good results in field.

V. SEED TREATMENTS AS AIDS TO GERMINATION

Materials and Equipment: 8 to 12, 200, 205, 227 to 230, 240, 241, 245, 259, 261, 262, 288, 289, 312, 314.

A. CHEMICAL TREATMENTS

Directions:

Blotters in germinators should be moistened every 12 hours. If this is not possible, moisten them at beginning and end of school day.

I. Sulphuric Acid Treatment:[1] (Fig. 23 and 32).

1. Count four lots each of honey locust, canna and asparagus (five seeds each).
2. Place each lot of one kind in individual 250cc beaker. Label "1," "2," "3." Do this for each of three kinds of seed.
3. Pour 5, 10, and 50% solutions of commercial sulphuric acid into three of 250cc beakers numbered "1," "2," and "3" respectively.
4. Pour water into beaker "4" to be used as check.
5. Allow seeds to remain in solutions 30 minutes.
6. Remove seeds.
7. Wash throughly by pouring fresh water on and off several times or wash in bicarbonate of soda and water.
8. Place seeds between blotters in flower pot saucer germinators or petri dishes

[1] See note Section 48, p. 51.

(Fig. 24). Cover saucers with glass. Label with same numbers as acid solution and beaker No. 4.

9. Place germinators in warm room to germinate seed.

10. Remove all seeds which have germinated every 24 hours. Count them and record results as removed. For record use form indicated later in exercise.

II. Chlorine Treatment:

1. Count two lots of radish seed (ten in each lot).

2. Place one for three hours in 250cc beaker, labeled "1," containing chlorine water (two drops saturated chlorine water to 60cc of water).

3. Place other lot, labeled "2," in distilled or tap water for same period.

4. Remove and wash seeds thoroughly.

5. Place in saucer germinators or petri dishes and cover with glass.

6. Observe results every 6 to 12 hours. Count and remove all seeds which have germinated.

7. Compare and record results using form below.

B. Hot Water Trearment

1. Count two lots of honey locust seed (ten seeds to lot).

2. Place one lot in 250cc beaker and label "1."

3. Pour boiling water into beaker and allow seeds to remain until water has cooled.

4. Place other lot, labeled "2," in tap water for same period.

5. Remove seeds and place in germinators. Cover with glass and label.

6. Observe results every 24 hours. Count, record and remove all germinated seeds.

7. Record data in form outlined below.

C. Mechanical Treatments

I. Scarification:

1. Rub 30 or more seeds of sour or bitter clover (Melilotus indica), vigorously between two boards faced with fine sandpaper (Fig. 35), until seed coats have roughened appearance.

2. Count and label 25 scarified seeds "1." Label 25 untreated seeds "2."

3. Place these lots between moist blotters in two different flower pot saucer germinators or petri dishes and label "1" and "2." Cover with glass. (Fig. 24).

4. Tabulate results every 24 hours. Count, remove and record seeds that have germinated in both saucers.

5. Record results as outlined.

II. Filing or boring:

1. File or bore holes in five canna, Moonflower or Abyssinian banana seeds. (Emery wheel may be used).

2. Place these in germinator, cover with glass and label "1."

3. Place five untreated seeds of same kind in another germinator, cover with glass and label "2." Keep blotters moist.

4. Check, note and record results every 24 hours as indicated in form page 468.

III. Cutting or Clipping:

1. Clip apex ends (Fig. 33c) of 25 olive seeds with farrier's nippers [1] or wire cutting pliers.

---

[1] From 1200 to 1500 seeds an hour can be clipped with practice. Appearance of seeds after clipping is shown in Figure 33. Device adopted for clipping seed is made from "farriers' nippers" 14 inches long with one-inch jaw, mounted on board (Fig.33) spring between handles keeps jaws open. Point of pit is clipped by inserting between jaws and then closing by pressing with foot on wire loop attached to upper handle. To prevent pit being inserted too far, shield of thin brass is riveted to immovable upper jaw. In this shield is slot $\frac{9}{32}$" wide for insertion of pit. To prevent cutting kernel, rounded notch is filed in each jaw, forming when closed hole $\frac{2}{16}$" in diameter vertically and $\frac{3}{16}$" horizontally. This hole is not circular, as it appears in Figure 33. This clipper is suited for small seeds, such as Redding olive, which seems most suitable variety for purpose.

2. Plant seeds in row in flat of sand, water and label row "1" with pot label.
3. Plant 25 untreated seeds in row in sand in same flat as check and label row "2."
4. Tabulate results when germination is complete. (Fig. 34).

Questions and Assignments:

1. Explain what action acid of various strengths has upon germination of seeds.
2. What strength acid would you recommend using?
3. Why are seeds scarified and with what seeds is scarification practiced commercially? How is it accomplished?
4. What method other than one in this exercise is used to hasten germination of olive seeds?
5. Is it always practical to treat seeds to hasten or increase germination?

METHOD OF RECORDING DATA—SEED TREATMENTS

Name of seeds	Treatment	6 or 12 hrs.	1st day	2nd day	3rd day	4th day	5th day	6th day	7th day	8th day	9th day	10th day	Total	Remarks
		Number of seeds germinated at end of												
Honey Locust	5% H_2SO_4 [1]													
	10% H_2SO_4													
	50% H_2SO_4													
	H_2O [2] (cold)													
Canna	5% H_2SO_4													
	10% H_2SO_4													
	50% H_2SO_4													
	H_2O (cold)													
Asparagus	5% H_2SO_4													
	10% H_2SO_4													
	50% H_2SO_4													
	H_2O (cold)													
Radish	Cl Sol [3]													
	(2 drops in 60 cc. water)													
	H_2O													
Honey Locust	H_2O (hot)													
	H_2O (cold)													
Bitter Clover	Scarified													
	Unscarified													
Canna	Filed or bored													
	Untreated													
Olive [4]	Cut or clipd													
	Untreated													

[1] H_2SO_4 = sulphuric acid. [2] H_2O = water. [3] Cl. Sol. = chlorine solution.
[4] It will take longer to germinate olive seeds than indicated by chart. Separate record of them must therefore be kept.

VI. STRATIFICATION OF SEEDS

Materials and Euipment: Nos. 13 to 22, 235, 245, 261, 313.

Directions:

A. MYROBALAN PLUM, PEACH AND WALNUT SEED [1]

In late autumn stratify seeds listed above according to directions following (Fig. 26).
1. In box place 1" sand layer.
2. Place one layer of seeds on sand.

[1] Plum and peach seed, following collection and drying, may be stratified between layers of moist moss in boxes and placed in cold storage at 36 to 38° F. for 10 to 20 days to break the rest period. This treatment has very materially increased germination. Figs. 27, 28, 29 and 30.

3. Cover seeds with 1" sand.

4. Continue in this manner until box is full (Fig. 26).

5. Place boxes for winter on north side of building exposed to weather.

6. Wet flats thoroughly and leave in place until spring. Wet when necessary during winter to keep sand always moist.

7. Observe for germination when warm weather arrives.

8. Plant seeds in nursery (Practicum XXXVI) when they split or just as hypo cotyl or caulicle appears.

B. Almond and Apricot Seed

These seeds germinate in two to four weeks following stratification, therefore, should not be stratified until two to four weeks before planting time in spring.

Stratify seeds as in A, but do not wet or expose to weather until four weeks before planting.

C. Cotoneaster, Pyracantha or Myrtus, Hawthorn, Oregon Hollygrade and Seeds of Similar Ornamentals [1]

1. Place layer of sand 3" deep in bottom of flat.

2. Place layer of cotoneaster seeds on sand.

3. Cover seed with $\frac{1}{2}$" to $\frac{3}{4}$" sand.

4. Place flat on bench in lathhouse or coldframe.

5. Continue as above till all other seeds listed are stratified in separate flats.

6. Allow seeds to remain stratified until they germinate and grow until second pair of true leaves begin to develop (Fig. 181). Resultant seedlings will be used in Practicum XXVIII.

D. Apple and Pear—Small Lots of Seeds [2]

1. Soak seed for 24 hours in cool water before stratifying. Change water each 12 hours.

2. Let seeds air one or two hours each day of soaking after pouring off water.

3. In flat, place sand layer 3" deep.

4. On sand place layer of seeds.

5. Cover with $\frac{1}{2}$" sand.

6. Place flats in cool situation such as lath house and keep moist.

7. When warm weather approaches seeds will germinate. Allow them to grow 2" to 4" high in flats. (Figs. 181 and 184). Transplant seedlings in spring (Practicum XXXVII) when just developing second pair of true leaves (Fig. 184).

E. Apple and Pear Seeds—Large Lots of Seeds in Cold Storage (Figs. 27 to 30).

1. Soak seeds 24 hours in cool water; pour off water and allow to remain exposed to air an hour or two daily.

2. Place seed in cheesecloth in ice house between layers of moist moss. *Note:* Do not place seed in cold storage where it freezes solid; temperature must not fall below 32° F.

3. In spring when warm weather approaches plant seeds in flats of sand and place in lath house to germinate.

Questions and Assignments:

1. Define stratification.

2. Why do we stratify seeds?

3. Give several methods of stratification or handling of peach pits before planting.

4. Give methods of handling almonds other than that employed in this exercise.

5. Name substitutes for stratification.

6. Why subject certain seeds to low temperatures before sowing?

---

[1] Execute this part of Practicum in spring.

[2] The cold storage treatment described in previous footnote applies to apple and pear seeds.

VII. COLLECTION AND PRESERVATION OF PLANT SPECIMENS AND WEED SEEDS [1]

Materials and Equipment: 7, 34, 192, 194 to 199, 205, 242, 243, 247, 290 to 295.

A. FIELD TRIP—COLLECTING PLANT MATERIALS AND SEED [2]

Directions:

1. Take vasculum or collecting can and tools for collecting plants.
2. Collect weed plants that cause damage locally and available crop plants. See Table 15 for list of worst weeds in United States.
3. Keep roots intact; wrap plants in moist burlap; place in collecting can.
4. Label and number plants with tree labels. Insert number of each in notebook with full information —— date and place of collecting, local common name of plant, kind of soil and habitat (woods, rocks, meadows, marsh, sand, etc.), approximate elevation of place, (as foothill or plain) and collector's name. At later date give family, genus, species and variety names. On card label accompanying mounted specimen, insert also name of person who identifies, with any additional information
5. Take notes as to uses, characters, color of flowers and other information which later will not be directly revealed by specimen.
6. Collect seeds of weed plants with plants when possible and place in small, numbered paper bags. Write on each bag common name of plant from which seed came. Enter numbers given seed, with common names, in notebook.
7. Take plant specimens back to class room, wrap in wet burlap or canvas and leave in cool place until following day.

B. LABORATORY WORK WITH COLLECTED PLANTS

Directions for Preserving Plants:

1. Spread material loosely on table.
2. Place one or more driers on table or floor, one on top of other when more than one are required, as with plants that contain much moisture.
3. On driers place folded paper approximately same size as drier. Newspapers are excellent for this because they are just proper size.
4. Open paper and spread on lower half, plant to be pressed.
5. Separate leaves and branches and spread out.
6. Bend plant to fit paper.
7. Label with slip of paper or page of notebook used when collecting. Add any additional information desired.
8. Place upper fold of paper over plant.
9. On this place two or more driers as required.
10. On top of driers place another paper and then a plant between folds of papers.
11. Then place two or more blotters over plant.
12. Continue in this manner until stack has been built up.
13. On top of stack place 40 to 50 pound flat stone or concrete block. This method is better than using strap driers, for straps loosen as plants dry, whereas weight of stone gives continuous pressure.
14. Change blotters daily for first three days then every second day for week. Allow longer periods to elapse between changes as drying progresses.
15. When plants have become thoroughly dried and pressed, pick them off newspapers and place on piece of glass previously smeared evenly with paste.
16. Remove plant from glass and place on sheet of herbarium paper.
17. Lay pasted plant between folds of newspaper for setting and drying paste.
18. Print or type following information on separate 3″ x 4″ label and attach to herbarium paper. (a) Scientific name; (b) common name; (c) family name of plant; (d) locality and notes; (e) collector's name.

---

[1] Although this is not a propagation subject, it is closely allied to seed testing so should precede such studies to acquaint students with weed seeds commonly found in crop seeds. Weeds interfere with plant propagation and culture; hence students should know weed plants so as to know how best to eradicate them.

[2] Table 15.

19. Make pile of these and weight down with stone until thoroughly dried.

20. File mounted plants between newspapers for future study.

Test good job of pressing is (1) retention of original color of flowers and leaves and (2) flexibility of foliage. If brittle foliage results, drying was probably too slow. More driers should have been used.

C. Weed Seed Preservation

Directions for Preserving:

1. Place collected weed seeds on paper plates to dry.

2. Write their numbers and names on plates, giving plate numbers corresponding to those on collecting bags.

3. When thoroughly dry place seeds in glass vials or jars provided by instructor.

4. Number and label vials of seeds, giving common names. Leave space in which to insert the scientific name when obtained.

5. Store vials on shelf until needed for study.

Questions and Assignments:

1. How many of weed plants collected are noxious? Name them.

2. Do you consider weed situation in your community serious? Why?

3. How would you control weed plants you collected?

4. Outline plan for community weed control.

5. Why is community effort necessary in most control work?

VIII. IDENTIFICATION OF WEED SEEDS, CROP SEEDS AND PLANTS

Materials and Equipment: 27 to 31, 205, 206, 295, 296. Use seed and plant material preserved in Practicum VII.

A. Identification of Crop Seeds

1. Rule piece of paper 8″ wide into two sections. Write numbers from "1" to "36" in two rows.

2. Identify and number crop seeds placed in glass vials on tables by instructor. Numbers on vials should correspond with names of seeds and numbers on paper.

3. After trial at identification, instructor will read names of seeds by number and give notes about each. Check those incorrect or with names missing and hand papers to instructor.

4. Instructor will pass out numbered list with names of seeds on it. With this key sheet go over seeds again. Using your notes, make careful study of outstanding characteristics of various seeds.

5. Prepare another numbered sheet after gaining confidence in identifying seeds.

6. With this sheet identify the seeds, entering names on sheet as before.

7. With key sheet check those named improperly and those not named, and hand paper to instructor.

B. Identification of Weed Seeds

Weed seed will be placed on tables. Proceed with these as with crop seed.

C. Identification of Weed and Crop Seed [1] (Figs. 38 to 40)

1. Separate weed seed from following crop seed: (1) white clover, (2) alfalfa, (3) rye grass, (4) vetch, and (5) rye.

---

[1] Instructor will do well to place among student's seed samples to be tested, locally important weed seeds identified by him. Their presence and identity should be noted by students. Samples of weed seeds in vials labeled with name of weeds should be at hand during test so students may refer to them for identification of seeds found in sample. Plants producing weed seeds should be on display so students may learn to recognize them. If seed has no foreign, inert material in it, add some to give student practice in complete test. Do same for other crop seeds.

2. List findings as outlined below:

	Name of weed seeds	Noxious Yes or no	Names of other crop seeds
(1) White clover	....	....	....
(2) Alfalfa	....	....	....
(3) Rye grass	....	....	....
(4) Vetch	....	....	....
(5) Rye	....	....	....

Below is list of seeds and material for an agronomy student's contest such as that held annually for high schools at the University Farm, Davis, California. From this list specimens are selected for identification in contest.

LIST OF PLANTS FROM WHICH SPECIMENS MAY BE SELECTED FOR AN AGRONOMY IDENTIFICATION CONTEST OR FOR CLASS STUDY

Crop seeds

1 Alfalfa	12 Common vetch	23 Oats	34 Sudan grass
2 Barley, naked	13 Dent corn	24 Onion	35 Burr clover—
3 Barley, 2-row	14 Flax	25 Pink bean	in burrs
4 Barley, 6-row	15 Flint corn	26 Popcorn	36 Sweet clover
5 Beet	16 Hairy vetch	27 Purple vetch	37 Sweet corn
6 Bermuda grass	17 Honey sorghum	28 Red kidney bean	38 Tomato
7 Black eye bean	18 Horse bean	29 Rice	39 Wheat
8 Buckwheat	19 Lettuce	30 Rye	40 White clover
9 Cabbage	20 Lima bean	31 Rye grass	41 White Egyptian
10 Chick pea	21 Millet	32 Small white bean	42 White yolo
11 Carrot	22 Milo	33 Spinach	

Weed seeds and plants

1 Dodder	6 Russian thistle	11 Chess	16 Pigweed
2 Foxtail	7 Star thistle	12 Crabgrass	17 Quack grass
3 Johnson grass	8 Shepherd's purse	13 Cocklebur	18 Smart weed
4 Lamb's-quarter	9 Pussley	14 Oxeye daisy	19 Sheep sorrel
5 Puncture vine	10 Black mustard	15 Wild carrot	20 Ragweed

D. IDENTIFICATION OF CROP AND WEED PLANTS

1. Using same methods as for seed identification, identify crop and weed plants placed before you by instructor.

Questions and Assignments:

1. Define weed.
2. Explain how plant is enabled to become weed by seeding habits; by habits of growth.
3. State some losses caused by weed seeds in crop seed lots.
4. Which if any of lots of seeds studied would you plant on your farm? Give reasons for or against planting.
5. What is noxious weed and what are considered noxious weeds in your state?
6. What are five most serious weed pests in your locality?
7. How are some losses brought about by weeds?
8. Are weeds ever beneficial? Explain.
9. How may weeds be spread?
10. How would you suggest attacking weed problem?
11. What are some control measures?
12. Is study of life history essential for control measures? Why?
13. Name some of natural enemies of weeds and tell how they act.

14. What are herbicides? Of what values (if any) are they in weed control?

15. Give methods of control of weeds in (1) orchard; (2) vineyard; (3) inter-tilled crops; (4) grain fields; (5) alfalfa fields; (6) lawns; (7) gardens; and (8) walks or courts.

IX. PURITY TEST FOR SEEDS[1]

Materials and Equipment: Nos. 27, 31, 89, 240, 205, 206, 209, 295, 297 to 300, 304.

Directions:

Test following seeds for purity: (1) White clover; (2) alfalfa; (3) rye grass; (4) vetch, (5) rye.

A. WHITE CLOVER

1. Mix sample of seed thoroughly by pouring from one 250cc beaker to another. (Fig. 40).

2. Make circle 5" or 6" in diameter in center of paper. Divide circle into sectors. Label as indicated (Fig. 39A).

3. After seed has been thoroughly mixed, dip half teaspoonful of it.

4. Place seed on paper (to one side) on which counting chart has been drawn (Fig. 39B).

5. Separate pure seeds from impurities with knife blade or piece of thin carboard.

6. Place respective separations in proper sectors of counting chart (Fig. 39A).

7. When completed, weigh contents of each division or sector of chart separately, at least to second decimal place in grams.

8. Record results as outlined below.

WHITE CLOVER

	Weight in grams [2]	Percentages of each [2]
1. Pure seed		
2. Inert matter		
3. Other crop seeds		
4. Weed seeds		
Total Weight............		
		Total percentage

9. Give names of weed seeds and crop seeds present and state if noxious. Use form given in Practicum VIII.

B. ALFALFA

Proceed with alfalfa in same manner as with white clover. Use slightly rounded teaspoonful of seed as working sample. Record results.

C. RYE GRASS

Proceed as with white clover but use one tablespoonful of seed as working sample. Record results.

---
[1] Table 11.

[2] These four component parts should each be weighed in grams and percentages by weight (based on sum of weights of component parts, not on original weight) determined and recorded. In cases of other crop seeds and weed seeds, separate seeds of each species where possible and record number or weight of each kind.

D. Rye

Use two tablespoonsful of seed and proceed as outlined above.

E. Vetch

Follow directions for rye in D.

Questions and Assignments:

1. Give five reasons or purposes for testing seed.
2. What seeds especially need testing for purity and why?
3. Refer to Table 11 and state which of seeds tested for purity you would like to plant on your farm.
4. Summarize losses incurred by using low grade seed.
5. Visit seed testing laboratory if one is within a reasonable distance of school.
6. When should duplicate analysis be run when conducting purity test?
7. How is true value of seed calculated?

X. GERMINATION OR VIABILITY TEST FOR SEEDS [1]

Materials and Equipment: Nos. 1, 2, 3, 12, 27 to 29, 31, 33, 35 to 41, 129, 165, 190, 191, 200, 205, 206, 241, 259.

A. Oats, Alfalfa, Bitter Clover, Rye and Wheat Seeds

1. Obtain 5 flower pot saucer germinators or petri dishes with pieces of glass to cover them (Fig. 24).
2. Cut pieces of blotter to fit bottoms of saucers. After thoroughly soaking saucers and blotters, place in saucers (Fig. 24A).
3. Count 100 seeds of each of oats, alfalfa, bitter clover, wheat and rye.
4. Place seeds of each kind on moist blotter used as substratum in germinator saucer. Label. (Note that no blotter covers seed in this case).
5. Cover germinator with glass plate, label and place in warm room.
6. Moisten blotter morning and evening. Never allow it to become dry.
7. At time of watering in evenings, count and remove sprouted seed. Record results as indicated in the form below.
8. Note any irregularity in germination. It is as undesirable as low germination percentage.

GERMINATION OR VIABILITY TEST RECORD FORM

Names of seeds tested	Date test started	Number of seeds at start	No. of seeds germinated	Date of count of germination	Total No. of seeds germ.	Total % of germ.	Date test closed
Oats (as example)	Jan. 30	100	50	Feb. 3	—		
			5	" 4			
			15	" 5	—		
			20	" 6	90	90	Feb. 7
Alfalfa							
Bitter clover							
Wheat							
Rye							

B. White Clover, Celery, Onion, Cucumber and Beet Seed [2] (Fig. 24B)

1. Place 10 pure seeds from lots listed above, in germinator as previously described. **In addition cover with blotter to fit dish.**

---

[1] See Table 7 and Figure 31.
[2] Covering this group of seeds with blotter facilitates germination. Note that first group of seed did not require blotter covering.

2. Proceed as described under A for remainder of test.

3. Make complete record of seed germination as indicated in record form page 474. Hand record to instructor when test is complete.

C. Corn, Bean and Pea Seed (Fig. 24C)

1. Cut pieces of canton flannel to fit saucer germinators.
2. Moisten flannel and place woolly side up in germinators.
3. Count one lot each of 100 seed of beans, corn, or peas.
4. Place each lot separately on flannel in germinators.
5. Cover seeds with another piece of flannel, woolly sides next seeds.
6. Place piece of glass over each germinator.
7. Proceed as described above for remainder of test.
8. Make and hand in complete germination record, using form illustrated above.
9. Moisten flannel in germinators twice daily.

D. Rye Grass, Lettuce, Bitter Clover (Fig. 24D)

1. Cut four pieces of common Scott tissue paper toweling for each germinator and place two moistened layers in bottom of each germinator.

2. Place 100 seeds each of rye grass, lettuce and sweet clover in germinators as directed under A.

3. Cover seeds with two pieces of moist toweling.

4. Proceed as with other seeds, making complete record.

5. Hand record to instructor.

Questions and Assignments:

1. Define germination.
2. What was percentage of germination in samples of: Alfalfa, oats, wheat, rye sweet clover? Are these good seeds? (Table 14.)
3. How does condition of weather at harvest time effect germination?
4. What effect has age upon germination? (Table 7.)
5. Are "hard" leguminous seeds viable?
6. Explain why irregular germination of seed is undesirable.
7. PROBLEM: Suppose you have field that requires 1000 pounds of perfect alfalfa seed to plant it properly and that you are offered two lots of seed: Lot X at 15 cents a pound, and Lot Y at 18 cents a pound. With plate or saucer germinator you have tested sample of each lot and found Lot X germinates 70% and Lot Y germinates 90%. How much savings would there be in buying the higher priced seed? The answer is $14.28. How do we get it?

XI. PROPAGATION BY LAYERS AND ROOT SPROUTS OR ROOT TIPS

Materials and Equipment: 48 to 50, 52 to 54, 56, 63, 66 to 72, 119, 123, 166, 170, 180 or 185, 239, 249.

A. Tip Layering (Fig. 56)

Directions:

Use blackcap raspberry, loganberry, trailing blackberry (or dewberry) plants.
1. Bend young cane tip down to ground using any of plants listed above.
2. Drive dibble or trowel into moist soil 4″ to 5″ deep. Push forward on handle to make opening in soil behind tool. (Figs. 188 to 190.)
3. Remove tool from ground.
4. Thrust cane tip into opening 2″ to 3″ deep.
5. Again insert tool in ground, near tip of cane. Push forward to force soil firmly against buried tip. (Figs. 56 and 57).
6. Fill hole left in soil. Completed job is shown in Figure 57.
In 4 to 6 weeks new plant will have developed from tip (Fig. 57).

B. Simple Layering (Fig. 54)

Directions:

Use any plant whose branches can be bent along ground (Fig. 54). Abelia, oleander or pyracantha will do.

1. Bend down branch and 18″ from tip wound it by shallow girdling below node, cutting out ring of bark (Fig. 54) or by notching to cambium directly below bud.

2. Place branch so wounded area will lie in shallow, short trench, (Fig. 54) leaving 10″ to 12″ of extremity uncovered to elaborate plant food. (Fig. 54C.)

3. Peg branch down with forked stick or wire. (Fig. 54B.)

4. Cover branch (except tip) with 2″ or 3″ of soil. (Fig. 54C.)

5. Branch will send out roots and shoots in spring and summer. Sever new plant from parent during fall, winter, or following spring and plant where desired.

C. Compound (Serpentine) Layering (Fig. 55C)

Directions:

Use grape, Virginia creeper or trumpet creeper.

1. With hoe open ground to form trench 3″ to 4″ deep running away from trunk of vine.

2. Bend cane of vine down to ground.

3. Twist cane vigorously through bud.

4. Place wounded node in trench. Stake down with forked stick or wire and cover with 3″ or 4″ of soil.

5. Skip one node; twist, bury and stake next one as with first.

6. Continue with cane wounding and burying every second node (Fig. 55C) but leave 6″ or 8″ of tip above ground.

7. Sever new plants from parent when well established.

D. Continuous Layering (Fig. 55B)

Directions:

Use Japanese snowball *(Viburnum)*, dogwood *(Cornus)*, grape vine or filbert. (Fig. 55X).

1. Open trench with hoe.

2. Pull down and wound limb on under side with sharp knife, or scrape it down to cambium full length of limb with knife or hoe.

3. Place limb in trench and stake down with forked sticks or wires.

4. Cover with 3″ or 4″ of soil, allowing 6″ or 8″ of tip to extend above ground.

5. Separate plants formed when well established and plant them.

E. Mound or Stool Layering (Figs. 55D and 61B)

Directions:

Use gooseberry, quince, paradise apple stock or currant.

Tops of these plants should have been cut back in late winter or early spring previous to fall layering to force strong growth of new sprouts which root readily when mound layered. It is possible, however, to get new plants from old wood.

1. Wound each new shoot below node close to ground as in simple layering.

2. Bury base of plant with soil, allowing tips of new shoots to protrude above surface. (Fig. 55D.)

3. After one season's growth separate new plants from parent plant and place where desired.

F. Chinese or Pot Layering [1] (Figs. 58 and 110)

Directions:

Use any of following plants: Dracena, oleander, croton, rhododendron, rubber plant or pandanus.

---

[1] Split pot is sometimes placed around limb to hold medium in place. (Figs. 59 and 60.)

1. With one of above plants in natural growing position, wound stem by girdling or notching just below node. (Fig. 54.)

2. Place mixture of small amount of soil and some moss around node and wounded area. (Figs. 58 to 60.)

3. Wrap with raffia or string to hold in place.

4. Water frequently to keep moss and soil always moist.

5. Roots will push from region of girdle or notch. When they have filled ball of moss, sever stem below wound.

6. If there is evidently too much leaf area for roots to sustain reduce it as when transplanting.

7. Set new plant in flower pot.

G. RUNNERS (Fig. 62)

Directions:

1. Note where and how runners on growing strawberry plants develop. (Fig. 62B.) Sever new plants from parent. Dig only first two plants next to parent on runner. These are strongest.

2. Plant in bed.

H. ROOT TIPS

Red Raspberry

1. Locate plants springing from roots of red raspberry.

2. Dig up with roots attached.

3. Transplant to nursery or field.

Questions and Assignments:

1. On layered branch, what gives rise to roots? To shoot which comes up and grows above ground?

2. Define: Simple layer, tip layer, compound or serpentine layer, continuous layer, pot layer and runner.

3. Give examples of plants layered by methods given in question 2.

4. When is proper time to layer plants?

5. What plant is commercially propagated by runners?

XII. PROPAGATION BY SEPARATION—BULBS AND CORMS

Materials and Equipment: 154 to 157, 166, 210 or 211, 234, 245, 261, 285, 286, 301.

A. BULBS (Fig. 76)

Directions:

When supply of material is small bulbs may be propagated by many various methods.

I. Scooping[1]

1. Hollow or scoop out hyacinth bulb, exposing lower parts of scales just above where they unite with base of bulb. (Fig. 80A.) Cutting in this manner destroys growing point and flower bud so all latent strength will be used to form baby bulbs or bulbels. Curved knife is best for this operation. (Figs. 82 and 84.) Scoop to extend into bulb for about one-half or more of its depth.

2. After scooping, dust bulbs with sulphur and place on trays in sunshine one day to dry.

3. Place trays in mild hotbed or propagating frame in greenhouse where ventilation and light can be controlled and where temperature is 75° to 90° F. Cover tray with slightly moist (not wet) moss. Keep it so.[2]

---

[1] As number and vigor of bulbels are proportionate to size and strength of mother bulb, strongest and best of mature bulbs are used for scooping.

[2] If mother bulbs are scooped in August and properly handled, they should produce fine lot of baby bulbs by November. (Fig. 80). Separate bulbels from mother bulb in spring and plant in pots, flats, lathhouse or open ground.

4. Give necessary treatment to make them grow into large marketable bulbs. This will take one to four years or more in bed. Operation is best performed in summer but may take place in fall.

II. Scoring

Directions:

1. Across base of hyacinth bulb make two to four cuts (Fig. 81), depending on size and extend through to about center of bulb.
2. Give bulb same subsequent treatment as for scooping method.

III. Scales of Easter Lily or Scaly Bulbs[1] (See Figs. 78 and 86)

Directions:

1. Carefully remove outer two or three tiers of scales of Easter or tiger lily bulbs. If possible, each scale should bear piece of main stem; but this is not absolutely necessary.
2. Sow in flat of one-half composted soil and one-half sharp sand.[2]
3. Cover with ¼″ to ½″ of soil and sand mixture, and keep slightly moist but not soaked in temperature of 45° to 60° F.
4. Place in coldframe, greenhouse or lathhouse. In three to ten weeks bulbel (sometimes two or more) will appear at base of scale (Fig. 78). After two or more summers' growth in beds most species will be ready for permanent planting and production of blooms.
5. Plant what remains of bulbs in lathhouse for production of blooms.

B. Corms

Directions:

1. Separate and plant new corms of gladiolus or crocus in flats of composted soil or in pot, greenhouse bench, bed, lathhouse or coldframe.
2. Save for planting baby corms or cormels formed around base of mother or large corms (Fig. 92).

Cormels—Gladiolus or Crocus

Directions:

1. Separate cormels from parent plant.
2. Plant in flats of composted soil or in outdoor beds.
3. Cover with 1″ of soil.
4. Give same subsequent treatment as bulbels.

Scooping and Scoring Corms

1. Wound gladiolus or crocus corm same as bulb was wounded and proceed as with bulbs. Practice both scoring and scooping. Little corms or cormels will form adventitiously much as described with bulbels.
2. Plant these cormels in flats and label flats with pot labels, giving variety name, date planted and your name.
3. Later plant outdoors in beds.

Questions and Assignments:

1. Define separation.
2. What is bulb? Corm?
3. Describe various kinds of bulbs and give examples.
4. Define bulbels, bulblets or bulbils and cormels, give examples of each and how produced.

---

[1] This form of bulb propagation, not normally separation, may be classed either as cuttage or division; but when it takes place in nature, it may be called separation.

[2] Another procedure may be followed: Scales may be placed on tray under bench of cool greenhouse or in cold frame shaded with muslin or covered with moist moss. (Fig. 86.)

5. From what countries does the United States import large quantities of bulbs? Could these be raised in this country?

XIII. PROPAGATION BY DIVISION—TUBERS, ROOTSTOCKS, OFFSETS AND CROWNS

Materials and Equipment: 73, 74, 158 to 162, 166, 234, 235, 250, 261.

Directions:

Put dahlia tubers in warm, moist place without soil for 7 to 10 days previous to this practicum so eyes will show sprouts in time. (Fig. 70.)

A. STEM TUBERS [1]

1. Cut Irish potato tubers, weighing 4 to 8 ounces, in half length-wise. (Fig. 117A.) They should be in proper stage of sprouting not too far advanced.
2. Continue to cut tuber into one to two ounce pieces, aiming to make cuts at right angles to each other in order to secure blocky rather than wedge shaped pieces. (Fig. 117B.) Each tuber piece must have at least one eye.
3. Plant tuber pieces 4″ deep in furrows or hills in well prepared ground.

B. ROOT TUBER DIVISION—DAHLIA

Directions:

1. Dig dahlia plant, keeping tubers intact in clump. (Fig. 69.)
2. Locate bud on stem and when separating from clump of each tuber remove bud and tuber intact. (Figs. 70B and 71.)
3. Plant in 6″ or 8″ flower pots and put in frame or greenhouse.
4. After bud has made reasonable growth and roots have become established, transplant to open beds. These may be planted immediately in open beds if ground is available.

C. OFFSETS—FRENCH ARTICHOKE, HOUSELEEK

1. Remove side slips, suckers, or offsets from artichoke plant.
2. Plant in rows 6′ by 6′ apart.
3. Remove offsets from houseleek plants and thrust stems into pots of composted soil to grow; or plant in open ground. (Fig. 67.)

D. CROWNS OR RHIZOMES—ASPARAGUS

1. Divide crowns of asparagus.
2. Plant one-year-old crowns, in trench about 8″ deep. (Fig. 67X.)
3. Spread fleshy roots laterally in prepared trench.
4. Spread 1″ fine soil over crowns.
5. After young shoots appear, move additional soil into trench and repeat at intervals of about two weeks.
6. By midsummer entire trench should have been filled.

E. ROOTSTOCKS—IRIS OR CANNA

1. Dig up clumps of iris or canna rootstocks. (Fig. 65.)
2. Note buds or "eyes" on them.
3. Divide rootstocks in pieces, each piece with an "eye." (Figs. 65-4, 65-6.)
4. Plant pieces 4″ apart each way in flat or in 8″ pots in composted soil, or better, plant directly to open beds.
5. When shoots appear above ground and have made 6″ or more growth, transplant new plants from flats or pots to open beds.

---

[1] Note: These tubers are characteristic of stems; having buds regularly arranged along their length.

Questions and Assignments:

1. Define division, separation, rootstock, crown, offset, rhizome, tuber and give example of each.
2. Has sweet potato buds like Irish potato has? Is it a tuber?
3. From what do slips start on sweet potato tuber?
4. Are methods of propagation used in this exercise sexual or asexual? Explain.
5. Is Irish potato tuber, root or stem? What is sweet potato?
6. From what do roots arise in Irish potato?

XIV. COLLECTION AND STORAGE OF MATERIALS FOR DECIDUOUS HARDWOOD STEM AND ROOT CUTTINGS [1]

Materials and Equipment: 48, 49, 55, 64, 66, 75, 103 to 109, 112, 113, 115 to 118, 122, 130, 134, 166, 167, 181, 235, 239, 245, 247, 261, 313.

A. STEM CUTTINGS

Directions:

Make 25 to 30 cuttings each of some deciduous varieties listed under materials and equipment.

1. Before severe freezing (if possible) collect wood from above mentioned deciduous plants. If winter is mild good results should follow.
2. Make hardwood stem cuttings of these, $3\frac{1}{2}''$ to $5''$ long, and root cuttings as directed below from material $\frac{1}{4}''$ to $\frac{1}{2}''$ in diameter.
3. Make top cuts of stem cuttings $\frac{1}{2}''$ above nodes and bottom cuts $\frac{1}{8}''$ below. (Figs. 103-3, 4, Fig. 48A.)
4. Tie cuttings in bundles of 25 each.
5. Attach copper wired tree label to each bundle, giving variety name of plant, date and student's name. (Use common lead pencil, not indelible pencil or ink on painted side of label. Iron wires soon rust and ink and indelible lead become blurred.)
6. Place layer of moist sand, sawdust, or sphagnum or peat moss in bottom of common lugbox or flat.
7. Place bundles of cuttings on this layer, butts up.
8. Pack material around edges of box.
9. Cover cutting butts $3''$ or deeper with moist moss, sand or sawdust.
10. Store in cool cellar or similar place to callus, but where cuttings will not freeze.
11. Store only one variety of cutting in each receptacle. Keep packing medium just moist.
12. In three or four weeks, or in spring after callusing, plant cuttings.

B. ROOT CUTTINGS

Directions:

Make 25 root cuttings of each of varieties directed by instructor. (Fig. 98.) Horseradish, flowering quince, quince, upright blackberry. and pyracantha roots are all excellent.

1. Make cuttings of roots $2''$ to $3''$ long (Fig. 97).
2. Pack loosely between layers of moist sand, sawdust or moss in flats.
3. Label flats with pot labels.
4. Store in same manner as hardwood stem cuttings and plant in flats or in open ground in spring.

Questions and Assignments:

1. Define hardwood cutting.
2. Describe method of storing hardwood cuttings.
3. Is it always necessary to store hardwood cuttings?
4. When are hardwood cuttings usually planted?
5. What is procedure in propagating by root cuttings from time roots are dug until cuttings are planted?

---

[1] Evergreen plants tend to mold in storage.

XV. PROPAGATION BY ROOT CUTTINGS

Materials and Equipment: 55, 66, 109, 115 to 119, 134, 167, 170, 182, 183, 203, 215, 235, 261, 264, 265, 266.

A. BLACKBERRIES [1] AND HORSERADISH

Directions:

1. Use stored blackberry and horseradish roots from $\frac{1}{4}''$ to $\frac{1}{2}''$ in diameter to make 2" to 4" cuttings. (Practicum XIV.) Plant in nursery as directed below. (Figs. 97, 98, and 273.)
2. Open furrows by shovel, single plow or garden cultivator with shovel attachment. (Fig. 294.)
3. Sow blackberry root cuttings horizontally in furrow approximately 6" apart; place horseradish cuttings vertically, square ends up, same distance apart.
4. Cover roots with soil 2" to 3" deep and pack firmly around by tramping.
5. After one season's growth in nursery set out in permanent planting plants that develop.

B. FLOWERING QUINCE, QUINCE, PEAR, HAWTHORN, APPLE AND PYRACANTHA ROOTS

Directions:

1. Wet and tamp sand in flat full of sand. (Fig. 99.)
2. Open trench in sand with piece of metal. (Fig. 100.)
3. Make cuttings 1" to 3" long.
4. Plant vertically so tips come just to surface of sand. (Fig. 97.)
5. Sprinkle thoroughly and tamp between rows. (Fig. 101.)
6. Cover cuttings with $\frac{1}{2}''$ of sand.
7. Wet down with fine nozzle sprinkler.
8. Set flat in lathhouse, cold frame or greenhouse.
9. When roots and shoots develop, pot plants. (Fig. 98.)

Questions and Assignments:

1. What kind of buds develop on roots? From what do root and top growth on root cuttings spring?
2. Name five plants propagated by root cuttings.
3. How are root cuttings cared for when taken from field and when are they planted?

XVI. HARDWOOD STEM CUTTINGS OF ORNAMENTALS

Materials and Equipment: 58, 59, 75, 77, 80, 82 to 87, 90, 91, 105, 106, 109, 112, 113, 119 to 128, 164, 167, 170, 203, 235, 261, 264 to 266, 285, or 286.

Directions:

1. Fill flat with medium to fairly coarse, clean, sharp sand and wet thoroughly.
2. Place 2" × 4" piece of wood on top of sand and pound over surface with mallet until firmly packed. (Fig. 99.)
3. Make 25 cuttings each $3\frac{1}{2}''$ to 5" long of one variety of plant material with knives or sharp pruning shears, preferably knives. Make lower cut of cutting $\frac{1}{8}''$ below the node or bud, and top cut $\frac{1}{2}''$ above node or bud. (Figs. 48A and 103—1 to 4.)
4. With evergreens leave but reduce top leaf or leaves by cutting in half. (Fig. 103-1, 2, 6 Fig. 48d.) Coniferous cuttings are best made with heel. (Fig. 103-5 and 48d.) With conifers leave section of foliage at top of cutting. (Fig. 103-5.)
5. When cuttings of first variety are completed place in flat "No. 1." Label with variety name and date on painted side.
6. Do same for each other variety and number flats "2," "3," "4," etc.

---

[1] If stored cuttings are not available, dig blackberries in spring and plant cut roots at once.

7. Plant one row of cuttings of one variety or species left at flat at your desk as described below. Then move to next flat and plant row. Continue until one row of each variety has been planted in each flat.[1]

8. With piece of sheet metal, open trench 1½″ from end of flat, (Figs. 100A and B) by pressing straight down on one, then other end of metal, then pushing it forward and backward. Furrow should extend to within ½″ of bottom of flat.

9. With cuttings in one hand force base ends of cuttings with other to bottom of furrow or trench. Cuttings should be ½″ apart in row.

10. When row has been planted, sprinkle it, using plenty of water to settle sand around cuttings. Allow flat to drain through holes in bottom.

11. With mallet tap piece of 1″ × 4″ board, standing on edge against one side of row firming sand against cuttings. Repeat on other side of row. (Fig. 101.)

12. Plant, sprinkle and tamp until flats are filled or materials are exhausted. When completed, planted flat should look like Figure 102B. If cuttings are easily pulled up job is not well done. (Fig. 102A.)

13. Place flats in coldframe, hotbed or greenhouse.

14. Keep sand moist by frequent sprinkling at two to four day intervals, but do not sprinkle until water is needed. If cuttings show evidence of wilting or if sand is drying on top, but not bottom, it is time to water. Too frequent sprinkling is bad practice; water thoroughly with longer periods intervening.

15. Cuttings of rose, willow, tamarix, fig, privet, quince, currant, gooseberry, and many other species may be planted with success in soil in open ground as well as in flats of sand.

Questions and Assignments:

1. Define hardwood cutting.
2. How are cuttings treated from time wood is collected until planted?
3. How are cuttings of coniferous plants propagated?
4. How are broad-leaved evergreens propagated?
5. What are best mediums in which to plant hardwood cuttings?
6. What is proper time to make hardwood cuttings?
7. May tuber cutting of Irish potato be classed as stem cutting?

XVII. PROPAGATION BY SEMI-HARDWOOD CUTTINGS

Materials and Equipment: 58, 82 to 90, 105, 119, 120, 127, 128, 167, 170, 203, 235, 245, 261, 264 to 266, 302.

Directions:

Instructor will direct as to what plants to use. Choose from above list. Figure 103B shows method of making cuttings. Fill needed number of flats to within ½″ of top when packed with sand—one for each species of plant from which cuttings are to be made.

2. Tamp sand as described in Practicum XVI.

3. Make cuttings 3½″ long. They should usually have not less than two nodes or buds, usually have three, four or more. Remove part of leaves from evergreen cuttings. (Fig. 103).

4. Follow same procedure of rotation, when planting, as in Practicum XVI.

5. Plant cuttings in trench ½″ asunder in rows, and rows 1¼″ apart. Tops of cuttings should extend just below top of flat to allow for placing of glass over flat after planting. Sprinkle and tamp between rows.

6. Place planted flats of cuttings in coldframe, greenhouse, or hotbed. Bottom heat will be beneficial.

7. Sprinkle and cover flats with glass.

Three to six weeks will be required to root semi-hardwood cuttings. Good plants can be obtained when placed in coldframe over winter in mild climate. These may be planted in beds in spring.

---

[1] This procedure is to give students experience in planting various varieties of cuttings and to maintain practise of only one variety to a flat.

8. Water cuttings when sand begins to dry on top but is still moist below; and do not water until these conditions exist.

9. Pot plants when rooted and roots are ¼″ to ½″ long.

Questions and Assignments:

1. Define semi-hardwood cutting.
2. At what time of year are plants usually propagated by semi-hardwood cuttings?
3. What type of wood has plants propagated by semi-hardwood cuttings?
4. How does wood of semi-hardwood differ from hardwood cuttings? Softwood cuttings?

XVIII. PROPAGATION BY SOFTWOOD AND LEAF CUTTINGS

Materials and Equipment: 65, 85, 88, 95 to 102, 105, 141, 142, 119, 120, 122, 166, 167, 170, 203, 235, 245, 261, 244, 264 to 266, 302.

A. Softwood Cuttings of Close or Hardwooded Plants

Directions:

Select softwood cuttings of close or hardwooded plants listed above. Softwood cuttings are taken from wood that snaps clean and does not string or squeeze when bent double. If it strings it borders on semi-hardwood.

1. Test softwood to see if in proper condition. (Fig. 109).
2. Fill flat with sand and proceed as in Practicum XVI.
3. Make short cuttings 2½″ to 3½″ long. Leave some leaves on upper part of cuttings. Large lower leaves are removed.
4. Drop cuttings in water as made. Do not keep them there too long, or bark will be loosened and they will turn brown after planting.
5. Plant cuttings and label flats as in Practicums XVI and XVII.
6. Place planted flat where it will have shade and bottom heat, in hotbed or on greenhouse bench with heat below. (Figs. 44, 148, 149).
7. Water and cover with plate of window glass as in Practicum XVII.
8. When surface indicates drying out, water (Practicum XVII). Too frequent watering is conducive to "damping off." Water only in mornings.
9. Take glass off for period each day for aëration.
10. Root formation is indicated by bright-colored, new foliage.

B. Succulent or Herbaceous Plants

Fuschia, passion vine, salvia, oxalis, begonia, hoya, coleus, geranium, impatiens and gloxinia.

Directions:

Make cuttings 2½″ to 3½″ long with amount of leaf surface retained as Figures 105X, 113. Plant as with preceding cuttings and give same treatment following planting.

C. Leaf Cuttings

I. Begonia rex, hoya, or gloxinia (parts of leaves)

1. Reduce fresh leaves of above plants approximately one-third to fan shaped pieces, (Fig. 116G). Wound veins with knife near bases.
2. Prepare flat as for softwood cuttings. (Above).
3. Open furrow and insert fan shaped pieces of leaves (stem ends down as with hardwood cuttings).
4. Firm sand around leaf pieces.
5. When flat has been planted, sprinkle and place glass over top.
6. Place flat in coldframe, hotbed, or greenhouse. Bottom heat may be used to advantage.

II. Bryophyllum and begonia rex—(whole leaves, Figs. 115, 116C and 116D).

1. Prepare flat as above.
2. Place whole bryophyllum and begonia leaves on surface of sand, top surfaces up.

3. Wound veins of begonia leaf with knife, but do not wound bryophyllum leaf veins. Peg begonia leaves down with toothpicks as indicated. (Fig. 115).

4. Cover leaves of bryophyllum with ½" of sand, but do not cover begonia leaves. Give these light sprinkling of sand to hold them down.

5. Keep sand moist.

6. Small plants will appear from notches in bryophyllum leaves in a week or two. (Fig. 116C). Remove, transplant to pots or flats of composted soil. New plants will spring from wounded veins of begonia leaves. Treat in like manner.

Questions and Assignments:

1. Why is it possible for softwood cuttings to continue growth and produce new roots after being severed from parent plant?

2. When is usual time for making softwood cuttings?

3. What is proper medium for planting softwood cuttings?

4. Why do we remove part of leaf surface from cuttings?

5. Name other plants which may be propagated by softwood cuttings?

XIX. PROPAGATION OF ROSES BY CUTTAGE [1]

Materials and Equipment: 82, 166, 167, 170, 180 or 185, 203, 235, 261, 264 to 266, 285 or 286.

A. COLLECTION STORAGE OF HARDWOOD ROSE CUTTINGS

Directions:

Use any climbing or cut flower roses.[2]

1. Collect strong, well-ripened shoots of past season's growth of various rose varieties [3] between time leaves fall and weather is freezing.

----

[1] Figures 113 and 114.

[2] Hybrid perpetual, hyrid tea, Bengal, Bourbon and China varieties may be used. These are usually grown for cut flowers.

[3] Recommended rose varieties: *Hybrid perpetual*—Baron de Bonstettin, Coquette des Alpes, Coquette des Blanches, Frau Karl Druschki, Gloire Lyonnaise, Margaret Dickson, Baroness Rothschild, Clio, George Ahrends, Heinrich Munch, Magna Charta, Mrs. John Laing, Anne de Diesbach, John Hopper, Jules Margottin, Paul Neyron, Ulrich Brunner, General Jacqueminot, Hugh Dickson, J. B. Clark, Prince Camille de Rohan.

Hybrid tea—Bessie Brown, British Queen, Kaiserin Augusta Victoria, Madame Jules Bouche, Nathalie Bottner, White Killarney, Antoine Rivoire, Arthur R. Goodwin, Joseph Hill, Madame Ravary, Marquis de Sinety, Mrs. A. R. Waddell, Ophelia, Queen Mary, Sunburst, Tipperary, Betty, Chrissie Mackellar, Jonkherr J. L. Mock, Killarney Queen, Konigin Carola, Lady Ashtown, Lady Ursula, La Tosca, Madame Segond Weber, Radiance, Chateau de Clos Vougeot, Ecarlate, Etoile de France, General McArthur, Grus an Teplitz, H. V. Machin, Laurent Carle, Lieutenant Chaure, Red Radiance, Red Letter Day.

Tea—Molly Charman-Crawford, Mrs. Herbert Stevens, Maman Cochet, W. R. Smith, Harry Kirk, Souvenir de Pierre Notting.

Polyantha (or "baby rambler")—Marie Pavie, Erna Teschendorf, Orleans, Triumphe Orleanais, Clothilde Soupert, Echo, Maman Turbat, Mrs. W. M. Cutbush, Perle d'Or.

Rugosa hyb.ids—Blanc Double de Coubert, Nova Zembla, Conrad Ferdinand Meyer, Mme. Lucien Villeminot, Amelia Gravereaux.

Pernetiana—Rayon d'Or, Madame Edward Herriot, Soleil d'Or.

Moss—Blanche Moreau, Crested Moss, Henri Martin, Princess Adelaide.

Climbing—Christine Wright, Climbing American Beauty, Dr. Walter Van Fleet, Paul's Scarlet Climber, Ruby Queen, Silver Moon, Avaiteur Bleriot, Crimson Rambler, Excelsa, Gardenia, Goldfinch, Lady Gay, Miss Heylett, Minnehaha, Sodenia, Source d'Or, Trier, American Pillar, Evangeline, Hiawatha, Milky Way, Newport Fairy, *Rosa setigera*.

Trailing—R. wichuraiana, R. rugosa prostrata.

Climbing sweet briar—Brenda, Meg Merrilies, Lady Penzance.

2. Each student make 25 cuttings 5″ or 6″ long with upper cut above bud and lower cut ⅛″ below node.

3. Tie cuttings in bundles of 25 with string or raffia.

4. Label bundles giving variety name, student's name and date made and stored.

5. Continue in same manner with remaining varieties.

6. Bury them butts up[1] in boxes containing sphagnum or peat moss or moist sand.

7. Place box of bundled cuttings in cool cellar. Cuttings may be planted in spring about corn planting time in open ground, care being taken not to injure callus which has formed. Plant so one or two eyes or not more than 1″ of cutting is above ground. This will leave 4″ or 5″ in ground.

B. Softwood or Greenwood Rose Cuttings[2]

Use any strong-growing hybrid tea, hybrid perpetual, Bengal Bourbon o: China varieties.

1. Collect wood for cuttings directly after blooming. Take current year's growth. Wood may be used that has or has not borne bloom.

2. Select only good, strong shoots.

3. Cut shoots to three eyes or buds.

4. Remove all leaves except top one and all leaflets except two.

5. Plant in flats of sand in same manner as softwood cuttings in Practicum XVIII.

6. Place planted flats in coldframe or spent hotbed with glass covering or in greenhouse with glass placed over flats.[3]

C. Semi-hardwood Rose Cuttings

1. Collect semi-hardwood or nearly mature wood, using same list of plants as for softwood cuttings. Wood should be taken either from forced plants in February or March, or from plants growing outdoors after blooming in summer, but later than softwood was taken.

2. Make cuttings 5″ to 6″ long, leaving same amount of leaf as for softwood cuttings.

3. Plant in flats in same manner as softwood cuttings.

4. Place in location similar to that where softwood cuttings were put.

Subsequent treatment is same as for softwood cuttings.

Questions and Assignments:

1. Name five roses usually propagated from hardwood stem cuttings.

2. What are other methods of propagating roses and when is each method used?

3. How are cut flower roses usually propagated? Name five rose varieties propagated by each of these methods.

4. Is it necessary to bud suckers or root-sprouts? Why?

5. How are roses propagated when budding and grafting are practiced? Explain in detail.

---

[1] Good results may be expected if cuttings are planted as soon as made, provided they are planted in flats of sand and placed in greenhouse. Where mild winters prevail, rose cuttings 8″ to 10″ long grow well when planted in open ground in November or December.

[2] Figures 114X and 114.

[3] Object of enclosed atmosphere is to prevent undue evaporation from leaves before roots have formed sufficiently to support plant. For few cuttings success may be had by inverting fruit jar over cuttings. (Fig. 114).

When roots have formed freely (Fig. 114XD), transplant in good soil. Water well and shade for few days from midday sun. Subsequent watering should be moderate until cuttings are well established. Rooted cuttings may be transferred to pots containing rich composted soil.

XX. PROPAGATION OF FRUIT TREES AND BUSHES BY HARDWOOD STEM AND ROOT CUTTINGS

Materials and Equipment: 48, 49, 103, 104, 115, 116, 130, 132, 167, 170, 203, 235, 246, 247, 261, 264 to 266, 302.

A. STEM CUTTINGS

Directions:

In late fall, make stem cuttings of well ripened wood of current year's or past season's growth from plants listed above.
1. Make cuttings 4″ to 5″ long.
2. Make base cut ⅛″ below node.
3. Make tip cut ½″ above node. (Fig. 103-3).
4. Plant cuttings in flats of sand as in Practicum XVI.
5. Plant but one variety in flat.
6. Place flat of orange cuttings on bench with bottom heat in greenhouse or hotbed. Use piece of glass to cover flat if using greenhouse bench.

B. ROOT CUTTINGS (Fig. 97)

Directions:

1. Make root cuttings from roots ¼″ to ½″ diameter, from same plants as used for stem cuttings.
2. Cut roots into 3″ lengths.
3. Plant in vertically as root cuttings in Practicum XV. (Fig. 97).
4. Compare stem cutting results with results obtained with root cutting.

Questions and Assignments:

1. What are advantages of propagating fruit trees from cuttings?
2. What are disadvantages?
3. How are cuttings difficult to root, handled?
4. Is propagation by cuttings a sexual or an asexual method?
5. From results and methods used in this exercise, would you say that root or stem cuttings are practical methods from which to propagate fruit trees?

XXI. PRODUCTION OF LILY BULBS FROM STEM CUTTINGS

Materials and Equipment: 170, 187, 203, 210 or 211, 235, 246, 251, 261, 264 to 266.

A. NATURAL METHOD—HEELING IN STEM BASES

Directions:

Select lily plants which have just completed blooming.
1. Cut stems about 18″ above ground or leave as they are if not many to handle.
2. Take firm grip with both hands about one third way down stem, give slight twist and sharp, quick jerk to one side to pull up stem.
3. Place stems in pile as removed and carry to planting bed either in open ground or in lathhouse.
4. With spade, open trench 4″ deep across 3′ bed. Make one side vertical, other sloping at angle of 45° or less. (Figs. 90 and 91).
5. Lay 25 stems on sloping side of trench with lower ends against vertical side. (Fig. 90).
6. When row is complete, open trench 12″ or more away and throw soil to cover set stems 12″ to 15″ at bases.
7. Lay stems in new trench and continue as before until all have been set and covered.
8. Leave stems thus 35 to 60 days [1] then remove and plant in permanent quar-

---

[1] Longer period will develop finest bulbs.

ters. They will have bulblets on about 6″ of their bases. (Figs. 89 and 91).

9. Cut off bases bearing bulblets[1] and plant as they are, in sunken bed. (Figs. 86 and 89).

10. After year or two in bed bulblets will be ready to dig as flowering bulbs.

B. Stem Cuttings Proper [2]

Directions:

Carry on this type of propagation in greenhouse or frame with glass, where temperature and moisture are under control.

1. Make 6″ or 8″ stem cuttings of one or more of following lily species: *Lilium longiflorum, L. testaceum, L. dauricum, L. umbellatum, L. leichtlini, L. elegans* (Fig. 89).

2. Cut off all leaves except top one within ¼″ of end of stem.

3. Plant half cuttings in sand same as if hardwood cuttings.

4. Place other half on wire tray under bench in greenhouse or in glassed hotbed frame outdoors and cover with moist moss.

5. Close space under bench in greenhouse with canvas or burlap.

6. Keep air saturated by liberal watering on soil beneath. Bulblets will soon form.

7. Plant bulblets in fields same as those from heeled-in stem bases.

Questions and Assignments:

1. What lilies may be propagated by stem cuttings? Stem bases? Stem proper?

2. How long does it usually take for bulblet to become flowering bulb?

3. Is production of bulblets from stem cuttings proper, usual practice?

4. What are advantages of propagation of bulblets by stem cuttings?

5. What are disadvantages?

XXII. MAKING AND STORING GRAPE HARDWOOD CUTTINGS

Materials and Equipment: 60, 167, 181, 247, 251, 303, 304.

A. Making Cuttings

Directions:

Each student make bundle of 100 cuttings from prunings furnished.

1. Select medium size wood (¼″ to ½″ in diameter), well matured, firm and with moderately short joints. (Fig. 119-3). Outer bark should be clear, color characteristic of variety and without dark blotches; inner bark green and full of sap; wood hard and free from dark specks or streaks; pith of moderate size, clear, firm and light colored.

2. Make cuttings not less than 12″ nor more than 18″ long from base to tip, base cut not over ¼″ below base node, top cut about 1″ above top bud. (Fig. 118).

3. Bundle cuttings in frame (Figs. 120 and 122), 100 in each bundle and make butts even. (Fig. 121).

Place tree label on cutting in center of bundle with following data on painted side: (a) variety name of vine and (b) number of cuttings in bundle. On unpainted side, name of student making cuttings. Write with common lead pencil, not ink nor indelible pencil.

When bundle of 100 cuttings is made and butts are even, tie securely with two wires, one near top, one near base of bundle. (Fig. 120).

B. Storage of Grape Cuttings

Either of two methods of storage may be used, first preferred.

---

[1] *Lilium candidum* should bear not less than 20 bulblets; *L. testaceum*, 12 to 15 and *L. umbellatum*, 50.

[2] In propagation by this method, cutting itself does not callus or form roots. Only development is of latent buds in leaf axils into bulblets. These form roots young, thus maintaining cutting through its progeny rather than through its own root system, as in ordinary hard or softwood cuttings.

I. Method A

1. Place pile of coarse sand, slightly moist, in protected location such as under shed.
2. Bury cuttings in this until spring, when they can be removed and planted.
3. Sprinkle sand when necessary to keep it moist, but do not overdo this.
4. Plant cuttings in nursery when warm spring weather arrives.

II. Method B

1. Dig hole slightly deeper than cuttings are long in high, well drained ground.
2. Place cuttings in hole, butts up, cover with soil 3″ or 4″ deep and cover with straw.
3. In spring watch cuttings closely and when first signs of growth appear (such as buds swelling) remove and plant in nursery.

Questions and Assignments:

1. Describe details to observe in choosing grape cuttings.
2. What is proper time for making cuttings?
3. Describe method of making cuttings for nursery planting; and for planting in open field or vineyard.
4. How do condition of soil and weather affect length of cutting?
5. Is any special part of vines preferable for cuttings? Explain.
6. Explain how cuttings are cared for until time of planting.

XXIII. PLANTING GRAPE CUTTINGS

Materials Required: 60, (cuttings), 182, 183, 246, 251, 305.

A. COMMON CUTTINGS

Directions:

1. Place wire in position where row is to be. Distance between rows should be 36″ to 40″; between cuttings 2″ to 4″.
2. Plow a furrow on one side of the planting line throwing the soil away from the line.
3. Use light subsoiler, if available, so soil in bottom of furrow will be loosened and pulverized 14″ from surface. Usually this can be accomplished by going over same furrow twice running subsoiler close to landside of furrow. If subsoiler is not available do work with a spade.
4. Place the planting boards in position with its edge exactly at edge of furrow, directly beneath line and throw loose, fine soil in the furrow to the depth of 6″.
5. Push cuttings into loose soil so they slant about 1 inch from vertical toward land side of furrow and so top bud is just above level of soil. Second bud may be at level of soil if internode is not over 3″ long.
6. Pack soil firmly about base of cuttings by tramping, planter working in trench and planting ahead of where he steps.
7. Complete filling furrow and firm soil.
8. Remove board and mound soil over row so top buds of cuttings (or bench grafts) are just covered with loose soil or sand.

Questions and Assignments:

1. Give precautions to take when choosing cuttings previous to planting.
2. Describe what should be condition and preparation of good nursery soil.
3. Describe preparation of ground for, and method of planting and handling grafted vines.
4. Describe fully operation of planting grape cuttings as performed for this exercise.
5. Are cuttings ever planted directly in field for permanent vineyard? What is your opinion of such practice?

XXIV. PREPARING COMPOSTED SOIL FOR POTTING AND MANURE FOR HOTBED

Materials and Equipment: 253, 267, 235, 251, 252.

A. PREPARING COMPOSTED SOIL FOR POTTING PURPOSES

Directions:

1. Secure good garden loam not too heavy nor too sandy (medium).
2. To this add enough sand to give good drainage.
3. Mix these together.
4. Throw up layer of loam 6" deep.
5. On top of this place 6" of manure.
6. On manure place another layer of loam.
7. Continue until pile has been built up 3' or 4' high.
8. Make top bowl-like to hold water when needed in dry weather.
9. Allow pile to set and manure to ferment and decay for year or more. After being mixed and sifted thoroughly, soil will then be ready for potting. (Fig. 159).
10. When time comes to remove soil for potting, spade vertically down through heap and throw composted soil in pile. (Fig. 159).
11. Turn this pile over with shovel several times to mix loam and rotted manure thoroughly. Screen composted soil through ¼" mesh screen. (Fig. 160). It is then ready for potting.

B. PREPARING MANURE FOR HOTBED

Directions:

1. Use fresh horse manure with straw litter.
2. Place so as to make flat-topped pile 4' or 5' high and any length desired.
3. If manure should be dry at time of piling, sprinkle as piled to start fermentation.
4. In day or two pile will start to steam and ferment. When well under way, turn pile with fork so interior of first pile becomes exterior of new pile.
5. In seven to twelve days from time of piling, manure will be ready for hotbed. Practicum (XXV) on hotbeds may then be executed.

Questions and Assignments:

1. Describe fully method of preparing potting soil other than one used in this exercise.
2. What are requirements for good potting soil?
3. Describe in detail method of preparing manure for hotbed?
4. What is proper time to start hotbed?
5. What is best heating element for hotbed?
6. What other methods of heating hotbed?

XXV. HOTBEDS AND COLDFRAMES—THEIR CONSTRUCTION, PREPARATION AND USES

Materials and Equipment: 37, 41, 44, 43, 203, 251, 304. Carpenter equipment for constructing a frame and materials for construction.

A. SKETCH OF PROPAGATING FRAME AND HOTBED

Directions:

Make sketch (to scale) showing top, end and side views of frame for hotbed and its pit. Sketch end view showing depth of manure and soil. (Figs. 138 and 139).

B. CONSTRUCTION AND PREPARATION OF HOTBED AND ITS FRAME

1. Lay out ground for hotbed. (Fig. 135).
2. Construct frame for hotbed referring to figures of this exercise. (Figs. 137 to 139).
3. Prepare hotbed by first digging pit 18" deep.

4. Put frame in place and fill pit to within 6" of top with manure previously prepared.

5. Throw in 6" of rich soil over manure and level surface. Carry out work as directed below.

C. PLANTING HOTBED

1. Sow seeds in hotbed from which to raise plants for early setting in vegetable garden. Such seeds as tomatoes, peppers, onions, lettuce, cabbage, cauliflower, melons, cucumbers and many others may be started in hotbed for early planting. Do not plant these seeds until two to four days following preparation of hotbed, so early extreme heat may pass off and temperature become moderate.

2. Provide for ventilation for half hour period or more daily by placing 4" block under sash.

3. Sprinkle in mornings only when bed plants show signs of needing water and do thorough job.

Questions and Assignments:

1. What is hotbed?
2. Describe desirable location for hotbed.
3. What are some uses for hotbeds and coldframes?
4. How is manure treated for use in hotbed?
5. Define coldframe and explain how it differs from hotbed.

XXVI. LATHHOUSE AND LATHHOUSE PRACTICES

Materials and Equipment: 235, 251, 184.

A. CONSTRUCTION AND PREPARATION OF LATHHOUSE

Directions:

1. Study plans given for size lathhouse instructor designates. (Fig. 156X).
2. Assist in construction under direction of instructor or shop teacher.
3. Lay out one or more walks through lathhouse depending on size.
4. On each side of walk or walks, lay out beds.
5. Make one sand bed with sand 3" to 4" deep in which to plunge potted plants.
6. Lay off beds to receive flats filled with cuttings.
7. Lay off one bed for planting lilies.
8. Lay out other beds for planting seeds and transplanting seedlings of whatever plants seem advisable.
9. Water plants when surface soil becomes dry. Do not water too often but give plenty of water at less frequent intervals. Soil in pots, after watering, should be wet to bottoms.

B. USES OF LATHHOUSE

1. Bring cuttings that have started in flats, in coldframe or hotbeds and any others not requiring bottom heat, into lathhouse during late spring and summer.

2. Take potted ornamentals into lathhouse from frames or greenhouse (thus making space for new plantings). Plunge pots into sand 1" or deeper. Do not place these potted plants in beds over 6' wide. This width does not cause one to reach over 3' from either side when necessary to remove certain pots from middle of bed.

3. Spade bed laid out for lilies and plant stem cuttings and bulbels started from bulb scales as directed (Practicum XII). Flowering bulbs may be planted in another bed as they will do well in lathhouse.

4. In another bed plant seedlings of ornamentals raised.

5. Plant semi-hardy ornamentals, yet not hardy enough to do well outdoors, in permanent quarters in lathhouse.

6. Visit nursery where lathhouse is used and observe other uses to which one may be put.

Questions and Assignments:

1. Why is lathhouse valuable asset?
2. List some uses as result of visit to nursery.
3. What is cost per square foot of land under lathhouse? How does this compare with greenhouse space costs?

XXVII. POTTING, SHIFTING, REPOTTING AND BALLING PLANTS [1]

Materials and Equipment: 26, 136 to 138, 163, 185, 195, 203, 234, 212, 234, 251, 255 to 258, Cuttings of plants which have developed roots $\frac{1}{4}''$ to $\frac{1}{2}''$ long.

A. POTTING

Directions:

Each student pot 25 or more plants.
1. Moisten composted soil two or three days before exercise and have in such condition it will not be too loose nor run together when used.
2. Mix thoroughly and screen flat full of composted soil.
3. Pile part of soil on bench, slightly at right. (Fig. 169A).
4. At left of pile place empty nested 2″ flower pots.
5. In front on bench place rooted cuttings. (Fig. 169A). If roots are long, trim back to about $\frac{1}{2}''$ before proceeding.
6. At right of soil place flat for potted cuttings. (Fig. 169A).
7. Working both hands at once, proceed as follows: [2]
   a. With right hand seize handful of soil.
   b. With left hand take up empty pot.[3] (Fig. 169B).
   c. Place pot in front of you and partly fill with soil from right hand. (Fig. 169B).
   d. With released left hand seize cutting. (Fig. 169C).
   e. At same time thrust index finger of right hand into soil in center of pot. (Fig. 169C).
   f. With left hand place cutting. (Fig. 169D).
   g. With right hand drop some of soil around cutting. (Fig. 169D).
   h. With both hands seize pot between first and second fingers, with index fingers on side of pot remote from body, holding pot firmly.
   i. With thumbs first parallel with, then at right angles to body, one on each side of cutting, press soil firmly and uniformly. (Fig. 169E). "Firmly" does not mean "packed hard."
   j. Sprinkle some loose soil over firmed soil. Pot should be filled to just above lower edge of top rim. (Figs. 168 and 169F).
   k. With right hand give filled pot sharp rap on bench and place in flat. (Fig. 169 lastly).
   l. With left hand seize another empty pot and proceed as before. (Fig. 169 lastly).
8. Label pots with pot labels, giving date and plant names.
9. Place potted cuttings on side benches of greenhouse, lathhouse or coldframe, water and shade them for time with muslin or cheesecloth.

Another method popular among professional potters is practised by a right handed man as follows: Bench piled with sifted soil from back almost to front; nested pots at left, laid on soil slope in short rows and not more than two or three tiers deep; cuttings also at left; flat to be filled with potted plants at right; no obstruction to soil directly in front; one boy to supply potter with pots and cuttings, another to supply empty flats, take full ones away and place plants on benches. Often two boys are needed for this latter job. With his left hand potter picks up rooted cutting and empty pot, almost as one operation, brings pot, with cutting inside, in

---

[1] If composted soil is not available, do not hesitate to use good garden loam and sand for potting soil; good results should be obtained.

[2] Left handed man will perhaps want to reverse this arrangement.

[3] In case pots are 5″ or more in diameter, place piece or pieces of broken pot over hole in pot to prevent soil from washing out and yet permit drainage of excess water.

front of his body; almost at same time right hand, palm upward, scoops soil and fills pot loosely. Thumbs held at right angles to body press soil firmly once; hands give pot quarter turn to left; thumbs press once; right hand gives pot slight shake and rap on bench and places it in flat; at same time left hand reaches for next cutting and pot. Left handed man works same way but arrangement of pots, cuttings and flats is reversed.

β. Shifting (Fig. 173)

Directions:

Each student shift 25 or more plants.
Shifting is a trade term for transferring potted plants to larger-sized pots.
Usually a plant is shifted to the next size larger than the one it has been in.
Remove or "knock out" plants to be shifted from pots as follows:
1. Place hand over top of pot containing plant, stem between second and third fingers, thumb alongside pot. (Fig. 171A).
2. Invert pot and tap rim on edge of bench to loosen ball of earth. One tap is usually enough if ball of earth is moist. This is called "rapping." (Fig 171B).
3. Lift off pot. (Fig. 171C).
4 "Shoulder" plant[1]—that is, rub part of surface soil off so fresh soil may take its place in larger pot in which to be placed. (Figs. 172 and 176).
5. Place enough soil in bottom of new pot to have top of earth ball within ¾" from top of pot. Place plant with left hand.
6. Firm soil. (Fig. 172C).

C. Repotting Pot-Bound Plants (Fig. 177)

Directions:

1. Stand pots with pot-bound root systems in water 30 minutes.
2. Knock pot-bound plants out of pots as in B 1, 2, 3 above (Fig. 177A).
3. Wash and work out earth from roots in tub of water or with gentle stream of water.
4. Trim up roots and tops. (Fig. 177B).
5. Pot plants in pots one or two sizes smaller than those they have been in, as previously directed for potting plants. (Fig. 177C).
6. Place repotted plants in shady place, water and keep there until danger of wilting has passed.

Questions and Assignments:

1. How is ideal soil for potting prepared?
2. What are some records for potting cuttings?
3. How do you determine when plant is ready to shift?
4. What is good test for proper condition of soil for potting?
5. Explain how to determine when plant in pot should be repotted.

XXVIII. TRANSPLANTING AND PRICKING OUT SEEDLING PLANTS[2]

Materials and Equipment: 136 to 138, 166, 182, 183, 203, 234, 245, 249, 261, 306.

A. Transplanting Plants to Open Ground (Figs. 195 to 197X).

I. Plants in 2", 2½" and 3" pots or in flats

Directions:

Make planting so it can be cultivated and irrigated with ease.
1. Select plants which have been in 2", 2½" and 3" pots, or in flats in hotbed, coldframe, greenhouse or lathhouse.

---
[1] Shouldering removes undesirable lower orders of plants growing on surface of potted soil.
[2] When possible, choose cool, cloudy or overcast day for this exercise.

2. Take to nursery well prepared for transplanting.

3. Lay out rows in nursery by using wire and stakes (Practicum XXXVI).

4. Plant along line, as outlined below, all plants of same variety in same section along line; that is, do not have mixed planting of varieties.

    a. Thrust dibble (Figs. 195 to 197) into soil and push first forward, then backward, to make hole.

    b. Knock plant out of pot (Fig. 171) being careful to retain ball of earth intact with roots.

    c. Place ball of earth and roots in hole.

    d. Pack earth firmly around ball with hands but do not break ball.

    e. Place garden label with variety name in front of first plant of each variety, working from left front to right rear of each row.

    f. Continue until all plants of this size have been planted.

II. Plants in Larger Pots than 3"

1. Use trowel to dig holes for plants in 4" to 6" pots.

2. Use shovel to dig holes for plants in pots larger than 6". Plant as directed above.

3. Label plants as planted. If ground is not already moist enough, water thoroughly as planting is completed.

B. PRICKING OUT PLANTS

1. Select seedling plants grown in flats (Practicum VI) and which are ¾" to 2" high. For this work second pair of true leaves should just be developing (Figs. 181 and 191).

2. Fill flat of moist composted soil, to within ½" of edge and tamp lightly with 2" x 4" block, smoothing surface.

3. Set flat along side of flat containing seedlings.

4. Remove plants from flat as follows: (a) Grasp top of seedling with left hand; (b) push knife blade under to pry plant out with right hand; trim roots if necessary so they will readily go into holes in composted soil made for them.

5. Use marker to make holes in soil. (Figs. 179 to 181).

6. If not necessary to trim roots, place roots with earth attached, in these holes. Otherwise trim roots and place plants in holes.

7. Firm soil around roots with fingers.

8. Continue until flat is full of plants.

9. It is best not to sprinkle until job is finished; but to have soil moist to begin with and sprinkle several days later. Set flat in greenhouse, lathhouse or frame. Do not sprinkle too often for this will encourage damping-off. Allow soil to become somewhat dry on top before sprinkling again. Sprinkle only in morning.

Questions and Assignments:

1. Define transplanting.

2. Why does plant tend to dry up and die when transplanted?

3. What kind of weather is best for transplanting?

XXIX. TOP GRAFTING—LABORATORY PRACTICE

It is advisable to have class execute grafting in laboratory before attempting field job. Students will then work with more efficiency and confidence in field.

Materials and Equipment: 164, 166 to 171, 185, 189, 213, 214, 268, 269, 307.

Directions:

Make following grafts as directed. Use wood furnished by instructor. Be sure of location of cambium of both stock and scion before starting to do any grafting (Fig. 206). When grafting, match cambiums of stock and scion.

A. CLEFT GRAFT

1. Select for stock, limb 2" to 5" in diameter.

2. Cut limb to length of 18".

3. Smooth off cut surface of stock with grafting knife.

4. Use grafting chisel and mallet on stock 4″ to 6″. (Fig. 239A).

5. Remove and reverse chisel. (Fig. 239B). Insert wedge of tool to open cleft so scion may be inserted. (Fig. 239A). Stocks too large for common cleft grafting demand different method (Figs. 251 and 253).

6. Prepare scion by making two strokes with sharp grafting knife at lower end. Cut surfaces 1¼″ to 1¾″ long. (Figs. 236X to 238). Outer edge of scion should be slightly thicker than inner edge. (Figs. 236X, 237B, C, and Fig. 238) This insures close contact with cambium layers of stock and scion. Scarf (cut or groove) on scion should have straight bevel. Results of irregular bevel are shown in Figure 237C. Bevel of scion should not come to straight point. Prepared scion set in place and method of inserting scions are shown in figures 236X, 237 and 238.

All new growth between stock and scion is formed from cambium—thin growing layer of tissue between bark and sapwood. (Fig. 206). Cambium of scion must come in contact with cambium of stock to insure union. (Fig. 236X and 238).

7. Leave two to three buds on scion, two preferred. Lower bud should be located near top of wedge. (Figs. 236, 236X and 237).

8. Place scion in cleft of stock. Make sure to match cambium of scion with that of stock. This means that when bark of stock is thick, scion must be set in some distance. (Figs. 236X and 238A).

9. Some operators slope tops of scions slightly outward. This insures crossing of cambiums of stock and scion at one point at least, but practice is doubtful. Although one point of contact is usually enough to make union, it is desirable to have greater union of cambiums.

10. If stock is more than 2″ in diameter, put in two scions. (Fig. 238).

11. If stock is large and pressure great, hold cleft open with small wedge to prevent crushing of scion. Remove wedge when scions have been placed.

12. When work is complete (before waxing), show job to instructor for instructions and approval.[1]

13. Next, apply what has been learned from inspection and improve technique. If necessary make more grafts until work meets instructor's approval.

14. After work has been approved, label graft and keep for reference. Waxing prevents drying out and fungous injury but is not advisable in laboratory jobs.

B. COMMON BARK GRAFT (Fig. 252)

1. Select limb, 3″ to 5″ in diameter, bark of which raises easily.

2. Cut it at a smooth place to leave stub 18″ long.

3. Smooth off top of cut with grafting knife.

4. Slit bark of stock 2″ with sharp knife. (Fig. 252A). This should be done on flat side of limb. (Fig. 255).

5. Prepare scion by making first cut 1½″ to 1¾″ long. Scion should have two to three buds. Scion wood small in diameter is best for bark graft except for walnuts where large wood at least ⅜″ in diameter is desirable.

6. Next, put shoulder[2] on scion (Fig. 252B).

7. On opposite side of scion from first cut, make another cut 1¼″ long (Fig. 252B). Make short cut. (Fig. 254). Scion is now ready to insert.

8. Loosen bark on both sides of slit in bark of stock, by inserting knife blade in slit and prying up bark each side. (Fig. 252A.)

9. Force scion down between bark and sapwood. Shoulder of scion should rest on top of stock. (Fig. 252E).

10. Drive two small nails through scion (Fig. 252E and F). Also nail down bark as shown.

11. Place other scions 3″ apart around stocks to foster rapid healing of wounded stock.

---

[1] Instructor should cut away bark next to scion, thus exposing cambiums of scion and stock. Thus union or non-union of cambiums can be seen. (Fig. 238).

[2] When small wood is used the scions may be cut somewhat differently, and the bark of the stock need not be split. Scion is forced between wood and bark and nailed. Tying is unnecessary. This type of bark graft is used on large stocks. Use No. 19 flat headed wire nails.

12. When all work has been approved by instructor, label it.

13. Put in bark graft on stock 5″ or more in diameter without splitting bark of stock, using scions of small diameter.

If small nail or brad is driven through scion to hold it in close contact with stock and two nails are placed to hold down bark, it is not necessary, though often desirable, to use tape or waxed cloth with which to wrap graft.

14. Make another bark graft, using method illustrated in Figure 250, 251.

C. BIEDERMAN'S BARK GRAFT (Fig. 257)

1. Make vertical cut about 2″ long down smooth portion of bark same as for common bark graft, but not over bud or limb base.

2. Separate bark from wood by inserting knife blade in slit and prying it up slightly.

3. Prepare scion. Make scarf on side opposite lowest bud, at lower end of and diagonally across scion 1½″ to 2″ long and with a concave surface. (Fig. 257E). Scion from ½″ to ⅝″ in diameter should be used for scions when grafting walnuts. Smaller wood does not give good results. Use only base portion of shoot for walnut grafting—that part with very small buds.

4. Make face of scarf concave its full length with least possible injury to cambium. Shape scion with one or more strokes of ¾″ half-round chisel. (Fig. 257).

5. Next, make short cut with grafting knife, ½″ long on back side of scion. (Fig. 254).

6. Insert scion between bark and wood of stock and force down as far as it will go. Leave about ¼″ to ⅜″ of upper end of scarf exposed. (Fig. 257F).

7. Bark at top of stock will thus be forced out slightly with insertion of scion. Remedy this by driving 1″ 19-gauge flat-headed nail on each side of vertical cut to hold bark against stock and keep it tight against scion. (Fig. 257E and F).

8. Drive 2 fine nails through scion to hold firmly in place. (Fig. 257E and F).

9. After graft has been approved by instructor, wrap scion and stock with Johnson's industrial tape, waxed cloth or string.

10. Fill in space left on each side of scion (between bark and wood) with soft paper before waxing.

11. Cover all exposed surfaces with melted grafting wax or tree seal when doing work in orchard but not in laboratory. Fill slit in bark by stroking lengthwise and crosswise with brush. Label graft.

C′. MAC COOPER'S BARK GRAFT

Refer to Figure 258A and execute a Mac Cooper's Bark Graft.

D. SIDE GRAFT (Figs. 247 and 249)

Side graft has one advantage: When using it stock is not cut back until graft has taken. Sometimes it need not be cut back at all.

1. Make oblique cut in piece of stock 1″ to 3″ in diameter, with aid of grafting or butcher knife and mallet or hammer. (Fig. 247D).

2. Cut scions wedge shape. Make scarf 1¼″ to 1¾″ long, on side toward stock. Make scarf on outer side 1″ long. (Fig. 247A, B, C).

3. Press and tap scion into incision in stock until cut surface or scarf is almost concealed in stock. (Fig. 247E).

4. Nail and wrap with grafting industrial tape, waxed cloth or soft twine. (Fig. 247F).

5. Take job to instructor for criticism before wrapping.

6. Fill opening between bark and wood with wax and wax all cut surfaces completely. Cover with waxed cloth, string or tape with wax when doing job in orchard but do not wax laboratory work.

7. Label graft.

E. SAW KERF OR NOTCH, INLAID GRAFT OR GROOVE GRAFT [1]

1. Cut off piece of limb 2″ to 4″ in diameter and 18″ long.

---

[1] This graft has also given satisfaction in working trees (such as black walnut) difficult to graft. It takes practice to do work rapidly and satisfactorily but efficient and rapid work can be done when skill has been developed. (Fig. 250 and 253).

2. Smooth off top of cut with grafting knife. Make groove in stock by cutting kerf 2" long with saw.[1] This should extend down side of stock 1½" and be ¾" deep, extending toward center of cut surface of stock. (Fig. 253).

3. Cut notch ½" wide at surface of stock. Extend down stock from 1" to 1¼" Make width and depth of grove at top same as diameter of scion to be used, or slightly less. Taper groove to point at bottom. Make groove with grafting knife. (Fig. 253G). Guard against making groove too wide. This is common mistake when doing work at first.

4. Next, shape scion. Instead of being wedge-shaped and inserted in cleft or split of stock, scions must be shaped to fit into V-shaped groove on side of stock. (Fig. 253H). Angle that cuts of scion make with one another should be slightly more obtuse than angle of groove. Thus, when scion is placed on stock contact will be firm at line of bark. This will insure close contact of cambiums. Figure 253H shows scion properly shaped to fit groove in stock.

5. Place scion on stock and secure firmly in place until new tissues grow together. This is accomplished most easily by nailing with two 1" 19-gauge, flat headed wire nails. (Fig. 253I).

6. Take work to instructor for judgment.

7. Wax all cut or exposed surfaces carefully when doing work in field.

8. Label graft.

F. Whip Grafting

1. Make up several whip grafts from wood ¼" to ⅜" in diameter. (Fig. 228 to 232).

2. Follow directions given under "Bench Grafting" (XXXI) and complete graft and tie as shown in Figure 232.

Questions and Assignments:

1. Define grafting.
2. Give objects of grafting.
3. Define stock, scion and cambium layer.
4. Describe selection and care of scion wood for grafting.
5. What is proper season of year for grafting methods covered in this Practicum.

XXX. TOP GRAFTING—ORCHARD PRACTICE [1 and 4]

Materials and Equipment: 166 to 171, 173, 185, 189, 213, 214, 247, 270, 271, 272, 397.

Directions:

Execute this exercise when buds start to swell in spring. Use methods covered in Practicum XXIX.

1. *Cleft Grafting:* Place two cleft grafts on each of three limbs of trees assigned by instructor. These limbs should be cut back where they are 1" to 4" in diameter or through secondary limbs of framework. Apply wax. Label grafts by tacking brad on limb grafted and tying tree label to it. On label give your name, date, variety of stock, variety of scion and grafting method used.

---

[1] Groove in stock is most conveniently formed by first making shallow, straight saw cut as long and as deep as groove is to be. (Fig. 253F). Then by means of sharp knife or leather cutting tool groove is widened at top and tapered to point at bottom. (Fig. 253G). When finished cut surface should be smooth and straight If rough and irregular good fit with scion cannot be secured.

[2] Keep in mind that dormant scion wood is necessary for successful grafting. If dormant wood is available, grafting may be carried on even as late as summer.

[3] For grafting walnut, scion wood ½" to ⅝" of past seasons' growth has been found best by authors. Use only base wood of shoots with immature buds. Tip wood will not usually give as good results. Wood with diameter of ⅜" is good for other trees.

[4] Figs. 243 and 244.

2. *Common Bark Grafts.* Put bark grafts on three limbs. Use any two methods of bark grafting practiced in laboratory. These limbs may be any size above 1½″ in diameter. Label as above.

3. *Side Graft.* (Fig. 247 to 249). On side of limb 1″ to 2½″ in diameter, insert three side grafts without heading back. (Practicum XXIX). Wax and label as above. When grafts have taken, cut stock back to 6″ or 8″ from scion. Later remove stub limb close to scion.

5. *Whip Graft.* If there are water-sprouts or small limbs ¼″ to ¾″ in diameter make five whip grafts. Wax and label.

6. *Saw kerf or notch graft.* This graft gives good results when working on black walnuts. Insert three notch or saw kerf grafts on each of three limbs (Practicum XXIX). Wax and label.

Remove water sprouts in direct competition with graft. (Fig. 270).

7. *Mac Cooper's Bark Graft.* This is even a better graft than saw kerf for working on black walnuts. Graft one limb 3 or more inches in diameter using this graft. (Fig. 258A). Re-wax thick barked grafts in 4 to 6 days.

8. Refer to Figures 245 and 249 and graft evergreens.

Questions and Assignments:

1. What are advantages Biederman bark graft has over common bark graft?
2. What trees, if any, respond better to budding than grafting?
3. What size stocks are best adapted to cleft grafting?
4. What method of grafting would you use on larger stocks than those on which it is advisable to use cleft graft?
5. Write discussion on subsequent care of grafts.

XXXI. BENCH GRAFTING FRUIT TREES [1]

Materials and Equipment: 166, 167, 173, 185, 239, 247, 270, 273.

Directions:

Make 24 root grafts, 12 using whole roots and 12 using piece roots 4″ to 6″ long. (Figs. 227 and 229).

1. Use whip graft, make sloping cut 1″ to 1¾″ long at base of scion and top of root. (Fig. 228 to 232).

2. Starting at point one-third distance from tip and above center of bevel scion and root, make reverse cut on each, sloping cuts slightly toward center (Fig. 229). Thin tongue of wood in both root and scion is thus formed which, when skillfully made, will interlock and fit snugly together. (Fig. 229).

3. See that cambium layers (under bark) of scion and root fit together on at least one side. If one piece is larger than other, as is usually case, they will coincide on only one side; but this is sufficient. (Fig. 230).

4. Tie graft with No. 18 waxed knitting cotton. (Fig. 232).

5. Wrap tightly to make union parts fit snugly together.

6. At end of wrap, tying is not necessary. Draw twine under tip of tongue. (Fig. 232).

7. Wrap grafts in bundles and tie with wire or heavy cord.

8. Label bundle with tree label, giving name of stock and name of scion, your name and date grafted.

9. Store bundles in moist sand, sphagnum or peat moss, or sawdust in cellar or other cool place and keep moist but not wet.

10. When spring comes grafts will be callused, knit together and ready to plant. Strings if not already rotted, must be removed as soon as growth swells plant. Figure 265 shows equally good results from budding or grafting.

Questions and Assignments:

1. What fruit trees are usually "bench" or "root grafted?"

[1] Root pieces of fair size make fair trees. Whole straight roots are usually preferred. Bench grafting is practiced more extensively in East than on Pacific Coast where budding is more popular.

2. What are advantages of "bench" or "root grafting?"

3. Give details of how and when scion wood and stock are collected and cared for previous to grafting.

4. Will root-grafted tree make as satisfactory growth as budded tree?

5. If you were to have choice of budding or grafting your nursery trees which operation would you perform? Why?

XXXII.   BENCH GRAFTING GRAPES

Materials and Equipment: 60, 166, 167, 174, 180, 181, 247, 275.

A. PREPARING STOCK AND SCION

Directions:

1. Each student make 25 cuttings of phylloxera resistant stock graded to sizes. If slot grader[1] is available, use it. (Fig. 118). Cuttings which fail to enter slot or that pass completely through are discarded as too large or too small. They should be approximately 10" or 11" for coast or cool regions and 12" or 14" for interior valleys or warm regions and as straight as possible.

2. Make cuttings proper length as indicated above and disbud all but top bud with sharp knife or pruning shears before grading.

3. Prepare one-bud scion cuttings. Cut each ½" above bud and with 1½" to 2½" of internode below. Scions should have been soaked previously for about 12 hours and then graded, always with buds pointing in same direction when being graded. Stocks and scions are now ready to be grafted.

B. GRAFTING OPERATIONS

1. Make 12 grafts using ordinary whip graft and 12 using short or modified whip Figure 262A. Modified whip graft is preferred when hot room callusing is practiced for it requires no tying.

A. *Ordinary Whip Graft* (to be used when sand callusing is practised), or grafts—Fig. 262B—are to be buried in soil:

(1) At end of prepared cutting, make slanting cut about ½ times as long as diameter of cutting at angle of less than 30° or approximately 1½" long.

(2) On each cutting make thin tongue with knife slightly across grain from first third of cut down, to second third, so tongue extends length of middle third of cut. (Fig. 262B.)

(3) Make similar cut and tongue on scion and fit stock and scion together.

(4) To facilitate operation open tongues by drawing out knife obliquely.

(5) Tie graft with raffia or No. 18 knitting cotton in spiral with turns separated by small interval. (Figs. 260, 261). This is necessary for even callusing. If raffia is used it must be moist.

B. *Short Modified Whip Graft,* to be used for hot room callusing (Fig. 262):

(1) After stocks and cuttings have been prepared and graded, cut bevel stock and scion with sharp grafting knife to give cut one and one-half times their diameter.

(2) Make tongue by cutting across grain from near top to near bottom of cut.

---

[1] Slot grader is not essential, for stock and scion can be matched rather closely by sight. When much grafting is to be done grading is best done with metal slot grader. The length of the slot, cut in the brass plate, is 7", with width ½" at one end and ¼" at other. Ends of slot are widened into circles 1¼" and 1½" wide, respectively. Plate is marked with guide lines which determine number and size of grades. Any desired number of grades and relations between grades can be obtained by varying position of guide lines. Percentage difference between grades is best. Five or six grades are sufficient.

Behind slot, a ¾" piece of iron as stop to hold cutting helps in grading accurately. With this marking of grader, six size grades of cuttings are made, each varying in same ratio from next

Tongue should be fairly thin to avoid splitting. (Fig. 262A).

(3) Prepare scion in same manner.

(4) Adjust stock and scion.

(5) When graft is well made it is so strong it needs no tying.

(6) Place untied grafts in boxes for callusing in hot room.

Questions and Assignments:

1. Why do we bench graft grapes? Why not always plant straight cuttings ot desired variety?

2. How have resistant stocks been produced?

3. What is good resistant stock for coastal regions, especially for fog belt of California?

4. What is most grown stock in this state and what are its limitations and advantages?

5. Name stock well suited to light, gravelly and loose soils.

6. What stock would you use in San Joaquin Valley of California?

7. If you had rich irrigated soil in hot climate, or central California Valley conditions, what would be likely stock?

8. Give names of other promising stocks and conditions for which suited in other state or states.

9. Write account of operations of this exercise.

XXXIII. FIELD GRAFTING GRAPES

Materials and Equipment: 60, 166 to 170, 214, 251, 277, 307.

Directions:

Use two methods: (1) *Ordinary cleft graft,* and (2) *groove graft.* (Fig. 253).
For holding scions use kerosene can cut horizontally through middle and provided with round stick across top for handle. It will hold 50 scions.

Put 1″ of water in container and cover with damp sack to keep scions fresh.

A. PREPARATION PRECEDING GRAFTING

1. Clear away earth around base of vine, making pit about 2′ in diameter and 3″ or 4″ deeper than level grafting is to be done. (Fig. 253A).

2. Clean earth off stem of vine and remove rough dry bark. (Fig. 253A).

3. Decapitate vine by sawing horizontally where smooth straight wood (about 2″) is at top. (Fig. 253A, B, C). If vines are over 1½″ in diameter cut tops off a day or two before exercise to prevent excessive run of sap at time scion is put in. Too much sap might drown scion.

B. CLEFT GRAFT

1. Choose place where bark is smooth, straight and sound.

2. Make cleft by splitting not cutting. (Fig. 253C).

3. Place edge of knife or grafting chisel or tool on part of sawed surface where cleft is to be made and which has previously been cleaned and smoothed with grafting knife. (Fig. 253C).

4. With slight blow of wooden mallet drive edge of grafting tool about ⅛″ into both wood and bark. Make sure bark and wood split at same place.

5. Place chisel or chisel end of grafting tool on mark sufficiently far from bark to allow insertion of scion. (Fig. 253D).

6. Drive chisel in sufficiently to open cleft wide enough (perhaps 1″ or even more) to allow entrance of scion.

7. Open cleft by pressing chisel sidewise.

8. Insert scion and match cambium with that of stock. (Fig. 253E.)

9. When chisel is released and removed, tension of wood will hold scion firmly in place. Do not allow cleft to extend quite across stock, for it would not hold scion so firmly or close up so well as if split only part way across.

10. With small vines it is impossible to prevent splitting so it may be necessary to tie scions with string or raffia. With large vines it may be necessary to place small wedges of wood immediately behind scions to prevent crushing.

11. Cut scion in wedge form somewhat thicker on side which comes nearest to bark. (Practicum **XXIX**). Length of wedge depends on character and size of cleft in stock. Wedge will usually be long and tapering but not come to sharp point.

12. Insert scion so line between bark and wood coincide with corresponding line on stock. As bark of scion is thicker than that of stock, outer surfaces of scion will be set in slightly from that of stock.

13. Do work rapidly and do not allow freshly cut surfaces to remain exposed long while doing job.

One scion to vine is sufficient if stock is 1½" or less in diameter. With larger stocks use two scions, removing weaker if both grow after it has helped to heal wound.

C. Groove Graft

Instead of making wedge-shaped scion for this graft, scions are shaped (Fig. 253H) to fit into V-shaped groove (Fig. 253G) on side of stock extending from top of stump downward from 1" to 1½". Make width and depth of groove at top same diameter as scion to be used or slightly less. Groove should taper to point at bottom. (Fig. 253G).

1. Fit scion into groove so cambium layers of stock and scion coincide as completely as possible. (Fig. 253I).

2. Make groove in stock by first making shallow straight saw cut as long and as deep as groove is to be. (Fig. 253F).

3. With sharp grafting knife or leather-cutting tool, widen groove at top and taper to point at bottom. (Fig. 253G). When finished cut surface should be smooth and straight to insure good fit, with cabium of scion and stock matching.

4. Shape scion so cambium of stock and scion coincide when placed together. Angle cuts of scion made with one another should be slightly more obtuse than angle of groove.

5. Place scion on stock so contact will be firm at line of bark. This will insure close contact of cambiums. Figure 253H shows scion properly shaped to fit groove in stock. After inserting scion in groove nail it firmly in place with two 1" 19-gauge, flat-headed wire nails. (Fig. 253I).

6. Use scions of two buds (Fig. 253H). There is often advantage in having them longer.

Three and even more buds have been used with advantage on large vines. With only two buds on such vines growth is often so rapid and so large as to be almost unmanageable. With several buds growth is divided among more shoots so no one is likely to grow so large as to be troublesome.

D. Covering the Scions

As soon as scion is in place, cover all cut surfaces of stock and scion carefully 2" or more with moist, well-pulverized soil (Fig. 253B, H), drive stake to support first growth of graft. Complete filling of hole may be deferred several hours, but not long enough to run risk of having scion become even slightly dry. In extremely hot, dry weather fill hole immediately. No wax, clay, or similar material is needed. Nothing is better to put around union than moist, loose soil. This gives conditions of moisture and aëration most favorable to uniting of tissues. With cleft graft it is good practice to cover cleft in stock with some clay, leaf, or anything else that will exclude soil; but unless cleft is large, this is not necessary. It is never necessary with groove graft. Filling hole with soil should be complete; whole scion may be covered unless soil has a tendency to bake. When finished, each graft will be in middle of wide mound of soil. Narrow mounds may become too dry.

Questions and Assignments:

1. What are reasons for changing variety of growing vines?

2. Explain how cuttings from which scions are to be secured are made and handled in field for greatest conservation of scion material.

3. What is proper season for grafting grape vines in vineyard?

4. Give directions for proper management of grafts during first growing season.

5. Give treatment of grafts after first year.

6. Is it possible to use any other method than grafting proper in changing tops of vines?

XXXIV. BRIDGE GRAFTING,[1] INARCHING,[2] NATURAL BRACES AND ARCHES

Materials and Equipment: 166 to 168, 185, 189, 214, 270, 271, 272, 307.

A. BRIDGE GRAFTING

If no trees girdled by rodents or through mechanical injuries are available use limb 2" or more in diameter for practice work.

1. Cut out 10" section of bark so it is like rodent injury (Fig. 224B).

2. Cut scions slightly longer than area to be bridged to give slight tension which will hold them in place when tree bends or sways in wind.

3. Bevel scion on each end and on same side. (Fig. 224C).

4. Insert one end of scion under bark and tack it with small ¾" No. 19 flat headed nail. (Fig. 224D at *n*).

5. Next slip other end under bark and nail. (Fig. 224D at *n'*). Scion should have slight bow in middle.

6. Place scions as close as possible around and across wounded area.

7. Wrap area of bark, covering ends of scions with industrial tape, waxed cloth or string.

8. Have instructor criticize work before wrapping and waxing.

9. After approval by instructor carefully cover wounded area and grafts with grafting wax or "tree seal" to insure protection against drying out and entrance of decay organisms.

B. INARCHING (Figs. 220, 221, and 222).

Each student place three inarches in one tree as directed below. It is assumed that seedling trees have been planted in spring around tree to be grafted. (Fig. 220). If trees have not been previously planted and work is being done in spring, planting and inarching may be done same day.

1. Beginning 12" from ground on trunk of tree to be inarched, make two parallel cuts, distance of cuts apart equal to diameter of seedling used. (Fig. 220A).

2. Make two cuts at right angles to these, 5" apart. (Fig. 220A).

3. Remove patch formed by cuts.

4. Bevel lower side of rectangular opening (Fig. 220A) to allow seedling to make straight entrance into opening.

5. Bring seedling against opening in trunk and cut it off at proper place to fit, (Fig. 220B and C).

6. Make cut 5" long on side of seedling to fit against trunk. (Fig. 220C).

7. Place end of seedling in opening, so it will fit snugly against upper end of opening in trunk.

8. Nail it firmly with three or four fine No. 19 1¼" flat headed nails. (Fig. 220D).

9. Wax job thoroughly, filling all cracks and covering exposed surfaces.

10. Keep seedling free from growth of buds by rubbing shoots off as they start. (Fig. 220A).

C. NATURAL BRACES AND ARCHES (Fig. 203)

I. Braces

1. Select two small branches on two limbs growing toward inside of a tree.

---

[1] Figures 224 and 225.

[2] Inarching which gives tree new root system, is practiced on Pacific Coast to put French roots on Bartlett and other pear trees originally on Japanese root. Such trees develop unmarketable "black-end" pears. (Fig. 223). Inarching is done with hope that French root influences will produce normal pears and replace so-called "Jap" roots.

2. Scrape bark off cambium on side of each so wounded surfaces meet.
3. Braid these two limbs around each other tightly. (Figs. 215, 216, and 218).
4. If deemed necessary to hold together wrap with tape or string.
5. Within year branches will have grown together, (Fig. 215) and made an apparently single-limbed brace. (Fig. 203).

II. Arches

1. Select two trees growing fairly close together.
2. Bend them together at tops and wrap secure with twine. In time they will grow together and make arch.

Questions and Assignments:

1. What are causes of tree injuries which call for bridge grafting as remedy?
2. What trees do and what do not lend themselves readily to bridge grafting?
3. At what time of year should bridge grafting be done?
4. Describe treatment of bridge grafts after being made.
5. When should scions be gathered and how are they cared for? What wood is taken for scions?
6. Under what circumstances would you do inarching or grafting by approach?

XXXV. GRAFTING WAX MAKING AND PREPARATION OF WAXED STRING AND CLOTH

Materials and Equipment: 81, 171 to 173, 175 to 179, 202, 208.

Directions:

Students work in pairs, each pair making one or more waxes of various formulas given in text.

A. WAXED STRING

1. Immerse ball of No. 18 knitting cotton in hot grafting wax. (Wax of Formula I is good.) Let wax cook thoroughly first.
2. Allow ball to remain in hot wax five minutes.
3. Turn ball frequently to insure complete saturation of string.
4. Remove ball and turn over several times while cooling to prevent hot wax from settling in lower side.
5. Wrap it, when cold, in oiled paper, for storage until ready to use.

B. WAXED CLOTH

1. Tear from sheets of unbleached muslin strips 6″ wide and 16″ long. Wrap these round sticks, leaving one end of the stick long for handle.
2. Immerse these in can containing hot grafting wax of formula I, II, or III.
3. All cloth should remain in boiling wax five minutes.
4. Remove cloth and place in another can to drain. Turn sticks often while cooling and draining.
5. Wrap in waxed paper and store for use.
6. When about to be used, tear waxed cloth into strips ½″ to ¾″ wide.

Figure 268 shows satisfactory grafting wax heater for small job, (distributed by Edwin C. Tyson, Flora Dale, Pa.).

Questions and Assignments:

1. When you execute Practicum XXX, use each of different waxes prepared in this exercise. Label limbs waxed, giving name of wax used. Hand instructor report on success with different waxes. State which wax you prefer.
2. Which formula for wax would you use during cold weather? During hot weather?

XXXVI. PROPAGATION OF FRUIT TREE ROOTSTOCKS AND ORNAMENTALS FROM SEED

Materials and Equipment: 14 to 17, seed of 118 to 121; 143, 182, 183, 215, 235, 246, 249, 250, 261.

A. Propagation of Nursery Trees for Rootstock from Seed

Directions:

1. Make sure ground has been prepared as follows:
(a) Plowed in fall (8″ to 10″ deep).
(b) Plowed in spring just previous to planting. This plowing may be shallow.
(c) Thoroughly worked down to fine seed bed. Use rake previous to planting and reduce all clods.
2. Tie wire full length of rows to two stakes.
3. Stretch wire taut for first row and drive stakes.
4. Lay off row along wire tramping wire into ground with feet. In this way mark is left on surface when wire is removed. Make rows 40″ apart.
5. Place permanent stakes or garden labels at ends of row.
6. Mark row by running over marked line lightly with shovel attachment wheelhoe. (Fig. 294).
7. Repeat operation several times, somewhat deeper each time until trench is 2″ to 4″ deep; depth depends on type of seeds to be planted. (Fig. 294).
8. Use seeds stratified previous fall [1] and which have started to germinate or crack seed coats. Start planting after furrow has been opened. Place sprouted seeds every 4″ or 5″ in row.
9. Plant almond, peach, apricot, black walnut and Myrobalan plum seeds 2½″ to 3½″ deep and cover with soil.
10. Firm soil over seeds by tramping lightly with feet.
11. Label rows beginning at front end of first row, starting at left and reading toward back. Follow in next row to right. On each label write name of variety, your own name and date of planting.
12. Where seeds were planted 2½″ or more deep, go over ground lightly in four or five days with wheelhoe equipped with weeding knives to rid plot of weeds started during week and to save labor later.
13. Keep plot free from weeds and well supplied with water.

B. Propagation of Ornamentals from Seed

Directions: *Plant only one variety in each flat.*

1. Prepare to plant seeds of ornamentals reduced from their coverings in Practicum II. Used seeds of myrtus, cotoneaster, pyracantha, Oregon hollygrape or hawthorn.
2. Fill flat with sand to within 1″ of top.
3. Mark rows in sand 1½″ apart and make trenches ½″ deep.
4. In trenches drop seeds 16 to inch.
5. Label rows with pot labels giving name of variety planted, date planted and student's name.
6. Cover with ¼″ to ½″ of sand.
7. Sprinkle lightly with water when flat has been planted.
8. Some seeds require period of after-ripening before they will germinate; one should, accordingly, not become discouraged if they do not germinate at once. (Tables 7 and 8).
9. When seeds have produced small plants, latter may be pricked off as directed in Practicum XXVIII.
10. Repeat operations, if thought desirable, using two-thirds composted soil and

---

[1] Excepting apricot and almond which should have been stratified three to four weeks previous to planting date. It will not be practical to plant all varieties of seeds in one day since they will not germinate at same time. Hence only those seeds which indicate that germination has started should be used. Student should complete this exercise later.

one-third sand as medium in which to plant. Shade is sometimes desirable for seed beds, especially for coniferous plants. (Figs. 21, 112, 145, 145X, 150, 156X, 296).

Questions and Assignments:

1. What is place where seeds or seedlings for rootstocks are obtained for propagating following fruit trees: (a) apple, (b) pear, (c) cherry, (d) peach, (e) almond, (f) plum, (g) apricot, (h) citrus?

2. What are advantages claimed for natural peach pits over pits from budded varieties usually obtained from canneries or dry yards?

3. Which method of propagation for rootstocks (seed or seedling planting in nursery) is recommended for following: Pear, apple, plum, cherry, peach, walnut, apricot and almond?

4. What rootstocks are used for English walnut, pear, peach, plum, apple, apricot, almond and phylloxera-resistant grape vines?

5. Describe method of sowing and handling small seeds of ornamentals.

6. Which are to be preferred, foreign or domestic supplies of seeds? Why?

XXXVII. TRANSPLANTING SEEDLINGS FOR ROOTSTOCKS

Materials and Equipment: 143, 166, 167, 182, 246, 249, 261.

Directions:

1. From flats of pear and apple seedlings started in Practicum VI select plants 2″ to 3″ high and with second pair of true leaves. (Figs. 181 and 191).

2. Lay off rows 36″ to 40″ apart with wire stretched between stakes as in Practicum XXXVI.

3. Open hole in ground and plant seedlings 5″ apart. Use dibble to make holes for planting. (Figs. 195 and 197).

4. Trim off ends of long roots.

5. Plant seedlings in holes (Figs. 195 to 197) being sure root goes straight down when planted.

6. Firm soil around seedlings with dibble and hands.

7. When planting is completed, sprinkle or irrigate plot if soil is not sufficiently moist. Better have soil moist in advance of planting than wet it afterwards.

Planting thus requires more labor than planting seeds; but grower is repaid by almost 100% stand of seedlings and branched root system without resetting trees after first year.

Questions and Assignments:

1. What are advantages of transplanting apple and pear seedlings over planting seeds for rootstock production?

2. What is proper time to transplant as to (a) season, (b) size of seedling?

3. Describe commercial method of transplanting seedlings.

4. Which is to be preferred in planting seedlings, moist soil before setting seedlings or watering after seedlings are set? Why?

5. Are fertilizers of value in growing seedlings?

6. What influence has spacing on seedling development?

7. How important is spacing of plants?

XXXVIII. "T" OR SHIELD BUDDING—LABORATORY PRACTICE [1]

Material and Equipment: 164, 166, 167, 173, 180, 181, 189, 268, 270, 272.

"T" OR SHIELD BUDDING

Directions:

1. Practice taking buds from bud stick until work has been approved by instructor.

---

[1] This laboratory exercise should precede field practise. It gives student confidence and some speed and skill when he attacks nursery job. Job will be better done than if students are taken to nursery first. For laboratory work any variety of wood will do if bark slips. Common creek willow is good. Pear and apple watersprouts are excellent.

a. Remove buds by taking bud stick in left hand with buds pointing toward you (Figs. 282 and 286). Extend index finger of left hand under bud to be removed. (Fig. 286).

b. Make cut with single slicing motion of knife blade,[1] beginning $\frac{3}{8}''$ ahead of bud and ending about $\frac{3}{4}''$ behind bud. Lift bud slightly and with slicing motion cut it off. (Fig. 286). Bud removed should be shield-shaped. (Fig. 282Bd). Some budders make first cut on stock. (Fig. 282B).

c. Remove small sliver of wood with and under bud. (Fig. 282Bd). Beginners take too much wood with buds. Guard against this.

2. After work has been approved, put 25 buds in pieces of stock $\frac{1}{2}''$ in diameter, as follows:

a. Make first cut in stock (Fig. 280) parallel to long axis of stock trunk and perpendicular to ground surface.

b. Make second or cross cut, at right angles to first and parallel to ground surface. (Figs. 280 and 281).

c. Pry up corners of two cuts with blade of knife to loosen bark so bud will slip in place readily.[2] (Figs. 280C and 281B). This is usually done while making second cut by twisting knife blade downward first on one side of cut then on other as cut is completed.

d. Cut bud from bud stick as directed above, holding it on knife blade with thumb. (Fig. 281C).

e. Insert bud directly from blade cut. (Fig. 281C).

f. Push bud in place with thumb. (Fig. 281D).

g. Tie half buds made with rubber,[3] (Fig. 280E and Fig. 282Be and f), remainder with string, and compare results of these methods.

h. Have work approved by instructor.

Questions and Assignments:

1. At what time of year is bulk of "T" or Shield budding done?

2. When else may it be practiced?

3. What method of budding usually is used in your section of the country in production of (a) apple, (b) pear, (c) cherry, (e) peach, (f) orange trees?

4. If budding is to be preferred to grafting, why and for what fruits?

5. Is rubber as good bud-tying material as raffia, tape or string? Better? Why?

XXXIX. "T" OR SHIELD BUDDING—NURSERY PRACTICE—LATE SUMMER OR FALL BUDDING [4]

Materials and Equipment: 164, 166, 167, 173, 180, 188, 189, 246, 270, 272, 279.

Directions:

Use bud wood from shoots of present year's growth.

1. In nursery, with pruning shears trim for distance of 8" or 10" above ground (Fig. 284) trees suitable for budding. Remove from main stem all shoots, branches and leaves that might interfere with placing buds.

2. Select bud wood of past season's growth. (Fig. 280A). Do not use butts of shoots nor tip for 1' from end of shoot.

3. Use same method as practiced in laboratory, bud and tie 25 trees. Tie some buds with rubber, some with string, some with wet raffia and compare methods.

---

[1] Budding knife should have edge capable of shaving hairs off arm before budding is attempted.

[2] A turkey quill, tapered and sharpened and thrust down the perpendicular cut on stock should be used by beginners. This will make for an easy entrance of the bud.

[3] Rubber is best material yet found to tie buds. It has advantage of not girdling seedling if its removal is delayed. As it rots off after its useful period ends it does away with extra operation of cutting ligatures.

[4] Figures 278 and 279. Budding may be practiced any time bark slips readily— spring, June and late summer or fall budding. In last period we are interested for this exercise. For summer or fall budding past season's growths of lead pencil size are used as bud sticks. Only vegetative not flower buds are used.

4. Put razor edge on knife before proceeding.

5. Bend seedling over slightly and hold between left arm and leg (Fig. 277), reach down for smooth place on bark; as near ground as convenient to work, make cuts in stock (Practicum XXXVIII and Fig. 281).

6. Cut bud from bud stick, (Figs. 282 and 286) with only small portion of wood from bud stick attached.[1]

7. Taking position shown in Figure 277, insert point of bud in opening at top of slit in bark of stock and push in place with thumb (Fig. 281). Insert bud directly from knife blade.

8. Wrap buds (Fig. 282e and f). (Fig. 280E).

9. Label parts of row budded, giving on garden label name, variety of bud inserted, name of stock, and date.

10. Following spring, cut back stock to bud. (Fig. 285A and 287).

Questions and Assignments:

1. How is bud wood not being used immediately cared for in field?
2. How is bud wood cared for when to be shipped long distances?
3. What are requirements for good budding knife?
4. Why is it usually desirable to bud as low as possible?

XL. "T" OR SHIELD BUDDING IN SPRING—"SPRING BUDDING"— ORCHARD PRACTICE

Collect bud wood while still dormant, in most sections in fall or early winter. Store in moist moss or sawdust in cool cellar until budding time. Avoid over-moistening moss or sawdust for this will cause mold or decay.

Materials and Equipment: 164, 166, 167, 173, 180, 189, 246, 272, 280.

Directions:

Using dormant bud sticks kept in cold storage, bud 25 trees with "T" or shield bud.

1. Remove all side branches and leaves from stocks up to 10" from ground. (Fig. 284).

2. Place buds holding stock in position. (Fig. 277).

3. Wrap buds with budding rubber, soft string or wet raffia. Rubber preferred.

4. At beginning of row budded, place garden label with following information: (a) stock used; (b) variety of bud; (c) date of budding; (d) student's name; (e) number of trees budded.

5. After bud has taken, cut stock one-third through so two-thirds of top of stock may be broken over as in June budding. This will stimulate growth from bud. (Fig. 284C).

6. When bud has started growth, cut off balance of stock just above bud. (Fig. 285).

Questions and Assignments:

1. When should wood be collected for spring budding?
2. What are advantages of "spring budding"?
3. What, if any, are disadvantages of spring budding?
4. When will spring budded tree be ready to plant?
5. Will spring budded tree make as great growth as fall budded tree? Why?

XLI. "T" OR SHIELD BUDDING IN JUNE—"JUNE BUDDING"— NURSERY PRACTICE

Under favorable conditions budding in June produces small trees by fall of same year. If properly grown under ideal conditions trees will then be ready for orchard planting. This method is popular in foothill districts of California and Southern

---

[1] Beginners have tendency to take too much wood with bud. Take just enough to give some rigidity to bud. Wood should lie only under bud; not full length of cut.

States where small trees are preferred for transplanting. In common practice, budding continues later in season, even to October first.

Materials and Equipment: 164, 166, 167, 180, 188, 189, 246, 270, 272, 281.

Directions:

Each student bud and tie 25 trees.

1. Cut off all branches and leaves on stock from ground up to 10" to remove any interference with budding. (Fig. 284).

2. Use same methods as in laboratory exercise on "T" or shield budding.

3. Take position when budding shown in Figure 277.

4. Wrap buds with budding rubber, soft string or wet raffia, rubber preferred. (Figs. 282e and f and 282Bc).

5. In two weeks check work for results. Bud will be dry and shrivelled if it has not taken but will be firm and plump if it has.

6. After bud has taken, bend tree over and partially break it so two-thirds of top is above break (Fig. 284C) to stimulate growth from bud. After bud growth has started, cut stock back to bud. (Fig. 285).

7. Each student label his section of row with garden label. Give following information: (a) stock used; (b) variety of bud; (c) date of budding; (d) student's name; and (e) number of trees budded.

Questions and Assignments:

1. Under what circumstances is "June budding" practiced?

2. What are advantages of "June budding"? Disadvantages?

3. What wood is used for bud sticks in June budding? Describe its preparation.

4. In June budding, how is growth forced into bud?

5. What is good day's work for expert budder? How does your work compare with his as to speed?

XLII. PATCH AND MODIFIED "H" OR WINDOW BUDDING— LABORATORY PRACTICE

Materials and Equipment: 164, 166, 167, 189, 269, 282, 283, 308.

Directions:

A. PATCH BUDS

1. Select past season's growth shoots of black or English or other thick barked wood walnut ½" to 1½" in diameter for bud sticks.

2. Choose older wood 1" to 2" in diameter as stocks.

3. Draw budding tool around stock at smooth place in bark to make two parallel cuts 1" apart. (Fig. 290A and 291).

4. With blade of grafting or budding knife make two cuts 1" apart at right angles to previous cuts (Fig. 290B) to make 1" square patch. (Fig. 290C and D).

5. Remove and use patch thus made as directed below.

6. Use same method to cut bud from budstick, but slip patch off instead of pulling or lifting it as may be done on stock. If patch is lifted off, core at base of bud on under side will be pulled out and leave hollow base on bud. This may cause bud to dry out and not "take." If patch is slipped off core is snapped off where it springs from wood and remains in base of bud. Slipping bud off is accomplished by lifting one corner of patch and then, with thumb pressure, sliding patch off bud stick.

7. Insert patch with bud into opening on stock.

8. Wrap tightly with industrial tape, rubber strips (best), or waxed cloth,[1] leaving only bud protruding. (Fig. 290H).

9. Present work to instructor for criticisms.

B. MODIFIED "H" OR WINDOW BUD

1. Select wood as for patch budding.

---

[1] Preparation of waxed cloth in exercise XXXV. Rubber strips are best however.

2. Draw budding tool around stock as before, (Fig. 292-1).

3. Next, make single cut in center, thus connecting parallel cuts and making flap on each side of vertical cut. (Fig. 292-2).

4. Pry up flaps outward with knife blade but close them at once to prevent drying. (Fig. 292-3).

5. Remove 1" patch with bud from bud stick as in patch budding.

6. Insert patch under flaps.

7. Wrap with industrial tape or waxed cloth, leaving only bud protruding. Do not wrap over bud. (Fig. 292-8).

Questions and Assignments:

1. What method of budding would you recommend for budding walnuts? Why?

2. Describe fully subsequent treatment of budded trees.

3. When is it possible to bud walnut trees?

4. Which bud do you prefer—patch or window bud? Why?

5. On what kind of trees is patch budding or its modifications practiced?

XLIII. PATCH AND MODIFIED "H" OR WINDOW BUDDING [1]— ORCHARD AND NURSERY PRACTICE

Materials and Equipment: 164, 166, 167, 189, 246 (or 247), 272, 280, 308.

Directions:

Patch and modified "H" buds are used with success on thick barked nut trees—pecan, chestnut, walnut.

A. PATCH BUDS

Place ten patch buds on black walnut stocks 5/8" to 2" in diameter as detailed in Practicum XLII, but in actual nursery or orchard work thoroughly wrap each bud with budding rubber, budding tape or waxed cloth, leaving only bud uncovered (Fig. 290H). Budding rubber is best.

B. MODIFIED "H" OR WINDOW BUD

Make ten modified "H" buds by same steps as in Practicum XLII and wrap as in XLII.

1. In 15 to 20 days remove cloth or tape. If bud has taken, it will be fresh and plump and white callus will have formed around edges of patch. If it has not taken, patch will be brown and somewhat dried.

2. If it did not take, place another bud nearby on stock.

3. If it has taken, allow it to go through winter dormant (provided it was made in August or fall).

4. In spring, when tree starts growth, remove part of stock above bud. Make cut 6" from bud to throw growth into bud. After growth 6" to 12" long has been made from bud, cut rest of stock off just above bud.

Questions and Assignments:

1. Explain fully subsequent treatment of patch budded trees.

2. What are some methods of budding walnut trees other than those used here?

3. If you had black walnut trees 2' in diameter and wished to change tops to English walnuts, what would be your program and methods of grafting or budding or both?

---

[1] Patch or modified "H" budding may be done in spring with active buds or during July, August, or September. If work is done in spring, bud wood collected during dormant season and stored in damp moss or sand in cool cellar may be used; but wood may be taken directly from tree. It is necessary to bring bud wood out of storage week before budding and place in warm, moist location to start cambial activity so bark will slip and buds be slipped off readily. If work is done during summer, past season's growth is used as bud wood.

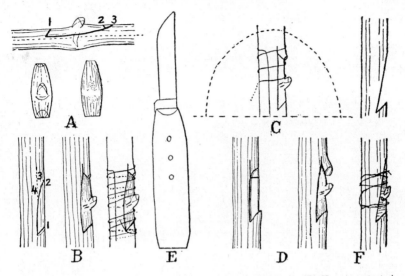

Fig. 293.—Yema grafts. (A) How to remove bud from scion cane. (B) How to cut stock, insert bud and tie graft. (C) How graft should be mounded up. (D) Modified Yema graft. (E) Knife used in Australia for Yema grafting. (F) New modified Yema graft.

XLIV. BUDDING GRAPES

Materials and Equipment: 60, 164, 166, 167, 180, 188.
Directions for Laboratory Study:
    Put in six buds for each of three methods (making total of 18 buds), as described below.

A. First Method

    1. With sharp budding knife prepare stock. (Fig. 293A, B, C, D, F).
    2. Remove bud (Fig. 293A).
    3. Place bud (Fig. 293B).
    4. Wrap with string or raffia.

B. Second Method

    1. Place bud (Fig. 293D and F).
    2. Make and wrap six buds.

C. Third Method. Any of your own.

Questions and Assignments:

    1. How does Yema bud or graft differ from "T" or shield bud?
    2. What is proper season to do grape budding?
    3. Which of three methods of putting in Yema bud did you find best? Why?

XLV. LAYING OUT ORCHARD [1]

Materials and Equipment: Refer to Chapter — "Laying out the Orchard" materials
    and direction needed in this practicum.

Directions:

    Lay out one acre plot by: (1) *square system,* and (2) by *hexagonal system.* (Chapter XX). (Figs. 328 to 335).

    [1] Figures 328 to 335.

Questions and Assignments:

1. Write full account of method of laying out orchard for planting by square system. Use sketches to illustrate. (Figs. 328 and 329).

2. What is proper planting distance for peach, apricot, plum, prune, almond, pear, apple and walnut?

3. Which system of planting do you prefer? Hexagonal or square? Why?

4. What are systems of planting other than those executed in this exercise?

XLVI. DIGGING AND PLANTING TREES FOR ORCHARD [1]

Materials and Equipment: 167, 251, 272, 309, horse and plow.

A. DIGGING NURSERY TREES FOR ORCHARD PLANTING

Trees should have shed their leaves and be dormant before being dug.

Directions:

Students work in pairs.

1. Plow furrow about 14″ away from trees on each side of row.
2. With sharp spade cut roots about 1′ from tree trunks.
3. With spade cut roots below trees.
4. After all roots are cut, allow trees to remain in place until cutting job is complete.
5. Trees may then be either planted, sold or stored.
6. When removed cover roots with wet burlap or heel them as shown in Figure 304.

B. PLANTING NURSERY TREES IN ORCHARD

It is assumed that field has been laid out and staked (Practicum XLV). Students in pairs plant 12 trees each.

1. When trees are taken from nursery or heeling-in ground cover roots with wet burlap.
2. Place planting board (Fig. 325B) in position over tree stake. Drive temporary stake at each end of board.
3. Remove planting board.
4. Remove tree marking stake.
5. Dig hole where tree stake stood, deep and wide enough to accommodate tree roots. (Fig. 326-4). Throw shovelful of top soil into bottom of hole.
6. Place setting board over temporary end stakes. (Fig. 325D).
7. Place tree in hole after pruning roots (Fig. 325E) so its trunk fits in center notch of board. (Fig. 326-5).
8. Spread roots out in natural position. (Figs. 325F and 326-5).
9. Throw in shovelful or two of top soil around roots.
10. Slightly lift and jar tree to work soil around roots.
11. Adjust tree so it will be at same depth as in nursery.
12. One student hold tree in place and push soil in place with hands while other throws in more soil. (Fig. 325G).
13. Tramp and firm soil while being thrown in. Get close around roots and trunk of tree with toes.
14. Do good job of firming as this is essential to successful planting. Firming does not mean to pack too tightly. (Fig. 325G).
15. Fill hole to level of ground.
16. Throw several shovelfuls of loose soil around tree and level ground. Do not tramp this.
17. Continue until 12 trees have been planted by each pair of students.
18. Whitewash trunks of set planted trees.[2] (Fig. 327).

---

[1] Figures 297 to 300.

[2] A simple good whitewash formula follows: "Slake fresh quicklime with water sprinkled on little by little till it forms a paste then thin it with skim milk and add one to three handfuls of salt to the mixture."

Questions and Assignments:

1. Give ideal method of preparing field for tree planting.
2. What is another method?
3. Describe care of trees from time of arrival until placed in ground.
4. What is "tree setting" board and how used?
5. Describe actual method of planting trees.

XLVII. PROPAGATION AND CULTURE OF VINES AND SMALL FRUITS

Material and Equipment: 49 to 57, 164, 166, 167, 235, 245, 249, 251, 261, 246, 266.

A. BLACKBERRY

Upright blackberries may be propagated by root suckers, root cuttings. Do work early in spring.

Directions: *Suckers.*

1. Dig shoots which have sprung from roots around established blackberry canes and cut tops back to 6" (Fig. 96).
2. Trim roots.
3. With spade plant in laid out field.
4. Set plants slightly deeper than they formerly were in ground 3' to 4' apart in row and rows 8' apart.
5. Destroy all suckers between rows with hoe and cultivator, except when it is desired to produce new plants.
6. Train plants by one system learned from reference reading.

Root Cuttings

1. In fall or early spring dig up blackberry roots ¼" or more in diameter.
2. Cut into pieces about 3" long.
3. Plant horizontally in trenches about 3" deep in well prepared nursery soil. By following fall these will have better root systems and be stronger plants than those made from suckers.
4. Set these new plants in field as in A 4 above.
5. After plants grow train them as in A 6 above.

B. TRAILING VARIETIES

Though trailing blackberries may be propagated by root cuttings, nearly all are usually propagated by tip layering in late summer or fall as detailed in Practicum XI.

B. LOGANBERRY

Loganberries are usually propagated by tip layering as detailed in Practicum XI.

C. RED RASPBERRY

Red raspberries are usually propagated by root cuttings, suckers or root tip plants. Methods are same as for blackberries. Section A, above.

D. BLACK RASPBERRY

See Practicum XI.

E. STRAWBERRIES

I. Narrow Rows—Raised Beds.

Directions:

If plants are to be held long they should be heeled-in.
1. Prepare bed as follows:

(a) Make beds 2' from center to center.
(b) Raise them above furrow 3" to 5".
2. Set plants as follows in center of bed:
(a) Trim roots.
(b) Move dibble backward and forward in ground to make hole for plant. (Figs. 195 to 197).
(c) Place and spread roots in hole.
(d) Insert dibble (Fig. 197B) in soil near plant.
(e) Press dibble toward plant thus firming soil around roots. Work may be done with spade.

II. Wide Matted Rows—Raised Beds.

Directions:

Actual setting plants is same as for narrow rows—raised bed system.
1. Make beds 5" above furrow between beds.
2. Make furrows between beds 24" wide.
3. Set double rows of plants on bed placing each row 4" from edge of bed and 16" apart.
4. Set plants 12" apart in rows.
5. Allow plants to spread toward edges of bed and toward center forming solid mass of plants.

III. Matted Row System—Level Planting

Under matted row system, plants are commonly set in winter or early spring 18" to 30" apart in rows 3½' to 6⁴ distant. Runners are allowed to root. Distance apart to set plants in row depends chiefly upon danger of loss of plants by drought and insects. If little danger, plants may be set 24" or more apart and runners trained to fill spaces thus forming solid mat of plants. Where loss from either cause is likely, plants should be set about 18" apart.

Directions:

1. Mark rows 40" apart with marker.
2. Along these marks set plants as previously described, 18" apart.
3. Allow all runners which appear to root.

IV. Hill System.

Under hill system plants originally set are kept for fruiting, no summer plants being allowed to root. In this way beds are formed. Single or double rows may be used in this system.

Directions:

Planting itself and distance between plants are same as for other systems.

I. Single Row Hill Sytem

1. Set the plants 18" apart and the rows 3' apart. An acre requires 9680 plants when set 1' x 54".
2. Remove all runners as they appear.

II. Double Row Hill System.

1. Set plants double rows 14" apart and plants in row 8" asunder. Make next double row 40" from center to center.
2. Remove all runners as they appear.

F. Gooseberry and Currant. (Fig. 55).

Gooseberries are ordinarily propagated by mound layers, but also by cuttings; currants almost entirely by cuttings of vigorous one year shoots.

Directions:

Students work in pairs. Each pair planting one flat. For detail see Practicum XX.

Cuttings in Flats. Houghton and Poorman gooseberry root readily from cuttings. Collect wood any time after it has matured in fall or until just before growth begins in spring. Choose strong healthy shoots of past season's growth.

1. Prepare flat of sharp, clean sand.
2. Make cuttings 6″ long.
3. Plant in flat.
4. When plants have developed shoots and roots, set in nursery.

Cuttings in Open Ground. This is usual method of planting these cuttings. Each student plant 25.

1. Make cuttings 8″ long.
2. Open trench with one straight side.
3. Place cuttings against straight side of trench.
4. Make rows 2′ apart and place cuttings 5″ asunder.
5. Leave at least one bud above ground when planting.
6. Cover soil around cuttings and firm well.
7. Give cuttings sufficient water to keep them moist but not wet.
8. When they have grown, dig and trim roots and tops and plant in field or garden.
9. In fall or winter, prune bushes.

Mound Layers. Gooseberry varieties like Downing do not root readily from cuttings so mound layering must be used. Plants should be cut back heavily in fall or winter. By midsummer many vigorous new shoots will have developed. Early in July, they should be mound layered as directed in Practicum XI.

Currants

Directions:

Nearly all varieties of currants root and grow readily from cuttings. Made any time after wood has matured in fall until just before growth begins in spring. They may be set at once in nursery or stored in a cool place in moist moss or sand until spring planting. Methods are detailed in Practicums XIV and XVI.

Questions and Assignments:

1. What is duration of plantation of blackberry, loganberry and dewberry?
2. Are bush fruits or strawberries desirable intercrop for young orchard? What are advantages? Disadvantages?
3. If you interplant small fruits in your orchard how long would you grow them?
4. How may upright blackberries, trailing blackberries, dewberries, red and black raspberries, loganberries, currants and gooseberries be propagated?
5. When is proper time for planting bush fruits in field?

XLVIII. PROPAGATION AND CULTURE OF VEGETABLES FOR HOME GARDEN

Materials and Equipment: 47, 182, 183, 184, 246, 250, 251, 267, 310. Manure.

A. APPLICATION OF FERTILIZERS FOR VEGETABLES

I. Manure

1. Apply manure at rate of 20 to 30 tons to acre in fall, if fall plowed, or well rotted manure just previous to plowing if spring plowed. Give manure opportunity to rot and become incorporated in soil before planting, so arrange for its application accordingly.

II. Commercial Fertilizers

When not possible to obtain manure use commercial fertilizers.

1. Apply complete fertilizer analyzing about 8% ammonia, 6% phosphoric acid and 6% potash, at rate of 1500 pounds to acre.

2. Increase amount of potash 1 to 8 or 10% on light soils.

3. Broadcast complete commercial fertilizer.

4. Thoroughly mix fertilizer with soil by using disk or harrow before seeds are shown or plants set.

All soils do not need fertilizer so it would be wasteful to apply when not needed.

B. PREPARATION OF GROUND

Prepare ground considerably in advance of rest of exercise either at home or on school grounds as directed.

1. If soil is heavy, plow in fall and leave rough for frost action on clods; if light, time of plowing is less important.

2. Plow in spring—second plowing where fall plowing is practiced.

3. Immediately harrow or rake to make surface fine after plowing and before soil has begun to bake.

4. Successful gardeners pulverize soil well before starting to plant.

C. PLANNING GARDEN

To insure regular year around supply of vegetables for family make planting plan.

1. Before starting to work garden make list of vegetables to be grown and sketch plan for their placing. Flowers with vegetables make attractive appearance.

2. Table 7 will help in making the list of vegetables.

3. After list has been made determine planting dates for each species and variety.

4. Next, determine approximate harvesting dates.

5. After determining time between planting and harvest make notations as to what crops to follow or rotate, and arrange for two plantings on same ground, setting down dates for second sowings.

6. Decide lengths of, and widths between rows. Note these on sketch.

7. Determine amount of seed necessary for each variety to plant.

8. When sketch and other planting information are completed, check to see that following items are included:

a. Length of rows. b. Distance between rows. c. Varieties of vegetables to be planted. d. Amount of seed required for each. e. Cost (estimated) of seed. f. Planting calendar. g. Harvesting calendar.

D. PLANTING THE SEED

Usually method of planting is covered by instructions on packet of seed.

1. Use hotbed and coldframe for starting seeds early in spring before weather outdoors is suitable for sowing. This work should start from two to five weeks previous to setting plants in open. Window box may be used for early starting of seeds (Fig. 140).

2. Many seeds will be started in open ground. Plant these as directed on seed packet, in text book or seed catalogs.

3. Lay out rows in straight lines. Do not make rows too short. This would make garden inconvenient to cultivate and irrigate.

4. Use wire stretched between stakes for laying out rows.

5. Keep garden free from weeds and well irrigated if rainfall is not sufficient for steady growth of plants.

6. Follow calendar of planting as closely as weather permits.

E. RECORDS

1. Keep full record of all operations.

2. Keep full cost record of production.

3. Keep full record of time, money for hired work done, or spent on garden.

4. Keep full record of vegetables consumed by family, estimate price and credit income from garden with this amount.

5. Keep record of vegetables sold.

Questions and Assignments:

1. Take into account expenses of garden, vegetables used and state whether home garden is paying project.

2. Write discussion on desirability of home garden.

3. Give description of desirable location for home garden and state how yours may be improved.

4. Describe how you prepared soil for your home garden.

5. What pests did you find in your garden? What are proper methods of controlling them?

XLIX. GREENHOUSES AND GREENHOUSE PRACTICES

Materials and Equipment: 44 to 46, 64, 82, 100, 102, 231, 311.

A. CONSTRUCTION OF GREENHOUSE[1] (Figs. 131 and 151 to 156).

Directions:

1. Under supervision of shop instructor give aid in constructing greenhouse (Fig. 156).

2. Make concrete foundations and side walls.

3. Imbed in concrete, 2″ iron pipe posts fitted with special post top fittings on which to attach wooden gutter.

Construction may be modified if instructor sees fit to use wooden posts and angle iron.

4. Read literature on greenhouse construction.[2]

5. If house is to be heated with hot water or steam, lay out pipe above which benches are to be and connect with main pipes from and to boiler.

6. Take care of such construction problems as how to put up superstructure, side and end walls, sash bars, how to ventilate, paint, and glaze, heat, supply water and install heating systems.

7. When house is completed put in walks and benches. (Figs. 155 and 156).

B. GREENHOUSE PRACTICES

Many plants may be grown to high perfection in greenhouse when they do not succeed outdoors. Handling requires attention to such factors as light, heat, humidity or air moisture, water, air, shade and soil.

I. Light and Heat from Sun

Light and heat of late spring and summer are too intense for many greenhouse plants so shade is necessary.

1. In spring mix enough white lead or whiting in gasoline to cover glass on greenhouse.

2. Make preparation thin but add more lead or whiting if necessary.

3. Apply outside to glass with a hand operated spray outfit.

II. Heat

1. Keep heat at uniform temperature especially during night.

Requirements range with type of crop to be grown. For instance, lettuce, violets and other cool climate crops do best at night temperatures of 45° to 50° F.; carnations 50° to 60°; tomatoes 60° to 65°, cucumbers 60° to 70°, and so on.

2. Keep temperature of soil same as that of air by using raised benches for planting and placing heat beneath.

3. Give artificial heat from October to March or April when necessary. For balance of year artificial heat may not be needed except during cold days.

---

[1] If it is desirable to construct larger house it will probably be best to hire work done, although under proper supervision it is possible for shop man and class to do work.

[2] U. S. Dept. of Agr. Far. Bul. 1318 discusses Greenhouse Construction and Heating.

III. Humidity of Air

1. Maintain humidity of 75% for most crops. This is done by watering walks as well as plants on all bright days.
2. Remember decrease in temperature will increase relative humidity and deposit moisture on leaves, so keep temperature where it belongs.

IV. Water

1. Water in mornings only.
2. Water to point of saturation only when plants need water. Too much water or water to saturation point for long periods excludes soil air which is essential to plant well being.
3. Provide ample drainage in benches and flats by boring $1/2''$ holes in bottoms.

Too much moisture and too little light at all times induce "damping off," since these conditions favor its development.

Surface watering, common method, may be done by hand with fine sprinkling nozzle or by overhead sprinkling system if house is properly arranged for it. Experimentally, sub-irrigation has given best results but this method is not yet practical.

V. Air

1. Give proper ventilation whenever weather conditions permit. On warm sunny days open ventilators.
2. Avoid drafts.
3. Open ventilators more or less during winter when outside temperature is not below freezing.
4. Fresh air is essential to healthy growth of plants.

VI. Soil

In class most work will be done in benches or in flats on tables.
1. Use medium textured to fairly coarse sharp, clean sand for propagating cuttings either in benches or in flats.
2. Use composted soil (Practicum XXIV) for benches where plants are to be grown for bloom or fruit.

C. PLANTS TO GROW

I. Crop Plants

Put composted soil in selected bench. Plant sections to any of following plants: a. Lettuce (Fig. 157); b. tomato (Fig. 157); c. cucumbers; d. radish; e. melon, or, f. mushroom.

II. Ornamental or Flowering Plants

Grow any of following plants or others in benches or beds: Rose, carnation, chrysanthemum, violet, tuberous begonia, orchid, azalea, primula, ferns, smilax, asparagus fern, begonia rex, coleus, vinca, impatiens, poinsettia, or cyclamen.

III. Preliminary Preparation of Greenhouse for fumigation

1. Examine carefully exposed glass surface of greenhouse.
2. Replace all broken glass.
3. Close all cracks carefully.
4. Arrange ventilators, as far as possible, so they may be opened from outside by disconnecting "machine," or gear, of top ventilators and attaching to central ventilator shaft (Figs. 196 and 200) an arm (a or b) which may be controlled by cord or wire extended through side of greenhouse. Gears on side ventilators may be disconnected so sash may be opened from outside. If only one ventilator can be opened, it should be on roof of greenhouse.

IV. Mixing Chemicals and Fumigating

Mix chemicals in following proportions: for each ounce of sodium cyanide use $1\frac{1}{2}$ fluid ounces of sulphuric acid and 2 fluid ounces of water.

1. Use one gallon earthenware jars.

2. Distribute jars throughout greenhouse before chemicals are mixed; placing them 20' to 25' apart, (Fig. 188,) so gas will be distributed uniformly.

3. Determine amounts of cyanide by using dosage tables (19 and 20) and computed cubic contents. (Fig. 197).

4. Divide cyanide evenly among number of jars. One ounce to jar is as small dose as is practical.

5. Mix chemicals invariably in following manner at temperature between 55° and 68° F.

    a. Fumigate after sundown. Post danger sign on door.

    b. Measure and place in each generator (jar) amount of water required.

    c. Measure and place in each generator (jar) amount of sulphuric acid required.

    d. Starting at generator farthest from door drop cyanide gently into diluted warm acid in each generator.[1]

    e. Immediately leave and lock greenhouse.

    f. Expose house to gas for one or two hours in evening or early morning before sunrise, former preferred.

    g. Allow gas to escape after not more than two hours.

    h. Thoroughly air greenhouse previous to sunrise.

    i. When job is over bury or pour residue into sink and wash both sink and generators before storing latter.

    j. Fumigate again at proper time.[2]

V. Fumigation with Cyanogas

Read text 214 to 220 in regard to fumigation and, if desired, use this method of fumigation in lieu of previously outlined method. Latter method is to be preferred. It is safer and just as effective. (Fig. 198).

Questions and Assignments:

1. Define greenhouse.

2. What is good location for greenhouse?

3. Take care of greenhouse for one week tending to ventilation of house and watering of plants.[3]

4. Write paper on propagation of cucumbers under glass.[4]

5. Do same for tomatoes and lettuce.[4]

L. PROPAGATION OF ORNAMENTALS FOR HOME AND SCHOOL GROUNDS

1. Materials and equipment will not be given here because propagation methods to be followed are not definitely known. Constant reference in this practicum must be made to other practicums and text where lists of materials are given.

---

[1] In case there are two rows of generators cyanide should be dropped simultaneously by two operators. As little time as possible should elapse between addition of acid and addition of cyanide, as heat liberated by mixing of acid and water assists in generation of gas.

[2] Interval between fumigations naturally must be governed by reappearance of insect to be controlled. With small dosages, which are imperative when fumigating greenhouse containing assortment of plants, it is possible to kill only larvæ of scale insects, adults and first larva stages of greenhouse white fly, adults of Florida fur caterpillar, greenhouse leaf-tyer, loopers and percentage of aphids. Eggs and pupæ of most greenhouse insects offer considerable resistance to gas so overlapping of broods necessitates several fumigations at short intervals. Three or four such fumigations will give practical control.

[3] Good plan to follow is to have different pair of students responsible for watering and care of greenhouse plants each week. This is better than having each individual student care for his plant material all time.

[4] U. S. Dept. of Agr. Far. Bul. 1431, Greenhouse Tomatoes, and No. 1418, Lettuce Growing in Greenhouses.

Directions:

1. Use plant lists made in practicums and check with plant lists in this book (pp. 519 to 526) to determine methods of propagating each plant used.

2. After propagation methods have been determined, refer to various practicums for instructions and proceed to propagate plants required by planting plans of home and school grounds.

3. When these plants have been grown to proper size in frames, greenhouse, nursery or lath house, harden them off and plant in place according to plans.

Questions and Assignments:

1. Make list of plants used for planting plans and state how each plant is propagated.

CULTURAL INSTRUCTIONS

1. ANNUALS AND PERENNIALS GROWN FROM SEED

CONDENSED CULTURAL INSTRUCTIONS

For Flower Seeds *

The letter opposite the plant name refers to the proper paragraph in the list which follows.

Abronia ... A	Cobæa ... D	Ice Plant ... A	Perilla ... D
Abutilon ... N	Coccinea ... F	Impatiens ... N	Petunia ... D
Acacia ... S	Cockscomb ... A	Incarvillea ... U	Phlox, annual ... F
Achillea ... V	Coleus ... D	Inula ... V	" hardy ... V
Acroclinium ... M	Collinsia ... U	Ipomœa ... F	Physalis ... A
Adlumia ... G	Convolvulus ... F	Ivy, English ... V	Pinks, annual ... U
Adonis ... F	Coreopsis, hardy ... V		" hardy ... V
Ageratum ... F	Cosmos ... A		Platycodon ... V
Agrostemma ... A	Cowslip ... C	Kaulfussia ... U	Polyanthus ... C
Alyssum ... A	Crepis ... U	Kenilworth Ivy ... V	Poppy, annual ... P
" perennial ... V	Cucumis ... F	Kochia ... A	" hardy ... V
Amaranthus ... A	Cuphea ... A	Kudzu Vine ... V	Portulaca ... F
Ampelopsis ... V	Cyclamen ... B		Primula, tender ... B
Anchusa ... V	Cypress Vine ... F		" hardy ... C
Anemone ... V		Lantana ... N	Pyrethrum, hardy ... V
Angelonia ... N		Larkspur, annual ... U	" golden-leaved .. Q
Antirrhinum ... A	Dahlia ... O	Lathyrus, latifolius.. V	
Aquilegia ... V	Datura ... F	Lavateria ... F	
Aralia ... N	Delphinium ... V	Lavender ... V	Rehmannia ... N
Arctotis ... V	Dianthus, annual ... U	Layia ... U	Rhodanthe ... M
Aristolochia ... V	" hardy ... V	Lemon Verbena ... N	Rhodochiton ... N
Arnebia ... A	Digitalis ... V	Leptosiphon ... U	Ricinus ... F
Asparagus	Dimorphotheca ... A	Linum ... U	Rocket ... V
verticillatus ... V	Dolichos ... F	Lobelia, annual ... Q	Rose, monthly ... I
" plumosa ... S	Dracæna ... N	" hardy ... V	" hardy ... V
" sprengeri ... S		Lupinus ... U	Rudbeckia, annual .. U
Asters ... A		Lychnis ... V	
Auricula ... C	Echinocystis ... F		
	Edelweiss ... V		Salpiglossis ... A
	Eschscholtzia ... U	Malope ... F	Salvia ... A
Balloon Vine ... F	Euphorbia ... F	Mallow ... F	Scabiosa ... F
Balsam ... A		Marigold ... F	Scabiosa ... F
Bartonia ... U		Marvel of Peru ... F	" perennial . V
Begonia ... S	Ferns ... S	Mathiola ... F	Schizanthus ... F
Bellis ... C	Fuchsia ... N	Matricaria ... D	Silene ... N
Bignonia ... V		Maurandia ... D	Smilax ... N
Brachycome ... F		Mesembryan-	Stevia ... A
Browallia ... A		themum ... F	Stocks, annual ... A
Bryonopsis ... F	Gaillardia ... F	Mignonette ... U	" biennial ... I
	" perennial ... V	Mimosa ... D	Stokesia ... V
	Geranium ... N	Mimulus ... D	Sunflower ... F
Cacalia ... U	Geum ... V	Mina ... J	Swainsonia ... S
Calampelis ... A	Gilia ... U	Momordica ... F	Sweet Pea ... E
Calandrinia ... P	Gladiolus Seed ... O	Moon Flower ... F	Sweet Sultan ... F
Calceolaria ... B	Globe Amaranth ... M	Morning Glory ... F	Sweet William ... V
Calendula ... F	Gloxinia ... S	Musa ... K	
Calliopsis, annual ... F	Godetia ... U	Myosotis ... C	
Campanula ... V	Goldenrod ... V		Tagetes ... F
Canary Vine ... F	Gourds ... F		Thunbergia ... F
Candytuft ... U	Grevillea ... N	Nasturtium ... F	Torenia ... D
" hardy ... V	Gypsophila ... F	Nemesia ... N	Tritoma ... O
Canna ... O	" hardy ... V	Nemophila ... U	Tropæolum ... F
Canterbury Bell ... V		Nicotiana ... D	
Carnation ... T		Nigella ... U	
Celastrus ... V		Nolana ... U	Valerian ... V
Celosia ... A	Helichrysum ... M		Verbena ... A
Centaurea ... U	Heliotrope ... N		Vinca ... N
" white-leaved Q	Helenium ... V	Œnothera ... A	Violet ... C
Centrosema ... V	Heuchera ... F	Oxalis ... F	Virginian Stock ... U
Chrysanthemum,	Hibiscus, annual ... F		Viscaria ... U
annual ... U	" hardy ... V	Pæonia ... V	
" perennial ... T	Hollyhock, hardy ... V	Palava ... U	
Cineraria ... B	" annual ... A	Pansy ... C	Wallflower ... V
" white-leaved Q	Honeysuckle ... V	Passion Flower ... N	Wistaria ... V
Clarkia ... U	Humea ... Q	Pelargonium ... N	
Clematis ... V	Humulus ... F	Pennisetum ... F	Zea ... F
Cleome ... F	Hyacinthus ... O	Pentstemon ... V	Zinnias ... F
Clianthus ... D			

Courtesy Peter Henderson & Co., New York

519

GENERAL RULES

To avoid repetition in the lettered rules below, the following general rules and notes have been cut from the Henderson original directions:

Where mentioned as necessary to grow seedlings, flats should not be over 2½ inches deep.

Seeds should be covered not more than four times their diameters.

Unless otherwise stated, seeds should be firmed in the soil.

Never let seedlings become dry.

Transplanting of seedlings is done when two or three true leaves have formed.

A Sow in flats in greenhouse, hotbed, or light window of dwelling in temperature of 60 to 70 degrees. Cover and firm the seeds. Water with fine spray. Transplant 1 inch apart in similar flats or 2-inch pots. Plant out in garden after danger from frost. Seed may also be sown in open ground after danger from frost is over.

B Sow in flats of light soil in greenhouse, hotbed, or light window, in temperature of 50 to 60 degrees, at any time except during hot weather (spring months preferred). Merely press the seed into the soil with firming board; rub a little light soil through a fine sieve over them until covered not deeper than 1-16 of an inch. Water with fine spray. Transplant 1 inch apart in flats. Pot off as soon as large enough. Shift as pots fill with roots until the sizes of the pots are 6 or 7 inches.

C For early flowering, sow in fall in bed of fine, well-pulverized soil. Cover and firm the seed. Transplant about 2 inches apart in cold frames; cover with mats during very cold weather. Sow also in spring in flats, in temperature of about 60 degrees, and transplant 1 inch apart in flats. Plant in the open as soon as frost has left the ground. The plants succeed best in a moist, loamy soil, partially protected from hot sun.

D Sow in light soil in flats, placed in hotbed, greenhouse, or window, in a temperature of 60 to 70 degrees. Cover seeds and press firmly. Water with fine spray. Transplant 1 inch apart in flats. Plant out in open garden after danger from frost, or pot in 2-inch pots and plant out from these, or shift into larger pots as the plants need root room—this last provided large plants in pots are desired.

E Sow in spring in open ground where plants are to grow, in deeply prepared soil. The sooner sowing can be done the better. Thin seedlings to 6 inches apart. Moist, loamy soil gives best results. Seeds should be 2 inches deep in soil; in lighter soil they should be 4 or 5 inches deep, and the soil should be well firmed upon them. If not allowed to go to seed they will flower much longer.

F Sow out of doors in well-pulverized soil when danger from frost is over. Cover and press soil firmly. Thin out so the plants are not crowded. If desired, early seed may also be sown in greenhouse, hotbed, or light window of dwelling. Transplant to flats and plant in open ground after danger from frost is over.

G Sow in spring in open ground where plants are to remain. Cover and firm, and thin seedlings as necessary so they do not crowd. Protect roots in winter by covering of leaves or straw.

I Sow in flats of light soil in greenhouse or hotbed. Cover and firm. Transplant in flats and plant out in open ground after frost danger is over. If sown early, they will flower the first year; if not, they will have to be taken up, in cold localities, potted off and kept in cool greenhouse, or heeled in in protected frames during winter. Sow also in well-pulverized bed in open ground in spring or summer, and care for in winter in the same way.

J Sow in light soil in flats in warm greenhouse, hotbed, or light window of dwelling. Cover. Transplant 1 inch apart. If profusion of flowers is desired, pot off when about 1 inch high into 2½-inch pots and allow to become pretty well root-bound, to check luxuriant growth and throw the vigor into flowers. Plant out in garden after danger of frost is over.

K Plant seeds in flats about 1 inch apart and ½ to 1 inch deep, in light soil mixed with cocoanut dust, leaf mold, or well-rotted manure. Place in warm situation at temperature of not less than 70 degrees, either in greenhouse, hotbed, or window. When seedlings are large enough, pot off singly into small pots, and shift into larger ones as necessary.

M Sow out of doors when danger of frost is over. Cover, press firmly, and thin out seedlings to prevent crowding. If desired early, sow in flats in greenhouse, hotbed, or light window, in temperature averaging 70 degrees, and transplant to similar flats. If desired to keep flowers as everlasting, cut when buds are a little more than half open and suspend in a dark, dry place with heads down until fully dry.

N Sow in flats of light soil in greenhouse, hotbed, or light window of dwelling house, in temperature averaging 65 degrees. Cover, press firmly, and transplant seedlings 1 inch apart into similar flats. Water with fine spray. Pot off as soon as large enough, and repot, as they grow, into larger pots; or they may be planted out in open ground for the summer, after danger of frost is over.

O Sow in flats of light soil in greenhouse, hotbed, or light window of dwelling, with an average temperature of 65 degrees. Transplant 1 inch apart to similar flats, and plant out in garden after danger of frost is over. In fall, take up roots and store in sand in cool, dry place, such as cellar. Sowings may also be made in open ground in spring, after danger of frost is over.

P Sow in open ground after danger from frost is over, in beds of well-pulverized soil. Plants should remain where sown, as they will not stand transplanting unless done with extraordinary care. Thin out carefully, so as not to disturb the remaining plants more than necessary. For succession of blooms, two or three sowings may be made at intervals during summer.

Q To get good sized plants for planting out in the spring, sow seed in flats in greenhouse, hotbed, or light window of dwelling as soon after January first as possible, in light soil, in temperature averaging 60 degrees. Cover, firm. Transplant to similar flats 1 inch apart. When large enough, pot in 2½-inch pots. Plant in open ground after danger from frost is over.

S Sow in flats of light soil, in temperature of 70 degrees, in greenhouse, or light window of dwelling. Merely press seed into soil. Always water with fine spray, so as not to disturb the surface. Place pane of glass over top, but allow a little space for ventilation. Put flats in shaded place. Transplant to similar flats and pot off when large enough.

T Sow in spring in greenhouse, hotbed, or light window of dwelling, where temperature will average 60 degrees. Use flats of light soil. Cover. Transplant seedlings 1 inch apart in flats. When 1 or 2 inches, pot in 2½-inch flats, and shift to larger ones as needed, or plant in open ground, where plants will form flowering clumps for fall and winter.

U Sow out of doors after danger from frost, and, for succession, at intervals during summer. For early flowering, sow in greenhouse, hotbed, or south or southeast window of dwelling, in flats, with average temperature of 60 degrees. Transplant to similar flats and plant seedlings in open after danger from frost is past. Also sow in garden in May in light soil; cover, firm, and water with fine spray.

V Sow out of doors after danger from frost is over, in beds of finely pulverized soil. Cover with light soil and firm. Thin out when necessary. Plant in permanent position as soon as seeds are large enough, so they may become firmly rooted or established before cold weather; or sow in early fall, carry plants over in coldframe, and transplant to permanent position in spring.

2. WOODY PLANTS

Acer ....A, B, I	Cornus ....G, I	Kerria ....E, G	Quercus ....A, I
Æsculus ....B, I	*Cratægus ....B, I	Kœlreuteria C	
Ailanthus ....B	Cytisus ....F, I		Rhamnus C
Akebia C		Laburnum ....C, I	Robinia ....B, H
Almond (dbl. fl.) I	Deutzia ....E	Larix I	Rose ....A, F, I
Alnus C	Diervilla ....E, G	Ligustrum ......B, F	
Amelamchier ...C, I		*Liquidambar ..A, B	Salix ....G, I
Amorpha I	Euonymus ......G, I	Liriodendron ....B, I	Sambucus ...C, D, G
Ampelopsis ....F	Elæagnus I	Lonicera ......A, B	Sassafras ....C, H
	Exochorda ......C, D		Sophora ....C, F, I
		Magnolia ...A, F, I	Spiræa ....A, F
Barberry ....B	Fagus ....B, I	Menispermum .....F	Stuartia .....C, D, F
Betula ....A, B, I	Forsythia ......E, G	Myrica ....A	*Styrax ....A, B, E
Bignonia ....F	*Fraxinus ......B, I	Mulberry ....G, I	Symphoricarpus .B, E
			Symplocus ......C, F
Calycanthus ....B, C	Ginkgo ....B, I	Nemopanthes ......A	Syringa ..D, E, G, I
Caragana ....D, H, I	Gleditschia ......B, I	*Nyssa ....B	
Carpinus I			Tamarix ....G
Catalpa ....B, E, I	Halesia ....B	Ostrya ....C, I	Taxodium ....C, I
Ceanothus ......B, D	Hamamelis C	Oxydendrum C	Tilia ....B, I
Celtis ....A, G	Hickory ....B, I		
Cephalanthus ....G	Hydrangea .....E, F		Ulmus ....A, I
Cercediphyllum ....E	Hypericum ...G, H	Paulownia ......C, G	
Chestnut ....B, I		Philadelphus ......G	Vaccinium C
Chinquapin I	Itea C	Phellodendron ......H	*Viburnum ......B, E
Chionanthus ...C, I		Populus ....A, G	
Cladrastis .....D, H	Juglans ....B, I	Ptelia ....A, I	Wistaria ......C, F, I
Clethra ....F	Juneberry ....B		
Colutea ....G			Xanthoceras ....C, H

* Seeds often require two years to germinate.

A Seeds sown as soon as ripe; hardy kinds in frames outdoors, tender ones in greenhouse.

B Seeds stratified over winter and sown in spring in nursery row.

C Seeds, spring or fall sown, in frames.

D Layers during summer.

E Soft or semi-mature cuttings in early summer.

F Soft or semi-mature cuttings in winter or spring, in gentle heat.

G Ripe wood cuttings in fall, winter, or spring.

H Root cuttings in spring.

I Named varieties and rare species grafted on seedling or cutting-grown stocks.

3. EVERGREENS

Abies ......A, D, E	Cistus ....A, H	Kalmia ....B, D	Pinus ....A, D
Andromeda .....B, F	Cotoneaster ....H		Pseudotsuga A, B, E
Azalea ....H		Ledum ....F	
	Daphne ....G	Leiophyllum ....C, F	
Buxus C		Leucothoë .....C, F	Retinospora .... A, D
	Empetrum ....H		Rhododendron .. A, D
Calluna ....H	*Ilex ....A, D	Mahonia ....H	
Cedrus ....A, D			Taxus .... A. D
Chamæcyparis ......A	*Juniperus ..A, D, H	Picea ....D, E	Thuya ....A, D

A   Sow seeds in spring. Transplant seedlings to nursery rows following spring.

B   Sow freshly ripe seeds thinly in peaty-sandy soil, or sphagnum, in pots or pans. Give ample air in coldframe. Plant out seedlings following spring, or, if too small, prick out in flats.

C   Sow newly ripe seeds in light, well-drained soil in coldframe.

D   Graft named varieties and sparse seeding species during winter on fall potted seedlings. Veneer grafts generally do best.

E   Set seedlings of growing tips in sand in shaded frame. Don't disturb from six months to a year.

F   Layers pegged down in September will root in a year or less.

G   Mature cuttings in fall in well drained pots of peaty soil in propagating bed. Keep cool during winter. Give gentle heat in spring. Pot rooted plants singly, and grow in mild but close heat till established. Harden off in fall.

H   Mature wood cuttings in late summer in sand, in coldframes or cool house.

4. VINES

Actinidia	Celastrus	Humulus	Periploca
Akebia	Clematis		
Ampelopsis		Ipomœa	
Apios	Decumaria		Rose, Climbing
Aristolochia		Lonicera	
Bignonia	Euonymus	Lycium	Wistaria

Seeds in late winter or early spring; layers during spring or summer; mature wood cuttings in summer or fall, in mild heat; greenwood cuttings in winter.

5. HARDY PERENNIALS

Acanthus	Aubretia	Delphinium	Hepatica
Achillea	Auricula	Dianthus	Heracleum
Aconite		Dicentra	Hesperis
Acorus	Baptisia	Dictamnus	Heuchera
Actæa	Bellis	Digitalis	Hollyhock
Adonis	Boconnia	Dodecatheon	Houstonia
Ajuga	Boltonia	Doronicum	Hyssop
Althæa	Borago	Dracocephalum	
Alyssum			Inula
Amsonia	Callirrhöe	Echinops	
Anchusa	Campanula	Elecampane	Liatris
Anemone	Caryopteris	Epimedium	Linaria
Anthemis	Cassia	Eryngium	Lobelia
Apios	Catananche	Eupatorium	Lychnis
Aquilegia	Centaurea		Lysimachia
Arabis	Centranthus	Gaillardia	Lythrum
Arenaria	Cerastium	Galega	
Armeria	Chelone	Gentiana	Mandragora
Arnica	Chrysanthemum	Geum	Menispermum
Artemisia	Cimicifuga	Gynerium	Mertensia
Arundo	Clematis	Gypsophila	Miscanthus
Asperula	Clintonia	Hæmodorum	
Asphodeline	Coreopsis	Hedysarum	Œnothera

Pentstemon	Ranunculus	Silene	Trillium
Phalaris	Rheum	Silphium	Trollius
Phlomis	Rudbeckia	Sisyrinchium	
Phlox		Stachys	Uvularia
Platycodon	Salvia	Staphylea	
Podophyllum	Sanguinaria	Statice	Verbascus
Polemonium	Saponaria	Stokesia	Veronica
Polygonatum	Saxifraga		
Polygonum	Scabiosa	Tansy	Wormwood
Potentilla	Shepherdia	Thalictrum	Yucca

Sow the above named species (1) outdoors after danger of frost in beds of finely pulverized, light soil, transplant to permanent place when large enough to become established before cold weather; (2) or sow the seed between midsummer and early fall in coldframes, protect over winter, and plant the seedlings in the spring; (3) start the seeds during midwinter in the greenhouse, transplant to small plots, and shift when rooted. In case three, plants kept growing sturdily will usually bloom the first season.

6. BULBS, CORMS AND TUBERS

Agapanthus	A	Crocus	B	Helleborus	A	Ornithogalum	B
Allium	B			Hemerocallis	A	Oxalis	B
Alstrœmeria	E	Dahlia	A	Hippeastrum	B		
Amaryllis	D	Dicentra	E	*Hyacinth		Pæony	E
Amorphophallus	D	Dioscorea	E			Polianthes	B
Anemone	E			Iris	A, B	Puschkinia	B
Anomatheca	E			Ixia	B		
Anthericum	E	Eranthis	E			Ranunculus	A
Apios	E	Eremurus	E	Kniphofia	B	Richardia	C
Astilbe	A	Erythronium	E				
		Eucharis	E			Scilla	B
Begonia	A			Leucoium	F	Sparaxis	E
Boussingaulia	A	Freesia	B	Lilium	B		
Bravoa	B	Fritillaria	A			Tigridia	E
		Funkia	A	Milla	B	Trillium	E
Caladium	C			Muscari	B	Triteleia	D
Canna	A	Galanthus	B			Tritonia	D
Chionodoxa	B	Galtonia	B			Tulipa	B
Colchicum	B	Gladiolus	B				
Convallaria	E			Narcissus	B	Zephyranthes	B

See—For special treatment.

A Seeds. Offsets, tubers, or divisions of old plants early in spring.

B Seeds. Bulbels or offsets fall planted under glass, or spring planted out of doors.

C Tubers, dried or rested. Divide large, healthy ones. Keep pots in moderate night temperature; syringe once or twice daily.

D Seeds. Offsets or divisions at any time.

E Seeds. Division of roots fall or spring.

F Bulbels as soon as possible after foliage matures.

7. GREENHOUSE AND HOUSE PLANTS

Abutilon ....A	Begonia ....A	Fuchsia ....A	Polianthes
Acalypha ....B	Bouganvillea ......F		Plumbago ....B
Acanthus C	Bouvardia ......B, C	Genista ....B	
Achyranthes ....A		Geranium ....A	Richardia C
Agapanthus ....B	Caladium ....C, G		
Ageratum ....A	Calla C	Hibiscus ....A, H	Sanseveriera ....E
Allamanda ....B	Canna C	Hydrangea ....A	Smilax ....E
Aloysia ....B	Carnation ....A		Swainsona ....A
Alternanthera ......A	Chrysanthemum ..H	Jasminum ......B, F	
Alyssum ....A	Clerodendron A, C, E		Thunbergia ....H
Amaryllis ....D	Clevia ....A	Lantana ....A	Tigridia ....D
Anthericum C	Cobœa ....A	Lobelia ....A	Tuberose ....D
Antirrhinum ....A	Coleus ....B		
Ardisia ....A	Colocasia ....G	Moonflower ....B	Vallota ....D
			Verbena ....A
Asparagus C	Dieffenbachia ......G	Pandanus ......B, E	Vinca C
Aspidistra ....E		Passiflora ....A	
Aucuba ....A	Eucharis ....D	Pelargonium ....A	Zephyranthes ....D

A　Green wood cuttings at any time, rather warm temperature; after rooting, pot in friable soil.

B　Greenwood cuttings, warm temperature; late winter or early spring.

C　Root division or root cuttings; autumn or early spring.

D　Offsets or divisions; whenever mature enough to remove.

E　Division, crown, or suckers at any time.

F　Semi-mature wood cuttings, warm temperature.

G　Tubers, dry or resting, moderate temperature; syringed daily at least once.

H　Semi-mature wood cuttings, fall, winter or spring. Low temperature.

8. FERNS

Acrostichum		Cyathea		Lastrea	*Platycerium
Adiantum	A	Cyrtonium		Lomaria	Platyloma
Alsophila		Cystopteris		*Lygodium	*Polypodium
Anemia					Polystichum　　A
Aspidium		*Davallia			Pteris
Asplenium	A	*Dicksonia		Nephrodium	
		Doodia		*Nephrolepis	
Botrychium		Doryopteris			Scolopendrium
					**Selaginella
Cheilanthes		Gleichenia		Onychium	
Civotium		Gymnogramma	A	*Osmunda	

* Propagated largely by division.
** Propagated by short cuttings in pots or pans in early spring.
　Steam sterilized soil at high temperature to destroy fern enemies.

Soil mixture: Two parts each garden loam and peat (or leaf mold) and one part clean, sharp sand. Use only sterilized (boiled and cooled) water for watering. Buy only best grade spores. Sow in March, July, or October. Use cans 12 inches square and 4 inches deep, or 6-inch ¾ pots, each a third full of drainage (cinders). Press soil firmly in pots or pans. Pass surface half inch through ⅛-inch screen, level, press and water. Wait four hours before dusting spores on surface. Use no more spores for 12-inch pan than will pile on a ¼-inch circle. Have no breeze while sowing. Don't cover with soil. Place shaded sash over frame and keep closed till germination starts, then give air, little at first, more gradually till fronds appear and are hardened enough to have sash removed. Use no water for first two or more weeks. Weed out undesirable plants. When pot surface is covered with little ferns, prick out in clumps of three to six just level with surface of other flats. When clumps have three or four fronds, transplant singly in other pans or flats, and later into 2 or 2¼-inch pots.

A　Certain ferns (among them species and varieties of genera marked **A** in the list) bear detachable buds, bulblets, or plantlets on fronds and pinnæ. These, planted in well-drained seed pans, usually take root in less than two weeks. Others may be divided just before the plants start to grow.

9. PALMS

Acanthophœnix	Clinostigma	Hyophorbæ	Pinanga
Acanthorhiza	*Cocos	Hyphæne	*Pecctocomia
Acrocomia	Corypha		Pritchardia
Archonphœnix	Cycas	Jubæa	Ptychosperma
Areca	Cyphophœnix		
Arenga	Cyphosperma	Kentia	Raphia
Astrocarpum		Kentiopsis	Rhapidophyllum
Attalea	Dictosperma		Rhapis
	Didymosperma	Latania	Rhopalostylis
	Dion	Licuala	Roscheria
*Bactris	Diplothemium	Linospadix	
Bacularia	Drymophlœus	Livistonia	*Sabal
Borassus	Dypsis	Lodoicea	Scheilea
Brahea			Seaforthea
	Elæis	Martinezia	
Calamus	Erythea	Maxiliminia	Thrinax
Calyptrogyne	Euterpe		*Trachycarpus
*Caryota		Nenga	
Ceratolobus	*Geonoma		Veitchia
Ceroxylon		Oreodoxa	Verschaffeltia
Certostachys	Hedyscepe		
Chamædorea	Howea	*Phœnix	*Wallichia
Chamærops	Hydriastele	Phytelephas	Washingtonia

* Easily grown from suckers.

Sow seeds thickly, ½-inch deep, in sandy loam in propagating frame in warm greenhouse. Give plenty of heat and moisture. Some species require two or three weeks to germinate, others two months, still others three years. Possibly the sulphuric acid method (48) may shorten those longer times. Keep night temperature 55 to 60 and day 70 to 75. Supply ample water. Prick off in small pots when first leaves are well formed, and shift to larger sizes slowly, but as needed. Use friable compost of rotted sod and stable manure, with peat, leaf mold and sand.

10. WATER PLANTS

Acorus ....A	Juncus ....A	Nymphæa ......B, F	Saururus ....H
Alisma ....B	Jussiæa (Jussieua) B		Scirpus (Juncus) ...A
Aponogeton .....B, C		Orontium ....A, B	
	Limnanthemum ....B	Ouvirandra .....A, B	Trapa ....B
Cabomba ....A, B	Limnocharis A, B, E		Typha ....A, B
Caltha ....A, B	Ludwigia ....B	Peltandra ....A, B	
Cyperus ....A, B	Lyriophyllum ......B	Pontederia ......A, B	Victoria ....G
Eichhornia .....A, B	Nelumbium A*, B, F	Sagittaria ......A, B	Zizania ....B

* Seeds should be cut to admit water.

A Division in spring.

B Newly ripe seeds in pots plunged in water, under glass.

C Off-sets at any time.

D Division after flower.

E Runners, or stolons.

F Cuttings of rhizome (12 inches long), kept under water when out of doors.

G Keep seeds wet from ripening till sown. Place in sandy loam in pots. Immerse 2 inches deep in water never less than 85 degrees, in well-lighted tank, near the glass.

H Sow in moist loam.

11. ORCHIDS

Acanthephippium	A	Broughtonia	A	Dendrobium	B	Phaius	A
Æceras	A	Bulbophyllum	A	**Disa	A	***Phalænopsis	B
Ada	A	Burlingtonia	A				
Aerides	B			Epidendrum	B	***Saccalobium	B
Aganisia	A					Satyrium	A
Anguloa	A	Calanthe	A	Lælia	A	Sobralia	A
Anœctochilus	A, B	*Calopogon		Lycaste	A	Stanhopea	A
Ansellia	A	*Calypso					
Aplectrum	A	Catasetum	A	Masdevallia	A	Thunia	B
		Cattleya	A	Maxillaria	A	Trichopilia	A
Barkeria	B	Cœlogyne	A	Microstylis	B		
**Batemannia	A	Comparettia	A	Miltonia	A	Vanda	B
Bletia	A, B	Cymbidium	A			Vanilla	A, B
Brassia	A	Cyprepedium	A	Odontoglossum	A		
				Oncidium	A	Zygopetalum	A

* Offsets usually employed. Difficult to handle.
** Offsets also.
*** Some species form plantlets on old flower stems when pegged down on moss; others form plantlets on the roots.

    Seeds. Hand pollination of cultivated orchids is necessary to secure seeds. Choose nearly related genera or species where hybrids are desired, because distantly related ones may not "take to each other," or the offspring may resemble the seed-bearing parent. Select for the seed-bearing parent a plant of vigorous health, free growth and flowering habit, because the offspring usually "take after the mother" in form, but after the "father" in flower color. To pollinate, place one or more ripe pollen masses on the right stigma of the female flower. Seeds require sometimes three to six months, but oftener a year, to ripen. Sow seed as soon as ripe by dusting on surface of pots or baskets in which healthy plants of the same genus are grown. Keep moist with very fine rose till seedlings are started. Spring-sown seed usually sprouts quickest. Some species require a year or more to germinate. When seedlings have two or three leaves, plant in flats, or singly in small pots, in compost suited to the parent, but finer. Should compost become sour, transfer seedlings to other soil.

A   Division. Choose none but sturdy plants. Carefully remove soil. Cut plant with keen knife so each piece will have at least one "lead." In some cases the procumbent rhizomes produce only one growth from the pseudo bulb. With these cut part way through the rhizomes two or three pseudo bulbs behind the leaf, in late winter or early spring. Count on one new bulb from the base of the bulb next the division. Do not separate till the lead is well established; then sever and pot.

B   Cuttings. Choose long-jointed species. In midwinter, just before plants start growth, cut old pseudo bulbs according to joints. Lay pieces on moist moss in warm propagating frame. When young offshoots have started well, pot whole piece and plantlet. Where the rhizomes form roots before cutting, leave such roots on the lower parts of the stems (at least a foot long), discarding the upper part. These stems produce new growths, which may be rooted later.

12. CACTI

Cereus	A	Epiphyllum		Opuntia	A	Phyllocactus
						Pilocereus
Echinocactus	A	Mamillaria	A	Pelecyphora	A	
Echinopsis	A	Melocactus		Pereskia		Rhipsalis

A   Sow seeds in sandy soil in semi-shade till sprouting starts; then expose to sun. Water with care. Seeds give best results particularly with species marked **A**.

B   Make cuttings, or make off-sets, with sharp knife. Lay in sun or on dry sand till wounds heal and roots start; then pot in sandy soil and syringe daily, or oftener.

C   Graft weak or sprawling kinds on strong or erect species (E.g., **Pereskia aculeapa,** p. **Bleo, Cereus Peruvanius** and **C. Tortuosus.** See 329.

BIBLIOGRAPHY

Allison, F. E. Nitrate assimilation by soil micro-organisms in relation to available energy supply. Soil Sci. 24, 79-94, 1927.

Arthur, J. M. and Guthrie, J. D. Effect of light, carbon dioxide and temperature on flower and fruit production. Mem. Hort. Soc. N. Y. 3, 73-74, 1927.

Arthur, J. M. Work to date at Boyce Thompson Institute for Plant Research on effect of light on plant growth. Trans. Engin. Soc. 19, 995-996, 1924.

Bailey, J. S. Effect of stock on scion, Mass. Exp. Sta. Bul. 226, 1926.

Barker, B. T. P., and Spinks, G. T. Investigations on apple stocks. Univ. Bristol Agr. and Hort. Res. Sta. Ann. Rpt., 1917.

Barton, L. V. Hastening the germination of southern pine seeds. Jour. Forestry 26, 774-785, 1928.

Bateson, W. Root cuttings and chimeras. Jour. Genet. 11, 1921.

Bergmann, H. F. The relation of aëration to growth and activity of roots and its influence on the ecesis of plants in swamps. Annals Bot. 34, 13-33, 1920.

———The effect of cloudiness on the oxygen content of water and its significance in cranberry culture. Am. Jour. Bot. 2, 50-58, 1915.

Bonns, W. W. and Mertz, W. M. Experiments with stocks for citrus. Calif. Exp. Sta. Bul. 267, 1916.

Bottomley, W. B. Some accessory factors in plant growth and nutrition. Proc. Roy. Soc. Lond. Ser. B. 88, 1914.

———Some effects of organic growth-promoting substances (auximones) on the growth of *Lemma minor* in mineral culture solutions. Ibid. 89, 1917.

Bray, R. H. Apparatus for measuring the hydrogen-ion concentration of the soil. Indus. and Engin. Chem. 20, 1928.

Bradford, F. C. and Cardinell, H. A. Eighty winters in Michigan orchards. Mich. Exp. Sta. Spec. Bul. 149, 1926.

Bregger, J. T. Apple stock variation and its relation to scion growth. Proc. Am. Soc. Hort. Sci. 1924, 313, *1925*.

Buchanan, R. E. Life phases in a bacterial culture. Jour. Infec. Dis. 23, 109-125, 1918.

Burkholder, L. C. and Greene, Laurenz. Influence of size of mahaleb seedlings on nursery grades. Proc. Am. Soc. Hort. Sci. 1930, 85, *1931*.

Bushnell, J. The relation of temperature to growth and respiration in the potato plant. Univ. Minn. Exp. Sta. Tech. Bul. 34, 1925.

Cannon, W. A. On the relation of root growth and development to the temperature and aëration of the soil. Am. Jour. Bot. 2, 211-224, 1915.

———Physiological features of roots with special reference to the relation of roots to aëration of the soil. Carnegie Inst., Washington Publ. 368, 1925.

Clausen. Beizversuche mit "Uspulum." *Deutsche Obst-und Gemüsebauzeit.* 69, 304-305, 1923.

Clements, F. E. Aëration and air content; the role of oxygen in root activity. Carnegie Inst., Washington Publ. 315, 1925.

Collison, R. C. and Conn, J. H. The effect of straw on plant growth. N. Y. (Geneva) Exp. Sta. Tech. Bul. 114, 1925.

Collison, R. C. and Harlan, J. D. Variability and size relations in apple trees. N. Y. (Geneva) Exp. Sta. Tech. Bul. 164, 1930.

Coville, F. V. Effect of aluminum sulphate on rhododendron and other acid soil plants. Part I, Florists Exch. 66, 1257, 1927.

———Ditto Part II, 1361, 1927.

Crocker, W. After-ripening and germination of rose seeds. Am. Rose, An., 34-37, 1926.

———Dormancy in hybrid seeds. Memoirs. Hort. Soc. N. Y. 3, 33-38, 1927.

Cruz, A. J. Non-gas electrodes for pH determinations. Philippine Agric. 16, 307-323, 1927.

Curtis, O. F. Stimulation of root growth in cuttings by treatment with chemical compounds Cornell Exp. Sta. Mem. 14, 1918.

Dachnowski, A. P. Quality and value of important types of peat material. U. S. Dept. Agr. Bul. 802, 1919.

Daniel, A. M. Operating a house heating plant. U. S. Dept. of Agr. Far. Bul. 1194.

Daniel, L. Réactions antagonistiques et rôle du bourrelet chez les plantes gréffes. Comptes Rendus Acad. Sci., Paris, 170, 1920.

Davis, O. H. Germination of seeds of certain horticultural plants. Flor. Exch. 63, 917, 922, 1926.

———Germination and early growth of *Cornus florida, Sambucus canadensis,* and *Berberis thungergi.* Bot. Gaz. 84, 225-263, 1927.

Davis, W. E. and Rose, R. C. The effect of external conditions upon the after-ripening of seeds of *Cratægus mollis*. Bot. Gaz. 54, 49-62, 1912.

Domontovitsch, M. Application of the quinhydrone electrode to the determination of the p^H plant juices. Mauch. Agron. Zhur. (Jour. Landw. Wiss.), 700-712, 1925.

Doryland, C. J. T. The influence of energy material upon the relation of soil micro-organisms to soluble plant food. N. Dak. Exp. Sta. Bul. 116, 319-401, 1916.

Emerson, F. W. Subterranean organs of bog plants. Bot. Gaz. 72, 359-374, 1921.

Eckerson, S. H. A physiological and chemical study of after-ripening. Bot. Gaz. 55, 286-299, 1913.

Finnell, H. H. Improving stands of grain sorghums by seed treatments. Okla. Exp. Sta. Bul. 159, 1926.

Fitch, C. L. Studies of health in potatoes. Colo. Exp. Sta. Bul. 216, 1915.

Free, E. E. The effect of aëration on the growth of buckwheat in water cultures. Johns Hopkins Univ. Circ., p. 198. March, 1917.

Garcia, F. Apples grafted on pears. N. Mex. Sta. Rpt., 1917.

Gardner, F. E. and Yerkes, G. E. Size of apple seedlings in relation to the growth of the scion variety. Proc. Am. Soc. Hort. Sci. 1930, 131, 1931.

Garner, W. W. and Allard, H. A. Further studies in photoperiodism, the relative response of the plant to relative length of day and night. Jour. Agri. Res. 23, 871-920, 1923.

Gehring, A. and Brothuhn, G. *Über die Einwirkung der Beizung von Rübenknaülen auf die biologischen Vorgänge des Bodens.* Centralbl. für Bakt. Abt. 2, 63, 67-101, 1924.

Gladwin, F. E. The behavior of American grapes grafted on vigorous stocks. N. Y. (Geneva) Exp. Sta. Bul. 508, 1924.

Göppert, H. R. *Ueber innere Vorgänge bei dem Veredeln Bäume und Stracher.* Cassel, 1874.

Gram, E. Afsvampningsunders gelser. II Forsg med Runkelroeog Sukkerroefr 1920-1925. Statens Forsgsvirksomhed I Plantenkultur Berening, 197, 337-402, 1926. (From the English Summary).

Grubb, N. H. and Amos, J. Some factors influencing root development. Ann. Rpt. East Malling Res. Sta., 110-113, 1923.

Guignard, L. Recherches physioligiques sur la greffe des plantes a acide cyanhydrique. Ann Sci. Nat. Bot. 9 Ser., 1907.

Gunness, C. I. Meteorological observations. Mass. Exp. Sta. Serv. Bul. 498, 499, 500, 1930.

Hahn, G. G., Hartley, C., and Rhodes, A. S. Hypertrophied lenticels on the roots of conifers and their relation to moisture and aëration. Jour. Agr. Res. 20, 253-265, 1920.

Harrington, G. T. and Hite, B. C. After-ripening and germination of apple seeds. Jour. Agr. Res. 23, 153-161, 1923.

Hansen, N. E. Concerning the value of the sand cherry as a stock. S. Dak. Sta. Bul. 87, 1905.

Hatton, R. G. Paradise apple stocks. Jour. Roy. Hort. Soc. 42, 1917; 44, 1919.

——A first report on quince stocks for pears. Ibid. 45, 1920.

——Suggestions for the right selection of apple stocks. Ibid. 45.

——Stocks for stone fruits. Jour. of Pomol. 2, 1921.

——Root stock investigations. Ann. Rpt. East Malling Res. Sta., 1922.

Hedrick, U. P. Grape stocks for American grapes. N. Y. (Geneva) Sta. Bul. 355, 1912.

——Stocks for fruit trees. Calif. Mo. Bul. Com. Hort. 3, 1914.

——A comparison of tillage and sod mulch in an apple orchard. N. Y. (Geneva) Exp. Sta. Bul. 383, 1914.

——Stocks for plums, N. Y. (Geneva) Exp. Sta. 498, 1923.

Heppner, N. J. A study of deciduous root stocks with special reference to their identification. Calif. Sta. Tech. Paper 6, 1923.

Hill, H. H. The effect of green manuring on soil nitrates under greenhouse conditions. Va. Exp. Sta. Tech. Bul. 6, 121-153, 1915.

Hitchcock, A. E. and Zimmerman, P. W. Variation in rooting response of cuttings placed in media of different p^H values. Proc. Am. Soc. Hort. Sci., 388-390, 1926.

Hitchcock, A. E. Effect of peat moss and sand on rooting response of cuttings. Bot. Gaz. 86, 121-148, 1928.

Hopkins, E. F. Studies in the germination of celery seed. Proc. 18th. Ann. Meet. Assoc. Official Seed Analysis N. Amer., 47-49, 1926.

Howard W. L. Discussion of the relative merits of different root stocks. Calif. Mo., Bul. Com. Hort. 7, 1918.

——progress report on rootstock experiments. Ibid. 8, 1919.

——The value of the different roots as stocks. Better Fruit. 14, 1919.

——More about root stocks. Calif. Mo. Bul. Com. Hort. 9, 1920.

——Rootstock studies in Europe. Proc. Am. Soc. Hort. Sci. 18, 1922.

Itano, A. Biological investigation of peat. Jour. Bact. 10, 87-95, 1925.

Jacobs, A. W. Hastening the germination of sugar pine seeds. Jour. For. 23, 919-931, 1925.

Jones, H. A. A physiological study of maple seeds. Bot. Gaz. 69, 127-152, 1920.

Jones, L. H. Effect of the structure and moisture of plant containers on the temperature of their soil contents. Jour. Agr. Research, 42, 375-378, 1931.

Kellerman, K. F. and Wright, R. C. Relation of bacterial transformations of soil nitrogen to nutrition of citrous plants. Jour. Agr. Research, 2, 101-113, 1914.

Kinzel, W. Frost und Licht in der Samenkeimung. Ulmer, Stuttgart, 1913.

Kiesselbach, T. A. Field experiments with seed corn treatments and crop stimulants. Neb. Exp. Sta. Bul. 218, 1927.

Kienitz, M. Über Ausführung von Kiemproben. Forstliche Blätter 16, 1880.

Knight, R. C. and Witt, W. A. The propagation of fruit tree stocks by stem cuttings. I. Observations of the factors governing the rooting of hard wood cuttings. Jour. Pomol. and Hort. Sci. 5, 248-266, 1926.

——The propagation of fruit tree stocks by stem cuttings. Ibid. 6, 47-60, 1927.

Knott, J. E. and Jeffries, C. D. Containers for plant growing. Penn. Exp. Sta. Bul. 224, 1929.

Kostoff, D. Studies on callus tissue. Am. Jour. Bot. 15, 565-576, 1928.

Kruger, W. and Schneidewind, W. Ursache und Bedeutung der Salpeterzersetzung im Boden, Landw. Jahr. 28, 217-252, 1899.

——Zersetzung und Umsetzungen von Stickstoffverbindungen im Boden duoch niedere Organismen und ihr Einfluss auf das Wachstum der Pflanzen. Ibid. 30, 633-648, 1901.

Kuster, E. Pathologische Pflanzenanatomie. First ed. (Transl. by Frances Dorrance), 1903 and 1913.

Larsen, J. A. Methods of stimulating germination of western white pine seeds. Jour. Agr. Res. 31, 889-899, 1925.

Lipkin, B. J. Der einfluss niedriger Temperaturen auf die Kiemfähigkeit von Waldsamen. Mitt. Gork. Ysch. Landwirtsch. Inst. 2, 182-197, 1925.

Livingston, B. E. and Free, E. E. The effect of deficient soil oxygen on the roots of higher plants. Johns Hopkins Univ. Circ. 182-185, Mar., 1917.

McCallum, W. B. Regeneration of plants. I. Bot. Gaz. 40, 97-120, 1905.

——Ibid. II, 40, 241-262, 1905.

Martindale, E. S. Humidity in house heating. Dominion Fuel Board, Ottawa, Canada. 1930.

Mason, S. C. and Jones, I. Grafting the apple. Kans. Sta. Bul. 65, 1897.

Melhus, I. E. Crowngall of apple nursery stock. Jour. Econ. Entomol. 19, 356-365, 1926.

Moore, J. G. Scion root production by apple trees in the nursery. Proc. Am. Soc. Hort. Sci. 16, 1920.

Mothes, P. Versuche mit der Saatbeize Tillantin B. Deutsche Obst und Gemüsebuazeit. 71, 389, 1925.

Muller, H. R. A. Onderzoekingen naar den invloed van eenige ontsmettingsmiddelen op de Keinkrachtvan Tomatenen Selderijzaad. Tijdschr over Pflantenziekten. 31, 75-85, 1925.

Muncie, J. H. A study of crown gall caused by Pseudomonas tumefaciens on rosaceous hosts. Ia. State Coll. Jour. Sci. 1, 67-117, 1926.

Nightingale, G. T. The chemical composition of plants in relation to photoperiodic changes. Univ. Wis. Exp. Sta. Res. Bul. 74, 1927.

Olsen, C. and Linderstrom-Lang, K. On the accuracy of the various methods of measuring concentration of hydrogen-ions in soils. Carlsberg Laboratories, Copenhagen, Compt. Rend. 17, 1927.

Pack, D. A. After-ripening and germination of Juniperus seeds. Bot. Gaz. 71, 32-60, 1921.

Pfeiffer, T. and Lammermann, O. Denitrifikation und Stallmistwirkung. Landw. Ver. Sta. 54, 386-462, 1900.

Phillips, J. F. The propagation of "stinkwood" (Ocotea bullata E. Mey.) by vegetative means. So. Afr. Jour. Sci. 23, 418-434, 1926.

Pickering, S, U. Relative cropping of apples on different stocks. Woburn Exp. Fruit Farm Rpt 15, 1916.

——Science and Fruit Growing. London.

Plaut, M. Die Wirkung von warmen Beitzmitteln und Versuche zur Stimulation, Angew. Bot. 7, 153-184, 1925.

Prayag, S. H. The influence of stock and scion and their relation to one another. Agr. Jour. India, 15, 1920.

Rahn, O. Die schadliche Wirkung der Strohdungung und dessen Verhütung, Ztschr. Tech. Biol. 7, 172-186, 1919.

Reddy, C. S. and Holbert, J. R. Experiments to show the effects of certain seed treatments ou corn, Phytopath. 14 44-45, 1924.

——, ——, and Erwin, A. T. Seed treatments for sweet corn diseases. Jour. Agr. Res. 33, 769-779, 1926.

Rehwald, C. Ueberpflanzliche Tumoren als vermeintliche Wirkung chemischer Reizung, Zeitschr. Pflanzenkrank. Pflanzenschutz, 37, 65-86, 1927.

Reid, M. E. Quantitative relations of carbohydrates to nitrogen in determining growth responses in tomato cuttings. Bot. Gaz. 77, 404-418, 1924.

Reimer, F. C. A promising new pear stock. Calif. Mo. Bul. Com. Hort. 5, 1916.

Riker, A. J. and Keitt, G. W. Studies of crowngall and wound overgrowth on apple nursery stock. Phytopathol, 16, 765-808, 1926.

Roberts, R. H. Some stock and scion observations on apple trees. Wis. Exp. Sta. Res. Bul. 94, 1920.

————Factors affecting the variable growth of apple grafts in the nursery row. Ibid. 68, 1926.

————Apple physiology. Wis. Exp. Sta. Bul. 68, 1926.

————The modified leader tree. Ibid. 354, 1923.

Rose, R. C. After-ripening and germination of seeds of Tilia, Sambucus and Rubus. Bot. Gaz. 67, 281-308, 1919.

Rubner K. Bedeckungstiefe und Keimung des Fichtensamens. Forstw. Centralblat. 49/5, 168-183, 1927.

Sax, K. and Gowen, J. W. The relation of tree type to productivity in the apple. Me. Exp. Sta. Bul. 305, 1922.

————, ————, The place of stocks in clonal varieties of apples. Genetics, 8, 1923.

————Bud and root selection in the apple. Ibid. 344, 1928.

————, and Gowen, J. W. Productive and unproductive types of apple trees. Jour. Heredity 12. 291, 1921.

————, ————, The cause and permanence of size differences in apple trees. Me. Exp. Sta. Bul. 310, 1923.

Sax, C. Bud and root selection in the propagation of the apple. Proc. Am. Soc. Hort. Sci. 20, 1924.

Scheimpflug, E. Elfolge und Erfahrungen mit der Saatbeize "Uspulum." Deutsche obst-und Gemusebauzeit. 70, 177-178, 1924.

Schmidt, W. Uber Vorquellung und Reizbehandlung von Koniferensaatgut. Zellstim. Forschungen I. 355-368, 1925.

Scott, L. B. Nursery stock investigations. Proc. Am. Soc. Hort. Sci., 1922.

Scott, W. W. Standard methods of chemical analysis. Vol. 2, 1922.

Shaw, J. K. The root systems of apple trees. Proc. Am. Soc. Hort. Sci. 12, 1916.

————The propagation of apple trees on their own roots. Mass. Sta. Bul. 190, 1919.

Shippy, W. B. An inexpensive and quickly made instrument for testing relative humidity. Bot. Gaz. 87, 152-156, 1929.

Simon, S. Experimentelle Untersuchungen über die Differenzierungsvorgänge im Callusgewebe von Holzgewächsen. Jahrb. Wiss. Bot. 45, 351-478, 1908.

Small, J. Propagation of cuttings in acidic media. Gard. Chron. 244-245, 1923.

Smith, E. P. Acidity of the medium and root production in Coleus. Nature 117, 339, 1926.

————A comparative study of the stem structure of the genus Clematis, with special reference to anatomical changes induced by vegetative propagation. Trans. Roy. Soc. Edinburg. 55, 633-664, 1928.

Smith, J. W. The effect of weather upon the yield of potatoes. Monthly Weather Rev. 43, 222-236, 1915.

Snyder, E. F. A comparative study of the quinhydrone and hydrogen electrodes for determining hydrogen-ion concentration of soils. Jour. Agric. Res. 35, 825-834, 1927.

Staniland, L. N. The immunity of apple stocks from attacks of woolly aphis. Jour. Pom. and Hort. Sci. 3, 1923.

Starnes, H. W. The Stringfellow root-pruning theory. Ga. Sta. Bul. 40, 1898.

Stringfellow, H. M. The New Horticulture, 1896.

Stewart, L. B. Methods of propagation. Jour. Roy. Hort. Soc. London. 52, 33-39, 1927.

Stuart, W. Influence of stock on scion. Vt. Sta. Rpt. 18, 1905.

Stuckey, H. P. Influence of stock on scion. Ga. Sta. Bul. 116, 1915.

Swarbrick, T. and Roberts, R. H. Relation of scion variety to root growth. Wis. Exp. Res. Bul. 78, 1927.

Sorauer, P. Manual of plant diseases, Third ed. Vol. I. (Trans. by Frances Dorrance.)

————A treatise on the physiology of plants. (Trans. by F. E. Weiss), 1895.

Stoll. Ueber die Bildung des Kallus bei Stecklingen. Bot. Zeit. 32, 737-742, 1874.

Swingle, C. F. A physiological study of rooting and callusing in apple and willow. Jour. Ag. Res. 39, 81-128, 1929.

Thompson, T. G. and Miller, R. C. Apparatus for the micro-determination of dissolved oxygen. Ind. and Eng. Chem. 20, 774, 1928.

Tisdale, W. H., Taylor, J. W. and Griffith, M. A. Experiments with hot water, formaldehyde copper carbonate, and chlorophol for the control of barley smuts, Phytopath. 13, 153-160, 1923.

Toumey, J. W. Seeding and planting, a manual for the guidance of forestry students, foresters, nurserymen, forest owners and farmers. 455, 1916. (p. 130.)

————and Stevens, C. L. The testing of coniferous tree seeds at the school of forestry, Yale University, Yale Univ. Sch. For. Bul. 21, 1928.

Tozawa, M. Methods of hastening germination of tree seeds. Bul. For. Exp. Sta. 5. Keijyo, Japan. 1926.

Trecul, A. Accroissement des végétaux dicotylédonés ligneux. Ann. Sci. Nat. 19, 157-192, 1853.

Tukey, H. B. Seedling fruit stocks. N. Y. (Geneva) Exp. Sta. Bul. 569, 1929.

————Identification of mazzard and mahaleb cherry rootstocks. Ibid. circ. 117, 1930.

————and Brace, K. D. The propagation of multiflora rootstocks for roses by softwood cuttings, Ibid. Bul. 598, 1931.

————, ————, Correlation studies of the growth of apple and cherry trees in the nursery from the seedling to the two year budded tree. Ibid. Tech. Bul. 185, 1931.

Vieheller, A. F. Investigations in the rooting of apple cuttings. Proc. Am. Soc. Hort. Sci., 250-255, 1923.

——Ibid. 20, 1924.

Viljoen, J. A. and Fred, E. B. The effect of different kinds of wood and of wood pulp cellulose on plant growth. Soil Sci. 17, 199-212, 1924.

Vochting, H. Über Regeneration and Polarität bei nöhern pflanzen. Bot. Ztgs. 64, 101-148, 1906.

Wahlenberg, W. G. Fall sowing and delayed germination of western white pine seed. Jour. Agr. Res. 28, 1127-1131, 1924.

——Sowing and planting season for western pine. Jour. Agr. Sci. 30, 245-251, 1925.

——Waugh, F. A. Propagation of plums. Vt. Sta. Rpt. 13, 1901.

——The graft union. Mass. (Hatch) Sta. Tech. Bul. 2, 1904.

Webber, H. J. Necessity of selecting stocks in citrus propagation. Calif. Citrog. 5, 1920.

——Selection of stocks in citrus propagation. Calif. Sta. Bul. 317, 1920.

——The relation of stocks to scions with special reference to citrus propagation. Proc. Am. Soc. Hort. Sci. 19, 1923.

——The basis of selection in the improvement of citrus nursery stock. Ibid. 1930. 114, 1931.

——The improvement of rootstocks. Jour. Heredit. II, 291, 1920.

Whitten, J. C. An investigation in transplanting. Mo. Sta. Bul. 33, 1919.

Weiss, F. Seed germination in the grey birch (B. populifolia). Am. Jour. Bot. 13, 737-742, 1926.

Wilkins, V. E. Research and the land. H. M. Stationary office. London, W. C. 2.

Wilson, R. E. Humidity control by means of sulphuric acid solutions, with critical compilation of vapor pressure data. Jour. Indus. Eng. Chem. 13, 326-331. 1921.

Winkler, L. W. Die Bestimmung des im Wasser gelösten Sauerstoffes. Ber Deutsch Chem. Ges. 21, 2843-2854, 1888.

Yerkes, G. E. Experiments in the propagation of fruit tree stocks. Proc. Am. Soc. Hort. Sci. 20, 1924.

Zacharawicz, E. Sur l'affinité de quelques greffons francais. Rev. Vit. 25, 1906.

Zoderbauer, E. Die Keimprüfungsdauer einiger Koniferen, Centralbl. Forstw. 32, 306-315, 1906

Zimmerman, P. W. Vegetative propagation with special reference to cuttings. Proc. Am. Soc Hort. Sci., 223-228. 1925.

INDEX TO PLANT LISTS

The numbers refer to the Plant Lists on the preceding pages

A

Aaron's Beard. See Hypericum, 2
Abies, 3
Abronia, 1
Abutilon, 1, 7
Acacia, 1
Acalypha, 7
Acanthephippium, 11
Acanthophœnix, 9
Acanthorhiza, 9
Acanthus, 5, 7
Acer, 2
Aceras, 11
Achillea, 1, 5
Achyranthes, 7
Aconite, 5
Aconite, Winter. See Eranthis, 6
Acorus, 5, 10
Acrachinium, 1
Acrocomia, 9
Acrostichum, 8
Actæa, 5
Actinidia, 4
Ada, 11
Adam's Needle. See Yucca, 5
Adiantum, 8
Adlumia, 1
Adonis, 1, 5
Ærides, 11
Æsculus, 2
African Corn Lily. See Ixia, 6
African Lily. See Agapanthus, 6
Aganisia, 11
Agapanthus, 6, 7
Ageratum, 1, 7
Agrostemma. See Lychnis, 1
Ailanthus, 2
Ajuga, 5
Akebia, 2, 4
Alder. See Alnus, 2
Alder, Black. See Ilex, 3
Alkanet. See Anchusa, 1
Allamanda, 7
Allegheny Vine. See Adlumia, 1
Allium, 6
Allspice, Carolina. See Calycanthus, 2
Almond, 2
Alnus, 2
Aloysia, 7
Alsophila, 8
Alstrœmeria, 6
Alternanthera, 7
Althæa, 5
Alum Root. See Heuchera, 1
Alyssum, 1, 5, 7
Amaranthus, 1
Amaryllis, 6, 7
Amazon Lily. See Eucharis, 6, 7

Amazon Vine. See Dioscorea, 6
Amelanchier, 2
Amorpha, 2
Amorphophallus, 6
Ampelopsis, 1, 2, 4
Amsonia, 5
Anchusa, 1, 5
Andromeda, 3
Anemia, 8
Anemone, 1, 5, 6
Angelonia, 1
Angræcum. See Ærides, 11
Anguloa, 11
Anœctochilus, 11
Anomatheca, 6
Ansellia, 11
Anthemis, 5
Anthericum, 6, 7
Antirrhinum, 1, 7
Apios, 4, 5, 6
Aplectrum, 11
Aponogeton, 10
Apple, May. See Podophyllum, 5
Aquilegia, 1, 5
Arabis, 5
Aralia, 1
Arbor-vitæ. See Thuya, 3
Archonophœnix, 9
Arctotis, 1
Ardisia, 7
Areca, 9
Arenaria, 5
Arenga, 9
Aristolochia, 1, 4
Armeria, 5
Arnebia, 1
Arnica, 5
Arrowwood. See Viburnum, 2
Artemisia, 5
Arundo, 5
Ash. See Fraxinus, 2
Ash Berry. See Barberry, 2
Asparagus, 1, 7
Asperula, 5
Asphodeline, 5
Aspidistra, 7
Aspidium, 8
Asplenium, 8
Aster, 1
Aster, Stokes. See Stokesia, 5
Astilbe, 6
Astrocarpum, 9
Atamasco Lily. See Amaryllis, 6, 7
Attalea, 9
Aubrieta, 5
Aucuba, 7
Auricula, 1, 5
Australian Feather Palm. See Ptychosperma, 9
Autumn Crocus. See Colchicum, 6

Avens. See Geum, 1, 5
Azalea, 2

B

Baby's Breath. See Gypsophila, 1, 5
Bactris, 9
Bacularia, 9
Bald Cypress. See Taxodium, 2
Balloon Flower, 1. See Platycodon, 5
Balloon Vine, 1
Balsam, 1
Bane Berry. See Actæa, 5
Baptisia, 5
Barberry, 2
Barkeria, 11
Barrenwort. See Epidedium, 5
Bartonia, 1
Basswood. See Tilia, 2
Bastard Indigo. See Amorpha, 2
Batemania, 11
Bay, Giant. See Rhododendron, 3
Bayberry. See Myrica, 2
Bay, Swamp. See Magnolia, 2
Bean, Sacred or water. See Nelumbium, Nymphæa, 10
Beard Tongue. See Pentstemon, 1, 5
Bear's Breech. See Acanthus, 5
Bear's Grass. See Yucca, 5
Beech. See Fagus, 2
Begonia, 1, 6, 7
Bellflower. See Campanula, 1, 5
Bellis, 1, 5
Bell, Silver. See Halesia, 2
Bells, Coral. See Huchera, 1, 5
Berberis. See Barberry, 2
Betonica (Bettony). See Stachys, 5
Betula, 2
Bignonia, 1, 2, 4
Bilberry. See Vaccinium, 2
Biota. See Thuya, 3
Birch. See Betula, 2
Birthwort. See Aristolochia, 1, Trillum, 5, 6
Bittersweet. See Celastrus, 1, 4
Bladdernut. See Staphylea, 5
Bladder Senna. See Colutea, 2
Blanket Flower. See Gaillardia, 1, 5
Blazing Star. See Liatris, 5
Bleeding Heart. See Dicentra 5, 6
Bletia, 11

533

PROPAGATION OF VEGETABLES FROM SEEDS

Kinds of Vegetables	Jan.	Feb.	Mar.	Apr.	May	June	July	Aug.	Sept.	Oct.	Nov.	Dec.
Artichoke, French ...	—	E	—	B	B	—	—	—	—	—	—	—
Artichoke, Jerusalem .	—	—	—	A	A	—	—	—	—	—	—	—
Asparagus	—	—	F	A	—	—	—	—	—	—	—	—
Balm	—	—	E	B	B	—	—	—	—	—	—	—
Basil	—	—	E	B	B	—	—	—	—	—	—	—
Beans, bush	G	G	G	A	C	C	C	A	—	—	—	—
Beans, pole and lima	—	—	—	—	A	A	—	—	—	—	—	—
Beets	—	—	E	E	A	A	A	A	—	—	—	—
Borecole or kale	—	—	—	—	B	B	B	—	—	—	—	—
Broccoli	—	E	E	B	B	B	—	—	H	H	—	—
Brussels Sprouts	—	—	—	—	B	B	—	—	—	—	—	—
Cabbage, all kinds ...	—	E	E	B	B	B	—	—	H	H	—	—
Cardoon	—	E	E	B	B	B	—	—	—	—	—	—
Carrot	G	G	F	A	A	A	A	—	—	—	—	—
Cauliflower	G	E	E	B	B	B	—	—	—	—	—	—
Celery and Celeriac ..	—	E	E	B	B	B	—	—	—	—	—	—
Chard, Swiss	—	—	E	E	A	A	A	A	—	—	—	—
Chervil	—	—	C	C	C	—	—	C	C	I	—	—
Chicory	—	—	F	A	A	A	—	—	—	—	—	—
Collard	—	—	—	—	—	—	A	A	A	—	—	—
Corn, field	—	—	—	A	A	A	—	—	—	—	—	—
Corn, pop	—	—	—	A	A	A	—	—	—	—	—	—
Corn, salad	—	—	F	A	A	A	—	—	H	—	—	—
Corn, sweet	—	—	—	C	C	C	C	A	—	—	—	—
Cucumber	G	G	G	E	A	A	—	G	G	—	—	—
Dill	—	—	E	B	B	—	—	—	—	—	—	—
Eggplant	—	G	E	B	B	B	—	—	—	—	—	—
Endive	—	—	—	B	B	B	B	—	—	—	—	—
Fennel	—	—	A	A	A	—	—	A	I	—	—	—
Kohl Rabi	G	G	E	B	B	B	B	—	—	—	—	—
Leek	—	E	E	B	B	B	—	—	—	—	—	—
Lettuce	G	E	E	B	C	C	C	A	J	J	H	—
Mangel	—	—	F	A	A	A	—	—	—	—	—	—
Marjoram	H	H	H	E	E	J	G	—	—	—	—	—
Martynia	—	—	—	—	A	A	—	—	—	—	—	—
Melon, musk	G	G	G	E	A	A	J	G	—	—	—	—
Melon, water	G	G	G	E	A	A	J	G	—	—	—	—
Mushroom	K	K	L	—	—	—	—	L	K	K	K	K
Mustard	M	M	M	A	A	A	—	A	A	M	M	M
Nasturtium	—	—	E	A	A	—	—	—	—	—	—	—
Okra	—	—	E	E	C	C	C	—	—	—	—	—
Onion	—	E	E	B	B	—	—	—	—	—	—	—
Parsley	G	G	E	A	A	A	A	—	—	—	—	—
Parsnip	—	—	F	A	A	A	—	—	—	—	—	—
Pea	—	—	F	C	C	C	C	A	—	A	—	—
Pepper	—	E	E	E	B	—	—	—	—	—	—	—
Peppergrass	M	M	M	M	A	A	—	—	M	M	M	M
Potato	—	—	—	A	A	A	—	—	—	—	—	—
Pumpkin	—	—	—	E	A	A	—	—	—	—	—	—
Radish	M	M	M	D	D	D	—	—	J	J	—	—
Radish, winter	—	—	—	—	—	—	A	A	—	—	—	—
Rutabaga	—	—	—	—	—	—	—	A	A	—	—	—
Sage	—	—	E	B	B	—	—	—	—	—	—	—
Salsify	—	—	F	A	—	—	—	A	A	—	—	—
Savory	—	—	E	B	B	—	—	—	—	—	—	—
Scorzonera	—	—	F	A	A	A	—	—	—	—	—	—
Sea kale	—	—	F	A	A	A	—	—	—	—	—	—
Skirret	—	E	E	B	B	—	—	I	I	H	—	—
Spinach	—	—	F	A	A	—	—	—	C	I	—	—
Squash	—	—	E	E	A	A	—	—	—	—	—	—
Thyme	—	—	E	B	B	—	—	—	—	—	—	—
Tomato	G	G	E	B	B	B	—	G	G	G	—	—
Turnip	—	A	A	—	—	—	A	A	—	—	—	—
Witloof	—	—	A	A	A	—	—	—	—	—	—	—

KEY TO VEGETABLE PROPAGATION TABLE

A. Sow in open ground; thin plants to proper distances. *B.* Sow in garden seed bed and transplant to permanent quarters. *C.* Sow twice in open ground during month. *D.* Sow thrice in open ground during month. *E.* Start in hotbed; plant in open when weather and soil favor. *F.* Sow outdoors as soon as open ground can be worked. *G.* Grow only in hotbed or greenhouse. *H.* Sow in coldframe; protect winter; plant out in spring. *I.* Sow in open ground; protect with litter during winter. *J.* Plant in frame; cover with sash and straw mats during cold weather. *K.* Plant in cellar, barn or under benches in greenhouse. *L.* Plant out-doors in prepared beds. *M.* Sow weekly in greenhouse or frame for succession.

Note 1. For last planting of bean, sweet corn, kohl rabi, pea, radish, and tomato use quickest maturing varieties.

Note 2. Late sowings of salsify and scorzonera may remain unprotected in ground over winter. Roots will be larger following fall than spring-sown ones.

APPENDIX

APPENDIX

Malling Rootstock Tests.—Interest in apple rootstocks in the eastern United States is in the production of smaller than standard trees, writes H. B. Tukey (condensed from *Farm Research,* July 1940), so that these may be planted more closely, bear early, remain small enough to facilitate spraying, thinning and harvesting, produce a high proportion of No. 1 fruit and, in time, be replaced by new trees, possibly of a new variety better adapted to changing market demands.

This interest seems more warranted each year by the performance of trees on various dwarfing and semi-dwarfing rootstocks, yet has obscured other valuable characters in clonal rootstocks which may be as important, and in some instances more important, than the characters of controlling tree size; e. g., adaptability to various soil conditions, particularly moisture.

Possibilities are indicated by results with eight rootstocks; viz., Malling I, II, IV, VII, IX, XII, XIII, and XVI, grown in soil of high, medium, and low moisture. From their general performance these stocks have been tentatively grouped as follows: (See Fig. 336.)

1. Generally successful in high, medium and low moisture— VII, I, and XIII.

2. Tolerant of high moisture—I, XVI, and VII.

3. Tolerant of low moisture—VII, I, and XIII.

4. Intermediate in tolerance of high and low moisture—IX and XVI.

5. Intolerant of low moisture—IV, XII, and II.

Results secured in these preliminary tests cannot be taken in themselves to indicate field adaptability to various types of soil and various soil moistures; however, they do agree in general with field observations at the station during several years. For example, trees on Malling I and XIII have been generally successful in both dry and wet years, trees on XVI and IX have seemed to prefer soil high in moisture, trees on XII have seemed to suffer during dry summers in comparison with those on the other rootstocks, and trees on II have been generally less well suited to a range of conditions and have also done poorly in a dry year.

Most of all, these results call attention to significant differences in the behavior of apple rootstocks in different soil environments.

They suggest the desirability of a more critical study of these rootstocks from this point of view.

Apple and Quince Rootstocks.—At the New York (Geneva) Experiment Station Malling rootstocks of apple and quince propagated by mound and trench layering, according to their inherent vigor, showed that these methods are commercially feasible. The number of shoots obtained per unit area increased for several years after the establishment of the beds, but the percentage of well rooted, salable shoots varied from year to year with growing conditions. Quince rooted more readily than apple. Malling I and IX

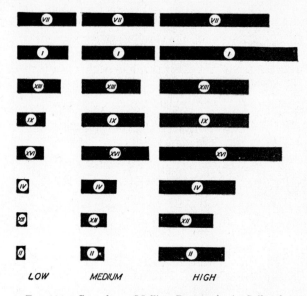

Fig. 336.—Growth on Malling Rootstocks in Soils of Varying Moisture Content. See text.

rooted easily, II rooted well, followed in descending order by XIII, XII and XVI. The apples were not injured appreciably by extreme low winter temperatures, but quince, from which salable shoots were removed in the fall, suffered severe damage.

Northern Spy Apple Rootstocks showed low power of recovery after transplanting when 47 trees of different ages were dug up and examined. The root systems were weak, sparse, poorly developed and with little fibre. The main roots were shallow, the deeper penetrating ones near the extremities. In general, this variety has a distinctive, natural root habit so cannot adapt itself to uncongenial environment. *Jl. Pomol. and Hort. Soc.* (British), Vol. 14, No. 3, p. 246. 1936.

Clon or Clone Stocks.—"At present it is not always possible from the literature to determine whether a rootstock is of clonal or of seedling origin, so unless one is familiar with the material used, he might not distinguish the facts that 'French Crab rootstocks' are seedlings and that 'Virginia Crab rootstocks' are a clone." (H. B. Tukey.)

Apple clonal stock appraisment has been experimentally outlined by F. B. Lincoln, of the University of Maryland as follows: "1. Budding on domestic seedlings to obtain a conception of their compatibility with domestic apples and capacity to produce dry matter. 2. A determination by the wire method of ability to root from the scion. 3. Observations on stock budding for general characteristics. 4. Budding of stocks with horticultural varieties. 5. Effect of stocks on root development. 6. Trench layering to test the capacity of the new stocks to reproduce by this method. A total of 185 clons for stock possibilities are under trial with this procedure."

Clonal Apple Stocks.—In 1924 the Massachusetts Experiment Station imported many Malling stocks which were budded with McIntosh and Wealthy apples. The resulting trees were planted in orchard form in 1928 with seedling-rooted and own-rooted trees as checks. Records show that production is correlated with size and only I and IV, when grafted to McIntosh, tended to promote early bearing. Wealthy was more variable on seedlings than on any clon, but McIntosh on certain clons may hold its fruit better near harvest time. In some cases the stocks seemed to influence the shape of the apples. On a basis of productivity, Malling XII and possibly XVI were better than seedlings or own-roots for both these varieties.

Stock and Scion Effects on Top-worked Apple Trees, in an orchard experiment at the Iowa Experiment Station, were established in 1930 with trees budded on roots of known varieties, on Hibernal Crab, French Crab and Virginia Crab intermediates with French Crab roots. It was observed that although the rootstocks had a rather distinct effect on the growth of the top, variability was not reduced materially by any set of stocks.

In growing seedlings from open-pollinated seed, the parents influenced definitely the vigor of the progeny. When budded on a recognized variety the vigorous seedlings produced the better trees. In trees limb-budded on Hibernal Crab and Virginia Crab there was less variability in the scion varieties on Virginia Crab than on Hibernal Crab, indicating that the intermediate stock had greatly influenced the uniformity of the trees and—in the author's opinion had an effect equal to, if not greater than, what could be expected with own-rooted trees. (T. J. Maney, H. H. Plagge and B. S. Pickett.)

Apple Stock Influence on Scion.—F. C. Bradford of the Michigan Experiment Station records a case of a cleft graft union of two Woodmansee apple scions on Longfield stock in which the callus tissue of the stock overgrew two inches above the original stub and gave rise to a small branch which bore Longfield apples. He suggests that such a phenomenon as this may have led to past conclusions that the stock influences the character of the scion.

Apple Stock and Scion Relationships.—Among observations upon digging 172 four-year old apple trees of 14 varieties worked on piece roots of Canada Baldwin seedlings at the British Columbia Experimental Station were differences in average weights of the root systems. Hyslop and U. S. D. A. No. 227 developed large tops, a comparatively large quantity of scion roots, and exceptionally vigorous growth of the seedling root system. Scion varieties differed in their capacity to overcome variation in the seedling roots, with indications that the more vigorous the scion, the more uniform the trees. The scion variety exerts a significant influence on the spread and depth of root development made by the seedling understock.

Fig. 337.—Callusing Box Showing Method of Filling.

Apple Stock Hardiness, as determined by the electrical conductivity of exosmosed electrolytes after subjection of scion roots to freezing at 15° F., was found by N. W. Stuart of the United States Department of Agriculture to be correlated with the known hardiness of the variety. In the material studied Oldenburg ranked first. The hardy roots contained slightly more sugar and less water than did the less hardy. All of the 25 varieties were hardier than French Crab seedlings. Observations on trees worked on clonal roots indicated an appreciable influence of the scion on the hardiness of the rootstocks, yet the tenderest clonal roots were produced under Wealthy, hardiest of the four varieties used. Conversely, hardiness of scions was not measurably influenced by hardiness of stock during one year's growth in the nursery.

Apple Stock Hardiness.—T. J. Maney and H. H. Plagge of the Iowa Experiment Station point out that in a commercial orchard planted in 1893-4, Grimes Golden, Gano and Jonathan apple trees double worked on Virginia Crab have lived longer than those on French Crab roots. From the general experience of Middle West fruit growers, top-working on hardy stocks is conducive to vigorous development, long life and productiveness.

Own-Rooted Apple Hardiness.—At the Indiana Experiment Station various varieties of apples, after becoming own-rooted, proved superior to the same varieties on French Crab. Virginia

Fig. 338.—Nursery Row-marker for Root Grafts and Small Plants.

Crab proved fairly resistant to woolly aphis. Grimes Golden, own-rooted on Virginia Crab, suffered no mortality from collar rot.

Ringing of Layered Apple Stocks in Denmark by means of copper wire tied tightly about the base of each shoot greatly increased the percentage of rooting. Apples are often grown on their own roots there. Certain varieties are as productive on their own roots as when grafted.

Apple Trees Double-worked in the Nursery, first in 1933 to Jonathan and again in 1934 to a Winesap sport, F. C. Bradford and

L. J. Oley of the Michigan Experiment Station experimented with four treatments: 1, All laterals removed from the immediate Jonathan stem; 2, three shoots averaging five leaves each left on the lower half of the intermediate piece; 3, three shoots left on the upper half; and 4, three shoots left on the lower and three on the upper portion.

Measurements of the top section showed the constantly largest diameter and longest shoots in group 1 and least in group 4. Foliage on the upper half of the intermediate piece had a more depressing influence on the scion than did that left on the lower half. Diameter increment of the intermediate piece just below the second budding point was greatest in trees which developed the largest top scions and least on those producing the smallest tops. Diameter increase of the intermediate stem just above the first bud point was apparently depressed by the absence of foliage on the lower half of the intermediate section. From a practical standpoint the best trees for orchard planting were those produced with no foliage on the intermediate stem.

Bridge- vs. Cleft-grafting Girdled Apple Trees.—T. A. Merrill of the Michigan Experiment Station suggests that the tops of girdled trees, smaller than 2″ in diameter, be cut off below the girdle and cleft-grafting instead of bridge-grafting them. Young trees treated thus made greater growth in the following years than did comparable bridge-grafted trees, but the new tops may suffer from winter injury because of their rapid growth the first year or two after grafting.

Stock and Scion Relationships with reference to "double worked" apple trees have been summarized by T. J. Maney of Iowa Experiment Station during 25 years, based on experimentation, observation and questionnaires covering the United States and Canada and a search through horticultural literature, especially the reports of the horticultural societies in the Northern States.

The prime purposes of this work were to discover exact information as to how various stocks respond when top-worked and to make recommendations as to their use. "The fact that a certain stock may be ideal for one variety is no indication that it might do well with another."

Hibernal and Virginia Crab have been used long and most extensively in the Northern States, due to their hardiness, deep rooting habit, resistance to disease, congeniality to many varieties and the wide angled crotch structure of the frame branches with the main trunk. Because of these qualities Maney concludes that "even under the extreme climatic conditions of the Great Plains States the use of these stocks may add 10 to 15 years to the life of top worked varieties."

The list of 45 varieties (*Am. Soc.Hort.Sci.Proc., 35,* p. 391. 1937.) includes the most important commercial ones, practically all of which have been used successfully with Hibernal and Virginia Crab. This latter, however, " gives somewhat peculiar reactions to different varieties." Members of the Winesap group show dwarfing; Stayman makes weak growth and smaller, poorer quality and colored fruit; Mammoth Black Twig is decidedly dwarfed, but the foliage, twig growth and fruit are normal; Paragon grows vigorously, thus proving it to be distinct from Mammoth Black Twig; Turley does well but Winesap is "perhaps half dwarfed." Rhode Island Greening makes healthy growth but from the behavior of 12-year-old trees it dwarfs about 25%. "This suggests that some stocks may be used very effectively in reducing the vigor of varieties which naturally attain to great size. This would be advantageous when considered from the standpoint of spraying, picking or other cultural operations.

"To deal with this problem intelligently we must not only know variety compatibility, but we must also know more about the adaptability of stocks to meet requirements of climate, soil, culture, and disease and insect control."

Apple and Cherry Growth Correlations.—Statistical analysis of records taken at the New York Experiment Station on French

FIG. 339.—Ridger Machine also Makes Deep Rows for Planting.

Crab and Mazzard cherry seedlings and on the growth of McIntosh apple and Montmorency cherry budded on such stocks, respectively, showed strong correlation between after-budding size of the one-year- and two-year-old trees and between one year and two year size. On the other hand, correlations between planting size and the after-budding size, between planting size and the size of one-year whips, and between planting size and the two-year tree were insignificant or approximately so. Correlations were higher for the same characters with cherries than with apples, a situation believed to be associated with a higher percentage of good trees in the cherry, apparently as a result of greater losses from imperfect unions.

Interpreting the results, the authors (H. B. Tukey and K. D. Brase) suggest the importance of the bud union in the production of a large nursery tree is of less magnitude than the development in size of the under stock during its first season in the nursery. Under the condition of rest, genetic differences between the seedlings were apparently masked by environmental factors, such as pruning, planting, culture, soil drainage, and general climatic conditions.

After five years, results showed that the original size of the root stock played little, if any, part in the development of the trees. Method of budding, time of budding, and conditions of the seedling stock at the time of budding appeared to have considerable effect on the development of the tree in the nursery row and after transplanting to the orchard. Re-transplanting to a new site after some time in the orchard apparently resulted in an equalization of the smaller and larger trees and helped to mask any possible differences in the inherent vigor of the rootstocks.

Layering of Root Grafts.—A ready method of obtaining self-rooted apple trees described by F. B. Lincoln of the Maryland Experiment Station (*Am. Soc. Hort. Sci. Proc.*, Vol. 35, p. 419. 1937.) has several advantages over three methods hitherto practised for obtaining self-rooted trees by means of nurse root; namely, 1, a long scion deeply planted; 2, wire girdle; 3, reversal of the nurse root, all of which depend upon the ability of the scion to develop roots. "With few exceptions the tendency of scions to develop roots cannot be depended upon for good yields of uniformly rooted plants in a short time. In fact, it can be considered abnormal for lignified tissue to develop roots."

Layering root grafts, however, is "a sure and quick means to obtain clonal stocks when only scion wood is at hand. . . . Its value does not seem to have been generally recognized, and it has not become a practise. Aside from the high degree of success in self-rooting apple scions by this method, an added advantage is its sim-

Fig. 340.—Experimental Equipment for Seedling Tree Planting. *Top*, Machine fed by six women who place seedlings for inflated inner tubes to press and paste between two strips of gummed paper tapes. *Middle*, Planting machine. *Bottom*, Planter at work. Notice rolls of tape and trees under hood of machine.

plicity to common nursery propagation practise. Where budding is the prevailing local method of propagating apple trees, buds may be set low and the shoots hilled, as are layered root grafts. Reasonable success in stem rooting may be expected, if the shoot which develops from the bud makes moderate growth.

"In the experiment, grafts were made so late that little callusing had occurred at planting time when the grafts were set upright in furrows with the uppermost bud slightly below normal ground level. The soil was settled by watering, thus leaving the top bud uncovered. Hilling was started when the scion shoot was an inch high, care being taken to keep the terminal leaves uncovered.

"In September, when these layered grafts . . . were inspected for root development from the scion, most of them showed no roots from the scion or its shoot," but by December had mostly made them. "Quite likely the group . . . not showing roots on the scion shoot by December will develop them by . . . the following spring or summer.

"In the future it is planned to remove the rooted scion shoots . . . in the fall, leaving the nurse roots in the soil to test their capacity to develop more shoots for rooting. It is quite possible that by using roots for grafting, which are dwarfing or show some degree of incompatibility with the scion, two or more of the buds of the scion might develop into shoots the first year.

"There are several advantages in obtaining self-rooted apple plants by layering root grafts; namely, saving of time when scion wood is scarce; avoidance of diseases and graft unions; production of normal, own-rooted trees by removing the seedling root and the graft union at the end of the first season; material for the study of preference for specific roots by the top, and the influence of the top on the production of specific root characteristics."

Apple Propagation by Etiolation.[1]—Growth of shoots in complete darkness results in blanching (etiolation). Best results in layering follow banking of shoots with earth as early as possible —before the tissues become woody.

To apply the above method to shoots on trees black, insulating tape, $2\frac{1}{2}$ to 3″ long, was wound spirally four or five times around young shoots as near the growing tip as possible. The partially expanded leaf or two near the tip were removed so as to increase shoot length. If bound to the stem, growth might be checked. Several thousand shoots may be covered in a day if the operator can work while standing on the ground.

When cuttings are to be made, the shoots are cut, the tape stripped off and the basal cut made in the etiolated area. By this

---

[1] F. E. Gardner, *U. S. Dept. of Agric.*, in *Am. Soc. Hort. Sci. Proc.*, Vol. 34, p. 323. 1936.

method 70% success is usual in the cutting bench—with McIntosh. When copper wire girdling of shoots early in their growth was practised, 100 per cent success followed. Girdling alone, however, was of no avail.

Experiments indicate that if the etiolation could be accomplished without allowing the tip to make its initial growth in the light, better rooting would probably result than under reverse conditions. In one experiment 78 out of 80 cuttings rooted in two weeks. In others, rooting ranged from 30 to 100%, depending on the shoot, the time of year and the variety. Some varieties are more inherently responsive than others. No variety has wholly failed.

The prompt rooting response—sometimes only three or four days—suggests that root primordia are pre-formed in the etiolated area during early growth.

In one experiment narrow, cylindrical bags about 10 inches long were made of heavy, black mulching paper and were fastened over individual shoots so that the few initial inches of growth could be made inside these rigid coverings. These bags were subsequently removed and tape applied as in a previous experiment. The rooting response of cuttings treated in this manner varied from relatively poor (30 to 40 percent) up to 100 percent, depending on the condition of the shoot, the time of year with respect to its resting period, and upon the variety. When tape is not applied to the shoots after the black bags are removed, the cuttings will not form roots.

A definite relationship exists between the time of year of taking the etiolated cuttings (reflected in their activity for growth) and the quickness and completeness of rooting response. Cuttings taken in early August and stripped of their leaves will root promptly and vigorously provided the shoots from which they are taken were not too vigorous and have had opportunity to accumulate some reserve carbohydrates at that date.

Prompt rooting can be secured as long as the top buds of the cuttings can be stimulated into activity, but as the shoot enters deeper into the resting condition the elongation of the primordia into roots becomes more sluggish as is evidenced by increasing slowness of rooting and the smaller number of roots per cutting.

The course of this rooting was followed by taking 25 cuttings of McIntosh at two-week intervals throughout the fall and winter months, beginning August 15, at which time 100% rooting was secured in 14 days. The rooting became progressively poorer until early spring when prompt rooting was again obtained after the rest period of the buds ended.

"Any method of rooting apple cuttings to prove commercially feasible should, it is believed, be adapted to field conditions. . . .

In the limited tests thus far made in the field, fall planting has been more successful than spring planting, due to the warm, friable condition of the soil which favored prompt rooting of the cuttings. As rooting occurs, a few small leaves unfold at the tops of the cuttings but the elongation of the stem does not proceed until spring. The percentage stand and the vigor of growth from fall planted cuttings have compared very favorably with the stand and growth from bench grafts of the same varieties on piece roots."

As bags and tape are troublesome to make, fasten over the shoots and later remove, also as many of the tender, white shoots are severely stunted or killed by the sun before they can produce chlorophyl, tubes ⅜″ in diameter and 5½″ long were made of black mulching paper and fastened with copper wire to the ends of shoots before growth started in spring. Their distal ends were made so that the shoot could gradually push into the sunlight and thus eliminate the risk of damage by the sun and also the troublesome necessity of removing the tubes in order to apply tape, for the tubes were left till cuttings were taken. From the standpoint of facility of application, this last method of etiolation is satisfactory though possibly it may result in somewhat reduced production of primordia.

Etiolation in the Tropics has been successful at the Malay Experiment Station when young shoots arising from pegged down and shallowly covered stems of the following plants were severed and planted separately: Lime and citron rooted freely, but *Achras sapota, Nephelium mutabile,* and *Citrus aurantium* needed to have wires twisted tightly about the base of each shoot some time before severing to induce callus formation and rooting. Better results were obtained when the plants were not pegged down until the young shoots were several inches long.

Citrus Propagation by Etiolation.—Branches of lime, lemon, Mandarin orange, guava and various species of *Eugenia* laid down horizontally and covered with soil proved successful in propagation, but too slow with chiku, rambutan, pulasan and mango. Better results were secured with marcottage in the case of chiku and with budding in that of rambutan, orange and pomelo. Shading and watering or mulching of the beds during dry periods proved beneficial. *Malayan Agr. Jl.,* Vol. 23, p. 526. 1935.

Vegetable Seed Vitality.—Studies with seeds of various species of vegetables in the Philippines showed little or no effect of differential storage temperatures on viability when stored over calcium chloride (to dry the air). On the whole, moisture was more detrimental to seeds in storage than temperature increases. From a practical standpoint the author, A. V. San Pedro, recommends either storing with calcium chloride or drying the seed and storing in hermetically sealed containers. When seed cannot be dried thoroughly they should be stored as near as possible to the freezing point. *Philippine Agric.*, Vol. 24, No. 8, p. 649. 1936.

Vegetable Seed Storage Experiments, conducted by L. V. Barton of the Boyce Thompson Institute, show that the viability of lettuce, onion and cauliflower seeds stored at room temperature

Fig. 341.—Seed Cleaning Machine.

may be prolonged markedly by adjusting the moisture content to 6 to 8%. Favorable results were also secured with tomato, carrot and eggplant. With pepper, moisture reduction was beneficial, but lowering the temperature was needed for successful storage beyond four years.

Germination tests of old and fresh seeds, stored for short periods at various relative humidities and temperatures, indicated that with relative humidities of 50% or lower the temperature may be as high as 35° C. (95° F.) for seeds with high germinative power and the storage period as long as three months without serious impairment of germination. Above 50% relative humidity storage temperatures of 20° C. or lower were required.

Peach Seed Germination.—Analysis of results obtained by the Illinois Experiment Station in peach seed sprouting indicated the need and value of after-ripening in a moist medium such as damp peat at about 40° F. Drying seeds before stratification had no influence on germination. When seeds from peaches kept in a bushel basket in storage at 35° to 37° F. without drying for 196 days were subjected to temperatures of 32°, 16°, 0°, and —10° F. for various periods, the seeds were killed almost in total at —10° and 0.° Practically no germination occurred in any of the uncracked pits at any temperature, but good germination was secured from cracked pits kept at 16° F. or above. In the case of Elberta seeds kept 112 days at room temperature, then held uncracked for 77 days at 40° F. in moist peat, the position of the seed in the soil had no significant effect on percentage of germination, but did influence the straightness of the stems and seedlings. An after-ripening period of 29 days is practically as good as 60 days for Elberta seeds either one or two years old. There was no marked difference between peat and sand as a stratification medium. The occurrence of dwarfed seedlings was traced to inadequate after-ripening, but after one summer the dwarfs took on normal growth.

Peach Seed Germinative Power Quickly Determined.—A simple method of determining the viability of peach seeds is outlined by F. Flemion of the Boyce Thompson Institute. The naked embryos were mixed with granulated peat moss and held at room temperature. In five to seven days at 20° to 25° C. the viable seeds showed hypocotyl development and in 10 days all embryos were growing or showing deterioration. The percentage germination compared favorably with that secured when seeds were after-ripened at 5° to 10° C. for the usual germination tests.

Peach Rootstocks Resistant to Nematodes.[1]—Seedling peach rootstocks commonly used are so severely attacked by nematodes (*Heterodera marioni*) in warm, well aërated soils of the Southeastern United States that peach nursery and orchard culture are impractical on heavily infested, deep, sandy and sandy loam soils. No orchard or soil management practises have been effective as controls.

Resistant rootstocks are promising preventives. At Fort Valley, Ga., plum, apricot, almond and several peach varieties were grown in experimental orchards from 1935 to 1936, with the result that two peach stocks (F. P. I. 63,850—Shalil—and F. P. I. 61,302) have proved nematode resistant.

Blenheim apricot seedlings were all resistant, "but peach trees

---

[1] Lee M. Hutchins, *Am. Soc. Hort. Sci. Proc.*, Vol. 34, p. 330. 1936.

propagated on them were noticeably less vigorous under orchard conditions than were trees propagated on peach rootstocks."

Japanese apricot seedlings (*Prunus mume*) "remained free from root-knot in heavily infested soil" . . . but trees so propagated "were strikingly dwarfed" so this stock is not regarded as satisfactory for commercial use.

Prunus hortulana is also "highly resistant" . . . but "it causes marked dwarfing" so "appears unsatisfactory." •

P. davidiana seedlings proved susceptible to nematode and crown gall and a dwarfing stock.

Arlington Farm No. 21,868 peach stock was "moderately susceptible to root-knot" and "not suitable for nursery culture on nematode-infested land."

F. P. I. 41,498 seedlings produced rapidly growing Early Hiley trees but were severely affected.

"Natural" seedlings were very susceptible.

Shalil peach produced seedlings some of which "appeared to be worthy of propagation, especially one numbered F. P. I. 63,850." Peach trees propagated on it "were among the best in the orchard . . . where nine different rootstocks were under test." This stock has also "shown complete resistance to root-knot in heavily infested soils. . . . It is regarded as a very promising selection for general use by nurserymen in securing vigorous, nematode-resistant seedling stock for budding to the commercial peach varieties."

As Shalil trees continue leafy long after other peach varieties are bare and as some flowers open during fall and winter only to be killed by frost, "it is believed that orchards for seed production should be grown in a climate where fall and winter temperatures are lower" than those of Georgia. This is further suggested by the habitat of the species, Kurram Valley, Northwestern Frontier Province, India, at about 5,600 ft. elevation where temperatures of 13° F. are reached, "a little milder than Salt Lake City, Utah." There the trees remain dormant from early November to early April.

"As a safeguard, it would be preferable to propagate Shalil trees for seed production by using bud or scion wood that is in direct line of clonal propagation from the original tree of F. P. I. 63,850 at Chico, California."

F. P. I. 61,302 is the resultant of a cross between Bolivian Cling peach and Quetta nectarine. Elberta peach budded on its seedlings "made unusually vigorous growth" and in three years were 1 to 3 feet taller than trees on any other rootstock than Shalil. The roots were found to be free from nematodes, whereas "natural" and other nematode-susceptible roots in the same orchard were galled by root-knot, as were also trees propagated by grafting on root pieces. In some cases, trees so propagated developed scion roots which became infested with root-knot.

About 4,000 root-grafted trees of Early Hiley planted in commercial orchards during 1931-1933 "are now in bearing; the trees are in excellent vigor, produce heavy crops for their age and the understocks have remained free from root-knot."

Avocado and Mango Propagation.—Tests by the United States Department of Agriculture of 16 media for germinating avocado seeds showed most rapid development during the rainy summer season in 10-mesh charcoal and in a mixture of carex peat plus sand and charcoal. In the cooler and drier period, cypress sawdust plus charcoal was also effective. The best seedlings were secured in the rainy season in sphagnum peat and cypress sawdust plus charcoal, and in the drier season in sphagnum peat, carex peat plus sand and charcoal. The Orlando fine sandy loam gave poor results with mango seeds. Good success was secured in sprouting immature avocado seeds and also the individual cotyledons or portions thereof. However, plants grown from half and quarter embryos were smaller than those from whole embryos. *Am. Soc. Hort. Sci. Proc.*, Vol. 30, p. 382. 1933.

Pear Stock Trials at the New York Station (Geneva) by Tukey and Brase proved that *Pyrus communis* rootstocks were uniformly successful for all varieties tested. *P. betulæfolia* succeeded with Bartlett, Seckel and Kieffer, but failed with Beurre d'Anjou, though the trees were free from leaf spot; *P. calleryana* was worthless for all varieties; *P. ussuriensis* worked with Kieffer but was unsatisfactory with the other varieties; *P. serotina* was similarly unsatisfactory. *Am. Soc. Hort. Sci. Proc.*, Vol. 30, p. 361. 1933.

Plum Root Stock Influences.—R. G. Hatton, J. Amos, and A. W. Witt, of the East Malling Research Station (England), point out certain combinations of stock and scion invariably give poor results suggestive of actual incompatibility. Pershore, Common Mussel and Brompton and certain well selected Myrobalan stocks gave consistent satisfaction. Victoria plums on Myrobalan gave practically double the growth of Victoria or Brussel during five years' test. Myrobalan, Brompton and Pershore stocks were vigorous. Habit of growth proved varieties on Myrobalan and Brompton roots produced more or larger growth than on other stocks.

Development of root suckers seems a varietal characteristic rather than due to the method of propagation. Common Mussel, Common Plum and Brussel were prolific of suckers. The scion variety exerted an influence on number of suckers. Brompton and Common Mussel were exceptionally strong rooted; Brussel and Pershore trees, easily blown by wind.

Rootstocks influenced time of blooming, but there was no correlation between time of blooming of stock and its effect on scion; e. g., late blooming Pershore apparently accelerated time of blooming of scion.

Rootstocks influenced proportion of blooming and non-blooming spurs on young trees. Actual number of flowers to spur was also affected. Preliminary fruiting records taken on 10 varieties showed stocks to have a significant influence: in 7, trees on Pershore yielded the heaviest crops.

In a later report the authors say that, in general, *Prunus cerasifera* rootstocks gave most vigorous trees, and stocks within the *P. institia* species, e. g., Common Mussel, Common Plum and some of the Saint Julien selections, may be expected to produce trees of moderate vigor. Growth and productivity were not necessarily closely associated, at least up to the end of the fourteenth year. Varieties on their own roots fruited as well as on precocious rootstocks, but there was evidence that the trees developed more rapidly on *P. cerasifera* roots. Marked variation in commercial stocks of Saint Julien and Black Damas was manifested by striking differences in fruiting and growth. Rootstocks were observed to affect time of maturity and size of the fruit in some cases. There were indications that trees on Common Plum recovered more readily from silver leaf and bacterial die-back diseases than on other stocks. It is believed that selection of desirable combinations of rootstock and scion is more important in plum than in apple.

Peach Variety Seedlings for Understocks.—In search of seed stocks to replace the diminishing supply of "natural" seed, germination and growth behavior tests were made by F. E. Gardner and P. C. Marth of the United States Department of Agriculture. In the 126 lots, germination varied from 0 in 10 kinds to 85.4% in Lemon Free. With 40% germination rated as a good stand, 24 exceeded this rating. In general, seedling growth was correlated with germination. The seedlings within a variety exhibited, for the most part, a notable uniformity. For the most part, freestones gave appreciably higher germination than did clingstones. A positive correlation was observed between ease of cracking the pits and germination. Several varieties germinated better the second season after planting.

Peach Bud Types in Relation to Nursery Practise.—A comparison, made by W. H. Upshall, of the Horticultural Station in Vineland, Ontario, between single or double and triple buds taken from bearing trees of Valiant, Veteran and Elberta varieties, showed, in the first two varieties, striking gains in the percentage of developing buds in favor of double and triple bud groups. It is recommended that nurserymen do not use plump single buds from bearing peach trees.

Citrus Clonal Characteristics.—Observations on two pairs of trees, all on sweet orange rootstocks but budded respectively with buds taken from the Paper Ring orange and from a nucellar seedling thereof, showed the tree derived from the asexually produced seedling to possess greater vigor, more upright growth, greater thorniness and lower seed content of fruit. The pair of trees from Paper Rind, on the other hand, came into fruiting earlier. The maximum seed content in the original clone was 27 and in the nucellar derivative eight. *Journal of Heredity*, Vol. 29, p. 417. 1938.

Lemon Trees Influenced by Rootstock Strains.—Records at the Citrus Experiment Station in Riverside, Cal., on yield and growth of Eureka and Lisbon lemon trees grown from buds taken from single trees and worked on seedlings of uniform genetic identity showed a clear effect of stock on scion. In general, sweet orange stocks were outstanding in value, and since records taken at two other widely separated points, Riverside and Sespe, showed the same varieties to be of high value, genetic origin rather than environment is considered the important determining factor. Added to the fact that many of the old lemon groves of the State are on sweet orange roots, the evidence strongly suggests the high value of sweet orange understocks for lemons. In general, there was a strong correlation between the effect of the stocks on yield and on growth.

Eureka Lemon Cuttings rooted well when the leaves were left on, but no roots formed when they were cut off. Nothing showed cutting trees to be inferior to budded ones.

Citrus Propagation Studies.—At the University of California trees on five rootstocks—sour, sweet and trifoliate orange, grapefruit and rough lemon—came into bearing one or two seasons earlier when budded on themselves than when not budded. The mere presence of a bud-union thus caused the trees to fruit earlier than naturally. Size differences are not believed important since the two lots appeared almost identical in this respect during their early years. Comparing sweet orange budded with standard varieties with sweet orange seedlings, in every case the seedlings were larger, more upright and decidedly later in coming into bearing. *Calif. Citrogr.*, Vol. 20, No. 12, p. 370. 1935.

Rootstock and Scion Influence in Citrus.—At the end of their seventh growing season, trees of trifoliate orange budded on trifoliate and rough lemon stocks, also of rough lemon budded on rough lemon and trifoliate orange were carefully dug and records taken of top and root growth by R. W. Hodgson, S. H. Cameron and E. R. Eggers of California. Using as standards for comparison the trees budded on themselves, it was found that the rough lemon scion had greatly stimulated trifoliate rootstock and reciprocally the trifoliate scion had markedly reduced the growth of the rough lemon rootstock. By far the largest tree of all was the rough lemon budded on itself. Rootstock and scion influences appeared to be reciprocal in nature.

Lime Rootstocks.—Observations on seven-year-old Bearss limes budded on sweet and sour orange, grapefruit and trifoliate orange rootstocks showed the largest trees on grapefruit, with yields almost equal on rough lemon and grapefruit. Trifoliate orange markedly dwarfed the limes, and the sour orange had a similar but less potent effect. The form of the bud unions was similar in all cases; namely, an overgrowth on the part of the scion. The fruits were apparently similar except for a tendency to be smaller on the trifoliate roots. Own-rooted lime trees were larger than those on either trifoliate or sour orange. *Calif. Citrogr.*, Vol. 21, No. 8, p. 280. 1936.

Pecan Propagation[1] is mostly done by patch budding, either with buds of the current season (not earlier than mid June), or with previous season buds in early spring. The latter is preferable because it gains several months' time. Bud wood may be cut from the trees as needed but it is more economical to cut it while dormant and to hold it in cold storage. It is then "seasoned" or brought into condition for use by providing suitable moisture and temperature conditions. When seasoned it may be used at once or returned to cold storage for later work.

As results of an investigation of bud storage covering the whole general subject, the author makes the following recommendations (condensed). Bud wood should be cut for storage perhaps only ten days or two weeks before the trees are expected to show signs of growth. A temperature range from 32° to 40° F. is effective to preserve and keep bud wood dormant. Packing material should be moist enough to prevent drying of the wood; additional moisture does not hasten the process. For quick seasoning the temperature should be 80° to 85° F. If not used within two or three days, bud wood stored while dormant and later seasoned should be returned to storage. Having been stored, it may be used during 18 to 25 days without greatly deteriorating the value of the buds.

Among the conclusions not covered in the recommendations it is stated that bud wood seasons more quickly in late spring or early summer than in early spring following the storage period, also that an influence similar to the one which prescribes the rest period of plants regulates the cambial activity and the resulting slipping of the bark of bud wood.

---

[1] F. R. Brison, *The Storage and Seasoning of Pecan Bud Wood,* Texas Experiment Station, Bulletin 478. 1933.

Pecan Seedling Production for Graftage Stock.[1]—After more than 15 years' experimenting, the Georgia Experiment Station has found no pecan variety among over 40 tested whose seedlings consistently gave best results as stock for grafting or budding. After trials of 12 different methods of storing the nuts from harvest to spring planting time, it has proved that highest average percentages of germination (66.75%) and the most vigorous seedlings resulted from burying the nuts about 6″ deep in soil immediately after harvest. The next best (45.25%) germination came from nuts stored in a refrigerator at just above freezing temperature in a saturated atmosphere. Third, from nuts stored at 32° F. at high humidity. Drying and heating, at any time, are both detrimental to germination in proportion to the intensity and duration of the treatment.

Patch Budding of Pecan is popular in Texas. Both current and previous season's wood are used. Wood cut late in the dormant period is held in cold storage at 32° to 38° F. until needed. Such wood needs seasoning after removal from storage. The amount of moisture in the storage sphagnum may vary widely without retarding the seasoning process.

Walnut, Butternut and Hickory Seed Germination.—Observations by L. V. Barton of the Boyce Thompson Institute, on the germination of *Juglans nigra, J. cinerea* and *Carya ovata* seeds gathered before frost and planted in flats in a mixture of sand, peat and soil showed that pre-treatment at low temperatures for two to four months in a moist medium is necessary for seedling production in black walnut and butternut. Hickory seedling production under similar conditions for one to five months at 3° to 10° C., was increased, but some seedlings were produced without pre-treatment. A period of high temperature preceding low temperature had no effect on this species. Good results were secured by fall planting when the seed beds were protected by mulch or boards from alternate freezing and thawing.

Bud-Grafting of Grapes[2] has been used to prevent destruction of European varieties by phylloxera. As practised for more than 15 years in the Federal experiment vineyards of California, it differs from budding of tree fruits mainly by the inclusion of considerable woody tissue. When carefully done, 90 per cent. or more of the buds should grow. Failures may be either spring-grafted (p. 310) or bud-grafted the following autumn.

Phylloxera-resistant varieties to be used as stocks have their mains roots shortened to about 5″ and the side rootlets all cut off.

---

[1] J. E. Bailey and J. G. Woodroof, *Propagation of Pecans,* Georgia Experiment Station, Bulletin 172. 1932.
[2] Condensed from U. S. Dept. of Agriculture Leaflet No. 173. 1939.

Their shoot growth is reduced to one, two or three spurs of two buds each and all buds on the main trunk removed to prevent the development of stock suckers. When thus trimmed they are planted so that 2″ or 3″ of the stumps are above ground level for budding with the desired varieties. After planting, the stumps are protected from drying during summer by heaping soil over them.

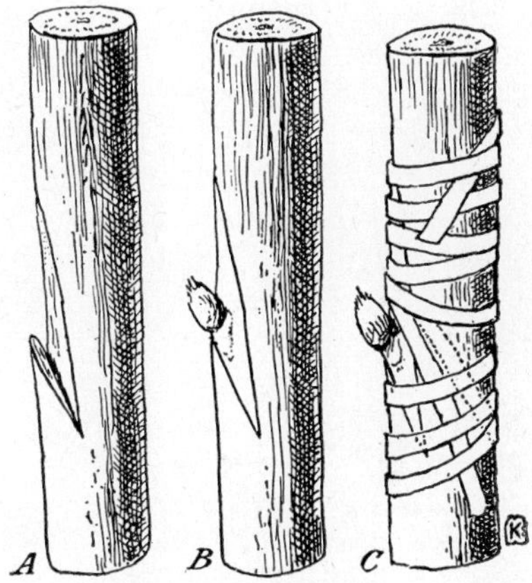

When possible, bud sticks should be cut fresh several times daily or be carefully protected from drying. To prevent off-type selection, vines that bear fruit typical of the desired variety should be used as scion plants and the shoots and buds to be chosen for budding should have turned brown at the nodes. This practically decides the season as late summer or early autumn.

FIG. 342.—Summer Bud Grafting. A, cut made in stock for bud; B, bud placed in position on stock; C, bud wrapped in place.

The position for inserting the bud must be a smooth area on the stock, somewhat above ground level to prevent development of roots from the scion. An oblique, downward ¾″ or 1″ cut is made in the stock with a shorter one below it and at an acute angle to remove a chip, as shown at A in Figure 343. Similar cuts are made in the bud stick to remove a chip of wood with its bud intact (Fig. 343 B). This chip is then fitted tightly in the rootstock notch (Fig. 343 C) with as much as possible of the cambium of stock and scion coinciding. The bud is then wrapped with raffia or ⅛″ rubber strip and buried with 6″ or 8″ of moist soil to protect it until the

FIG. 343.—Autumn Bud-grafting Operations. A, stock with wood chip removed; B, scion bud chip inserted; C, scion bud chip wrapped in place; D, completed graft covered with soil.

following spring (Fig. 343 D.) when it will start to grow. While
dormant, stock shoots may be shortened to get rid of excess wood.

In spring, when growth begins, the soil is scraped away (Fig. 344
A), the stock cu 1 or 2″ above the bud (Fig. 344 B), all scion roots
(if any) growing from the bud chip (Fig. 345 C) cut cleanly off
(Fig. 345 D), the strands of raffia or rubber below the bud cut but

Fig. 344.—Spring Care of Bud-grafted Vine. A, mound of soil removed after
growth has started; B, stock cut off above vinifera bud; C, stock and bud surrounded by roll of heavy paper; D, growth from bud tied to stake.

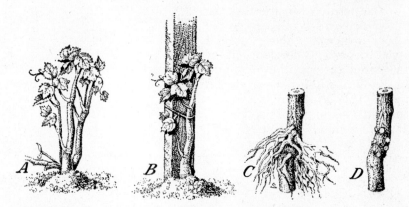

Fig. 345.—Summer Care of Bud-grafts. A, several shoots growing from vinifera bud-graft; B, thinned to one main shoot tied to stake; C, scion roots
growing from base of stem that developed from bud chip; D, scion roots
cleanly removed

the upper ones left intact (Fig. 344 A) to hold the bud chip firmly
in place. Then 1 or 2″ of earth are heaped over the bud to prevent
drying of stock and scion during the growing season. If the soil is
clayey or sticky a small cylinder of heavy, waterproof paper about
6″ long is placed over the vine and filled with coarse sand—an inch
or two over the top of the vine (Fig. 344 C). This will prevent
baking of the earth and will assure a straight scion shoot. During

the growing season the shoot must be tied vertically to a stake set beside it (Fig. 345 B).

Though several shoots may develop from the bud chip (Fig. 345 A) all but the most vigorous one should be cut off when this is 8″ or 10″ long and become somewhat woody at its base (Fig. 345 B). This will assure development of a strong, straight trunk with a favorable height of head during the first season.

FIG. 346.—Growth from Buds Inserted Previous Season. This picture, made June 20, illustrates variability in time of growth starting.

Grafted vines must be examined annually to cut off scion roots and stock shoots. They may be expected to begin fruiting the second summer after planting the rootstocks.

Machine Grafted Grapes.—Using the basic ideas of an Austrian patent [1] H. E. Jacob of the California Experiment Station has been successful with machine grafting. As built for his experiments, (Fig. 347) the machine consists of four 8-inch, planer-type, circular saws, each $\frac{1}{16}″$ thick, mounted in a gang head on the shaft of a $\frac{1}{2}$ hp., 3,600 r. p. m. ball-bearing electric motor. Spacer discs $7\frac{1}{2}″$ in diameter and $\frac{1}{16}″$ thick separate the saws and also limit the depth of the cuts to $\frac{1}{4}″$. Stocks and scions are pushed endwise (radially) against the saws (Fig. 348).

This action forms a slip joint of one to four tenons, according

---

[1] The status of the Albert Hengel patent in the United States would have to be determined before the machine could be safely manufactured and used for commercial purposes.

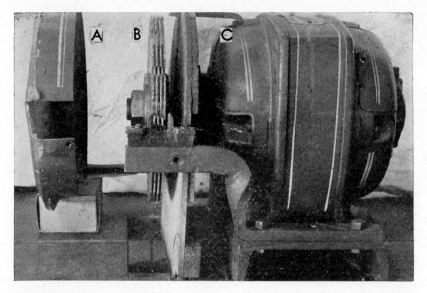

FIG. 347.—Multiple-saw Grafting Machine. A, safety cover removed to show construction details; B, four saws; C, motor.

to the diameter of the stock (or scion) and the corresponding indentures, those on the stock being at the upper end, those on the scion at the lower. When the stock is held against the right hand guide and the scion against the left, or vice versa, a good fit is assured between the two, provided they are of the same size and

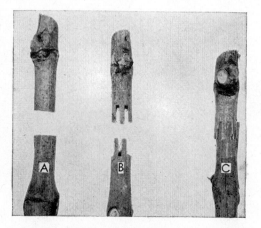

FIG. 348.—Steps in Making Multiple-saw Grafts. A, ends of stock and scion squared; B, tenons and and corresponding indentures; C, completed graft ready for callusing.

the end of each has been cut square across before the slip joint is sawed.

With this machine three reasonably fast men can make 700 to 1,000 grafts in an hour. Good, straight, hard wood, carefully graded as to size, is necessary for fastest work. In carefully conducted tests grafts made with this machine were comparable to short-whip grafts made by hand by a skilled workman. Over sev-

Fig. 349.—Treatment of Bench Grafts. A, newly planted nursery. Rows in foreground partially uncovered to show vines; B, correct method of heeling-in vines and bench grafts.

eral years, the average of machine-made grafts that grew into No. 1 rooted one-year-old vines has been slightly less than from skilled hand grafts because in hand work defective stocks and scions were discarded, whereas with the more rapid machine operation some defective material escaped detection.

Grape Grafting Tests.—At the California (Davis) Experiment Station, placement of stock cuttings in a warm room (75° to 80° F.) for 10 days prior to grafting increased the percentage of vines obtained from grafts—65% and 20% of success in two tests as against 2% in both controls. Benefit was obtained in most cases by immersing the stock cutting in water at 122° for various periods up to 25 minutes.

Grape Root Stocks—Observations on 42 grape stocks planted in the spring of 1932 at Poplarville, Miss., showed 9 to rate good or better in vigor after several years' trial and 11 to fail completely. Of the 9 superior forms, 4 are of *Vitis champini* origin.

Nursery Stock Needs Fresh Ground.—According to W. H. Upshall and G. N. Ruhnke of the Horticultural Experiment Station in Vineland, Ontario, growth of fruit tree stocks planted on an area from which a peach orchard had been removed showed striking differences. Weak growths almost exactly coincided with the former locations of the trees. Even six years after the tree removal and when all old peach roots were almost completely disintegrated it was still possible to detect the locations of the peach trees by the inferior growth of the young stock.

Digging Nursery Stock at Various Stages of Maturity.—Observations at Arlington Experiment Farm, Virginia, on seedlings dug at weekly intervals from September 22 to November 24, indicated that digging before a certain degree of maturity is reached is decidedly harmful. In the case of Mazzard cherry the September 22 lot averaged only 10.5% survival when lined out the next spring after being heeled in all winter in the nursery, as compared with 99% with stock dug November 3. Notes on growth conditions of the terminal buds, ease of separation of the bark, ease of stripping the leaves and the pigmentation of the stems and leaves are given for Mazzard and Mahaleb cherries, Bartlett pear seedlings, *Pyrus calleryana*, French Crab, and Myrobalan plum. *Am. Soc. Hort. Sci. Proc.*, Vol. 32, p. 338. 1934.

Storage Experiments with Nursery Stock at the New York Experiment Station (Geneva) by H. B. Tukey and K. D. Brase have been summarized in part as follows: The most important consideration in the storage of nursery stock is the treatment prior to placing in storage, such as growing, spraying, exposure to sun and wind during digging and freezing of roots. Cording carefully in bins and covering the roots with moistened kraut according to the

Fig. 350.—Front and Rear Views of Modern Tree Digger. Curved knife passes deeply beneath trees in rows, cuts roots and partially lifts stock for hand removal.

approved nursery practise is satisfactory for cherry trees; paraffining is of no added benefit. Roses, however, may be benefited by so treating the tops. Paraffining the roots as well as the tops of cherry trees is harmful, whereas similar treatment of roses results in little or no dying, although it is not a recommended practise. Cold emulsions sprayed on the tops with a power paint sprayer offer a rapid and convenient method of paraffining nursery stock already corded in bins, but no particular brand of emulsified paraffin should be used until its effect upon the plants has been determined, since some may result in severe injury. Trenching in the nursery

FIG. 351.—Blade of Tree Digger Shown in Figure 350.

cellar is no improvement over cording in bins; in fact it results in early starting and injury to the stock in handling. *Am. Soc. Hort. Sci. Proc.*, Vol. 28, p. 494. 1931.

Citrus Propagation by Twig Grafting depends for its success upon the same conditions as those necessary for rooting citrus cuttings; namely, using twigs with healthy, mature leaves taken from trees in vigorous condition, maintenance of high humidity in the propagating frame by frequently sprinkling the cuttings to keep the leaves turgid, and maintenance of a sand temperature of about 75° F.

One advantage of the twig graft is the fact that plants suitable for experimental purposes can be obtained in about three months; whereas at least two years are required to grow budded trees to the same stage. Moreover, the rootstock of the latter is a seedling which, in critical experiments, is an objectionable feature.

In this method two stem cuttings of the desired varieties are tongue-grafted together and rooted like an ordinary cutting. A further development of the "twig graft" makes possible the grafting of three different species and then inducing the one serving as a rootstock to root in sand like an ordinary citrus cutting. The use-

Fig. 352.—Workmen Lifting Trees Loosened by Digger. Notice long roots, practically complete, with trifling injury.

fulness as plant material for critical investigations concerning scion stock relationships is stressed. *Am. Soc. Hort. Sci. Proc.*, Vol. 34, p. 289. 1936.

Crown Grafting Improved.[1]—Comparison of the following description and drawing (Fig. 353) with those on page 305 will show: 1. The scions are cut in semi-wedge form instead of full wedge

---

[1] J. E. Bailey and J. G. Woodroof, *Propagation of Pecans*, Georgia Experiment Station, Bulletin 172. 1932.

form (as in cleft grafting) or with a notch as in ordinary crown grafting; 2. the tough, outer bark is partly pared away to facilitate scion insertion and close fitting; 3. the scion after insertion is tightly held in place by a cord which crosses the slit and the scion at least four times; 4. the bark of the stock is made to fit closely against the scion by the insertion of a wedge (a) beneath the cords on each side. Waxing follows wedging. As shown on page 305, several scions may be inserted in large stocks.

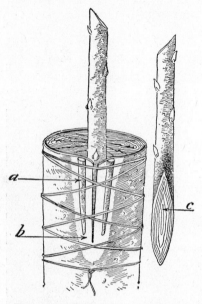

FIG. 353.—Bark Graft Inserted. a, wedge placed between waxed twine and bark to close opening on each side of scion; b, bark pared down to make it pliable and prevent splitting; c, method of cutting scion.

This method is particularly useful with thick barked trees such as walnut and pecan.

Ring Grafting and Stock Effect.—The replacement of a ring of bark, removed by R. H. Roberts of the Wisconsin Experiment Station from young Whitney Crab, Winesap and Yellow Transparent nursery trees, with other rings of known varieties resulted in differences of growth, with a significant relation between the accumulation of starch above the rings and the amount of new shoot growth. Certain combinations of stem and bark gave somewhat different results in different years, apparently because of seasonal differences.

When rings of bark were inverted from the normal position the tops were dwarfed, with dark green leaves, slender shoots and a delayed accumulation of starch.

The variety of ring exerts an effect on subsequent growth of the scion. A ring which gives good growth on one variety may give poor growth on another.

The new xylem formed under Hopa (a variety with red wood and red bark) was red, indicating its origin in the cambium of the bark. When the Hopa bark did not entirely surround the stem, a gap of tissue from the stock formed between the areas of red colored bark.

Bridge Grafting Stone Fruits.—Elberta peach, Burbank and Lombard plum scions were used by S. Johnson of the Michigan Experiment Station in an attempt to save mice-girdled, three-year-old trees. The results were that all the peach scions failed, three of the 14 Burbank plum scions lived and 21 of the 27 Lombard scions grew satisfactorily. However, where girdling was complete the trees did not recover, even with bridge grafting, thus indicating doubtful value of the operation.

Bud Stock Packing.—Three years' experiments by W. H. Upshall of the Vineland (Ontario) Experiment Station, with bud wood of apple, pear, plum, cherry and peach, show that seasonal conditions make great differences in the results of various treatments.

Lots with the leaves left on were kept from wilting by being placed upright individually in a heavy cardboard box containing *an abundance of moist moss* and the box wrapped in heavy waterproof paper. The results were that the petioles remained intact from two to seven days longer than in any other treatment. After being wrapped up for seven days the "handles," except in peaches, were generally usable in inserting the buds. For peaches there is some doubt about the advisability of using this packing method. The waxing treatment appears to be much better.

The waxed lots came second in retention of "handles." For shipments likely to be en route more than ten days, especially when they must pass through the hands of customs' and inspection men, this method is probably safest.

Apple buds withstand storage conditions better than the other fruit tree buds.

As to other treatments, the order of decreasing value seems to be oiled paper, moist moss, wet paper, and wet moss. This order suggests prolonged contact with water in liquid form may injure the buds. *Am. Soc. Hort. Sci. Proc.*, Vol. 29, p. 363. 1932.

Budding Ties.—After four years' comparison experiments with raffia and rubber strips at the Vineland Experimental Station (Ontario), W. H. Upshall concludes that on the whole gray rubber strips have given a slightly better stand of buds than raffia. Some nurserymen have been afraid to use them because they do not

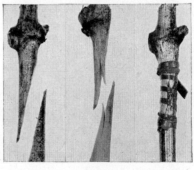

A   B   C

Fig. 354.—Long Whip Graft. A, sloping cuts on stock and scion; B, tongues cut and opened out; C, completed graft, tied with rubber strip, ready for callusing.

cover the wound as completely as raffia, but, judging from results in the tests, this is not a disadvantage. Heavier rubber, 4 x $\frac{3}{16}$ in., was used in one experiment but as it gave no better results than the smaller, less expensive strips, they were not used again. When the time of preparing raffia is considered, there is little difference in cost per tie between rubber strips and raffia. A further advantage in using rubber strip is the saving of labor in that no cutting away from the stock is necessary after the bud has united. *Am. Soc. Hort. Sci. Proc.*, Vol. 29, p. 362. 1932.

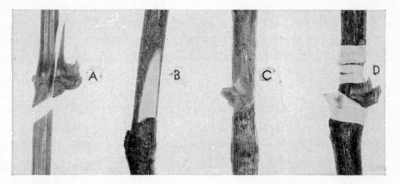

FIG. 355.—Steps in Budding Grapes. A, bud removed from bud stick; B, notch made in stock to receive bud; C, bud in place on stock; D, finished and tied, ready for covering with moist soil.

Half-H Budding [1] is an improvement over ring budding for propagating thick barked trees such as pecan. Two parallel cuts an inch or so apart are made about three-quarters around the stock to be budded, preferably with a double bladed knife (Fig. 356) and their ends joined by two other cuts at right angles to them (Fig. 357). Similarly, a bud is cut from scion wood and snugly fitted on the stock immediately after the removal of the severed piece. This reduces the risk of drying and thus insures the greatest likelihood of successful union. Wrapping and waxing follow.

Advantages of the method are: it can be practised on smaller trees than can patch budding; the strip of bark opposite the scion bud helps hold the scion in place while being wrapped; and healing follows rapidly (Fig. 358).

Shield Budding Technique.—As results of experiments at East Malling, England, comparing the English method of removing the wood from the bud with that of American propagators' practise of leaving the wood intact, apples, pears, plums and cherries showed small but significant increases from successful unions in favor of the

[1] J. E. Bailey and J. G. Woodroof, *Propagation of Pecans,* Georgia Experiment Station, Bulletin 172. 1932.

English method. However, there was no significant difference in height of trees at the end of the first year, and since the American method is more rapid and less wasteful of buds the author, R. J. Garner, suggests its trial by British propagators.

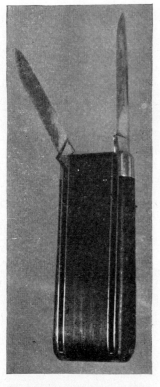

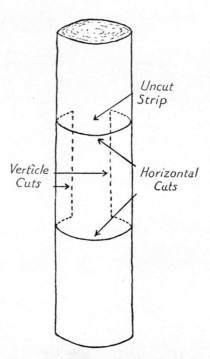

Fig. 356.—Double Bladed Knife. This tool cuts both stock and scion bark accurately for patch and ring budding.

Fig. 357.—Diagram Showing Position of Cuts for Modified Bark Graft. Half-H Budding.

Own-Rooted Fruit Trees.—For the northern prairies and similar climates, W. L. Kerr, of the Manitoba Station at Morden, reports that "seedling stocks are prepared as for the commonly practised methods of root grafting. The scion is then grafted into the base end of the stock, or piece root, rather than its apical end. By this method the stock is in an inverted position when planted out. Apparently the stock is able to nurse the scion, but the scion fails to nourish the stock sufficiently. The restriction, if such is the case, stimulates root growth just above the union. . . . In all cases the average growth of the scion at the end of the first season was approximately 6″ shorter than the average where stock was not inverted." This method may prove valuable in the propagation of some ornamentals. *Am. Soc. Hort. Sci. Proc.*, Vol. 33, p. 355. 1935.

Own-Rooted Old Home Pear Trees.—One-year-old trees of Old Home pear budded on one-year-old quince cuttings were planted with the unions 4″, 8″, and 12″ below the soil surface. Four years

Fig. 358.—Growth of Bud in Bark Graft
Shown by Arrow. Half-H Budding.

later two of the 12″ trees had developed good Old Home roots which in time apparently would dominate the quince roots. At 8″ there were fewer and smaller pear roots and at 4″ there were only a few. L. H. Day, Univ. of Calif.

Cherry Rootstocks.—Of six *Prunus* rootstocks tested in Vermont—Mazzard, Mahaleb, *serrulata, pennsylvanica, virginiana* and *serotina*—for propagating sweet and sour cherries, the last two made such poor unions with the scions that they were discarded. Early Richmond grew and fruited better on Mazzard than on Mahaleb—began in four years from the graft. Windsor did best on *P. serrulata*.

Summer-budded vs. Winter-grafted Roses.—Matchless, Madame Butterfly and Templar on Manetti stocks grown in the greenhouse by F. F. Weinard and S. W. Decker of the Illinois Experiment Station, showed that well-grown summer-budded plants were as valuable both as to number and quality of flowers as were winter-grafts, though there was some indication of differences in varietal response to the two types of propagation.

Summer Cuttings of Trees and Shrubs.—Iliein states that admixture of sphagnum moss to sand increased the percentage of rooting of summer cuttings of *Acer dasycarpum* (silver maple) and *Fraxinus lanceolata* (green ash). Cutting under water increased the rooting of these two trees and of *A. platanoides* (Norway maple) but not of *Quercus rubra* (red oak), *Cotinus coggygria* (*Rhus cotinus*—common smoke tree) and *Betula verrucosa* (*B. alba pendula*—European weeping birch). Cuttings taken from a 2-year-old *Q. robur* (English oak) rooted more readily than those from a 15-year-old tree. Ringing increased rooting in *Q. robur, F. lanceolata,* and *C. coggygria*. Abbreviating the length of day increased rooting in several species. Translation from Trudy Prikl. Bot. Genet., i Selek. Leningrad (*Bul. Appl. Bot. Genet., and Plant Breeding, Sup. 61*, p. 284.)

Blackberry and Raspberry Leaf Bud Cuttings.—Leaf buds of these two fruits resemble the buds in shield budding, except that the leaf is retained together with the bud in its axil and a small attached bit of bark and wood—cut between mid July and mid August, placed in a rooting medium of sand or sand and peat. With ordinary cutting bed management 100% success is often attained.

This method is of particular value in propagating new or rare varieties when wood is scarce, varieties that do not root well from either suckers or tips and would therefore be of no commercial value. Also, it might be used to supplement other methods in emergencies when spring-applied methods, such as hardwood or root cuttings, have failed. It is not successful with red raspberry and those varieties of purple raspberry that reproduce by means of suckers.

Leaves from the central part of the cane and with a substantial heel were most successful. Clean, sharp sand, regular watering and high humidity all appeared essential. Cuttings taken in late September developed a rosette type of growth. Good success was also had with rose, mock orange and gooseberry.

Repeated trials with Chief and Latham (red varieties) were unsuccessful, despite abundant callusing. Some success was secured with blackberry cuttings in a peat and sand mixture. *Am. Soc. Hort. Sci. Proc.,* 30, p. 278. 1933.

Dahlia Leaf Bud Cuttings.—The following method has given at least five times as many plants as can be secured from stem cuttings. Dahlia roots were placed in a mixture of sand and granulated peat in flats in early February and held at 60° F. When the shoots had reached 8 or 10 inches in height they were used for making cuttings by cutting each leaf with a piece of stem attached. If the leaf blade was large it was cut off. The cuttings were then inserted in sand in an open propagating bench with gentle bottom heat. *Mich. Stat. Quar. Bul.,* Vol. 16, p. 253. 1934.

Rhododendron Propagation by the usual commercial methods of rooting cuttings generally results in a low percentage of success. L. C. Chadwick and W. E. Gunesch treated cuttings taken in early October in various ways and placed them in a grafting case maintained at 60° to 65° F. A mixture of sand and peat proved better than peat alone. Favorable results were secured from treatment with permanganate of potash prior to planting. Sucrose combined with permanganate had an apparently favorable reaction on semi-mature cuttings. Chemical treatment of the rooting media had no advantage and may be actually harmful. *Am. Soc. Hort. Sci.*, Vol. 34, p. 607. 1936.

Fig. 359.—Plant Protector. Workman placing protector in cone-shaped metal placer; B, placer pressing cone over plant; C, earth covering frill of protector; D, operation complete.

Hardwood Cutting Selection.—Experiments, conducted by L. C. Chadwick of the Ohio Experiment Station, with hardwood cuttings taken monthly between November and April inclusive indicate that better results occur with those taken in late winter or early spring, the possible explanation being the shorter storage period, the consequent lessened risk of drying out and of damage by bacteria and fungi. Other probable factors are the changes in the nature of the food supply in the plant tissues during winter. These influence the formation of root initials and healing tissues. It is possible that changes in the food supply are more favorable to rooting when the cutting wood is still attached to the plant in its normal condition than when stored as detached individuals in some storage medium. *Am. Soc. Hort. Sci. Proc.*, Vol. 28, p. 455. 1931.

Blueberry Cuttings.—Straight, heel, and mallet—of newly formed shoots of low bush blueberry set in German peat moss, sorbex and a 50—50 mixture of peat moss and acid sand, gave good results in all cases. Highest average rooting (81.7%) was secured with heel cuttings; mallet type poorest (61.7%). Use of short laterals taken in early June permitted more rapid increase than was possible with dormant, hardwood cuttings when material is limited. Straight cuttings of highbush varieties (Adams and Rubel) gave better results than did heel or mallet cuttings. *Mich. Stat. Quar. Bull.*, Vol. 19, No. 1, p. 60. 1936.

Geranium Propagation Studies.—Among various factors concerned in the loss of geranium cuttings taken in late autumn, temperature was found most important by H. E. White of the Massachusetts Experiment Station. At 60° F. more than 90 per cent. rooting occurred—more than twice that obtained at 80°. Stem rot diseases (important factors in the losses) were favored at the higher temperature. The kind of media had little influence on rooting. Steam sterilization of the soil and treatment of the cuttings with permanganate of potash did not reduce losses from rots. Synthetic substances had some effect on rooting, but not in the presence of rots. Bordeaux mixture spray was actually detrimental.

Papaya Cuttings Successfully Rooted.—H. P. Traub and L. C. Marshall found that the application of bottom heat is highly beneficial in stimulating root response of papaya. Of four types of cuttings—1, the entire branch, including the naturally swelled base; 2, distal cuttings from branches; 3, median parts; and 4, the basal part including the natural swelling—all gave good results in a solar frame. Treating the bases of the cuttings for 42 hours in a 1—10,000 solution of β—indoleacetic acid increased the percentage of success and quantity of roots per cutting. No significant differences due to variety or sex were noted. The best size of cuttings for convenient handling range from 0.5 to 1 inch in diameter. No important difficulty was met in transplanting the rooted cuttings.

Leaf Bud Propagation of Rubus was successful with species as follows: *R. armeniacus, R. ellipticus, R. fraxinifolius, R. glaucus, R. parviflorus,* and *R. leucodermis.* All these species naturally root from cane tips indicating a correlation between the cane tip habit and capacity to propagate by leaf bud cuttings. The cuttings were placed in clean, sharp sand in a heated frame. C. C. Thomas in *Am. Soc. Hort. Sci. Proc.,* Vol. 33, p. 377. 1935.

"Vegetative Propagation of Conifers is essential to rapid improvement through forest tree breeding, because valuable parental stock and hybrids could be multiplied and tested by this means; but comparatively little is known concerning the factors affecting successful propagation of cuttings from any varieties of trees. The position of the cutting on the tree is one of the factors to be considered. It is possible that there are physiological differences in sprouting and response of cuttings taken from the upper and lower regions of the spruce, since the upper region bears the female flowers, the lower the male, and the wide-spreading lower branches of some varieties have a tendency to layer. Accordingly, an experiment was carried out in the greenhouse of the National Research Laboratories (Canada) to investigate this point.

"Cuttings from the upper and lower regions of a Norway spruce tree were treated with talc only, and with talc containing 1,000 ppm[1] indoleacetic acid. Ten weeks after being planted in sand, 43% of the upper and 75% of the lower cuttings were rooted. Hormone treatment increased the number of roots per rooted cutting but decreased the mean length of individual roots significantly. Nineteen weeks after being planted, the cuttings not rooted at ten weeks were re-inspected, and gave final rooting values for the experiment of 48% for upper cuttings and 86% for lower. Physiological differences are consequently suggested in cuttings taken from the upper and lower regions." *Can. Jl. Research,* Vol. 17, Sec. C, No. 6, p. 178 1939.

Root-Inducing Treatment of Cutting,[2] after several years' experimental work has resulted in various methods of application. Though each has proved effective on certain plants the tendency is to simplify procedures. Methods in which treatment lasts only a few seconds simplifies application, but introduces complications associated with concentrations 10 to 1,000 times higher than standard 24-hour treatments.

---

[1] ppm=parts per million.
[2] *Comparative Activity of Root-inducing Substances and Methods for Treatment,* A. E. Hitchcock and P. W. Zimmerman, Contrib. Boyce Thompson Institute, 10 (4): 461-480, July-September, 1939.

Results with powder preparations are complicated because talc, the commonly used carrier, consistently caused better rooting than did nontreated or tap water controls, also the effectiveness of powder preparations was noticeably dependent upon the mechanical fineness of the powder. Hence, results of different workers may not always agree unless strictly comparable preparations are used.

Indolebutyric, naphthaleneacetic and indoleacetic acids and their potassium salts were the principal root inducing substances used in these experiments, in standard solution, concentrated solution, and in powder form—the last in two types.

Data secured from the treatment of 64 species and varieties of herbs, evergreens, vines, deciduous trees and shrubs show that the optimum concentration of indolebutyric acid varied with the species regardless of whether the root-inducing substance was applied as a relatively dilute solution, as a concentrated solution or as a powder. Various species responded to relatively low concentrations with all three methods. Also, certain species that responded best to relatively high concentrations with one method likewise required relatively high concentrations with the other two methods. The concentrated dip method was generally more critical than the other two methods but the results obtained with the former were particularly satisfactory with species difficult to root.

The same correlation between the average number of roots per cutting and concentration reported for the standard immersion method was found to hold for the powder and concentrated solution dip methods. It is believed that this relationship is a far more reliable criterion of the relative activity of different rooting substances than is the percentage of cuttings rooted, since marked differences may be shown when all cuttings (including controls) are rooted.

Concentration requirements in these experiments varied not only with the species but also with the relative age of the cutting with particular reference to the degree of hardness where the basal cut was made. Both types of cuttings may be secured from the same plant or from shoots on plants grown under different conditions. The relative age of the cutting is thus an important limiting factor in determining the rooting response of cuttings treated with powders and with concentrated solutions.

The time of year treatments were administered also proved an important limiting factor in the response of cuttings to root-inducing substances. For instance, results showed that named varieties of French lilac can be rooted readily, so that there should be no necessity for grafting them.

Cuttings of many species require higher concentrations of indolebutyric acid when taken in October or November as compared with other times of year. Considering these results, it appears that regardless of the method of application, a given concentration of a root-inducing substance does not produce optimum rooting for all species and not even for the same species at all times of the year and under all conditions normally met with in propagation procedures. In general, cuttings of evergreens have shown more variation than have cuttings of deciduous plants. For this reason the approximate optimum concentrations for the two dip methods cover a wider range than in the case of evergreens treated according to the standard immersion method. Strict agreement in results of different workers cannot be expected unless the principal factors which determine concentration requirements for a given root-inducing substance have been accounted for.

In general, any beneficial effects of bottom heat (78° to 80°F.) consisted mainly of quicker rooting and a more rapid rate of root growth. Many species rooted better at 70° to 73°F. than at 78° to 80°F. These latter results were due primarily to the poor condition of the cuttings held at the higher temperature. A favorable temperature of the medium may act in effect the same as a higher concentration. Hence, temperature is a limiting factor when determining minimum concentration requirements for rooting of cuttings.

Since control cuttings treated with talc showed consistently a slightly better rooting than non-treated controls immersed in tap water, the effect of talc itself must be accounted for in experiments relating to results with comparative methods. The effect of talc appears to be due at least in part to differences which involve water relations. However, in many species there was no evidence of wilting but the talc controls showed better rooting and better callus formation than non-treated controls or tap water controls.

There is general agreement in published reports that indolebutyric and naphthaleneacetic acids are more effective for rooting cuttings than is indoleacetic acid, and that indolebutyric acid is the most effective of the three, from all standpoints, for practical use.

Potassium salts of indolebutyric, indoleacetic and naphthaleneacetic acids were generally more effective than the acids. The higher efficaciousness of the salts for root formation was particularly noticeable in the case of the two dip methods. In most cases the tests constituted a comparison between the acid and the salt of one or two substances. However, in one test the three principal acids and their corresponding potassium salts were compared simultaneously in three concentrations. Results obtained with the dip methods indicated that the salts are sufficiently more active than the acids to be of practical value in propagation.

The high effectiveness of the concentrated solutions (1 to 20 mg./cc.),[1] particularly for species relatively difficult to root, makes this method worthy of further consideration.

Growth Substance Treatment of Deciduous Fruit Cuttings. —More than 2,000 softwood cuttings of sour cherry, apple, pear and *Prunus tomentosa,* after treatment with synthetic growth substances were grown in 50—50 peat moss and washed sand. Different species and varieties within species responded differently to treatment with indolebutyric acid, indicating the need of careful trials with each plant material. The inability to produce roots was not overcome by chemical treatment, but plants which would root under favorable conditions rooted much more freely after treatment. In the Montmorency cherry, softwood cuttings taken shortly before the shoot became completely woody responded favorably to the indolebutyric acid treatment. K. D. Brase, N. Y. (Geneva) Experiment Station.

Root-inducing Substances in Amide Form.—The apparently hitherto untried amide derivatives of several well known growth substances,[2] as tested by V. T. Stoutemyer,[3] seem to be remarkably devoid of toxic effects, but highly effective in promoting root initiation. Compared with the action of naphthaleneacetic acid and, to a lesser extent, with the indole acids, they showed responses unlike those of any of the free acids or their salts or esters now in use as growth substances. With the amides, increases in dosage even to excess rarely produced the usual signs of toxicity other than diminution or inhibition of root formation, while the cuttings remained in an apparently healthy condition. The amide group in these chemicals apparently gave to the cuttings much latitude of dosage and an even greater freedom from toxic effects than is possessed by the indole compounds.

The amides usually appeared to be about as active in root formation as the free acids—sometimes definitely superior. Strong root-forming action cannot be explained on the basis of solubility, since the amides are less soluble than the free acids.

Phenylacetamide produced excellent rooting of softwood cuttings, particularly when the dosages were increased over those normally used with the most common growth substances in talc dust mixtures. Though the various phenol compounds produce excellent responses on leafy softwood cuttings, they often fail on hardwood cuttings or with difficult subjects—where most needed.

The chemicals used in these trials were mixed with talc [4]—one part of growth substance to 1,000, 250, 100 and 50. The powders

---

[1] Milligrams to the cubic centimeter.
[2] Phenylacetamide, 1-naphthylthioacetamide and 1-naphthylacetamide.
[3] V. T. Stoutemyer, Bureau of Plant Industry, U. S. Dept. of Agriculture.
[4] See *Talc as a Carrier of Root-forming Substances,* page 584.

were applied by dipping the moistened basal ends of the cuttings in the mixtures and tapping them lightly to remove excess amounts.

Since good conditions for propagation were maintained, the percentage of rooting was frequently high in all lots. The heaviness of the roots in the various treatments was compared by grading the cuttings in several arbitrary classes based on the number and length of roots produced. Usually cuttings having only one or two long or less than a half-dozen short ones were classed as "light rooting," those having exceptionally vigorous root systems as "heavy rooting," and those intermediate as "medium rooting." There was also an "over-treatment" group—cuttings whose roots emerged both at the base and up the stem for a considerable distance. This type of rooting, though not necessarily injurious, is often considered undesirable. It indicates that growth substance has been applied in excessively high concentration.

Comparisons of the amides with indolebutyric and indoleacetic acids on an equal weight basis have usually shown the naphthylacetamide to have some advantage, although this is probably a coincidence resulting from the selection of test species.

Talc as a Carrier of Root-inducing Substances.[1]—As practical use of growth substances in solution by unskilled operators is impeded by diversity of concentrations and by the difficulty of providing storage for large quantities of cuttings being treated, the greater simplicity of application and increased latitude in permissible dosages where talc is used as a carrier warrant careful appraisal of this vehicle by conservationists, nurserymen and others interested in large-scale propagation by cuttings.

In several series of experiments, V. T. Stoutemyer of the United States Plant Introduction Garden used various dust and aqueous concentrations of indolebutyric and naphthaleneacetic acids, the latter alone and also combined with thiourea.

Crystals of the growth substances were dissolved in 95 per cent. ethyl alcohol to make a pasty mixture when stirred into pharmaceutical talc. This was then dried and stored in the dark in glass containers. The aqueous solutions were prepared from concentrated alcoholic solutions of the crystalline substances. All aqueous treatments lasted 24 hours.

Rather liberal application of the dust was given the cuttings, previously moistened with a bulb spray. The cut basal ends were plunged about 1 centimeter deep. Excess powder was lightly tapped or shaken off. The cuttings were inserted at once in sand, in shaded greenhouses with bottom heat of 65° to 70°F. thermostatically controlled.

---

[1] *Am. Soc. Hort. Sci. Proc.,* Vol. 36, p. 817. 1938.

Plants used included species that require different dosages with aqueous treatment.

Toward the end of the tests it was apparent that many species would stand dusts even more concentrated than 1 to 250, so the test plants were tried again with 1 to 100 dusts of both indolebutyric and naphthaleneacetic acids. The results were practically identical with both substances. Cuttings of some species were killed, but others were not injured—even gave 100% rooting without the slightest sign of toxicity, though they are sensitive to strong dosages in aqueous solution.

Toxicity resulting from too high concentrations was not consistent in repeated trials. Apparently it varies with many factors both in the cutting and in the propagation conditions. Tabulation of rooting is complicated by the occasional occurrence of injury at the base of well rooted cuttings along with the formation of unusually heavy roots.

Trials on a less extensive scale with dusts of methyl indolebutyrate and potassium naphthalene acetate gave results similar to those obtained with indolebutyric and naphthaleneacetic acids.

Results show that the dust treatment is, in general, as effective as the aqueous solution treatments. That there is greater latitude of dosage with dusts than with solutions is shown particularly in cases where cuttings were killed by high concentrations of naphthaleneacetic acid in aqueous solution, but were not injured with high concentrations in dust form. Nevertheless, despite the greater latitude, varying optimum concentrations were evident as with the aqueous solutions.

Dusts were noticeably effective in promoting rooting even at the low concentration of 1 to 4,000 though the resulting roots were scanty. This concentration was definitely much too low. The 1 to 2,000 dusts were effective though not as reliable as the concentration of 1 to 1,000. This latter concentration was satisfactory for general use though the experiments show the frequent desirability of higher concentrations. Dusts of 1 to 500 were also tried with satisfactory results. The dusts having a concentration of 1 to 250 were exceedingly effective, but caused injury to cuttings of a few sensitive plants. This toxicity, however, was often inconsequential, even on some subjects which seem to require low dosages.

No one dust can be ideal for use with all cuttings, but satisfactory compromises are possible. The 1 to 1,000 concentrations seem to be a close approximation to a single general purpose dust.

Several substances which have been used to break dormancy in plants were incorporated with various dusts containing growth substances. The adddition of thiourea gave particularly consistent and promising results. The numerical counts suggest, rather than prove, definite increases in rooting due to the thiourea, but the increased heaviness in rooting was unmistakable in some lots. In no case was the substance deleterious although the concentrations may have been far from optimal.

The importance of apparently trivial details was illustrated by an experiment with both wide and narrow trenches in the sand. The narrow trench was formed with a knife. Some of the dust is inevitably rubbed off the cuttings in inserting them in such a narrow fissure. The wide trench was made with a wood label about 1 centimeter thick. Some of the cuttings were treated by applying the dust carefully to the cut basal surface only. Others were dipped in the dust 1 centimeter deep. The results indicate the desirability of applying the dust freely along the base and also of precautions to prevent loss of the powder while inserting the cuttings in the propagating bench.

The relative stability of the various growth substances when mixed with talc or other dust carriers will be an important factor in practical usage. Dusts containing indoleacetic acid quickly turn pink, probably caused by an oxidative change to urorosein. Those containing either indolebutyric acid or methyl indolebutyrate turn brownish with exposure to light. No color changes have been noticed in dusts containing naphthaleneacetic acid or potassium naphthalene acetate. Possibly the naphthalene compounds are the more stable of the growth substances. Unfortunately little information on this important matter is available.

The advantages of the dust treatment are: 1. Low cost, as the amount of dust used per cutting is small. Slender cuttings require from 10 to 15 gr. per 1,000 cuttings; thicker ones, from 15 to 25. The amount of dust adhering depends to some extent upon the moisture present. In general, 1 ℔. of dust might be expected to treat 20,000 to 40,000 cuttings. 2. The saving of time is great as the dust is quickly applied. The cuttings may be inserted at once in the propagating bed. 3. The method is simple and requires no apparatus. Charts of dosages are not essential. The treatment is safe in the hands of inexperienced workmen. 4. The method is exceedingly effective in practise. Hastening of rooting, increase in size of the root system, and percentage of survival are equal or even superior to results obtained with solutions. The solution treatment may be retained for certain special cases, though results show the high efficiency of the dust method with exceedingly difficult subjects.

Further study may show that the higher concentrations usable may make dusts more effective than solutions with some particularly difficult material.

Ericaceous Rooting Response to Auxin Treatment.—Summer cuttings of many ericaceous genera, such as Kalmia, Rhododendron, Erica and Leucothoë, rooted without special treatment but with the majority treated with indolebutyric acid resulted in a higher percentage of success. The auxin treatments hastened rooting by an average of two weeks and resulted in larger root systems. Indolebutyric acid was more effective than was indoleacetic acid. Inferior or negative results were secured with six of the 45 species tested. H. T. Skinner, *Am. Soc. Hort. Sci. Proc.*, Vol. 35, p. 830. 1937.

Vitamin B_1 as a Growth Substance.—Vitamin B_1 is sometimes referred to as a growth substance. Very definitely it has special physiological activity when applied to excised roots as shown by Dr. W. J. Robbins of the New York Botanical Garden; but the practical use of it for horticultural purposes, though receiving recent wide publicity, has not been definitely established. The compound is a product of both green plants and microorganisms. Wherever these microorganisms are active, as in soils containing organic matter, Vitamin B_1 is sure to be a by-product which is added to the soil. Green leaves and other parts of the plants also synthesize Vitamin B_1 which supplies the plant as a whole. As very small amounts are required, the soil is almost certain to be supplied with large enough quantities to permit of maximum plant growth. There have been many extravagant claims concerning the practical value of Vitamin B_1. These, however, come as a rule from amateurs who have not checked their results with control plants. The consensus of opinions among scientists is that Vitamin B_1 has been badly exploited and has no practical value as recommended for horticultural practise.

Gladiolus growth and flowering studies at the Iowa State College *(Research Bulletin 253, 1939)* indicate that "a certain shape of gladiolus corm can not be claimed as possessing qualitative flowering abilities. Certain quantitative growth and flowering results concerning high and low crowned corms were marked with considerable variation as was expected. In general, high crowned as well as low crowned corms within a given variety varied somewhat in certain growth and flowering aspects from one season to the next. In comparisons of high and low crowned corms within varieties, low crowned corms of most varieties completed their sprouting in less time and generally produced taller flower spikes. Low crowned corms always produced greater total leaf area, more spikes and a greater number of florets per corm than high crowned corms. Differences in the number of florets between high and low crowned corms were not significant. It was distinctly obvious that the high crowned corm did not produce a more superior flower spike than the low crowned corm.

"Many gladiolus growers claim to recognize a condition in corm termed 'running out.' The condition is characterized in some varieties by poor growth and flowering results, apparently caused by constitutional weakening of the corm the farther it is removed in vegetative generations from the cormel stage. Diseases play their part in the 'running out' of gladiolus varieties as they do in potato tubers. . . . The grandiflorus type of gladiolus does not propagate vegetatively as fast as the primulinus type, neither is it considered as disease resistant. A number of varieties of the primulinus type have been grown in the Iowa State College trial grounds for the past 14 years without indication of increasingly poor flowering performance. It is conceivable that if the grandiflorus type were subjected to optimum environment and horticultural treatment, the condition of 'running out' should not be prevalent."

Gladiolus Reproduction.—One of the most successful methods of hastening reproduction "is to cut the corms into sections so that there is one bud and part of a corm to each section. They are then coated with sulphur to lessen the possibility of disease inoculation, and are planted. This method is very satisfactory with many varieties but some do not respond well to it. It is employed frequently with the rarer varieties, stock of which is limited and which it is desired to increase rapidly." P. R. Krone, Mich. Experiment Station.

Gladiolus Cormel Sprouting.—The rate of germination of small gladiolus cormels in soil at room temperature after storage at $3°$ to $35°C$. for 28 to 97 days was increased. High temperature storage ($35°C$.) gave germination earlier than room temperature only in later stages of the rest period. Ethylene chlorhydrin was of only slight stimulating effect to corms stored at low temperature, but gave large gains in germination of corms previously stored at room temperature or higher. (F. E. Denny, Boyce Thompson Institute.)

Seed germinators in the past have proved so unreliable—in direct ratio to their dependence upon human attention—that efforts toward improvement have resulted in self-regulating styles of which Figure 360 is typical.

This apparatus, designed and developed by the manufacturer in consultation with seed analysts, maintains uniform temperatures and produces accurate results with minimum attention. The even temperature in all parts is maintained by electric current which warms a water jacket around the seed chamber. Current is controlled by a thermostat which keeps the temperature at the desired degree, thus eliminating risk of possible failure incident to other forms of heating. Quick changes of temperature, even to those of near freezing, can be made through connection with running water and refrigeration built into the apparatus. Moisture and ventilation (with filtered air) are also provided for.

Onion Seed Storage and Germination.—J. H. Beattie and
V. R. Boswell's (U. S. Dept. of Agric.) experiments show how onion
seed vitality may be prolonged. Germination tests were started in
1930 with seeds stored in sealed and non-sealed containers and
under various temperatures and degrees of moisture. High moisture content (10%) was less harmful at 20°F. than at higher temperatures. For the first three or four years 40°F. gave better germination than 20°F., with the reverse true thereafter. Seeds sealed
with low moisture content and stored at 20°F. maintained their

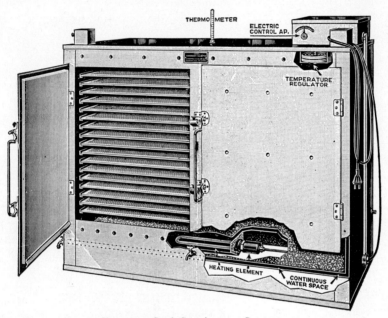

Fig. 360.—Seed Germinator. See text.

vitality without significant loss over a nine-year period. High temperature and moisture were harmful, particularly when both
occurred at the same time. It is recommended that for the maintenance of viability onion seed be reduced to a moisture content of
not over 6% and stored in sealed containers held at 40°F. or lower.
The superiority of initially high viability was indicated in the fact
that such seed held up best during the tests.

Flower Seed Storage.—Using as material 64 samples of flower
seeds representing 30 genera, tests were conducted as to viability
over a ten-year period. Some genera showed little loss for years,
then fell off rapidly. The average length of time the samples retained planting value was six years. Several samples with a low

original test retained 50% or more of their original vitality for the full ten years. Eighty-six per cent of all samples retained 50% or more of their original vitality for three years or more, 66% for five and 25% for 10 years or more. It is suggested that stored flower seeds should be tested for germination at least once every year, preferably just prior to the planting season. *California Dept. of Agric. Bull. 26.*

Quick Germination of Pome Seeds.—R. von Veh Züchler soaked freshly gathered apple, pear and quince seeds in tap water, removed their outer coats and germinated them in petri dishes at room temperature. He found that it was desirable to place the embryos upon a layer of ground cork floating on the water. In 10 to 14 days the seedlings were transferred to a mixture of half peat and half sand. In early spring the young plants were moved to an outdoor bed and exposed to frost. When returned to the greenhouse, rapid development ensued. With this technique plants were developed in eight months to a size reached ordinarily in 20 months.

Seeds of several cherry varieties were similarly treated, the flotation separating potentially viable and non-viable seeds, those with well developed embryos sinking to the bottom. Water is apparently an important factor in determining the early development of cherry seeds. While surrounded by the nucellus, the water-assimilation capacity is distinctly hindered.

Hop Seed Germination.—Of various treatments tested at the Oregon Experiment Station as means of stimulating germination of hop seed, that which provided 5 days' incubation in a standard germination chamber followed by 5 weeks' refrigeration at 5°C. (41°F.) resulted in the highest germination. Though germinability was often below 10% in untreated lots, percentages as high as 80% were obtained in the treated series. Varietal differences in reaction to temperature and moisture treatments were not established. Individual seedling plants varied markedly with respect to germinability of their seed. No differences attributable to treatment were noted in vigor of the seedlings. Under open field conditions climatic factors are believed to overcome dormancy.

After-ripening of Grape Seed.—Studies of seeds of *Vitis œstivalis, V. bicolor,* Concord and Delaware at the Boyce Thompson Institute, showed that all would germinate at warm temperatures, but that such germination was sporadic and slow. Much higher and more uniform germination was obtained when seeds were mixed in a moist medium and subjected to a period of several months at about 41°F. prior to planting at 70°F. Good seedling production was obtained in spring from seeds stored over winter in a mulched coldframe. The removal of part of the seed coat over the radicle reduced germination.

Cotoneaster Seed After-ripening and Germination.—At the Boyce Thompson Institute seeds of *Cotoneaster dielsiana* and *C. zabeli* gave nearly 100% germination after four months' storage in granulated peat held at 10°C. (50°F.), whereas those of *C. acutifolia, C. apiculata, C. horizontalis* and *C. lucida,* germinated poorly even after 10 months. However, when seeds of the last four species were held in a coldframe for two months they gave excellent germination the second spring. The author, J. Giersbach, concludes that dormancy in Cotoneaster results from two factors, an impervious coat and the need of after-ripening after the seed coat is penetrated. The coat effect was removed by treatment with acid or by mechanically removing the seed coat.

Rosa Seed After-ripening and Germination.—Of experiments at Wisley Gardens (England) to hasten germination of various *Rosa* species including cutting the pericarp, increasing the oxygen supply, dry storage at several temperatures and stratification in cool, moist sand, only the last gave consistently beneficial results. Fluctuation in temperature and water content seemed necessary; for example, prolonged inclosure in ice failed to cause rapid germination. The author advises that some acceleration may result from storage in moist sand or other medium at temperatures of —2° to +2°C.

Black Locust Germination Studies at the Cornell Experiment Station with seed obtained from California and locally showed that immersion in boiling water for at least two minutes was more effective than steeping in hot water allowed to cool to room temperature and that the optimum duration of sulphuric acid treatment varied with the different lots of seed, being 6 hours in one case and 10 in another.

Cacao Seed Viability After Storage.—Observations on cacao pods stored at 50°, 60°, 70° and 80°F. for 10, 20, 30, 40 and 50 days showed the greater loss in weight at the higher temperatures. After 20 days at 80°, when the pods had lost nearly half their weight, the seeds were still reasonably viable. Treatments with various antiseptics, such as mercuric chloride, formalin and carbolated vaseline did not reduce materially the losses from latent and incipient infections, but in certain treatments did prolong the life of the seed and reduce water losses. Temperatures below 60°F., even for short periods, were harmful. *Trop. Agri.* (Trinidad) Vol. 11, No. 12, p. 303. 1934.

Avocado Seed Size Correlation to Tree Size.— Statistical studies by R. W. Hodgson and E. R. Eggers at the University of California indicate that under like conditions large seeds tend to produce large seedlings and vice versa; and that when budded with known varieties the large seedlings tend to produce larger nursery trees than do the small seedlings. Trees resulting from the autumn start of buds were larger and more uniform than those started in spring.

Jerusalem Artichoke Rest Period.—At Arlington Experiment Farm, Virginia, tubers of four varieties of Jerusalem artichoke dug before freezing and treated with various chemicals to shorten the rest period started to grow 15 to 150 days sooner than untreated controls, but later growth in all cases was much slower than when the rest period was broken by low temperature. At Arlington, the rest period begins about September 1 and lasts 160 to 180 days.

Hybrid Amaryllis was rapidly increased by H. P. Traub of the United States Department of Agriculture by partially quartering blooming-size bulbs and placing them in clay flower pots containing a mixture of sand and loam. When the bulbs were completely severed into quarters, root formation was apparently retarded to some extent. Sand gave rise to disease-free plants, whereas those in loam showed some red rust.

Germination of Vegetable and Larkspur Seed.—Pre-treatment of lettuce seed on a moist medium at 25°C. or below permitted germination at high temperatures which are ordinarily prohibitive. Pre-treated seed may be dried at room temperature for at least three days, after which a germination of 50% can still be secured at 30°C., and 25% at a temperature of 35°C.

Vigorous carrot, eggplant, onion, tomato and lettuce seedlings were secured from six-year-old seed stored under favorable conditions. A slight initial retardation of growth was noted in cases of unfavorable storage conditions.

At room temperature and at —5° C.,—in some cases dried with calcium oxide—eggplant and tomato kept well under all conditions, but carrot, onion, lettuce and pepper seeds were injured by sealed storage at room temperature unless the seeds were dried. With drying, sealed storage was superior to open storage at room temperature. Lettuce seed gained in its capacity for seedling production with increased length of the storage period up to the maximum of three years. Germination of lettuce, on the other hand, remained practically constant throughout the period. The author, L. V. Barton, of the Boyce Thompson Institute, concludes that under conditions existing at Yonkers, N. Y., open storage at room temperature will maintain vitality for two years in the majority of cases. With reduced moisture content and sealing, vitality was assured for at least three years.

Annual larkspur seed, which does not germinate well at high temperatures, was induced to grow at prohibitive temperatures by previous treatment in moist condition at low temperature. It is suggested that treatment last for one to three weeks at 10° to 15°C.

or the seed be held in a refrigerator. Good germination can then be gained at constant temperatures up to 30°C. Though perennial larkspur was not so sensitive to high temperatures as annual larkspur, low temperature pre-treatment also gave favorable results up to 35°C.

FIG. 361.—Hulling Machine. This machine works on the impact-and-rebound principle at speeds which may be varied from 1,200 to 3,000 R.P.M.

Seed Treatment with Fungicidal Dusts, such as Ceresan, Semesan, Merko and Barbak, to control smuts and various other seed-borne diseases, is best done by machines, of which the one described and illustrated in Minnesota Experiment Station Circular 58 is a good example. According to the author, M. B. Moore, it can not only do a thorough job when properly built and operated, but it need not cost more than $3.50. Figures 362 and 363 show its construction and operation; when the trough A is tilted the layers of seed and fungicide slide into the chute where they are turned as they descend spirally over five or more baffles or through the holes in these.

Seed to be treated is spread evenly from end to end of the trough, sprinkled with fungicide dust and raked by nails or pegs driven in the edge of a short board. Other layers of seed and dust are added and similarly raked. When full, the trough is tilted so the mixture will pour down the chute and into a bag at the bottom.

In operating this apparatus the following precautions are necessary; 1. Fill the trough exactly as described, being sure to apply a separate dose of dust to each layer of seed. 2. Clean the treater thoroughly before changing from one variety or crop to another. 3. Use the exact amount of disinfectant recommended by the maker. 4. Avoid breathing the dust, as most dusts are poisonous. 5. Work outdoors when possible, otherwise in a well ventilated room. 6. Wear a dust mask when treating large quantities of seed. 7. Catch the treated seed in a sack fitted closely to the bottom of the chute.

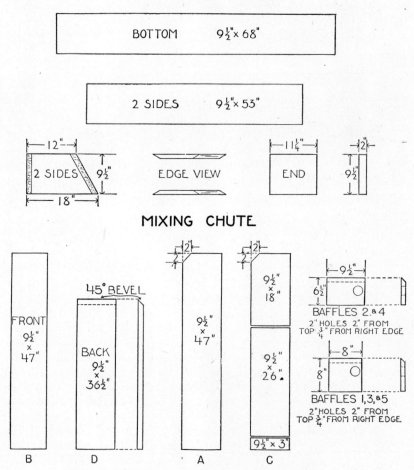

Fig. 362.—Construction Details for Seed Duster.

8. Wash hands and face thoroughly after work and especially before eating.

After-ripening of Fruit-tree Seeds.—Studies by I. C. Haut of the Maryland Experiment Station, to determine factors which may affect after-ripening and subsequent germinating in fruit seeds have been summarized (somewhat condensed) as follows:

Drying seeds at room temperature prior to after-ripening does not adversely affect the percentage of germination, provided the dried seeds are subsequently after-ripened at low temperature and in moist condition.

Seeds stratified dry at low temperature do not after-ripen.

In a stratification medium of sand held at approximately moisture capacity, after-ripening occurs but germination is reduced somewhat below the maximum.

Drying following after-ripening results in marked reduction

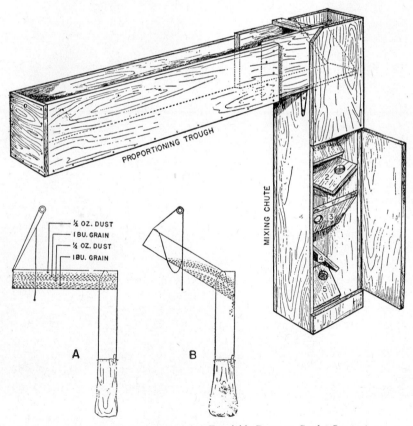

Fig. 363.—Apparatus for Applying Fungicide Dusts to Seed. See text.

in viability. Apparently seed completely after-ripened is susceptible to injury by dessication. The re-stratification of such dried seed consequently results in low germination.

Temperatures of 0°, 3°, and 8° C. were found effective for the after-ripening of McIntosh apple, Elberta peach, Mazzard and Mahaleb cherry seeds. However, slightly higher germination followed after-ripening at 3° C. A freezing of —3° C. and an alternating temperature of —3° + 3° C. proved to be relatively ineffective.

Fig. 364.—Electrically Sterilized Soil. Left, treated soil; right, untreated— notice weeds.

A high percentage germination was obtained following an after-ripening period of 45 days with pear, 60 days with apple, 75 days with peach, 88 days with Mahaleb, and 100 days with Mazzard, using a temperature of 3° C.

Allowing the pulp to disintegrate while the fruit remains in piles results in considerable injury to the seeds of peach. It is recommended that the fruit be not allowed thus to disintegrate, even though recovery of the seeds is thereby facilitated.

The percentage germination of Elberta peach and Mazzard cherry seeds may be considerably reduced by the mechanical resistance offered to the expanding embryo by the endocarp. This may also explain why the germination of these seeds in the nursery often is delayed until the second year after planting.

Attempts to after-ripen French pear and domestic apple seeds by various methods of stimulation other than low temperature proved unsuccessful.

No significant changes in fats, total sugars, sucrose, free reducing substances, titrable acid, and alcohol-soluble and insoluble nitrogen were found during the after-ripening process in seeds of the above named fruits.

The catalase activity progressively increased until the seeds were fully after-ripened when an activity about twice that of un-after-ripened seeds was attained.

It is suggested that in future studies a clearer differentiation be made between after-ripening changes and changes in seeds which are already germinating.

Stone Fruit Seed Germination Delay Decreased.—Working with plum, sweet cherry, sour cherry and peach seeds, F. Hilkenbäumer (*Landw. Jhrb.*, Vol. 82, No. 6, p. 883. 1936) found that the seeds of various mother trees within a species exhibit material variation in their germination. When seeds were not removed immediately from the flesh at harvest, or the fruits were fermented for a short time, germination was delayed and reduced. Of four media, peat, sand, sand and peat, and peat and soil, peat was the most effective in hastening germination. Germination was increased by peat only with Mahaleb cherry and peach. Low and varying temperature in damp storage reduced germination except in the peach. Storage and seed bed temperature over 12° C. hindered germination. Temperatures from —10° to —65° C. had no beneficial or harmful effects on air-dried seeds.

The several species had different optimum germination temperatures. Immersion in water at 12° C. had no effect on germination, except with Mahaleb cherry. At 24° C. germination was decreased and delayed. Various chemical agents, such as sulphuric acid and chloride of lime, were tested and for the most part accelerated germination. The bony seed shell delayed germination somewhat. The causes of delayed germination are said to rest in the specific nature of the seed and not in external factors such as seed shell.

Seed Germination in Live Sphagnum Moss has been proved highly successful by A. W. Close who has had good results with about 2,500 species embracing 300 genera and 50 plant families. This material "seems to confer the advantage of the organic media in requiring little watering, and at the same time to offer but little foot-hold for fungus diseases. In comparison with dead sphagnum and peat it has the springiness that is perhaps beneficial to germination. If glass coverings are used, condensation is generally less over sphagnum than over sand or soil.

"That the advantages secured are principally physical in nature is suggested by the data presented in Table 32.

"It will be noted that the seed covered with soil failed utterly to germinate, while sowing on soil and covering with fine sifted gravel or with sphagnum gave satisfactory results. The contrast between peat and sphagnum is striking.

TABLE 32.—GERMINATION OF *HAPLOPHYTON CIMICIDUM* IN VARIOUS MEDIA

Medium	Number of seed sown.	Germination percent.
Potting soil, covered with same.................	200	0.
Potting soil, covered with gravel................	700	85.7
Potting soil, covered with live sphagnum........	720	96.5
Peat, covered with peat........................	200	0
Live sphagnum, no covering....................	200	100.
Live sphagnum, covered with same.............	250	100.

"It is particularly valuable in several families, such as *Ericaceæ*, which give trouble in germination. Repeated sowings of *Anoromedia, Bruckenthalia, Calluna, Enkianthus, Erica, Gaultheria, Leucothoë, Pieris, Rhododendron, Vaccinium, Zenobia, Menziesia, Pernettya*, have invariably germinated successfully. Small seeded members of *Saxifragaceæ*, such as *Astilbe, Bergenia, Deutzia, Escallonia, Francoa, Heuchera, Hydrangea, Philadelphus* and *Schizophragma* have germinated readily on this medium and in many cases before watering becomes necessary. All of the genera in *Bignoniaceæ* with which the writer is familiar, including *Adenocalymma, Bignonia, Incarvillea, Jacaranda, Tabebuia, Tecoma* and *Tecomaria* gave similar results.

"Many rosaceous genera, such as *Fragaria, Physocarpus, Potentilla, Sanguisorbia*, and *Spiræa* germinate readily on sphagnum. With many genera of this family, however, such as *Chænomeles, Cotoneaster, Cratægus, Pyracantha, Rhodotypos, Rosa* and *Stauvesia*, better results have been obtained with other media, when the seed is after-ripened in the flat. Sphagnum ordinarily does not 'hold up' more than three months under these conditions.

"Seed of many *Compositæ* have been successfully germinated on sphagnum, but required transplanting at a very early stage.

"**Method of Preparation.**—After all the foreign matter has been removed by hand, the sphagnum is rubbed through a hardware cloth sieve having three meshes to the inch. Three-quarters of an inch of sphagnum as a top dressing is placed upon whatever base soil is used (peat and sand is preferable). It is important to leave an air space of ½ inch between the top of the flat and the surface of the moss. To prevent a compact and glossy surface, which might encourage the growth of algæ, the sphagnum is kept rather dry until it is in place, and then the flat receives a good watering and is allowed to drain for 1 hour before the seed is sown. This gives the moss surface time to become springy and porous, forming cavities into which seed may settle. After the seed is sown, the flat is covered with a pane of glass and protected from the direct rays of the sun. If the sphagnum is properly prepared and watered, many seed will have germinated before another watering becomes necessary."

Convenient Germinator.[1]—To avoid the cost of commercial germinators, the attention required by "rag doll" styles and the inconvenience of sand and sawdust boxes, the "milk can germinator"

Fɪɢ. 365.—Variety Breeding. Each cheese-cloth cylinder contains a plant whose flowers are protected against possible contamination with pollen from undesired sources.

has been evolved by H. R. Pettigrove of the Michigan Experiment Station.

In a 10-gal. can whose opening is equal to or greater than one-half its diameter, drill a $\frac{3}{16}$" hole 3" above the bottom inside. From a board cut two half circles which together will form a diameter about 1" less than that of the can. In each half bore several 1" holes to insure free air circulation. Complete this rack by nailing two $3\frac{1}{2}$" legs with one nail each to each half of the disc, placing one leg at the center of the circumference, the other on the straight side about 2" from the outside edge and extending beyond this edge

---

[1] *Mich. Stat. Quar. Bull.*, Vol. 20, No. 4, p. 229, 1938.

(Fig. 366A) so the other half disc may rest upon it when these edges are brought together (Fig. 366B).

To operate, open and fold two sheets of newspaper lengthwise. Thoroughly wet them and lay them out flat. Leaving a 6″ margin at each end, scatter 100 seeds for germination over the paper so no two are within an inch of each other. Roll a piece of paper into a core 1″ to 1½″ in diameter, dip in water and place on one end of the flat sheet. Roll the sheet loosely around this core, using enough pressure to hold the seeds in place.

When rolled, fasten each end loosely with string or a rubber band. Label, dip in water and stand upright in the can. When all the rolls are in place put the cover loosely on the can to allow for some free air circulation, keep at room temperature (70° to 75°) by day and not lower than 50° at night. Several rolls at a time give somewhat faster and more reliable germination than only one or two, since sprouting generates heat of its own.

In about a week remove the rolls one at a time, spread out and count the percentage of sprouted seeds. (Fig. 366C.) Dead seeds usually become moldy by that time; weak ones will produce smaller sprouts than strong ones.

This method of testing works well with all seeds except beets, mangels and chard which seem unable to absorb enough water to sprout.

A can may be used without a hole drilled in its side, provided the cover is removed twice daily and the rolls moved briskly back and forth across the can mouth to create a change of air. If sealed tight the seeds will sprout poorly or not at all because the carbon dioxide given off by germination cannot escape and be replaced by oxygen.

After each use both the can and the rack should be sterilized with boiling water or steam.

Weed destruction in forestry seed beds by hand weeding has proved so costly that other methods of eradication have been developed in recent years. In Scotland, burning over the surface with a blow torch just prior to germination has proved successful and has materially reduced the cost. The method is practical because the weed seeds germinate sooner than the forest tree seeds. Hence, a large number of weeds are above ground when the burning is done.

Among various chemicals tested zinc sulphate (8 gr. to 250 cc. of water) to the square foot gave most satisfactory results.

In an experiment at Michigan Experiment Station, untreated beds required 102 and 52 minutes, respectively, for hand weeding the first and the second years, total, 154 minutes; chemically treated beds, 31 and 56 minutes, respectively, total 87 minutes; and burned beds, 47 and 33 minutes, total, 80. Burning requires a

Fig. 366.—Milk-can Germinator. See text.

minimum of 5 seconds to the square foot. It is done just as the tree seeds are on the verge of bursting above ground.

Burning possibly has an advantage over chemical treatment in its effect on the soil. Continued use of zinc sulphate will tend to increase acidity, which, unless guarded against, might react unfavorably on the soil. Both methods eliminate the heaviest weedings which occur during the first few weeks of the life of the tree seedlings when they are least able to withstand disturbance. *Mich. Stat. Quar. Bul.*, Vol. 15, No. 4, p. 254. 1933.

"Burning out" greenhouses consists in applying heavy doses of calcium cyanide after all plants have been removed and before the houses are to be re-used. Preliminary to this treatment: 1. The whole place should be given a thorough clean-up and all trash burned to destroy pests lurking in such material. 2. The sand, soil or other propagative medium should be soaked four or five days prior to treatment so as to assure humidity of the air. 3. The dosage should vary with the type of pest to be controlled. For white fly, aphis, mealy bug and other easily killed insects, 4 oz. to the 1,000 cu. ft. should suffice, but for red spider, two to eight times that amount, depending upon such factors as serious infestation and tightness of the house.

Soil sterilization by calcium cyanide has proved highly successful in controlling sow bugs, millipedes, slugs, snails, grubs and the adults and larvæ of various "soil insects" without harming beneficial bacteria. When applied to moist soil, this chemical breaks down to form three important simpler compounds—hydrocyanic acid gas which does the sterilizing, nitrates which act as fertilizers, and lime which has several favorable actions upon the soil and the plants to be propagated in it. Thus this fumigant has an advantage over other chemicals used for similar purposes.

Just as in "burning out," the greenhouse must be empty of plants, but the ventilators should be open during the treatment so the gases may escape easily. A lapse of 10 to 15 days should occur between fumigation and putting plants in the greenhouse, so there may be no vestige of gas left in the soil.

Successful treatment depends upon penetration of the soil by the gas. In ordinary, friable greenhouse soils a distance of 12″ from the point of application is considered maximum; in sand, peat moss and other loose propagating media it might be double that radius. Best results are obtained when the soil is fairly dry, when two men work together, when about 5 lbs. of the material are distributed uniformly and systematically to 100 sq. ft. of surface, either in shallow trenches or in holes and when the surface is covered with sailcloth, roofing paper or other dense material to help confine the gas to the soil.

Trenching Procedure: 1. Dig a furrow 1' deep and 8" or 10" wide across the bed (narrow way). 2. Scatter fumigant evenly on the bottom of the furrow. 3. Immediately cover with just enough soil to hold the gas until— 4. Throw soil from the next trench to fill the first. Repeat this sequence until the whole bed has been trenched. Half an ounce to the foot is satisfactory for most species of soil pests.

Hole Procedure: 1. Fork over the bed, break clods and rake smooth. 2. Punch holes 1' deep and 6" apart in staggered rows with a pointed dibble or a sharpened broom handle. 3. In each hole drop a teaspoonful of fumigant and immediately fill with soil.

Fumigating new soil and compost outdoors is best done by building the material in a flat topped pile with a square base so as to facilitate calculation of the cubical contents (length times width times height). Satisfactory doses are 1 lb. to each 12 cu. ft. of soil. The most satisfactory way to proceed is as follows: 1. Prepare a space beside the pile of soil to be fumigated. 2. Sprinkle fumigant on this area. 3. Quickly cover the fumigant with about 6 in. of the soil or compost. 4. Repeat this sequence until all the soil is in the new pile. 5. Wait at least two weeks before using the treated soil for potting or filling the greenhouse benches.

Nematode destruction in greenhouse soils can hardly be expected to reach 100% because the worms protect themselves by encysting. As it is usually impossible to determine when all are not in this condition, treatment cannot be expected to reach them. Soil treatments produce the highest "kill" under the following procedure:

1. Remove and burn as many root knots as possible when soil is to be used a second time. 2. Keep the beds very moist for 2 or 3 weeks before treatment to help rot the remaining galls and to favor hatching the worm eggs. 3. Have the soil fairly moist at the time of fumigation to prevent the creatures from forming shells (encysting) which would protect them from the gas. 4. Follow routine of soil fumigation.

The theoretical concentration of hydrocyanic acid gas in a greenhouse when using the standard dosage of $\frac{1}{4}$ oz. of calcium cyanide per 1,000 cu. ft. is approximately 40 parts of HCN per million in the air. With regard to the toxicity of this concentration to human beings and animals, competent authorities have determined that it produces slight symptoms after several hours of breathing. However, since the rate of evolution of the gas is not instantaneous, the theoretical concentration just mentioned is never reached, especially in a greenhouse which is always subject to considerable leakage.

Calcium Cyanide Fumigation, Quick Method.—Recent investigation has proved that all-night fumigation (p. 253-255) is not necessary because practically all the insect destruction is performed during the first three hours of exposure, so little if anything is to be gained by leaving the gas in the greenhouse longer.

Outstanding advantages of the three-hour exposure are: 1. The kill of insects is satisfactory. 2. Unnecessary to check the temperature throughout the night. 3. Allowing the gas to escape at the end of the three-hour period reduces the risk of possible pocketing of the gas in localized spots and thus injuring the plants there. 4. The risk of gas absorption by free moisture on the foliage due to sharp reduction of temperature is similarly reduced, if not wholly prevented. 5. The quantity and cost of material ($\frac{1}{4}$ ounce or less and one cent or less per thousand cubic feet) are so small and the ease of application so favorable, that regularity of treatment (at seven to ten day intervals) is encouraged and the prevention of insect infestation assured.

Essentially, the old and the new methods are the same. After the fumigant has been spread on the walks, the house is kept closed for three hours. Then the top ventilators are slightly opened—1″ or 2″—so the gas may escape gradually and without causing draft or quick reduction of temperature. Should the outdoor temperature be very low, thus making the chilling of the house risky, extra steam should be applied as a precaution.

Compost Sterilization.—At the John Innes Horticultural Institution (England) it was found that calcium materials should not be added to compost before sterilizing. Addition of superphosphate after sterilizing gave highly beneficial results, probably by correcting the existing deficiency of phosphorus in the compost and also by offsetting the check of growth commonly following sterilization. Addition of peat moss to a compost before sterilization was particularly harmful. Evidently all fertilizers should be added to the compost after the sterilizing process.

Potting Soil Prepared with Peat.—Experiments at the University of Minnesota to determine if peat may be substituted for manure in potting soils indicated that as good or better results may be secured with many species—coleus, calendula, annual larkspur—when it replaces a considerable part of the manure. On the other hand, French marigold, *Browallia,* and *Schizanthus,* thrived best in full manure quota. A *Begonia* species did well with all the manure replaced by peat. Composting peat with manure or chemicals for a year in advance gave no better results than did fresh mixing at potting time.

Transplanting Responses.—Using a soil mixture consisting of one part each of manure and sand and two parts loam, with a pH

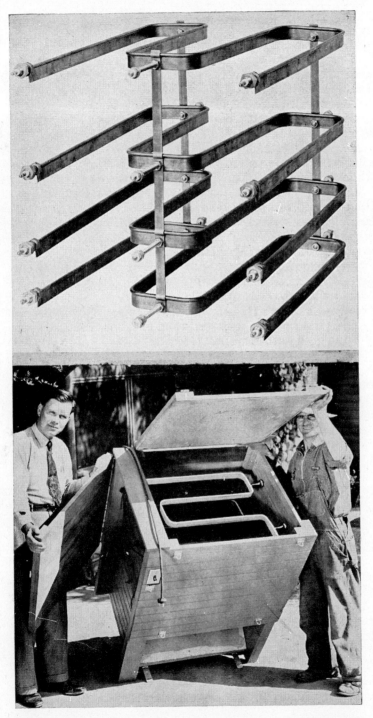

FIG. 367.—Electric Soil Sterilizer. Controls damping-off, kills weeds, soil insects and prevents many diseases.

of 7.65, various nutrient materials were compared for use at the time of pricking-off from the seedling flats. Nitrogen applications resulted in large, succulent top growth and inefficient root systems. In combination with potassium permanganate, nitrogen gave favorable results with tomatoes. Phosphorus gave good results with all types of vegetables, and a combination of potash and dextrose gave good results with head lettuce. Both potassium permanganate and dextrose, when used alone, stimulated root development. Temperature had a prounounced effect on the development of transplants, with the various species having different optima according to their nature. (V. E. Iverson, *Montana Experiment Station.*)

Lanolin as Wound Dressing on Trees.—Since lanolin used alone and with indoleacetic acid caused callusing of the upper ends of apple cuttings G. M. Shear of the Virginia Experiment Station tested their value as wound dressings.

Most wound dressings have been used to prevent entrance of decay—a theory not satisfactory practically; they become ineffective after the first season and subsequent treatments are seldom made. Practically all these materials are toxic to living plant cells. Until their fungicidal value is lost wound healing is retarded; hence, more harm than good may result.

Treatments undertaken by Shear included hydrous lanolin U. S. P., indoleacetic acid, white lead paint and asphalt. Indoleacetic acid was dissolved in lanolin (1 part to 200). Treatments were made within an hour of branch cutting of sugar maple, linden, Grimes Golden and seedling apple trees. Branches ranged from 1¼ to 1½ in. in diameter.

Within three weeks callus growth was noticeably better on wounds treated with plain lanolin. Wounds treated with paint gave the poorest growth. Callus tissue covered approximately one-fifth more area where plain lanolin was used than on untreated wounds.

Most, if not all, beneficent effect was due to lanolin preventing the drying of the cambium and young callus. Its consistency is such that a film is maintained over the growing callus thus permitting unimpeded growth. *Am. Soc. Hort. Sci. Proc.*, Vol. 34, p. 286. 1936.

Cheshunt compound for damping off is prepared and used as follows: Thoroughly mix finely powdered copper sulphate (2 oz.) and ammonium carbonate (11 oz.) and store for 24 hours in an airtight receptacle to prevent loss of ammonia. As needed, dissolve 1 oz. of this dry mixture in a little hot water and then dilute to 2 gals. with cool water in a wooden or crockery—not metal—receptacle. Sprinkle the dilute solution on soil about to be used for planting or that already planted. It will kill damping-off fungi and also increase plant vigor, but will not cure plants already attacked.

When soil is suspected of being infected, adopt the following technique: 1. Seed pans. Water thoroughly after sowing and covering seed. One pint is generally enough for a pan 14″ x 9″ x 2″. 2. Pots. Water with the solution immediately after planting, the soil being 1 inch below pot rim. If plants are left untreated over night many will be infected and treatment useless. 3. Houses. Remove each plant attacked. Water the hole with 1 pt. of solution. Place a healthy plant in the hole and give a second watering. The nitrogen in the solution acts as a stimulant fertilizer. The solution should be more dilute than the above for delicate plants. (W. F. Bewley, Experiment and Research Station, Cheshunt, Herts, England.)

Fig. 368.—Electrically Heated Cutting Bench. Cable rows laid seven inches apart; sand for cuttings placed on cable.

Electric Heating of Hotbeds and Cutting Benches.—After six years' testing, T. E. Hienton and J. H. MacGillivray of the Indiana Experiment Station present their conclusions (condensed) in Circular No. 226 as follows:

1. Soil-heating cable is superior to individual heaters in ease and cost of installation, and cost of operation.

2. Cabbage and tomato seeds germinate sooner and plants grow faster with the cable installed on the soil surface or in the soil and air or at a depth of 3 inches than when it is six inches below the surface.

3. Records of 35 electrical hotbeds operated in Indiana for six years show a variation in consumption from 0.22 to 3.60 kilowatt-hour per 3- by 6-foot sash per day. Of the entire group, 8 used

less than 1.0 kilowatt-hour per sash per day, 12 used from 1.0 to 1.5, 7 used from 1.5 to 2.0, 4 used from 2.0 to 3.0, and 4 used more than 3.0.

4. Covering hotbeds at night reduced consumption, and cinder insulation under and around the beds saved 20% of electricity. Banking the frames with soil and fitting sash tightly to the frames likewise reduced energy consumption.

5. Control of heating by thermostats showed no electric energy saved over manual control, but eliminated the necessity for close personal attention to temperature regulation.

Fig. 369.—Relative Size of Tomato Plants. Electric and steam heat compared. Stakes A and B are of equal height above ground. Plants from electric bed, A, produced 10.4 tons of tomatoes to the acre; those from steam heated bed, B, 9.4 tons.

Sand Culture.—"From the practical standpoint sand is advantageous because yearly replacement may be eliminated, accumulation of soluble salts avoided, known quantities of fertilizers at specified periods need not vary, control of soil moisture simplified, soil aëration troubles reduced, and finally through drenching and sterilization soil pests may be eliminated. From the scientific viewpoint, it is the only accurate approach to the problem of nutrition, since recommendations based on soil plot methods are not always applicable to all conditions and environments." Alex Laurie, *Am. Sci. Hort. Sci.*, Vol. 28, p. 427. 1931.

Sand Culture of Seedlings to Control Damping Off.—At the Connecticut Experiment Station (New Haven Bulletin 380, 1936), A. A. Dunlap compared sand washed with hot water and supplied with liquefied inorganic nutrients before planting, with composted soil and with composted soil sterilized or treated with formaldehyde, as media for growing of flower, vegetable and forest seeds. In one case seed was treated with cuprous oxide powder prior to planting in untreated soil.

In nearly every case seedling production was higher in the sand and much superior to that in untreated soil or cuprous oxide treatment. Also, the sand-grown seedlings were larger and had better root systems for transplanting. Though various sands were suitable, colored sand proved better than pure quartz.

FIG. 370.—Conservation of Heat by Coverings on Cold Nights. Tight-fitting frames reduce consumption of electric current.

Calcium nitrate and sodium nitrate were satisfactory sources of nitrogen, provided some potash was also supplied. Organic sources of nitrogen were not satisfactory because either the nitrogen was not readily available or organic matter encouraged fungi. Nitrate of soda proved superior to sulphate of ammonia, but in some cases the slower growth from the latter was beneficial in reducing length of stem. A real advantage is that sand can be used repeatedly if washed each time with hot water.

Sub-Irrigation of Seed Flats.[1]—Since earlier experiments with the use of wicks for watering seed pans and pot plants had proved successful,[2] similar experiments were carried out with seed flats and

[1] Sub-Irrigation of Seed Flats. Kenneth Post, Cornell University, Ithaca, N. Y. Florists' Exchange and Horticultural Trade World, May 3, 1941.

[2] Sub-Irrigation for House Plants. Kenneth Post, Cornell University, Ithaca, N. Y. Florists' Exchange and Horticultural Trade World, December 28, 1940.

produced successful results. Flat fiberglass, cotton wicking, and cheese cloth rolled into wick form were used as successfully as round wicking and were less expensive. One grower in New York State has used burlap wicks for more than three years.

In these experiments the flats were first thoroughly watered by dipping. Thereafter water was supplied by the wick, one in the bottom of a 16 inch x 22 inch flat being sufficient. Each flat was placed on a gallon crock with the wick hanging in the water. Depths of soil varying from 1½ to 3 inches were found to work equally well. The surface of the soil appeared to be at the optimum moisture content when it was about 4 or 5 inches above the water, the flats being properly adjusted to give this distance. If the soil surface became excessively moist, the flat was raised slightly, but experience showed that the water would not move up successfully if it was more than 6 or 8 inches below the top of the soil. Flats failed to re-establish proper capillarity if the crock was empty for one day.

The soil mixture consisted of one-third peat and two-thirds loam; some was sterilized with electricity, some with formaldehyde. More than 60 seed flats and some 25 seed pans were used in these experiments in the spring of 1941. One flat, among several sown to Petunias, for some reason showed poor growth directly over the wick. Three seed pans, sown to Kalanchoë, became so wet that growth of algae was a serious problem, but this condition was corrected by raising the pans an additional 3 inches above the water.

Seeds of more than 45 species and varieties have been germinated by this method, all of which responded favorably to the treatment. The following genera were used in comparison with the standard method of watering: Acroclinium, Anagallis, Arctotis, Aster, Begonia semperflorens, Begonia tuberous rooted, Brachycome, Calendula, Campanula, Candytuft, Celosia, Centaurea, Chrysanthemum, Cotula, Cuphea, Delphinium, Dianthus, Dimorphotheca, Euphorbia, Grevillea, Gypsophila, Hollyhock, Hunnemannia, Kalanchoë, Kochia, Lobelia, Marigold, Mesembryanthemum, Mignonette, Morning-Glory, Nemophila, Nierembergia, Nigella, Pansy, Petunia, Poppy (annual varieties), Portulaca, Pyrethrum, Scabiosa, Snapdragon, Stock, Thunbergia, Venidium, Xeranthemum, and Zinnia.

Conclusions drawn from the experiments are as follows:

1. Germination was not better than when the flats were surface watered, but the sub-irrigated flats required much less attention.
2. The root systems were excellent and the seedlings transplanted well.
3. The soil remained loose in the flats and the roots did not suffer for lack of air.
4. The seedlings were easily removed from the soil and the roots

FIG. 371.—*Top*: Flat of seedling Stocks showing how wick carries up water from container underneath. *Center*: Same flat showing even stand of seedlings. *Bottom*: Profile view of flat with wick. Height of flat above water is determined by depth of soil.

were injured less than in removing from flats which were watered on the surface.

5. Damping-off occurred in five flats but the same varieties of seedlings were affected when surface watered.

6. There was little difference between the two methods of watering as far as the spread of the disease was concerned. However, great care was taken in surface watering.

7. The wick method will not prevent damping-off but at least it is certain that the disease will be no worse than with surface watering.

8. The wick method appears to be desirable for summer use with snapdragon and other fine seeds.

Post reported that shallow flats of sand, watered by the wick method, gave good results in the rooting of miscellaneous cuttings including Geranium, Coleus, Petunia, and Ageratum. A bench equipped with wicks was used successfully in rooting Hydrangea and Chrysanthemum, but the amount of time saved is questionable because of the small amount of water required by such cuttings. Cuttings subject to leaf diseases might be benefited since the foliage would never be wet. In the light of present knowledge sub-irrigation for cuttings should be conducted on an experimental basis.

Hastening Propagation of Easter Lilies by Scaling Methods.[1]—For several years work has been in progress at the U. S. Horticultural Station, Beltsville, Md., aimed at the development of superior types of forcing lilies. Many promising seedlings have been secured which are being propagated and tested for ultimate introduction into commerce. The entire lily project is being conducted cooperatively by the U. S. Department of Agriculture, the Society of American Florists and Ornamental Horticulturists, the Louisiana State University and the University of California.

In the first method, involving rapid production in the greenhouse, scales were taken from bulbs that had been grown and flowered under glass. Scaling was done during August and September, 1940. Some of the bulbs had just finished blooming; others had flowered several months previously and had been dried off completely. In both instances the scales gave satisfactory propagation with the exception of those from a few bulbs which were so dry that the scales had become soft and limp. Such scales were inclined to decay without bulbil formation.

The scales were placed in flats of sharp sand, 4 inches deep, in rows 1½ inches apart, with approximately 30 scales per foot. Each

[1] D. V. Lumsden, Associate Physiologist, and N. W. Stuart, Associate Physiologist, Div. of Fruit and Vegetable Crops and Diseases, B.P.I., U.S.D.A. The Florists' Exchange and Horticultural Trade World. April 12, 1941.

scale was set upright (base down), about one-half exposed above the sand according to recommendations made by Tincker.[1] Following the work of Griffiths,[2] the flats were placed in a darkened chamber in which the temperature was closely controlled at 80° F. and the relative humidity ranged from 70 to 80 percent. After a period of one month under these conditions most of the scales had produced one to several bulbils with roots at their bases. They were then

FIG. 372.—Creole Easter Lily scales, "sown" in the open ground, U. S. Horticultural Station, Beltsville, Md., in August, 1939. In one year such scales produced bulbs up to the size shown in Fig. 373.

transferred to soil in a greenhouse bench and grown during the winter at a night temperature of 60° F. Such scales produced bulbs, some of which flowered within one year from the time of the scaling operation. Although this treatment is not practical for commercial propagation, it can be used advantageously to hasten maturity in an experimental breeding problem, for the rapid increase of a clonal type, or when it is necessary to hasten production of planting stock.

In the second method, which has greater commercial possibilities, large quantities of scales were set out in August, 1939, in an open field in a light, well drained soil. The beds were 3 feet wide, the rows running across the bed (Fig. 372). The scales were taken from selected bulbs of seedling origin which had been grown during the previous year in Louisiana or California, harvested when mature and shipped to Beltsville for propagation. Such scales were "sown" 2 inches deep without regard to their position, about 75 to each 3 foot row.

FIG. 373.—Creole Easter Lily bulbs produced in one year from scales in the open ground at Beltsville, Md. (Planted, August, 1939; dug, August, 1940.)

Some of the resulting bulbils produced leaves during the fall while others did not show leaf growth until the following spring. Over winter the beds were protected with a straw mulch about 2 inches thick which was removed before growth started in the spring. Later the beds were top-dressed with a one-half inch layer of well rotted manure.

Despite a January with the lowest mean temperature in 20 years, a good propagation had been secured when the beds were dug in August, 1940. Approximately 11,000 scales had been set out and over 11,300 bulbs were harvested, ranging up to 5 inches in circumference with an estimated average between $2\frac{1}{2}$ and 3 inches (Fig. 373).

A preliminary report on the response of lily scales to certain plant hormones shows that scales of the Creole Lily, dipped in or shaken with talcum powder mixtures containing 0.5 to 10 parts of indolebutyric acid per 1,000 parts of talc by weight, have produced far more uniform and heavier roots than untreated scales (Fig.

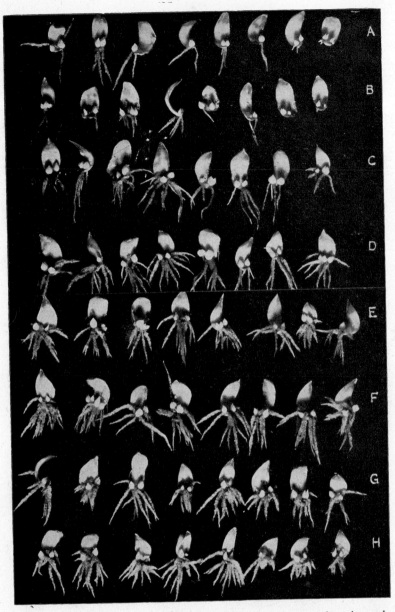

Fig. 374.—Creole Easter Lily scales treated August 15, 1940, and set in sand; photographed September 13, 1940. A, untreated; B, talc alone; C, talc containing 0.5 part of indolebutyric acid per 1,000 parts talc; D, 1 part per 1,000; E, 2 parts per 1,000; F, 4 parts per 1,000; G, 8 parts per 1,000; H, 10 parts per 1,000.

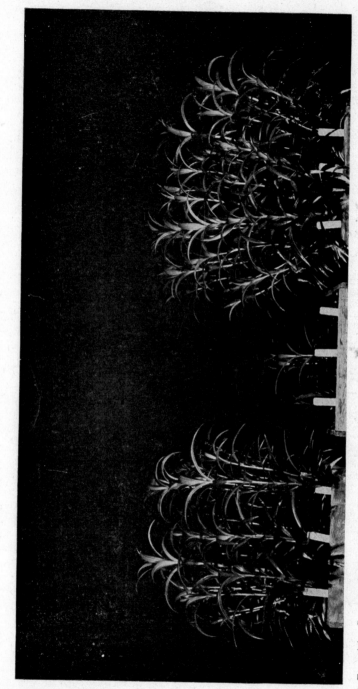

FIG. 375.—Comparative growth in the greenhouse from Creole Easter Lily scales. Bulbs stored five weeks before scaling; scales treated with indolebutyric acid powder, set in sand one month, planted in soil September 14, 1940, and photographed March 7, 1941. *Left*: bulbs stored at 32° F. *Center*: 50° F. *Right*: 70 to 80° F.

374).   Concentrations of one or two parts of indolebutyric acid in 1,000 parts of talc by weight appear to be very satisfactory.

Similar responses have been obtained by soaking the basal portion or the entire scale overnight in water solutions containing 10 to 100 milligrams of indolebutyric acid per liter of water.   If a higher concentration is used the scales should be soaked for a shorter period.

Naphthalene acetic acid and naphthalene acetamide are also effective in stimulating the rooting of scales but these materials appear to be somewhat more toxic than equivalent amounts of indolebutyric acid and consequently should be used at lower concentrations.

No delay or reduction in bulbil formation has been observed as a result of treatment with favorable concentrations of root-inducing chemicals.   Field tests involving more than 25,000 scales are now in progress.

Preliminary experiments also show that varying temperatures of storage for Creole Lily bulbs do not affect the response of such scales to indolebutyric acid powders, all rooting equally well in four weeks' time.   However, when such rooted scales were replanted in the greenhouse, those from bulbs which had been stored at low or high temperatures gave better growth response (Fig. 375).

INDEX TO APPENDIX

INDEX

Note: Except the numbers of tables all figures are page numbers

625

AN AUTHORITATIVE TEXT AND REFERENCE BOOK
FOR THE TEACHER AND STUDENT

Florist Crop Production and Marketing

**The Application of Scientific Facts to the Production and Marketing of Florist
Cut Flowers, Potted Plants and Bulbs Grown in the Greenhouse or in the Field**

By KENNETH POST, Ph.D.

**Professor of Floriculture and Ornamental Horticulture, New York
State College of Agriculture, Cornell University, Ithaca, N. Y.**

This book gives the practical application of science to the production and
marketing of cut-flowers, potted plants and bulbs grown in the greenhouse,
clothhouse, under lath or in the field. A complete guide and reference book for
the commercial producer of Florist Crops. It is a well organized and complete
text for a formal course in the growing and marketing of Florist Crops and a
ready reference for the Floricultural scientist.

The reader interested in the original research with the many florist crops,
will find the meat of the research woven into the story of production. Direct
references to the literature cited will enable him to obtain the complete and
original research with any one crop or subject.

The various methods used in Florist Crop Production in different parts of the
world, and the fundamental reasons why certain crops grow well in some areas
but poorly in others are covered. Crops suitable for potted plants; cut-flowers
under glass, under cloth or in the field are given with the season and areas of
their production. The complete culture of crops which are finished by the florist
such as bulbs and azaleas is given.

The text is cross-referenced to enable the reader to get the maximum tie-in
between crops and methods of production. The cross-references will help the
reader interested in obtaining a greater knowledge of science as applied to
Florist Crop Production when his training in the scientific fields is limited.

The author received his B.S. degree from Michigan State College, his M.S.
degree from Iowa State College and his Ph.D. from Cornell University. He has
worked among florists since 1928 to help them solve their production problem.
He has taught the commercial floricultural courses at Cornell since 1930 and has
been in charge of floricultural research at Cornell during this period. Through
the application of research the author has been directly responsible for many
changes in the growing and marketing of Florist Crops. He has presented many
phases of research as applied to Florist Crop Production at short courses and
meetings throughout America. The author's travels and wide acquaintance with
florists and their problems have made this volume most valuable to the florist.

ELABORATELY ILLUSTRATED

A marked feature of this book is the exclusiveness of its many superb
illustrations. It contains a series of charts and graphs especially drawn for this
book together with 427 drawings and photographs all of which were assembled
for this volume at great cost. They add to the information most sought and
will prove of greatest value to everyone.

WELL INDEXED AND PRINTED

The work here offered is fresh in every detail and is thoroughly indexed
under common and scientific names. Every topic can easily be found. It is
beautifully printed on a good grade of paper, from clear type that can easily
be read and is substantially bound in buckram with gold side and back stamping.
The book should find a place in the library of every commercial producer of
Florist Crops.

906 Pages.   Profusely Illustrated.   Buckram.   6x9.

Our Shade Trees

**A Simply Written Text Book and Guide for Tree Owners
— Field Workers — Tree Wardens — City Foresters
— Superintendents of Estates and Those Engaged
in the Planting and Care of Shade Trees**

By EPHRAIM PORTER FELT
Director Bartlett Tree Research Laboratories

In this new revised and enlarged edition is also incorporated the more important lessons of the 1938 hurricane, particularly those relating to the methods of growing trees to make them more resistant to storms. The matter in relation to windstorms has been largely rewritten and considerably amplified. The evidence in regard to the disappearance of the tap root in trees thirty years old or thereabouts and that in relation to sweeping salt spray injury, deals with phases usually ignored. Later there was the extensive and serious ice storm of March 1940, covering a wide coastal territory from northern New Jersey and Rhode Island.

The unusual storm damage to trees in the past three years aroused a wide interest in estimating losses which could be deducted from income taxes. We are of the opinion that the method of appraisal, amplified in this new edition, is the most logical way of estimating tree losses and their effect on real estate values. Included also is a general account of Winter drying resulting from the extremely unusual weather conditions during the late Winter and Spring of 1941. The account of home grounds and trees should prove of special interest to those who take a personal interest in developing their premises.

Illustrated.   320 Pages.   5½ x 8.   Cloth.

A Living from Bees

By FRANK C. PELLETT

This book is the result of a lifetime of association with the bees. First as a child the author spent much time with his grandfather among the bees. In young manhood he followed honey production as a means of livelihood and for a time he served the State of Iowa as its first official Apiarist.

As Field Editor of American Bee Journal he has visited most of the important honey producing areas in the United States and Canada and is personally acquainted with hundreds of the most successful beekeepers.

As the title suggests this book is designed to explain how a living can be made from bees. The fundamentals of honey production are explained and the reasons given for each necessary manipulation.

Conditions under which beekeeping is practical as an exclusive business and when it is better to be followed as a sideline are discussed at length.

Illustrated.   About 306 Pages.   5½ x 8½.   Cloth.

Making Pigeons Pay

A Practical Manual on the Selection, Breeding, Feeding and Marketing of Pigeons

By WENDELL M. LEVI, A.B., J.D.

The Author has addressed his remarks mainly to beginners in the business who have a limited amount of capital and experience and to whom the operation of plants of several thousand birds is of no interest further and as an illustration of the possibilities of the business. Beginners, however, cannot start with such plants and must of necessity commence business in a way commensurate with their experience and capital, and for such the Author has selected from his forty-five years of experience, a simple definite plan which will be a safe guide to the novice, saving him the inevitable experimenting, resulting from the reading of numerous books. In the development of the plan unusual attention is given to the small but important details from purchasing of breeding stock to the time that the produce is marketed. In addition this work contains much that is new and of value to the most experienced commercial pigeon raiser.

Profusely Illustrated.   About 300 Pages.   5 x 7½.   Cloth.

ARTIFICIAL MANURES

By ARTHUR B. BEAUMONT

The importance of animal manures for crop-production has long been recognized by practical farmers and gardeners. The rapid decline in the horse population in recent years, due to the increase in the number of motorized vehicles and farm tractors, has created a problem of obtaining substitutes for natural manures. Commercial fertilizers alone are not satisfactory. Soil scientists have discovered that the benefits from animal manures are not limited to the plant nutrients in them, but are due in a large measure to the organic matter they contain.

This book treats the problem of soil organic matter broadly and practically, with particular attention to the preparation and use of artificial manures, including cover crops and green manures. Introductory chapters on soils and conservation supplement and balance those on organic matter, which comprise most of the book. The subject matter will be found helpful in practical ways to the home gardener, market gardener, truck farmer, general farmer, orchardist, and greenhouse operator, particularly in times like these when all are asked to produce more crops with less fertilizer.

Illustrated.   **160 Pages.**   **5 ½ x 8.**   **Cloth.**

HOW TO RAISE RABBITS FOR FOOD AND FUR

This Helpful Book Will Tell You in Plain Language All About Raising Rabbits Profitably for Meat and Fur of High Quality

By FRANK G. ASHBROOK

This book is written for the man or woman in the city, in the suburbs, on the farm or in the classroom who is primarily interested in raising rabbits for meat and fur. The Author makes a special appeal to raise rabbits to replace rationed meats because of its quick and easy production.

Rabbit meat for the family, its importance in the Food for Freedom campaign, back yard rabbitry for home consumption, how to make a start, location of the rabbitry, and choosing a breed are all discussed in this book. The care and feeding of the doe and her litter, and the fattening of the young for market including the self-feeding system are all given in detail. The killing, dressing and marketing of rabbits, advising how to dispose of the meat and fur to best advantage and the greatest profits are discussed. Domestic rabbit meat provides a most attractive and tasty variation to a meal that otherwise might be meatless.

Fully Illustrated.   **256 Pages.**   **5 ½ x 8.**   **Cloth.**